MODERN CONTROL THEORY

McGRAW-HILL ELECTRICAL AND ELECTRONIC ENGINEERING SERIES

Ahrendt and Savant, Servomechanism Practice
Angelo, Electronic Circuits
Aseltine, Transform Method in Linear System Analysis
Atwater, Introduction to Microwave Theory
Bailey and Gault, Alternating-current Machinery
Beranek, Acoustics
Brenner and Javid, Analysis of Electric Circuits
Brown, Analysis of Linear Time-invariant Systems
Bruns and Saunders, Analysis of Feedback Control Systems
Cage, Theory and Application of Industrial Electronics
Cauer, Synthesis of Linear Communication Networks
Chen, The Analysis of Linear Systems
Chen, Linear Network Design and Synthesis
Chirlian, Analysis and Design of Electronic Circuits
Chirlian and Zemanian, Electronics
Clement and Johnson, Electrical Engineering Science
Cote and Oakes, Linear Vacuum-tube and Transistor Circuits
Cuccia, Harmonics, Sidebands, and Transients in Communication Engineering
Cunningham, Introduction to Nonlinear Analysis
Eastman, Fundamentals of Vacuum Tubes
Evans, Control-system Dynamics
Feinstein, Foundations of Information Theory
Fitzgerald and Higginbotham, Basic Electrical Engineering
Fitzgerald and Kingsley, Electric Machinery
Frank, Electrical Measurement Analysis
Friedland, Wing, and Ash, Principles of Linear Networks
Geppert, Basic Electron Tubes
Ghose, Microwave Circuit Theory and Analysis
Greiner, Semiconductor Devices and Applications
Hammond, Electrical Engineering
Hancock, An Introduction to the Principles of Communication Theory
Happell and Hesselberth, Engineering Electronics
Harman, Fundamentals of Electronic Motion
Harman, Principles of the Statistical Theory of Communication
Harman and Lytle, Electrical and Mechanical Networks
Harrington, Introduction to Electromagnetic Engineering
Harrington, Time-harmonic Electromagnetic Fields
Hayt, Engineering Electromagnetics
Hill, Electronics in Engineering
Huelsman, Circuits, Matrices, and Linear Vector Spaces
Javid and Brenner, Analysis, Transmission, and Filtering of Signals
Javid and Brown, Field Analysis and Electromagnetics
Johnson, Transmission Lines and Networks
Koenig and Blackwell, Electromechanical System Theory
Kraus, Antennas
Kraus, Electromagnetics
Kuh and Pederson, Principles of Circuit Synthesis
Ledley, Digital Computer and Control Engineering

LePage, Analysis of Alternating-current Circuits
LePage and Seely, General Network Analysis
Ley, Lutz, and Rehberg, Linear Circuit Analysis
Linvill and Gibbons, Transistors and Active Circuits
Lynch and Truxal, Introductory System Analysis
Lynch and Truxal, Principles of Electronic Instrumentation
Lynch and Truxal, Signals and Systems in Electrical Engineering
Millman, Vacuum-tube and Semiconductor Electronics
Millman and Seely, Electronics
Millman and Taub, Pulse and Digital Circuits
Mishkin and Braun, Adaptive Control Systems
Moore, Traveling-wave Engineering
Nanavati, An Introduction to Semiconductor Electronics
Pettit, Electronic Switching, Timing, and Pulse Circuits
Pettit and McWhorter, Electronic Amplifier Circuits
Pfeiffer, Linear Systems Analysis
Reza, An Introduction to Information Theory
Reza and Seely, Modern Network Analysis
Rogers, Introduction to Electric Fields
Ryder, Engineering Electronics
Schwartz, Information Transmission, Modulation, and Noise
Seely, Electromechanical Energy Conversion
Seely, Electron-tube Circuits
Seely, Electronic Engineering
Seely, Introduction to Electromagnetic Fields
Seely, Radio Electronics
Seifert and Steeg, Control Systems Engineering
Siegman, Microwave Solid State Masers
Siskind, Direct-current Machinery
Skilling, Electric Transmission Lines
Skilling, Transient Electric Currents
Spangenberg, Fundamentals of Electron Devices
Spangenberg, Vacuum Tubes
Stevenson, Elements of Power System Analysis
Stewart, Fundamentals of Signal Theory
Storer, Passive Network Synthesis
Strauss, Wave Generation and Shaping
Terman, Electronic and Radio Engineering
Terman and Pettit, Electronic Measurements
Thaler, Elements of Servomechanism Theory
Thaler and Brown, Analysis and Design of Feedback Control Systems
Thaler and Pastel, Analysis and Design of Nonlinear Feedback Control Systems
Thompson, Alternating-current and Transient Circuit Analysis
Tou, Digital and Sampled-data Control Systems
Tou, Modern Control Theory
Truxal, Automatic Feedback Control System Synthesis
Valdes, The Physical Theory of Transistors
Van Bladel, Electromagnetic Fields
Weinberg, Network Analysis and Synthesis
Williams and Young, Electrical Engineering Problems

JULIUS T. TOU

Professor of Electrical Engineering
Director of Computer Sciences Laboratory
The Technological Institute
Northwestern University

McGRAW-HILL BOOK COMPANY

New York San Francisco
Toronto London

MODERN CONTROL THEORY

MODERN CONTROL THEORY

Library of Congress Catalog Card Number 64-18905

65076

TO MY WIFE LISA

PREFACE

The trend of research in control and information science today demands great emphasis on modern concepts and on the new techniques of analysis and design which have been actively developed only within the past seven or eight years. The need for a textbook in this branch of modern engineering to clarify and codify these modern approaches has been basic and urgent, both in academic and industrial circles. Although there are a great many textbooks in the field of control engineering, they tend almost uniformly to treat the subject from the conventional point of view. In an effort to fill the gap for his students, the author first prepared a set of lecture notes which were used for some years in his classes at Purdue and later at Northwestern University. When requests for information from outside this immediate milieu began to reach the author, this book became the natural outgrowth of those lecture notes: it presents the first integrated treatment of automatic-control systems through the modern approach and reflects, in its new point of view, the trend and direction of current research in the field.

There are three major categories into which the important approaches to the design and synthesis of automatic-control systems may be classified. The first, based on the transform methods in the s domain or the z domain, is the familiar trial-and-error design procedure. The second category is that which uses as a measure of performance an infinite-time integral of square error or mean-square error. Together, these two approaches make up what is commonly accepted as the classical control theory, which formed the basis of the major techniques for designing automatic-control systems during World War II and in the decade that followed. These two components of the classical control theory have served, in addition, as the main topics of almost all the textbooks now available to the field of control-system engineering. Though more than a hundred such textbooks and monographs expounding the classical control theory have been published, until now almost no textbooks have been written on modern control theory. It is the third major approach to control- and information-system design with which this book is exclusively concerned.

The advent of high-speed digital computers revolutionized the philosophy of design and analysis of control systems. The impact of the digital computer upon system design and analysis had such tremendous consequence that the older methodology and tools became cumbersome: optimum design of the new complex systems demanded a computer program or an algorithm which could be processed on a digital computer. The classical approach was limited in its ability to solve problems of complex systems subject to large numbers of inputs and constraints. Control theory kept pace with the computer—it, too, advanced; and what it required was more significant and powerful tools.

To fill this requirement, the third approach to design and synthesis of automatic-control systems was formulated. Based upon the state-space characterization of a system, this design philosophy involves mainly the determination of an extremum of a functional. This, while it may be classed as a broad generalization of the second category, is nonetheless far in advance and is, specifically, the modern approach. Essentially, its basic idea is that a functional on the plant variables and control variables is selected or prespecified; physical constraints are imposed on these variables; and a control law or control sequence is determined to minimize or maximize the functional by some variational method.

This concept, this application of modern approach to control-system design, was introduced into the field of control engineering only a decade ago, yet both its pragmatic and theoretical values were so instantly visible and its advantages so significant that it gained immediate acceptance and, within a few years, widespread popularity. More recently, this modern approach has rapidly become the major technique applicable to the design of automatic-control systems.

Despite the many and apparent advantages of the modern treatment and the pronounced trend to research in this direction, only a few of the more recent textbooks have, though cursorily, included one or two of the modern concepts of control-system design; some give no more than a passing mention; most totally ignore them. Yet the scientific and technological development of the past decade has set the stage for a new approach to control- and information-system engineering: the requirements of these times call for a different point of view than has hitherto been expressed in textbooks. Until now there have been no books devoted entirely to the modern approach despite its many advantages, and the brief mentions cannot be expected to fill the hiatus.

It was because of this lack that this book came to be written. It is a book devoted entirely to modern concepts of control-system design: it attempts to put within one cover these techniques and principles which are of fundamental importance in modern control engineering and to organize and unify them coherently. A certain amount of original material has been included, although, as evidenced by the numbered references, most of the contents has been derived from other sources in the literature.

This volume is intended for use both as a graduate-level textbook and as a reference work for scientists, engineers, and system analysts. The material is arranged to form a logical progression from the simple to the more difficult problems. Though a good deal of higher mathematics was involved in the development and evolution of the theories and techniques here discussed, all mathematics throughout the text is presented on a simple, easy-to-follow level so that it may readily be understood by both student and engineer. For the student it presents a step-by-step discussion of basic theory and important techniques. For the practicing engineer it provides a systematically arranged source of ready reference. It is assumed that, as preparation, the reader has adequate background, represented by an introductory course on feedback control systems and some working knowledge of linear algebra, matrix theory, and ordinary differential equations.

Serving as a brief review of the background material, Chapter 1 introduces the control problems and describes the major approaches and design procedures, and Chapter 2 reviews the mathematical foundations which play an important role in the development of modern control theory. In teaching, the author has generally omitted parts of this chapter until the need for such material arose somewhat later in the course. Chapter 3 presents the analysis of control systems by the state-space method. Both continuous and discrete systems are discussed, the former being treated as a special case of the latter. Analysis of nonconventional sampling systems is emphasized. Chapter 4 studies the design of control systems from the state-space point of view. Topics covered in this chapter include optimum control of nonlinear discrete systems; time-optimal control for saturating systems; and the concept of controllability and observability. Chapter 5 surveys variational calculus in optimal control. Optimum-control problems are treated as problems of Lagrange, Mayer, and Bolza. The principle of maximum is studied in Chapter 6. Application of the maximum principle to the design of minimum-time control, terminal control, and minimum-integral control is discussed in some detail. Chapter 7 is devoted to the application of dynamic-programming theory to optimum-design problems. Design of the three basic optimum-control schemes via dynamic programming is studied in depth, and the problem of adaptive and learning control is investigated. The book concludes with a chapter on computer control theory, emphasizing design of the optimum controller and optimum estimator. Since stability analysis by the Lyapunov second method is amply treated in several recent textbooks on control systems, it has not been included here.

Many numerical examples are worked out in each chapter to clarify the development of each theory and of the various methods discussed. In addition, some 140 problems of various types and degrees of complexity are included for the purpose of permitting the student, through actual practice in problem solution, to clarify for himself the points discussed in the text. Some of these problems may also serve as guideposts for further investigation of the subject and as a supplement to the development of the text.

Citations are generally avoided in the text. However, a list of numbered references is included which covers the contributions of many workers in the field. In view of the enormous literature on this subject published in technical journals of many countries, the included list of references must remain incomplete. To those contributors to the field whose publications are inadvertently omitted, the author wishes to express his apology.

One enjoyable aspect of teaching modern control theory is the interest and challenge most students find in the subject. Because of this, they have enthusiastically worked out, at length, many illustrative examples and homework problems. The author is deeply indebted to a number of individuals who thus assisted in the preparation of the manuscript. During the period of writing the book, he received invaluable inspiration from Prof. Y. H. Ku of the Moore School of Electrical Engineering, University of Pennsylvania. The encouragement extended by the Office of Naval Research to write this book and to include the accomplished work under their sponsorship is gratefully recorded. Finally, the author would like to mention his secretary, Mrs. Gerta Houston, who typed the final manuscript and helped in proofreading it and with some of the editorial work.

Julius T. Tou

CONTENTS

1

INTRODUCTION

This introductory chapter presents a general discussion of the automatic-control problem, emphasizing the importance of feedback principles. The modern concept of control-system design is contrasted with classical design philosophy. This comparison brings into focus the advantages of the modern approach over the classical approach. The formulation of the design of optimum control as a variational problem is described, and the methods of attack are outlined.

1.1 THE AUTOMATIC-CONTROL PROBLEM

Recent trends in the development of modern civilization have been in the direction of optimum control. The limited supply of natural resources and the immense pressure of business competition have forced all types of industry—chemical, steel, automobile, food processing, aircraft, machine tool, textile, etc.—to begin to seek greater and greater efficiency through optimum control. The businessman strives to get the most out of his investment. The plant manager endeavors to maximize production and to minimize cost. The weapons engineer attempts to design weapons systems with maximum destructive power within physical constraints. The space technologist wishes to achieve an optimum-ascent trajectory of a satellite which results in maximum payload in orbit. During the past decade the need for better controls in industrial, military, and space applications has stimulated a great deal of interest in problems of optimal control and system optimization.

Among current scientific and technological developments, automation is of special importance. It is commonplace these days to hear that the world has plunged into a second industrial revolution, the era of automation. This time it is not man's muscles which are to be replaced and extended, but rather man's brain. Automation is generally regarded as one of the most significant developments of our time. With it comes a massive growth in the productivity of labor; it puts into practice the most daring dreams of many generations of mankind and opens up new horizons for various branches of industry. One of the major contributions to modern automation is feedback control. Systems which utilize feedback for control purposes have become essential elements in modern technology, ranging from the manufacture of simple toys to the most complex automatic factories and production equipment. Feedback control is in a large measure responsible for ever-increasing productivity and a rising standard of living.

It is difficult to conceive of any control process not involving feedback that is scientifically interesting and significant. The thermostat of a house is often used as a common example of feedback control. Suppose that an open-loop temperature control for a house is designed deliberately. The average temperature that the house ought to have during the winter months is estimated, and a timing cycle to turn the heat on and off is precalculated. Since changes of weather are rather unpredictable, the observed result will be that, during the winter, it will be either too hot or too cold some fraction of the time, even if the estimated average temperature and the precalculated timing cycle are well determined. This is certainly the specific drawback of open-loop control. When it is too hot, the people who live in the house are likely to open the windows to let out the heat. When it is too cold, since they are unable to do anything about the furnace, they will put on more clothes. In effect, they will be taking action based upon the difference between what the temperature ought to be and what it actually is; that is, they will develop a new feedback loop to control the situation.

There are, in fact, many reasons why open-loop control is unsatisfactory. In the fabrication of the control system it is necessary to allow tolerances in manufacture. The parameters of the control system may undergo changes due to time, aging, fatigue, temperature, etc., and in processes of moderate complexity, the dynamic characteristics may be only partially known.

In addition, there are external disturbances which are uncontrollable and often unpredictable. Apparently, open-loop control can hardly cope with fluctuations in the system caused by these factors. Except for extremely simple situations, control systems that do not utilize feedback are doomed to be unsuccessful.

Feedback control processes are observed everywhere—in living organisms, in automata which man builds, in the society which man organizes. When a stimulus is exerted upon a sensory organ, some form of energy absorption and transduction will occur. As a result, a neural signal will be generated and transmitted along the nerve fibers, linking it to some reflex center, where a decision is made and a control effort is issued to respond to the stimulus. In the pupillary-reflex system of the eye, the iris acts as a diaphragm to control the amount of light flux reaching the photoreceptor elements on the retina. As more light falls on the retina, the photoreceptor

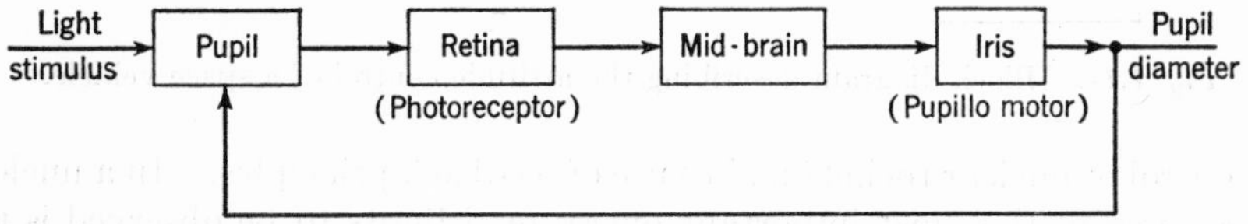

Fig. 1.1-1 Block diagram describing the pupillary reflex for a single eye.

increases the strength of the outgoing neural signals, which, when transmitted to the muscles of the iris, reduce the diameter of the pupil. The feedback control loop consists mainly of neural paths with appropriate transducers at the retina and at the iris, as illustrated in Fig. 1.1-1.

The problem of controlling automatic flight of aircraft is solved by feedback principles. The quantity to be controlled is, normally, the flight path, which is dependent upon the motions of the aircraft. Control forces and moments are imposed upon the airframe by actuating the control surfaces, which consist of the elevator, rudder, and ailerons, or such composite control surfaces as elevons, and special-purpose surfaces like dive brakes. Sensors are used to detect motions of the airframe, and various types of servomechanisms are used to actuate these controls to achieve the desired overall system operation.

Attitude control of space vehicles is another application of feedback principles. Here the system performs two major functions: (1) attitude change and (2) attitude stabilization; i.e., the control system is required to turn the vehicle in a prescribed manner to a prescribed degree and to stabilize the heading, or attitude, in a desired direction despite the disturbing action of unwanted torques. The structure of a space-vehicle attitude control system is shown in Fig. 1.1-2. As may be seen in the illustration, this feedback system consists of a space vehicle, a performance evaluation, and a controller. The performance evaluator includes sensors of vehicle behavior, a comparison with a reference behavior, and an interpretation of the discrepancies in terms that are usable by the vehicle. The controller operates on the information which formulates the control law to govern and optimize the performance of the vehicle. The sensor might be a solar eye producing a voltage output that varies over a certain range, depending upon the direction between it and the sun.

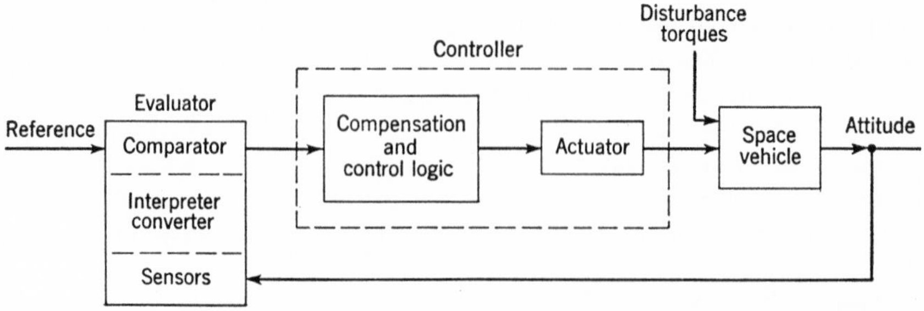

Fig. 1.1-2 Block diagram describing the attitude control of a space vehicle.

Control of nuclear rockets makes use of feedback principles. In a nuclear rocket, one of the most important operational limits to be observed is the rate of neutron multiplication. This rate should always be slow enough to permit the control to move fast enough to avoid a runaway multiplication. This function is most stringently demanded in the startup maneuver. A second control requirement is that the maximum gas temperature be obtained without damage to the material of the reactor. Another problem

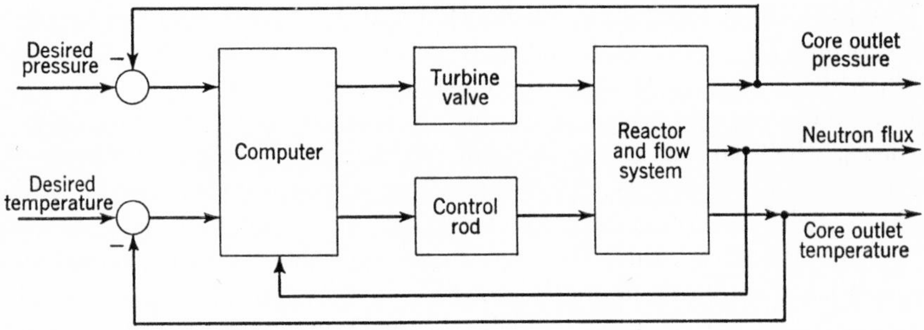

Fig. 1.1-3 Control for maximum power operation of a nuclear rocket.

associated with the core is the wide range of neutron flux that must be sensed for safe control. One possible scheme utilizes the measurement and feedback of reactor-outlet gas temperature, reactor-outlet pressure, and neutron flux to manipulate turbine valve and control rod, as shown in Fig. 1.1-3. Such a control scheme would satisfy most of the required functions, provided a dependable temperature sensor is available. The flux sensor supplies a signal to permit rapid calculation of the rate of change of flux, particularly during startup. The computer determines the decision for dispatching commands to the valve and control rod based upon a knowledge of the dynamic behavior of the system and the measured values of core-outlet pressure, core-outlet temperature, and neutron flux, so that maximum power operation of the nuclear rocket is attained.

In recent years scientists have been faced with the most complex scientific problems of automatic control. It is difficult to overestimate the significance of these problems. Success in solving them will create a basis for rapid growth of technological progress. It is necessary to develop the fundamental theory of optimum control systems, the construction principles of optimizing control devices, and the design techniques for systems with adaptive, learning, and self-organizing capabilities. This book attempts to introduce to the reader the modern approaches to the solution of automatic-control problems.

1.2 BASIC CONCEPTS OF CONTROL–SYSTEM DESIGN

The design of an automatic-control system usually starts with certain specific information. This includes a mathematical description of the plant or process to be controlled, specified performance requirements under dynamic and static conditions, constraints and limitations on the system components, the inputs to the plant and the variables, the statistical properties of the external disturbances, and a statement of the output variables which can be measured directly or can be estimated. In addition, extra requirements such as the introduction of sampling and quantization, the use of special equipment such as a digital computer, and the specification of certain control-system configurations or modes of control may be imposed. In some cases the solution of the problem may be unique; i.e., there is a system which is best; in other cases compromises may lead to several satisfactory solutions, depending upon the individual designer.

A distinction is made between analysis, design, and synthesis. By analysis is meant that the control system has been designed and what is required is an investigation of its performance under specified conditions. Design is often used in the sense that a control system which satisfies the statement of the problem must be found. In general, the procedure is not straightforward, but requires engineering judgment. Synthesis is reserved for the more ideal situation, where there is a clear procedure, usually entirely mathematical, for going from the problem statement to its solution. Examples of synthesis procedures are those for finding certain optimum control systems and linear networks and filters.

The approaches to the design and synthesis of control systems may be classified in three categories. The first is the well-known approach based upon transform methods, including the s domain and the z domain, or upon the root-locus method. This is often referred to as the trial-and-error design procedure. The designer is given a set of more or less arbitrary specifications in time domain or in frequency domain and possibly a system configuration. Gain margin, phase margin, M peak, output impedance, rise time, settling time, and peak overshoot are among the most commonly used specifications. The designer seeks to satisfy the specifications by gain adjustment or equalizer compensation. The second approach, which has been referred to as analytical design, uses an infinite-time integral of squared-system error or a mean-square error as a measure of performance. These performance criteria were first suggested by Wiener and Hall. The design procedure yields a compensation network for a linear-control-system configuration upon application of classical variational methods to minimize the performance measure. The method includes linear systems subject to both deterministic and stochastic inputs and linear systems operating on discrete data.[136]†

During World War II and in the decade following, the first and second approach constituted the major techniques for the design of automatic-control systems. These techniques, which are deeply rooted in practicing

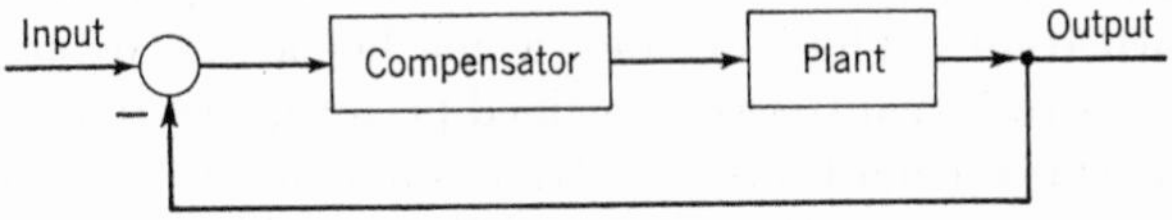

Fig. 1.2-1 Block diagram of a feedback control system.

control engineers, may be referred to as the classical approach. The block diagram of a typical classical feedback control system is illustrated in Fig. 1.2-1, which consists of a controlled plant and a compensator. A number of systems with different performance and quality may be designed to meet the same requirements. The configuration of the control system is more or less fixed ahead of time, which is usually not an optimum configuration of control. In a classical feedback system, only the input and the output are compared to yield an actuating signal. In systems of moderate complexity, this may not provide sufficient information for achieving optimum control. Classical approaches of system design are confronted by severe limitations and difficulties when applied to the design of multivariable and time-varying systems. Applications usually are limited to idealized and relatively simple feedback control systems. To summarize, the outline of the trial-and-error design method and that of the analytical design method are given in Tables 1.2-1 and 1.2-2, respectively.[123]

The third approach is a broad generalization of the second and has developed in many different ways. If, however, one restricts his interest to the control of linear processes, a rather clear pattern of design procedures

† Superscript numerals are keyed to the References at the end of the book.

TABLE 1.2-1 OUTLINE OF THE TRIAL–AND–ERROR METHOD

I. Specifications
- *a.* Dynamics of the control process
- *b.* Input signal and desired output
- *c.* External disturbances
- *d.* Tolerable error and degree of stability

II. Design procedure
- *a.* Determine the system gain on the basis of error specification
- *b.* Design the compensator to meet the stability requirement
- *c.* By analysis, check to see if the specifications are met
- *d.* If not, repeat procedure, using elaborate compensation

appears. The essential idea is that a functional on the plant variables and control variables is specified or selected, constraints are imposed upon these variables, and a control law or sequence is derived by finding an extremum of the functional by some variational method.

The concept of this approach to control-system design was first introduced into the control engineering field only a decade ago and has gained great popularity in recent years. It is often referred to as the modern design procedure, and is rapidly becoming the major technique for the design of automatic-control systems. The core of the modern approach to system design lies in the determination of a control law or an optimum-control policy so as to minimize or maximize a set of performance criteria. The control law is an expression of the control variables as functions of plant variables; i.e., a feedback system results. For relatively simple systems, the generation of the optimum-control law can be accomplished by incorporating a filtering device or an active network. In the case of complicated situations, a digital computer is generally used to advantage to generate the optimum-control law. Utilizing the information fed into the digital com-

TABLE 1.2-2 OUTLINE OF THE ANALYTICAL DESIGN PROCEDURE

I. Specifications
- *a.* Dynamics of the control process
- *b.* Input signal and desired output
- *c.* External disturbances
- *d.* Performance criterion
- *e.* Degree of freedom allowed in compensation

II. Design procedure
- *a.* Determine the classification of the problem—fixed, free, or semifree configuration
- *b.* If the configuration is fixed, express the performance index in terms of the free parameters; then minimize or maximize the performance index by appropriate adjustment of these parameters
- *c.* If the configuration is free or semifree, apply the method of spectral factorization to design the compensator which minimizes or maximizes the performance index
- *d.* Check to see if the compensation thus determined satisfies the performance criterion. If so, the theoretical design is completed and physical realization may begin. If not, the specifications cannot be met and must be altered

puter from the control process, the computer is instructed to generate a sequence of numbers which constitute the optimum-control policy. This approach of control-system design requires the feedback of all the information describing the dynamics of the process so as to accomplish dynamic optimization of the system.

The modern concept of control-system design has many advantages over the classical techniques. It simplifies the design of time-varying and multivariable systems and will yield an optimum configuration of the control for the system. Modern synthesis procedure takes into account arbitrary initial conditions. The modern concept facilitates the solution of a large class of more realistic control problems which can hardly be treated by conventional methods. Many of these problems are characterized by the necessity for satisfying multiple performance requirements and constraints. In such systems, the design of the control by classical approaches may prove extremely difficult. Modern techniques enable one to devote time to analytical studies alone, leaving the computational drudgery to a digital computer. The calculations necessary for the design are of a systematic numerical nature and can be programmed on a digital computer. In fact, with the advent of electronic digital computers, the trend in engineering analysis and design has been affected considerably. Analytical design techniques are now evaluated, not only with respect to their mathematical elegance, but also in relation to their computational feasibility. Although more than a hundred books and monographs have been written on classical control theory and techniques, until now practically no textbooks have been written on modern control theory, despite the many advantages of the new approaches and research interest in this direction. The need for a book devoted to modern control theory has become urgent. To meet the lack, this book on the modern approach to automatic control is written.

1.3 THE OPTIMUM-DESIGN PROBLEM

The central problem in the development of modern control theory is that of optimal control. A typical process or plant has associated with it four kinds of variables:

1. *Independent variables,* which are the manipulating variables for the control or monitoring of the process

2. *Dependent variables,* which serve to measure and describe the state of the process at any instant of time

3. *Product variables,* which are used to indicate and measure the quality of the operating performance of the control system

4. *Disturbances,* which are the uncontrollable, environmental variables

The general problem of optimum control of a process consists of the way in which the product variables are maintained at their optimum values in spite of the fluctuations caused by disturbances and parameter variations. The product variables are used to describe the performance index of the control system. Thus the optimum-control problem involves the minimization or maximization of the performance index.

A physical system of nth order can usually be described at any time t by means of a finite set of quantities $x_1(t), x_2(t), \ldots, x_n(t)$. These quantities are referred to as the state variables of the system, and constitute the components of the state vector $\mathbf{x}(t)$ of the system. The meaning of state variables and state vectors is elaborated in Chap. 3. To relate the time changes in the system to the state of the system, a simple and useful assumption is made that the derivative of the state vector, $d\mathbf{x}/dt$, depends only upon the current state of the system and not upon its past history. This basic assumption leads to a mathematical characterization of the process by means of a vector-matrix differential equation,

$$\dot{\mathbf{x}}(t) = \frac{d\mathbf{x}(t)}{dt} = \mathbf{f}[\mathbf{x}(t); \mathbf{m}(t), t] \tag{1.3-1}$$

with initial condition $\mathbf{x}(0) = \mathbf{x}_0$. In Eq. (1.3-1), $\mathbf{m}(t)$ denotes the control vector, and $\mathbf{f}$ is a vector function of the state variables, the control signals, the time, and possibly the environmental variables or external disturbances. At each moment, the control vector $\mathbf{m}$ must satisfy the condition

$$\mathbf{g}(\mathbf{m}) \leq 0 \tag{1.3-2}$$

which reflects the restrictions imposed upon the control system. The function $\mathbf{g}$ is a given vector function of the control signals. The problem of optimum design of a control system may be roughly stated as follows: Given a plant or a process to be controlled, determine the control law or sequence so that a set of specified performance indices is minimized or maximized. The optimum-control law is to be generated by the optimum controller or by the digital computer, which is incorporated in the control system.

The state variables of a system are sometimes all accessible for measurement and observation. For linear systems with this feature, the determination of the optimum-control law as a function of the state variables can be worked out even in the presence of measurement noise. However, it happens quite frequently in engineering systems that the state variables are not all accessible for measurement and observation. The optimum-control law is then determined as a function of the best estimates of the state variables, which are calculated from the measured output signals of the system. Consequently, the more general case involves both optimum estimation and optimum control.

As an illustration, consider the aircraft-control problem.[54] The equations of motion of an aircraft can be derived from a consideration of the aerodynamic forces and moments and from the application of the fundamental laws of mechanics. The resulting equations are then linearized under the assumption that the deviation from the equilibrium flight condition is small. The geometry of an aircraft in flight is illustrated in Fig. 1.3-1. When the aircraft landing system is considered, it can be assumed that the glide-path angle β is very small, the longitudinal motion of the aircraft is governed by the elevator deflection $\delta(t)$, and the velocity V of the aircraft is

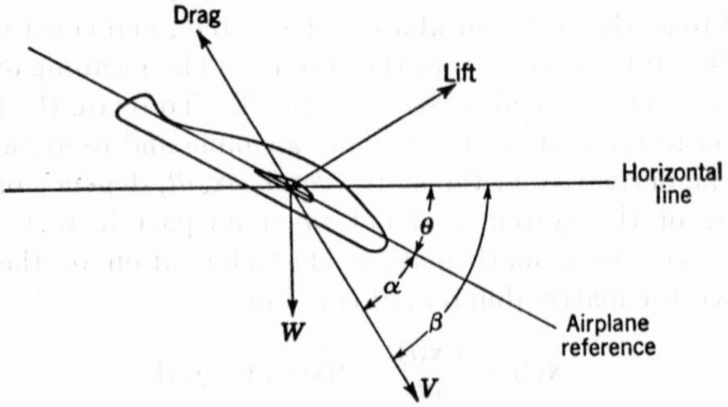

Fig. 1.3-1 Geometry of an aircraft in flight.

maintained essentially constant during the landing by the use of throttle control. These simplifying assumptions lead to the linearized short-period equations of motion of the aircraft as

$$\frac{d^3\theta(t)}{dt^3} + 2\zeta\omega_0 \frac{d^2\theta(t)}{dt^2} + \omega_0^2 \frac{d\theta(t)}{dt} = KT_0\omega_0^2 \frac{d\delta(t)}{dt} + K\omega_0^2\delta(t) \quad (1.3\text{-}3)$$

In this equation, ζ, ω_0, K, and T_0 are the aircraft parameters, which are defined as

ζ = short-period damping factor
ω_0 = short-period resonant frequency
K = short-period gain constant
T_0 = path time constant

The pitch angle θ and the altitude h are related by the differential equation

$$T_0 \frac{d^2h(t)}{dt^2} + \frac{dh(t)}{dt} = V\theta(t) \quad (1.3\text{-}4)$$

where the aircraft velocity V is assumed constant. In the above equation, zero initial conditions are assumed.

Combining Eqs. (1.3-3) and (1.3-4) by eliminating θ yields

$$\frac{d^4h(t)}{dt^4} + 2\zeta\omega_0 \frac{d^3h(t)}{dt^3} + \omega_0^2 \frac{d^2h(t)}{dt^2} = KV\omega_0^2\delta(t) \quad (1.3\text{-}5)$$

By letting

$$x_1 = h \qquad x_2 = \dot{x}_1 = \frac{dh}{dt} \qquad x_3 = \dot{x}_2 = \frac{d^2h}{dt^2} \qquad x_4 = \dot{x}_3 = \frac{d^3h}{dt^3}$$

and

$$m = \delta$$

Eq. (1.3-5) may be expressed as

$$\begin{aligned} \dot{x}_1 &= x_2 \\ \dot{x}_2 &= x_3 \\ \dot{x}_3 &= x_4 \\ \dot{x}_4 &= -\omega_0{}^2 x_3 - 2\zeta\omega_0 x_4 + K_1 m \end{aligned} \tag{1.3-6}$$

where x_i's may be referred to as the state variables of the aircraft. As will be discussed in Chap. 3, by defining

$$\mathbf{x} = \begin{bmatrix} x_1 \\ x_2 \\ x_3 \\ x_4 \end{bmatrix} \tag{1.3-7}$$

Eq. (1.3-6) may be reduced to the vector-matrix form as given in Eq. (1.3-1). To design the optimum control for the aircraft-landing problem, the state variables should be accessible for measurement and observation. The altitude h can be measured with a radar altimeter, and the rate of ascent dh/dt can be measured with a barometer rate meter. However, both d^2h/dt^2 and d^3h/dt^3 are not readily measurable. In Chap. 3 it is shown that this difficulty may be circumvented by choosing other quantities as state variables.

The aircraft landing system is subjected to several constraints on the aircraft variables. For instance, the pitch angle θ of the aircraft at the desired touchdown time $t = T_f$ must lie between 0 and 10°, for practical reasons. During the flare-out, the elevator deflection $\delta(t)$ is constrained between two limiting values. The optimum design of the landing system and the other flight control system of the aircraft aims at maximizing the comfort of passengers in the plane within the limitations imposed by physical constraints.

Modern control theory starts with the characterization of systems by state variables and the design of systems by state-space techniques. In a general formulation, the design of optimum control is usually viewed as a variational problem.[142] There are many possible variational methods for minimizing or maximizing a functional over a function space. The range is from classical methods in the calculus of variations to numerical and successive approximation techniques of experimental or model systems. Among the commonly used methods in control-system design are:

1. The calculus of variations
2. The maximum principle
3. The dynamic programming

In all cases the object is to find the optimum-control law or sequence such that the given functional of the performance indices is minimized or maximized. It is of interest to note that what is common in all three methods is the use of the variational principles. Each of these methods is related to well-known formulations in classical mechanics: the first to the Euler-Lagrange equation, the second to the Hamilton principle, and the third to the Hamilton-Jacobi theory. The maximum principle employs a more or less direct procedure of the calculus of variations, whereas dynamic programming, while still following the variational principles, uses the recurrence relationship or the algorithm of partial differential equations. This book is devoted to system analysis and synthesis by the state-space techniques and the design of optimum control by the calculus of variations, the maximum principle, and dynamic programming.

1.4 REVIEW OF MULTIVARIABLE–SYSTEM DESIGN BY THE CLASSICAL METHODS

As a prelude to control-system design by the modern techniques, this section reviews the classical approach to the design of control for multivariable processes. These are processes with r control inputs and n outputs, where $r > 1$ and $n > 1$. The input and output variables can represent

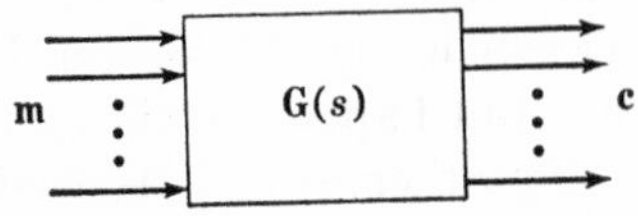

Fig. 1.4-1 Block diagram of a multivariable process.

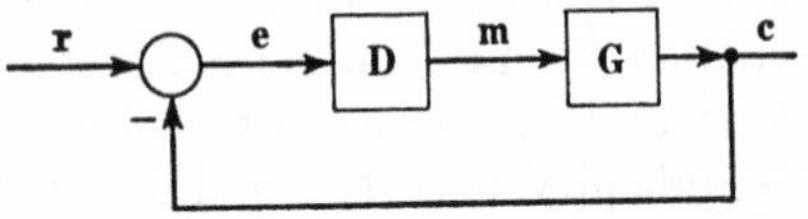

Fig. 1.4-2 Block diagram of a multivariable feedback control system.

different physical quantities such as voltage, current, velocity, displacement, temperature, pressure. Examples of multivariable processes exist in abundance: chemical processes, oil refineries, steel mills, guided missiles, and space vehicles, to name a few. In fact, most control systems encountered in practice are of the multivariable type. The control processes discussed in most textbooks are treated as single-variable processes, because it is assumed that the other variables are maintained at a contant value.

In the following discussions, it is assumed that the control inputs and the output variables are related by linear functions. A linear multivariable process may be described by a transfer matrix, as shown in Fig. 1.4-1. The change of one control variable will affect practically all the output variables. In some applications, e.g., the boiler control in a power plant, it is desired that variation of each reference input quantity will cause only one controlled output variable to change, and each output variable is affected only by changes in the corresponding reference input variable. This feature of a multivariable feedback system is referred to as noninteracting control.[139]

Shown in Fig. 1.4-2 is the block diagram of a multivariable feedback control system, in which vector **c** represents the n output variables, vector **m** represents the r control variables, vector **r** denotes the q reference input variables, vector **e** denotes the q actuating signals, matrix **G** is the transfer matrix of the process, and matrix **D** is the controller matrix which is to be determined. For the sake of simplicity, it is assumed that $r = q = n$. The transfer matrix of the process is given by

$$\mathbf{G} = \begin{bmatrix} G_{11}(s) & G_{12}(s) & \cdots & G_{1k}(s) & \cdots & G_{1n}(s) \\ G_{21}(s) & G_{22}(s) & \cdots & G_{2k}(s) & \cdots & G_{2n}(s) \\ \cdots & \cdots & \cdots & \cdots & \cdots & \cdots \\ G_{j1}(s) & G_{j2}(s) & \cdots & G_{jk}(s) & \cdots & G_{jn}(s) \\ \cdots & \cdots & \cdots & \cdots & \cdots & \cdots \\ G_{n1}(s) & G_{n2}(s) & \cdots & G_{nk}(s) & \cdots & G_{nn}(s) \end{bmatrix} \tag{1.4-1}$$

where $G_{jk}(s)$ denotes the transfer function from m_j to c_k, which are the jth element of **m** and the kth element of **c**, respectively. The controller matrix is defined as

$$\mathbf{D} = \begin{bmatrix} D_{11}(s) & D_{12}(s) & \cdots & D_{1k}(s) & \cdots & D_{1n}(s) \\ D_{21}(s) & D_{22}(s) & \cdots & D_{2k}(s) & \cdots & D_{2n}(s) \\ \cdots & \cdots & \cdots & \cdots & \cdots & \cdots \\ D_{j1}(s) & D_{j2}(s) & \cdots & D_{jk}(s) & \cdots & D_{jn}(s) \\ \cdots & \cdots & \cdots & \cdots & \cdots & \cdots \\ D_{n1}(s) & D_{n2}(s) & \cdots & D_{nk}(s) & \cdots & D_{nn}(s) \end{bmatrix} \tag{1.4-2}$$

where $D_{jk}(s)$ denotes the transfer function from e_j to m_k, which are the jth element of **e** and the kth element of **m**, respectively.

With reference to Fig. 1.4-2, the following relationships are derived:

$$\mathbf{C} = \mathbf{GDE} \tag{1.4-3}$$

and

$$\mathbf{C} = [\mathbf{1} + \mathbf{GD}]^{-1}\mathbf{GDR} \tag{1.4-4}$$

where **R**, **E**, and **C** are the Laplace transforms of **r**, **e**, and **c**, respectively. Since noninteracting control of a multivariable system implies one-to-one correspondence between a reference input and a controlled output, it is required that the matrix **GD** be a diagonal matrix. The off-diagonal element of matrix **GD** is zero. This leads to the following conditions:

$$[P_{kk}(s)]\{D_{jk}(s)\} = -D_{kk}(s)\{G_{jk}(s)\}$$
$$j \neq k;\ k = 1, 2, 3, \ldots, n;\ j = 1, 2, 3, \ldots, n \tag{1.4-5}$$

where the element P_{kk} of matrix $[P_{kk}]$ is a minor of the determinant $|\mathbf{G}|$ associated with the element $G_{kk}(s)$, and $\{D_{jk}(s)\}$ and $\{G_{jk}(s)\}$ are column matrices defined by

$$\{D_{jk}(s)\} = \begin{bmatrix} D_{1k}(s) \\ D_{2k}(s) \\ D_{3k}(s) \\ \cdot \\ \cdot \\ \cdot \\ D_{nk}(s) \end{bmatrix} \quad \text{and} \quad \{G_{jk}(s)\} = \begin{bmatrix} G_{1k}(s) \\ G_{2k}(s) \\ G_{3k}(s) \\ \cdot \\ \cdot \\ \cdot \\ G_{nk}(s) \end{bmatrix}$$

By defining a column matrix

$$\{F_{jk}(s)\} = -[P_{kk}(s)]^{-1}\{G_{jk}(s)\} \qquad j \neq k \tag{1.4-6}$$

Eq. (1.4-5) is reduced to

$$\{D_{jk}(s)\} = \{F_{jk}(s)\}D_{kk}(s) \qquad j \neq k \tag{1.4-7}$$

In view of the diagonal nature of the matrix **GD**, the multivariable feedback control system may be represented by n single-variable subsystems. Since the matrix **GD** for noninteracting control may be expressed as

$$\mathbf{GD} = \begin{bmatrix} \sum_{k=1}^{n} D_{k1}(s)G_{1k}(s) & 0 & \cdots & 0 \\ 0 & \sum_{k=1}^{n} D_{k2}(s)G_{2k}(s) & \cdots & 0 \\ \cdots & \cdots & \cdots & \cdots \\ 0 & 0 & \cdots & \sum_{k=1}^{n} D_{kn}(s)G_{nk}(s) \end{bmatrix} \tag{1.4-8}$$

each of the subsystems has n channels in the forward branch, as illustrated in Fig. 1.4-3. Thus the design of the multivariable control system is now

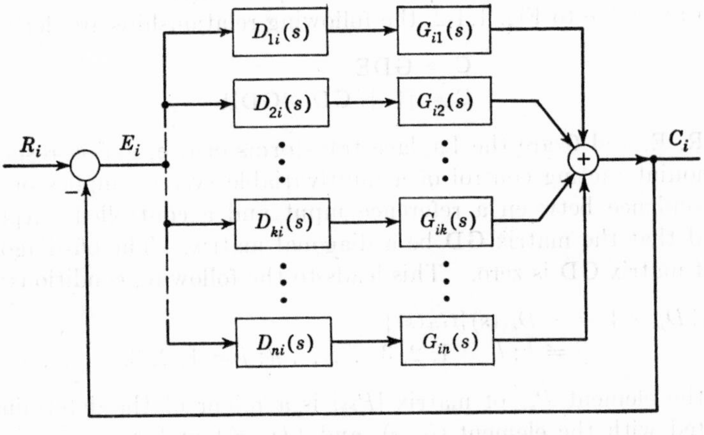

Fig. 1.4-3 Block diagram of a subsystem.

converted into the design of the n subsystems, which requires the determination of the transfer functions $D_{jk}(s)$ in the n parallel channels. It should be noted that the design of the subsystems can be greatly simplified if use is made of the relationship given in Eq. (1.4-7). Utilizing this relationship reduces the block diagram of Fig. 1.4-3 to that shown in Fig. 1.4-4, in which the transfer functions $G_{ik}(s)$ are given and the functions $F_{ki}(s)$ can readily be computed from Eq. (1.4-6). Hence, for this subsystem, $D_{ii}(s)$ is the only unknown transfer function which can be determined by means of the classical techniques. Once all $D_{ii}(s)$ are found, the other elements of the controller matrix **D** can be determined from Eq. (1.4-7).

Although the above design procedure appears quite straightforward, the labor involved in the determination of the controller matrix is tre-

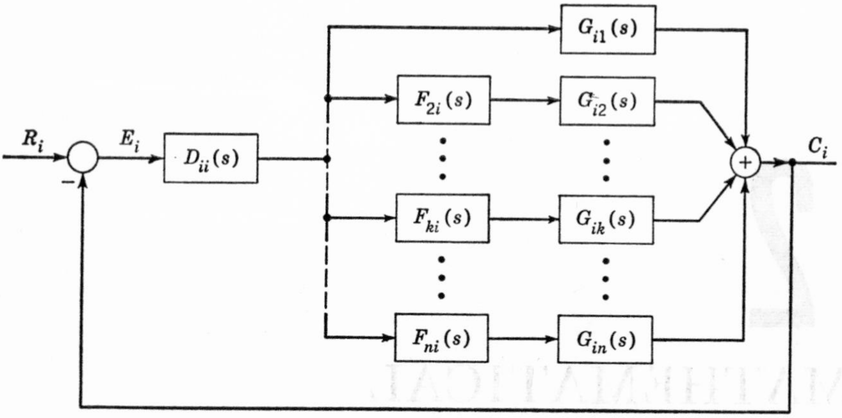

Fig. 1.4-4 The modified block diagram of a subsystem.

mendous. Furthermore, if noninteracting control is considered undesirable, the design of multivariable control systems by the classical approach may prove extremely difficult. As will be seen in later developments in this book, the modern approaches may facilitate the design of multivariable feedback control systems.

2

MATHEMATICAL FOUNDATIONS

This chapter presents a concise introductory discussion of several mathematical concepts and techniques which are fundamental in modern control theory. It is a current trend that engineering analysis and design rely heavily upon mathematical methods. As a result, many engineering schools offer to their undergraduates as standard such courses as Fourier transforms, Laplace transforms, z transforms, and transfer-function analysis. While these undergraduate courses undoubtedly provide the basic mathematical foundations for the analysis and design of conventional control systems, they fail to provide the engineering student with sufficiently adequate mathematical background to cope with modern control problems. A sound knowledge of set theory, vector spaces, eigenvalue problems, and generalized coordinates would appear both desirable and necessary in the development of modern control theory. This chapter attempts to fill partially the gap which is created by the recent rapid advance in control theory and the delay in the modernization of undergraduate curricula in some engineering schools. By so doing, we hope to place at the disposal of computer, control, and system engineers the basis of an intelligent working knowledge of a number of facts and techniques relevant to modern control engineering. This chapter gives, then, an introductory account of such topics as set theory, finite-dimensional vector space, eigenvalue problems, vector-matrix differential equations, quadratic forms, and generalized coordinates. A substantial understanding of these basic underlying principles plays an important role in the efficient use of the facts and techniques. Consequently, care has been taken throughout the chapter to state the desired results and theorems in simple, easy-to-understand language, to provide physical and geometrical interpretations, and to point out some engineering applications. For a more complete discussion from the classical point of view, the reader is referred to standard textbooks on these topics.

2.1 INTRODUCTION TO SET THEORY

The notion of a set is so basic that it is somewhat difficult to define in terms of even more fundamental ideas. A well-defined collection of objects is known as a *set*. This concept, in its complete generality, is of great importance in engineering, since all engineering principles could be developed by starting from it. The set X is usually written as

$$X = \{x_k\} \tag{2.1-1}$$

where the x_k represent the elements of the set. The notation

$$x_k \in X \tag{2.1-2}$$

is commonly used to signify that x_k is an element of X, and the notation

$$y_k \notin X \tag{2.1-3}$$

indicates that y_k is not an element of X. A convenient representation for the set X is given by

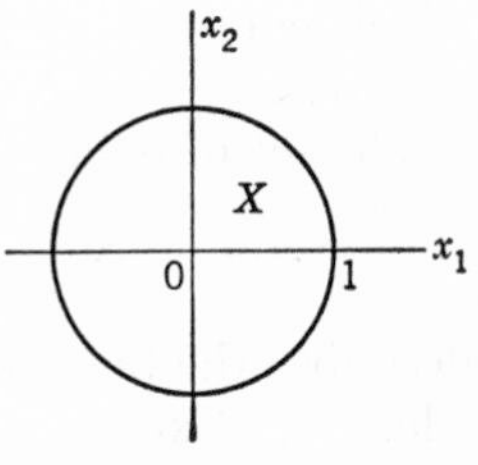

Fig. 2.1-1 Set of points described by

$X = \{[x_1, x_2]: x_1^2 + x_2^2 \leq 1\}$

$$X = \{\mathbf{x}: P(\mathbf{x})\} \tag{2.1-4}$$

which means that the set X represents the set of all points $\mathbf{x}$, each of which has the property $P(\mathbf{x})$. For instance,

$$X = \{[x_1, x_2]: x_1^2 + x_2^2 \leq 1\} \tag{2.1-5}$$

describes the set of points which lie inside and on the circumference of the unit circle with its center at the origin, as illustrated in Fig. 2.1-1.

The sets whose elements are points in a finite-dimensional vector space are called *point sets.* In the following paragraphs, some basic properties and operations on sets are first outlined. More advanced concepts of set theory are discussed later.

Basic Properties and Operations

A set that consists of some members of another set is referred to as a *subset.* Thus a set Y is said to be a subset of a set X if all the elements of Y are in X. However, not all elements of X need to be in subset Y. The notation

$$Y \subset X \qquad \text{or} \qquad X \supset Y \tag{2.1-6}$$

is commonly used to indicate that Y is a subset of X. Two sets X and Y are said to be *equal* if they contain the same elements, i.e., if every element of X is also an element of Y, and conversely.

The *union* of two sets X and Y is the set

$$Z = X \cup Y = \{z_k\} \tag{2.1-7}$$

which contains all elements in either X or Y or both.

The *intersection* of two sets X and Y is the set

$$Z = X \cap Y = \{z_k\} \tag{2.1-8}$$

which contains all elements common to X and Y; that is, $z_k \in X$ and $z_k \in Y$.

The set of points

$$X = \{\mathbf{x}:\mathbf{x} = \alpha\mathbf{x}_2 + (1 - \alpha)\mathbf{x}_1 \qquad \text{all real } \alpha\} \tag{2.1-9}$$

describes the line passing through points $\mathbf{x}_1$ and $\mathbf{x}_2$ in a euclidean space E^n, where $\mathbf{x}_1 \neq \mathbf{x}_2$.

The set of points

$$X = \{\mathbf{x}:\mathbf{x} = \alpha\mathbf{x}_2 + (1 - \alpha)\mathbf{x}_1 \qquad 0 \leq \alpha \leq 1\} \tag{2.1-10}$$

defines the *line segment* joining two points $\mathbf{x}_1$ and $\mathbf{x}_2$ in E^n.

The set of points

$$X = \{\mathbf{x}:\mathbf{a}'\mathbf{x} = c\} \tag{2.1-11}$$

describes a *hyperplane* in E^n, where $\mathbf{a} \neq \mathbf{0}$ is a given $n \times 1$ column vector, c is a specified scalar, and the prime denotes the transpose of the matrix. Thus the equation for a hyperplane is

$$\mathbf{a}'\mathbf{x} = c \tag{2.1-12}$$

It is noted that $\mathbf{a}$ is a vector normal to the hyperplane. Equation (2.1-12) indicates that the hyperplane passes through the origin if and only if

$c = 0$. In a two-dimensional space,

$$\mathbf{x} = \begin{bmatrix} x_1 \\ x_2 \end{bmatrix} \quad \text{and} \quad \mathbf{a} = \begin{bmatrix} a_1 \\ a_2 \end{bmatrix} \tag{2.1-13}$$

$$\mathbf{a}'\mathbf{x} = a_1x_1 + a_2x_2 = c \tag{2.1-14}$$

which is the equation of a straight line. In a three-dimensional space,

$$\mathbf{a}'\mathbf{x} = a_1x_1 + a_2x_2 + a_3x_3 = c \tag{2.1-15}$$

which defines a plane.

A hyperplane $\mathbf{a}'\mathbf{x} = c$ in euclidean space E^n divides all E^n into three mutually exclusive and collectively exhaustive sets. These sets are

(1) $X_1 = \{\mathbf{x}:\mathbf{a}'\mathbf{x} < c\}$
(2) $X_2 = \{\mathbf{x}:\mathbf{a}'\mathbf{x} = c\}$
(3) $X_3 = \{\mathbf{x}:\mathbf{a}'\mathbf{x} > c\}$

The first and the third set describe open half-spaces. The sets

$$X_4 = \{\mathbf{x}:\mathbf{a}'\mathbf{x} \leq c\} \quad \text{and} \quad X_5 = \{\mathbf{x}:\mathbf{a}'\mathbf{x} \geq c\}$$

describe closed half-spaces. It is noted that

$$X_2 = X_4 \cap X_5$$

In euclidean space E^n, n points are needed to determine a hyperplane. However, not any arbitrary set of n points provides a unique definition. Only a set of n points $\mathbf{x}_1, \mathbf{x}_2, \ldots, \mathbf{x}_n$, which can be numbered in such a way that the $n - 1$ vectors $\mathbf{x}_1 - \mathbf{x}_n, \mathbf{x}_2 - \mathbf{x}_n, \ldots, \mathbf{x}_{n-1} - \mathbf{x}_n$ are linearly independent, describes a unique hyperplane. Any point $\mathbf{x}$ on the hyperplane has the property that $\mathbf{x} - \mathbf{x}_n$ can be written as a linear combination of $\mathbf{x}_1 - \mathbf{x}_n, \mathbf{x}_2 - \mathbf{x}_n, \ldots, \mathbf{x}_{n-1} - \mathbf{x}_n$.

By letting

$$\mathbf{n} = \frac{\mathbf{a}}{|\mathbf{a}|} \quad \text{and} \quad \delta = \frac{c}{|\mathbf{a}|} \tag{2.1-16}$$

when $|\mathbf{a}|$ represents the magnitude of vector $\mathbf{a}$, Eq. (2.1-12) reduces to

$$\mathbf{n}'\mathbf{x} = \delta \tag{2.1-17}$$

where $|\mathbf{n}| = 1$, and the vector $\mathbf{n}$ is referred to as a *unit normal* to the hyperplane. In euclidean space E^n, the distance of the hyperplane $\mathbf{a}'\mathbf{x} = c$ from the origin is

$$|\delta| = \frac{|c|}{|\mathbf{a}|} \tag{2.1-18}$$

Two hyperplanes are parallel if they have the same unit normal; that is, the hyperplanes $\mathbf{a}_1'\mathbf{x} = c_1$ and $\mathbf{a}_2'\mathbf{x} = c_2$ are parallel if $\mathbf{a}_1 = \alpha\mathbf{a}_2$, $\alpha \neq 0$.

The set of points

$$X = \{\mathbf{x} : |\mathbf{x} - \mathbf{a}| = r\} \tag{2.1-19}$$

describes a hypersphere in euclidean space E^n with center at $\mathbf{a}$ and radius $r > 0$. Thus the equation of a hypersphere in E^n is

$$|\mathbf{x} - \mathbf{a}| = r \tag{2.1-20a}$$

or

$$\sum_{i=1}^{n} (x_i - a_i)^2 = r^2 \tag{2.1-20b}$$

For instance, in E^2, Eq. (2.1-20) defines a circle with center at (a_1, a_2); and in E^3, Eq. (2.1-20) defines a sphere with center at (a_1, a_2, a_3).

A point $\mathbf{x}$ is called an *interior point* of the set X if there exists a neighborhood about $\mathbf{x}$ which contains only points of the set X. If every ϵ neighborhood about a point $\mathbf{x}$ contains points which are in the set X and points which are not in the set, the point $\mathbf{x}$ is called a *boundary point* of the set X. A set X which contains all its boundary points is called a *closed set.* Hyperplanes are closed sets. A closed half-space is also a closed set. A set X which contains only interior points is called an *open set.* If any two points in an open set can be joined by a polygonal path lying entirely within the set, it is a *connected set.*

For a set X, if there exists a vector of finite components $\mathbf{c}$ such that, for all $\mathbf{x} \in X$, $|\mathbf{x}| \leq |\mathbf{c}|$, the set is referred to as *bounded from above.* If there exists a vector of finite components $\mathbf{c}$ such that, for all $\mathbf{x} \in X$, $|\mathbf{x}| \geq |\mathbf{c}|$, the set X is referred to as *bounded from below.* If there exists a positive number c such that, for every $\mathbf{x} \in X$, $|\mathbf{x}| < c$, the set X is said to be *strictly bounded.*

Based upon the properties described above, the concepts of convex sets, convex hull, and convex cones are presented in the following.

Convex Sets

A *convex set* is defined as the set X in which the line segment joining any two points $\mathbf{x}_1$ and $\mathbf{x}_2$ of the set also lies in the set. This implies that, if $\mathbf{x}_1, \mathbf{x}_2 \in X$, then every point in the set

$$\mathbf{x} = \alpha\mathbf{x}_2 + (1 - \alpha)\mathbf{x}_1 \qquad 0 \leq \alpha \leq 1 \tag{2.1-21}$$

must also belong to the set X. A hyperplane and a half-space are convex sets. The intersection of a finite number of convex sets is also a convex set. The intersection of a finite number of hyperplanes or half-spaces or of both is also a convex set. The intersection of a finite number of hyperplanes or closed half-spaces or of both is a closed convex set. The set of solutions to a system of m linear equations in n unknowns is also a closed convex set. It should be noted that a convex set is a connected set. For example, the set

$$X = \{[x_1, x_2] : x_1{}^2 + x_2{}^2 \leq 1\}$$

is a convex set.

A point $\mathbf{x}$ of convex set X is called an *extreme point* if and only if no distinct points $\mathbf{x}_1$, $\mathbf{x}_2$ exist in the set such that

$$\mathbf{x} = \alpha\mathbf{x}_2 + (1 - \alpha)\mathbf{x}_1 \qquad 0 < \alpha < 1 \tag{2.1-22}$$

This definition implies that an extreme point cannot lie between any other two points of the set. In other words, it cannot lie on the line segment joining two points of the set. An extreme point is a boundary point of the set; however, not all boundary points of a convex set are necessarily extreme points.

A point is called a *convex combination* of a finite number of points $\mathbf{x}_1$, $\mathbf{x}_2$, . . . , $\mathbf{x}_m$ if it can be described by

$$\mathbf{x} = \sum_{k=1}^{m} \beta_k\mathbf{x}_k \qquad \beta_k \geq 0, \ \sum_{k=1}^{m} \beta_k = 1 \tag{2.1-23}$$

Equation (2.1-23) implies that a convex combination of m points can be likened to the center of mass of these points, with the mass assigned to each point being a fraction of the total mass. The set of all convex combinations of a finite number of points $\mathbf{x}_1$, $\mathbf{x}_2$, . . . , $\mathbf{x}_m$ may be written as

$$X = \left\{\mathbf{x}:\mathbf{x} = \sum_{k=1}^{m} \beta_k\mathbf{x}_k \qquad \text{all } \beta_k \geq 0, \ \sum_{k=1}^{m} \beta_k = 1\right\} \tag{2.1-24}$$

which is a convex set.

Among the many classes of convex sets, those having useful engineering applications are convex hull, convex polyhedron, convex cone, and convex polyhedral cone, which are discussed in the following paragraphs.

The *convex hull* of a set Y is defined as the smallest convex set X which contains the set Y. Consider the set of points

$$Y = \{[x_1, x_2]:x_1^2 + x_2^2 = 1\}$$

which describes the circumference of a unit circle with center at the origin. Then, according to the above definition, the convex hull of the set Y is the convex set

$$X = \{[x_1, x_2]:x_1^2 + x_2^2 \leq 1\}$$

which describes the circumference of the unit circle and its interior. Furthermore, it is noted that the convex hull of two distinct points $\mathbf{x}_1$ and $\mathbf{x}_2$ is the set of all convex combinations of the points

$$X = \{\mathbf{x}:\mathbf{x} = \alpha\mathbf{x}_2 + (1 - \alpha)\mathbf{x}_1 \qquad \text{all } \alpha, 0 \leq \alpha \leq 1\} \tag{2.1-25}$$

Since the intersection of all convex sets containing Y is the smallest convex set which embeds Y, the convex hull of a set Y may be defined more rigorously as the intersection of all convex sets which contain set Y. It can be shown that the convex hull of a finite number of points $\mathbf{x}_1$, $\mathbf{x}_2$, . . . , $\mathbf{x}_m$ is the closed set of all convex combinations of the points $\mathbf{x}_1, \mathbf{x}_2, \ldots, \mathbf{x}_m$ as given in Eq. (2.1-24).

The *convex polyhedron* generated by a finite number of points is defined as the convex hull of these points. The convex polyhedron generated by m points cannot have more than m extreme points since it is the set of all convex combinations of the m points. Any point $\mathbf{x}$ in a convex polyhedron can be described by a convex combination of the extreme points of the polyhedrons, thus:

$$\mathbf{x} = \sum_{k=1}^{m} \beta_k \mathbf{x}_k^* \qquad \beta_k \geq 0, \sum_{k=1}^{m} \beta_k = 1 \tag{2.1-26}$$

where the points $\mathbf{x}_k^*$ stand for the extreme points. However, it should be noted that not every convex set with a finite number of extreme points has the property that any point in the set can be described by a convex combination of the extreme points.

A special case of a convex polyhedron which is the convex hull of any set of $n + 1$ points from E^n not lying on a hyperplane in E^n is called a *simplex*. Since in a simplex the $n + 1$ points do not lie on a hyperplane in E^n, n points must be linearly independent. A set of points is said to be linearly independent if no point in the set of points can be written as a linear combination of the others. Thus, a set of points $\mathbf{x}_1, \mathbf{x}_2, \ldots, \mathbf{x}_n$ from E^n is linearly independent if the relationship

$$c_1\mathbf{x}_1 + c_2\mathbf{x}_2 + \cdots + c_n\mathbf{x}_n = 0 \tag{2.1-27}$$

holds only when $c_1 = c_2 = \cdots = c_n = 0$. In a two-dimensional case, a triangle and its interior form a simplex.

If point $\mathbf{x}$ is in a set X, so is $\beta\mathbf{x}$ for all $\beta \geq 0$; then the set $X = \{\mathbf{x}\}$ is said to generate a *cone* C. Symbolically, a cone generated by a set X is described by

$$C = \{\mathbf{y} : \mathbf{y} = \beta\mathbf{x} \qquad \text{all } \beta \geq 0 \text{ and all } \mathbf{x} \in X\} \tag{2.1-28}$$

For example, in a three-dimensional case, a cone generated by the set of points

$$X = \{[x_1, x_2, x_3] : x_3^2 + x_1^2 \leq 1 \qquad x_2 = c\}$$

is illustrated in Fig. 2.1-2. It is clear that a cone is never a strictly bounded set. The dimension of a cone C is defined as the maximum number of linearly independent vectors in C.

A cone contains as an element the point $\mathbf{0}$, which is called the *vertex* of the cone. The negative of a cone $C = \{\mathbf{y}\}$ is the set of points

$$C^- = \{-\mathbf{y}\} \tag{2.1-29}$$

The sum of two cones $C_1 = \{\mathbf{a}\}$ and $C_2 = \{\mathbf{b}\}$ is denoted by $C_1 + C_2$, which is the set of all points $\mathbf{a} + \mathbf{b}$ such that

$$\mathbf{a} \in C_1 \qquad \text{and} \qquad \mathbf{b} \in C_2 \tag{2.1-30}$$

It can be shown that the smallest subspace containing a convex cone C is $C + C^-$. The *polar cone* C^+ of a cone $C = \{\mathbf{a}\}$ is defined as the collection of points $\{\mathbf{b}\}$ such that $\mathbf{b}'\mathbf{a} \geq 0$ for each $\mathbf{b}$ in the set and all $\mathbf{a} \in C$. In a two-dimensional case the polar cone C^+ of a cone C is formed by the half-lines perpendicular to the edges of the cone at the origin, as shown in Fig. 2.1-3.

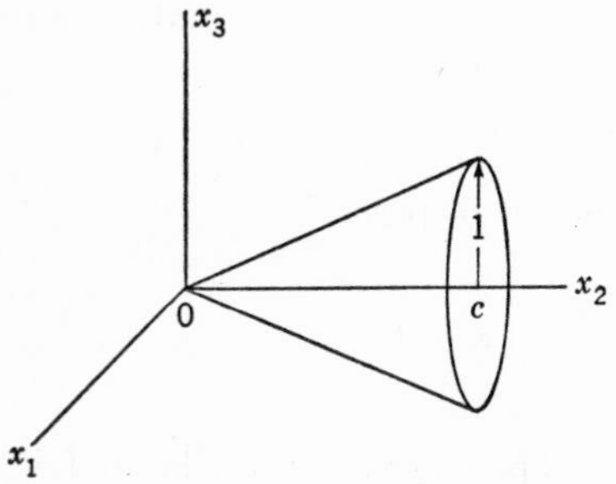

Fig. 2.1-2 A cone generated by the set of points

$X = \{[x_1, x_2, x_3]: x_3^2 + x_1^2 \leq 1,\ x_2 = c\}$

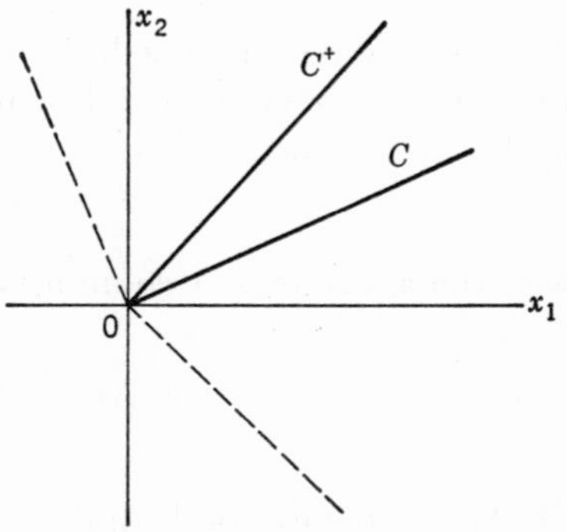

Fig. 2.1-3 Polar cone.

A cone is said to be a *convex cone* if it is generated by a convex set. Putting it in a more precise way, a set of points X generates a convex cone if and only if:

1. The sum $\mathbf{x}_1 + \mathbf{x}_2$ lies in the set X when $\mathbf{x}_1$ and $\mathbf{x}_2$ are in the set X.
2. $\beta\mathbf{x}$ is in the set when $\mathbf{x}$ is in the set X for any $\beta \geq 0$.

A convex cone has the property that the sum of two convex cones is also convex.

The definition of a cone given in Eq. (2.1-28) suggests that a *half-line* may be defined as the set

$$L = \{\mathbf{y}: \mathbf{y} = \beta\mathbf{p} \qquad \text{all } \beta \geq 0\} \tag{2.1-31}$$

where $\mathbf{p}$ stands for a given single point and $\mathbf{p} \neq \mathbf{0}$. The polar cone of a half-line is a closed half-space containing the origin $\mathbf{0}$ on its bounding hyperplane and is described by the set

$$H = \{\boldsymbol{\mu}: \mathbf{p}'\boldsymbol{\mu} \geq 0\} \tag{2.1-32}$$

Thus, the polar cone H of a half-line L is the set of points $\boldsymbol{\mu}$ such that $\boldsymbol{\mu}'\mathbf{y} \geq 0$ for all $\mathbf{y} \in L$.

The concept of half-lines may be used to describe a *convex polyhedral cone*, which is defined as the sum of a finite number of half-lines. Thus

$$C = \sum_{k=1}^{n} L_k \tag{2.1-33}$$

If the point $\mathbf{p}_k$ generates the half-line L_k, the set of points

$$\mathbf{y} = \sum_{k=1}^{n} \beta_k \mathbf{p}_k \qquad \text{all } \beta_k \geq 0$$

defines the convex polyhedral cone C. The cone generated by a convex polyhedron is a convex polyhedron cone. If $\mathbf{A}$ is an $m \times n$ matrix which may be written as

$$\mathbf{A} = (\mathbf{a}_1, \mathbf{a}_2, \ldots, \mathbf{a}_n)$$

where the $\mathbf{a}_k$ are $m \times 1$ column vectors, the set of points

$$\mathbf{y} = \mathbf{A}\mathbf{x} = \sum_{k=1}^{n} \mathbf{x}_k \mathbf{a}_k \qquad \text{all } \mathbf{x} \geq 0$$

describes a convex polyhedral cone in E^m. The columns $\mathbf{a}_k$ of the matrix $\mathbf{A}$ generate the half-lines the sum of which forms the polyhedral cone.

A cone is said to be orthogonal to a cone C if it is generated by the set of all vectors $\mathbf{x}$ in E^n such that each vector $\mathbf{x}$ is orthogonal to some vector $\mathbf{y} \in C$. An orthogonal cone, which is often denoted by the symbol $C^\perp$, is thus defined by the set

$$C^\perp = \{\mathbf{x} : \mathbf{x}'\mathbf{y} = 0 \qquad \text{all } \mathbf{y} \in C\} \tag{2.1-34}$$

The orthogonal cone to a half-line is a hyperplane, and is often denoted by P. For a half-line generated by a given point $\mathbf{p} \neq \mathbf{0}$, it can readily be shown that the orthogonal cone is a hyperplane passing through the origin described by the set

$$P = \{\mathbf{x} : \mathbf{p}'\mathbf{x} = 0\} \tag{2.1-35}$$

2.2 FINITE-DIMENSIONAL VECTOR SPACE

Vectors are frequently employed in many branches of mathematics and in the physical and engineering sciences. At the most elementary level in engineering and physics, a vector is used to describe a physical quantity possessing both magnitude and direction. Typical examples are force, velocity, acceleration, and momentum. It is customary to represent vectors by letters in boldface type. Instead of characterizing a vector by magnitude and direction in the most elementary sense, an equally satisfactory description can be achieved by the terminal point of a vector of proper magnitude and direction emanating from the origin of the coordinate system. In three-dimensional space, a vector $\mathbf{x}$ may be written as

$$\mathbf{x} = (x_1, x_2, x_3) \tag{2.2-1}$$

which implies that $\mathbf{x}$ is a vector drawn from the origin to a point in space E^3 with coordinates (x_1, x_2, x_3). The numbers x_k, $k = 1, 2, 3$, are called the components of the vector along the coordinate axes.

This concept of vector representation leads to the definition of a vector as an ordered array of numbers which should not be limited to a quantity containing at most three components. A vector can be generalized to contain an ordered array of n numbers which are referred to as an ordered n-tuple of numbers. Thus an n-component vector $\mathbf{x}$ is an ordered n-tuple of numbers, which may be written as a $1 \times n$ row matrix

$$\mathbf{x} = (x_1, x_2, \ldots, x_n) \tag{2.2-2}$$

or as an $n \times 1$ column matrix

$$\mathbf{x} = \begin{bmatrix} x_1 \\ x_2 \\ \cdot \\ \cdot \\ \cdot \\ x_n \end{bmatrix} \tag{2.2-3}$$

An n-component vector is also called an n-dimensional vector. The x_k, $k = 1, 2, \ldots, n$, which are assumed to be real numbers, form the components of the vector. A column matrix may be written as

$$\mathbf{x} = (x_1, x_2, \ldots, x_n)' \tag{2.2-4}$$

where the prime denotes the transpose of a matrix. The representation of a vector as either a row matrix or a column matrix is immaterial. These two representations are considered to be geometrically equivalent, though column representation is used more often than row representation. In this book, boldface capital letters are used to describe matrices. Vectors are $n \times 1$ matrices and are denoted by boldface lowercase letters.

Just as (x_1, x_2) and (x_1, x_2, x_3) are used to represent points in two- and three-dimensional spaces, respectively, the notation $(x_1, x_2, \ldots, x_n)$ can be used to describe a point in an n-dimensional space, where the x_k are the coordinates of the point. The n-dimensional space is referred to as the euclidean space, or euclidean vector space, which is often represented by the symbol E^n.

As a prelude to the study of finite-dimensional vector spaces, several commonly used basic vectors must first be defined, and the basic vector operations and properties must be described: A *null vector* is defined as a vector with all its components equal to zero. A null vector is denoted by $\mathbf{0}$ and is thus given by

$$\mathbf{0} = \begin{bmatrix} 0 \\ 0 \\ 0 \\ \cdot \\ \cdot \\ \cdot \\ 0 \end{bmatrix} \tag{2.2-5}$$

A *unit vector* is defined as a vector with one of its components equal to unity and all other components zero. The symbol $\mathbf{e}_k$ is commonly used to represent a unit vector with the kth component equal to 1 and all other components equal to zero. For instance,

$$\mathbf{e}_1 = \begin{bmatrix} 1 \\ 0 \\ 0 \\ \cdot \\ \cdot \\ \cdot \\ 0 \end{bmatrix} \tag{2.2-6}$$

A *sum vector* is defined as a row vector with all components equal to 1; that is,

$$\mathbf{1} = (1, 1, \ldots, 1) \tag{2.2-7}$$

The row vector defined in Eq. (2.2-7) is referred to as a sum vector, because the matrix product of $\mathbf{1}$ and a column vector $\mathbf{a} = (a_1, a_2, a_3, \ldots, a_n)'$ yields the sum $\sum_{k=1}^{n} a_k$.

The basic vector operations are described below.

1. *Vector addition.* The simplest operation acting on two vectors is *addition*. The sum of two vectors

$$\mathbf{x} = \begin{bmatrix} x_1 \\ x_2 \\ \cdot \\ \cdot \\ \cdot \\ x_n \end{bmatrix} \quad \text{and} \quad \mathbf{y} = \begin{bmatrix} y_1 \\ y_2 \\ \cdot \\ \cdot \\ \cdot \\ y_n \end{bmatrix}$$

is defined as the vector

$$\mathbf{x} + \mathbf{y} = \begin{bmatrix} x_1 + y_1 \\ x_2 + y_2 \\ \cdot\ \cdot\ \cdot\ \cdot\ \cdot \\ x_n + y_n \end{bmatrix} \tag{2.2-8}$$

2. *Vector subtraction.* The difference between two vectors **x** and **y** is defined as

$$\mathbf{x} - \mathbf{y} = \begin{bmatrix} x_1 - y_1 \\ x_2 - y_2 \\ \cdot \;\cdot \;\cdot \;\cdot \;\cdot \\ x_n - y_n \end{bmatrix} \tag{2.2-9}$$

3. *Scalar multiplication.* Multiplication of a vector $\mathbf{x} = (x_1, x_2, \ldots, x_n)'$ by a scalar c is defined by the relation

$$c\mathbf{x} = \mathbf{x}c = \begin{bmatrix} cx_1 \\ cx_2 \\ \cdot \\ \cdot \\ \cdot \\ cx_n \end{bmatrix} \tag{2.2-10}$$

4. *Equality.* Two n-dimensional vectors **x** and **y** are said to be equal if and only if their corresponding components are equal; that is, $\mathbf{x} = \mathbf{y}$ if $x_k = y_k$ for $k = 1, 2, \ldots, n$.

5. *Inequality.* Given two n-dimensional vectors **x** and **y**, then $\mathbf{x} \geq \mathbf{y}$ means $x_k \geq y_k$, $\mathbf{x} \leq \mathbf{y}$ means $x_k \leq y_k$, $\mathbf{x} > \mathbf{y}$ means $x_k > y_k$, and $\mathbf{x} < \mathbf{y}$ means $x_k < y_k$, where $k = 1, 2, \ldots, n$.

6. *Inner product of two vectors.* The inner product of two n-dimensional vectors **x** and **y** is a most important scalar function of two vectors. This function is written as $(\mathbf{x}, \mathbf{y})$ or $\mathbf{x}'\mathbf{y}$ and defined by the relation

$$(\mathbf{x}, \mathbf{y}) = \mathbf{x}'\mathbf{y} = \sum_{k=1}^{n} x_k y_k \tag{2.2-11}$$

The importance of the inner product lies in the fact that $(\mathbf{x}, \mathbf{x})$ can be considered to represent the square of the "length" of the real vector **x**. This provides a method for evaluating nonnumerical quantities. From the definition of the inner product, the following properties are derived directly:

$$\begin{aligned}
(\mathbf{x}, \mathbf{y}) &= (\mathbf{y}, \mathbf{x}) \\
(\mathbf{x}, \mathbf{y} + \mathbf{z}) &= (\mathbf{x}, \mathbf{y}) + (\mathbf{x}, \mathbf{z}) \\
(\mathbf{x} + \mathbf{y}, \mathbf{z}) &= (\mathbf{x}, \mathbf{z}) + (\mathbf{y}, \mathbf{z}) \\
(\mathbf{x} + \mathbf{y}, \mathbf{z} + \mathbf{w}) &= (\mathbf{x}, \mathbf{z}) + (\mathbf{x}, \mathbf{w}) + (\mathbf{y}, \mathbf{z}) + (\mathbf{y}, \mathbf{w}) \\
(c\mathbf{x}, \mathbf{y}) &= c(\mathbf{x}, \mathbf{y}) \\
(\mathbf{x}, c\mathbf{y}) &= c(\mathbf{x}, \mathbf{y})
\end{aligned}$$

Basic Properties of Vectors

1. *Orthogonality.* Two vectors **x** and **y** are said to be orthogonal if their inner product vanishes; that is,

$$(\mathbf{x}, \mathbf{y}) = 0 \tag{2.2-12}$$

The unit vectors are orthogonal because $(\mathbf{e}_i, \mathbf{e}_j) = 0$ for $i \neq j$. This implies that the coordinate system in n-dimensional space defined by the unit vectors is an orthogonal coordinate system analogous to the orthogonal coordinate systems for two- and three-dimensional spaces.

2. *Norm.* The norm of an n-dimensional vector $\mathbf{x}$ is defined as

$$\|\mathbf{x}\| = (\mathbf{x}, \mathbf{x})^{\frac{1}{2}} = \left(\sum_{k=1}^{n} x_k^2\right)^{\frac{1}{2}} \tag{2.2-13}$$

3. *Distance.* The distance from the vector $\mathbf{x}$ to the vector $\mathbf{y}$ is defined as

$$|\mathbf{x} - \mathbf{y}| = (\mathbf{x} - \mathbf{y}, \mathbf{x} - \mathbf{y})^{\frac{1}{2}} = \left[\sum_{k=1}^{n} (x_k - y_k)^2\right]^{\frac{1}{2}} \tag{2.2-14}$$

The distance between two vectors possesses the following properties:

$$\begin{aligned} |\mathbf{x} - \mathbf{y}| &> 0 \qquad \text{unless } \mathbf{x} - \mathbf{y} = \mathbf{0} \\ |\mathbf{x} - \mathbf{y}| &= |\mathbf{y} - \mathbf{x}| \\ |\mathbf{x} - \mathbf{y}| + |\mathbf{y} - \mathbf{z}| &\geq |\mathbf{x} - \mathbf{z}| \end{aligned}$$

4. *Length.* The length of a vector $\mathbf{x}$ is the distance from the origin to the vector $\mathbf{x}$. It is also called the norm of vector $\mathbf{x}$.

5. *Schwarz inequality.* It can be shown that, for any two n-dimensional vectors $\mathbf{x}$ and $\mathbf{y}$,

$$|(\mathbf{x}, \mathbf{y})| < |\mathbf{x}|\,|\mathbf{y}| \tag{2.2-15}$$

where $|(\mathbf{x}, \mathbf{y})|$ denotes the absolute value of the inner product, and $|\mathbf{x}|$ and $|\mathbf{y}|$ stand for the length of the vectors $\mathbf{x}$ and $\mathbf{y}$, respectively. Equation (2.2-15) is called the Schwarz inequality.

6. *Triangle inequality.* For any two n-dimensional vectors $\mathbf{x}$ and $\mathbf{y}$,

$$|\mathbf{x} + \mathbf{y}| \leq |\mathbf{x}| + |\mathbf{y}| \tag{2.2-16}$$

which is referred to as triangle inequality.

7. *Angle.* The angle θ between two n-dimensional vectors

$$\mathbf{x} = (x_1, x_2, \ldots, x_n) \qquad \text{and} \qquad \mathbf{y} = (y_1, y_2, \ldots, y_n)$$

is given by

$$\cos\theta = \frac{(\mathbf{x}, \mathbf{y})}{\|\mathbf{x}\|\,\|\mathbf{y}\|} \tag{2.2-17a}$$

$$\cos\theta = \frac{\sum_{k=1}^{n} x_k y_k}{\left(\sum_{k=1}^{n} x_k^2\right)^{\frac{1}{2}} \left(\sum_{k=1}^{n} y_k^2\right)^{\frac{1}{2}}} \tag{2.2-17b}$$

In statistics, the cosine of the angle between two vectors $\mathbf{x}$ and $\mathbf{y}$ defines the correlation coefficient for the sets of data represented by these two vectors.

8. *Linear combination.* Given m n-dimensional vectors $\mathbf{x}_1, \mathbf{x}_2, \ldots, \mathbf{x}_m$, a linear combination of these m vectors for any scalars c_k, $k = 1, 2, \ldots, m$, is defined as the n-dimensional vector

$$\mathbf{x} = \sum_{k=1}^{m} c_k \mathbf{x}_k \tag{2.2-18}$$

Making use of the basic vector operations described in the preceding paragraphs, it can readily be shown that any n-dimensional vector can be expressed as a linear combination of the n unit vectors; i.e.,

$$\begin{aligned} \mathbf{x} &= (x_1, x_2, \ldots, x_n)' \\ &= \sum_{k=1}^{n} x_k \mathbf{e}_k \end{aligned} \tag{2.2-19}$$

Clearly, this is a straightforward generalization from two- and three-dimensional cases to higher dimensions. In E^2, a two-dimensional vector is expressed as

$$\mathbf{x} = x_1\mathbf{e}_1 + x_2\mathbf{e}_2$$

and in E^3, a three-dimensional vector is written as

$$\mathbf{x} = x_1\mathbf{e}_1 + x_2\mathbf{e}_2 + x_3\mathbf{e}_3$$

In operations with two- and three-dimensional spaces, the unit vectors lie along the coordinate axes of the system. This concept can easily be extended to spaces of higher dimensions. A coordinate system for n-dimensional space can be obtained if one imagines that a coordinate axis is drawn along each of the n unit vectors. The origin of the n-dimensional coordinate system is represented by the null vector $\mathbf{0}$, and the kth component of an n-dimensional vector $\mathbf{x}$ is the component of $\mathbf{x}$ along the kth coordinate axis. This representation of an n-dimensional vector leads to the *generalized coordinate system* in classical mechanics.

9. *Linear dependence.* An n-dimensional vector $\mathbf{x}_k$ in a set of vectors from euclidean space E^n is said to be linearly dependent on the other vectors if $\mathbf{x}_k$ can be expressed as a linear combination of some of the other vectors in the set. The set of vectors is also said to be linearly dependent. On the other hand, if no vector in a set of n-dimensional vectors can be expressed as a linear combination of the other vectors, the set of vectors is said to be linearly independent. The condition for linear dependence of a set of vectors may be stated as follows: A set of n-dimensional vectors $\mathbf{x}_1, \mathbf{x}_2, \ldots, \mathbf{x}_m$ from euclidean space E^n is defined as linearly dependent if there exist scalars c_k not all zero such that

$$\sum_{k=1}^{m} c_k \mathbf{x}_k = \mathbf{0} \tag{2.2-20}$$

If the above equation holds only for c_k all equal to zero, the set of vectors is defined as linearly independent. On the basis of the above definitions, the following statements concerning n-dimensional vectors may be inferred:

a. If a set of n-dimensional vectors is linearly independent, any subset of these vectors is also linearly independent.

b. If a set of n-dimensional vectors is linearly dependent, any larger set of vectors containing this set of vectors is also linearly dependent.

c. If a subset of r vectors in a set of m n-dimensional vectors $\mathbf{x}_1, \mathbf{x}_2, \ldots, \mathbf{x}_m$ from euclidean space E^n is linearly independent, $r < m$ being the maximum number of linearly independent vectors in the set, every other vector in the set can be expressed as a linear combination of these r linearly independent vectors.

d. The null vector is linearly dependent on every other vector in a set, and no set of linearly independent vectors can contain the null vector.

Geometrical considerations indicate that any two vectors which are not parallel to a line are linearly independent in two-dimensional space and that any three vectors which are not parallel to a plane are linearly independent in three-dimensional space. An analytical criterion for linear dependence of a set of vectors with real components may be expressed in terms of the Gram determinant, or *Gramian*, of the set of vectors. By successively forming the scalar products of $\mathbf{x}_1, \mathbf{x}_2, \ldots, \mathbf{x}_m$ into both sides of Eq. (2.2-20), it will be found that the coefficients c_k must also satisfy the equations

$$c_1(\mathbf{x}_k, \mathbf{x}_1) + c_2(\mathbf{x}_k, \mathbf{x}_2) + \cdots + c_k(\mathbf{x}_k, \mathbf{x}_k) + \cdots + c_m(\mathbf{x}_k, \mathbf{x}_m) = 0$$

for $k = 1, 2, \ldots, m$. These conditions clearly require merely that the left-hand member of Eq. (2.2-20) be simultaneously orthogonal to the vectors $\mathbf{x}_1, \mathbf{x}_2, \ldots, \mathbf{x}_m$. According to Cramer's rule, this set of m equations in m coefficients c_k can possess a nontrivial solution only if the determinant

$$G = \begin{vmatrix} \mathbf{x}_1^2 & (\mathbf{x}_1, \mathbf{x}_2) & \cdots & (\mathbf{x}_1, \mathbf{x}_m) \\ (\mathbf{x}_2, \mathbf{x}_1) & \mathbf{x}_2^2 & \cdots & (\mathbf{x}_2, \mathbf{x}_m) \\ \cdots & \cdots & \cdots & \cdots \\ (\mathbf{x}_m, \mathbf{x}_1) & (\mathbf{x}_m, \mathbf{x}_2) & \cdots & \mathbf{x}_m^2 \end{vmatrix} \qquad (2.2\text{-}21)$$

vanishes. This determinant is referred to as the Gram determinant, or Gramian of the set of vectors $\mathbf{x}_1, \mathbf{x}_2, \ldots, \mathbf{x}_m$. Thus a set of vectors is linearly dependent if and only if its Gramian vanishes. It can be shown that, for a vector with complex components, this theorem is still true if the scalar products in the definition of the Gramian are replaced by hermitian scalar products.

The set of all vectors $\mathbf{x}$ which can be expressed as the linear combination

$$\mathbf{x} = \sum_{k=1}^{m} c_k \mathbf{x}_k \qquad (2.2\text{-}22)$$

is called the *vector space* generated by the vectors $\mathbf{x}_k$. If r and only r of the m vectors $\mathbf{x}_k$ are linearly independent, the set of vectors is said to be of rank r. When $r < m$, it is noted that $m - r$ of the vectors $\mathbf{x}_k$ can be written as linear combinations of the r independent vectors $\mathbf{x}_k$, and Eq. (2.2-22) can accordingly be expressed equivalently as a combination of only r linearly independent vectors, so that only r independent coefficients of combination are indeed available in such a case. In a space of n dimensions, any vector $\mathbf{x}$ can be generated by any set of vectors of rank n in the form

$$\mathbf{x} = \sum_{k=1}^{n} c_k \mathbf{x}_k \tag{2.2-23}$$

where the n vectors $\mathbf{x}_k$ are linearly independent. The concept of vector space is further discussed in the following paragraphs.

Vector Space and Subspace

A vector space is defined as a collection or a set of vectors which is closed under the operations of addition and multiplication by scalars. This definition implies that, if $\mathbf{x}$ and $\mathbf{y}$ are two vectors in the vector space V, the sum $\mathbf{x} + \mathbf{y}$ and the multiplication by a scalar c as $c\mathbf{x}$ and $c\mathbf{y}$ are also in the same collection of vectors. If a vector space V is a collection of all finite n-dimensional vectors, V is called an n-dimensional vector space V_n. A real inner-product vector space is referred to as a euclidean space and is denoted by the symbol E^n. Its complex analog is called a unitary space. A Hilbert vector space is defined as the vector space of infinite-dimensional vectors,

$$\mathbf{x} = (x_1, x_2, \ldots, x_\infty)'$$

of complex numbers, but with finite value of its norm. The dimension of a vector space is equal to the maximum number of linearly independent vectors contained in it.

A subspace S_n of the n-dimensional vector space V_n is defined as a subset of V_n, which is itself a vector space. The dimension of a subspace S_n is defined as the maximum number of linearly independent vectors in the subspace. A subset is a subspace if it is closed, under addition and under multiplication, by scalars. If V_n is a vector space and S is a subset of V_n, the set W of all vectors dependent on S is a subspace of V_n. Moreover, $W = V$ if and only if the dimension of W is equal to the dimension of V.

Consider a set of n-dimensional vectors $\mathbf{x}_k$ such that they form an n-dimensional vector space V_n. A linear combination of $\mathbf{x}_k$ is also defined in V_n. Suppose that A is an appropriate $n \times n$ matrix. Then the new vector

$$\mathbf{y} = \mathbf{A}\mathbf{x} \tag{2.2-24}$$

is in the same collection of vectors. Equation (2.2-24) describes a linear transformation, and the vector space V_n is said to be invariant under linear transformation represented by $\mathbf{A}$. When $\mathbf{A}$ is an $m \times n$ matrix, each point of V_n is transformed or mapped into a point in V_m. Of course, if $m \neq n$, then $\mathbf{y}$ and $\mathbf{x}$ cannot be considered to be points in the same space. Under linear transformation, addition and multiplication by a scalar are preserved. A linear transformation T on the space V_n can be defined as a process which maps each vector $\mathbf{x}$ of V_n into a vector $T(\mathbf{x})$ of V_m such that, for all vectors $\mathbf{x}_i$ and $\mathbf{x}_j$ in V_n and all scalars a_i and a_j, the following relationship holds:

$$T(a_i\mathbf{x}_i + a_j\mathbf{x}_j) = a_iT(\mathbf{x}_i) + a_jT(\mathbf{x}_j) \tag{2.2-25}$$

When matrix $\mathbf{A}$ of Eq. (2.2-24) is an $m \times n$ matrix, the matrix $\mathbf{A}$ is said to map all vectors of space V_n into space V_m. Since any $m \times n$ matrix $\mathbf{A}$ can be written as a row of $m \times 1$ column vectors,

$$\mathbf{A} = (\mathbf{a}_1, \mathbf{a}_2, \ldots, \mathbf{a}_n) \tag{2.2-26}$$

Eq. (2.2-24) may be expressed as

$$\mathbf{y} = \mathbf{A}\mathbf{x} = x_1\mathbf{a}_1 + x_2\mathbf{a}_2 + \cdots + x_n\mathbf{a}_n \tag{2.2-27}$$

where the x_i can take on all possible values. The range of the linear transformation, which is defined as the subspace generated by the $\mathbf{y}$, is then the subspace of V_m generated by the columns of $\mathbf{A}$, with the dimension equal to the maximum number of linearly independent columns in matrix $\mathbf{A}$.

A linear transformation of vectors is very important in the theory of vector space. Consider a linear combination of vectors $\mathbf{x}(k)$ of the form

$$\sum_{i=0}^{k} \mathbf{A}_i\mathbf{x}(i)$$

where $\mathbf{A}_i$ is an appropriate linear-transformation matrix. If $\mathbf{A}_i$ is an $n \times n$ matrix, this collection of vectors constitutes an n-dimensional vector space V_n. When $\mathbf{A}_i$ is an $m \times n$ matrix with $m < n$, it is noted that, as $\mathbf{x}(i)$ ranges over the entire vector space V_n, $\mathbf{A}_i\mathbf{x}(i)$ ranges over only a certain part of V_n. This part of V_n is called a subspace S. Thus a subspace of a finite-dimensional vector space V is itself a vector space, with dimension less than or equal to that of the vector space V.

Now consider the linear transformation

$$\mathbf{y}(k) = \mathbf{M}\mathbf{x}(k) \tag{2.2-28}$$

where the measurement matrix $\mathbf{M}$ is an $m \times n$ matrix, with $m < n$. Equation (2.2-28) appears again in the optimum-estimation problems discussed in Chap. 8. The dimension of $\mathbf{y}(k)$ is less than or equal to that of $\mathbf{x}(k)$. A collection of $n \times 1$ vectors $\mathbf{x}(i)$ forms a vector space of dimension n,

$$V = \sum_{i=0}^{K} \mathbf{A}_i\mathbf{x}(i) \tag{2.2-29}$$

where $\mathbf{A}_i$ is an appropriate $n \times n$ matrix. In a like manner, a collection of $m \times 1$ vectors $\mathbf{y}(i)$ constitutes a vector space of dimension m,

$$S = \sum_{i=0}^{K} \mathbf{B}_i \mathbf{y}(i) \tag{2.2-30}$$

where $\mathbf{B}_i$ is an appropriate $m \times m$ matrix. Since $m < n$, the vector space S is a subspace of the vector space V.

Concept of a Basis

A set of vectors $\mathbf{x}_1, \mathbf{x}_2, \ldots, \mathbf{x}_k$ from vector space V_n is said to generate V_n if every vector in V_n can be written as a linear combination of $\mathbf{x}_1, \mathbf{x}_2, \ldots, \mathbf{x}_k$. This set of vectors is referred to as a generating set. If a vector space V_n has finite dimension n, any linearly independent set with n vectors is a basis for V_n, and every basis for V_n has n vectors. Thus a basis for V_n is defined as a linearly independent subset of n vectors from V_n which spans the entire space. If vector space V_n has finite dimension n and the set $S = \{\mathbf{x}_1, \mathbf{x}_2, \ldots, \mathbf{x}_k\}$ is any linearly independent set in V_n, then, for $k < n$, there exist vectors $\mathbf{x}_{k+1}, \mathbf{x}_{k+2}, \ldots, \mathbf{x}_n$ such that the set $\{\mathbf{x}_1, \mathbf{x}_2, \ldots, \mathbf{x}_n\}$ is a basis for V_n. The representation of any vector in terms of a set of basis vectors is unique. However, a basis for vector space V_n is by no means unique. The n unit vectors $\mathbf{e}_1, \mathbf{e}_2, \ldots, \mathbf{e}_n$ form a basis for vector space V_n.

Given a set of basis vectors $\mathbf{x}_1, \mathbf{x}_2, \ldots, \mathbf{x}_k$ for vector space V_n and any other vector $\mathbf{y} \neq \mathbf{0}$ from V_n, if in the expression of $\mathbf{y}$ as a linear combination of the $\mathbf{x}_i$,

$$\mathbf{y} = \sum_{i=1}^{k} \lambda_i \mathbf{x}_i \tag{2.2-31}$$

any vector $\mathbf{x}_i$ for which $\lambda_i \neq 0$ is removed from the set $\{\mathbf{x}_1, \mathbf{x}_2, \ldots, \mathbf{x}_k\}$ and $\mathbf{y}$ is added to the set, the new set of k vectors is also a basis for vector space V_n. A set of n mutually orthogonal vectors of unit length from vector space V_n forms an orthogonal basis for V_n.

Orthogonal Projection

Consider two vectors $\mathbf{x}$ and $\mathbf{y}$ which are different from zero. The vectors $\mathbf{x}$ and $\mathbf{y}$ are said to be orthogonal if their inner product $(\mathbf{x}, \mathbf{y})$ is zero. This idea can be extended to a system of vectors. The nonzero vectors in an n-dimensional vector space V_n are said to be orthogonal if their inner products are zero. Let $\mathbf{x}_1, \mathbf{x}_2, \ldots, \mathbf{x}_n$ be an orthogonal system of vectors. Then

$$(\mathbf{x}_i, \mathbf{x}_j) = 0 \qquad \text{for } i \neq j \tag{2.2-32a}$$

$$(\mathbf{x}_i, \mathbf{x}_j) = \|\mathbf{x}_i\|^2 \qquad \text{for } i = j \tag{2.2-32b}$$

A system of vectors is said to be orthogonal if any two vectors of the system are orthogonal to each other. The vectors forming an orthogonal system are linearly independent. Let $\mathbf{x}_1, \mathbf{x}_2, \ldots, \mathbf{x}_n$ be the vectors in the vector space V. This system of vectors is linearly independent if every relation of the form

$$\lambda_1\mathbf{x}_1 + \lambda_2\mathbf{x}_2 + \cdots + \lambda_n\mathbf{x}_n = \mathbf{0} \tag{2.2-33}$$

implies that $\lambda_1 = \lambda_2 = \cdots = \lambda_n = 0$. Now, if $\mathbf{x}_i$ is orthogonal to every vector in V, then

$$\begin{aligned}(\mathbf{0}, \mathbf{x}_i) &= (\lambda_1\mathbf{x}_1 + \lambda_2\mathbf{x}_2 + \cdots + \lambda_n\mathbf{x}_n, \mathbf{x}_i)\\ &= \lambda_i(\mathbf{x}_i, \mathbf{x}_i)\end{aligned} \tag{2.2-34}$$

Since $(\mathbf{x}_i, \mathbf{x}_i)$ is larger than zero, it follows that $\lambda_i = 0$.

Consider any subspace S of the vector space V. The set of all vectors in this vector space V which is orthogonal to every vector in the subspace S is called the orthogonal complement of the subspace S. The orthogonal complement of a vector $\mathbf{x}$ in a vector space V is the set of all vectors of the space which are orthogonal to the vector $\mathbf{x}$. In the three-dimensional space, the orthogonal complement of a vector is the set of all vectors perpendicular to the given vector.

Let $\mathbf{x}$ be any vector of the vector space V and let S be a subspace. The vector $\hat{\mathbf{x}}$ is said to be an orthogonal projection of $\mathbf{x}$ on the subspace S if the following conditions are satisfied: (1) The vector $\hat{\mathbf{x}}$ is in subspace S, and (2) the vector $\tilde{\mathbf{x}} = \mathbf{x} - \hat{\mathbf{x}}$ is orthogonal to every vector in the subspace S. This vector $\tilde{\mathbf{x}}$ is referred to as the normal component of $\mathbf{x}$, that is, the perpendicular dropped from $\mathbf{x}$ on the subspace S. It is to be noted that the vector $\mathbf{x}$ and its normal component $\tilde{\mathbf{x}}$ are not in the subspace S, while its orthogonal projection is a vector in subspace S. It can be shown that the orthogonal projection $\mathbf{x}$ (sometimes simply called the projection of $\mathbf{x}$) always exists for any vector $\mathbf{x}$ on a subspace S. The concept of orthogonal projection is to be applied to the study of optimum-estimation problems in control systems. Some of the useful properties of orthogonal projection are outlined below:

1. The orthogonal projection $\hat{\mathbf{x}}$ is in the subspace S of the vector space V.
2. The vector $\mathbf{x}$ is equal to the sum of the orthogonal projection $\hat{\mathbf{x}}$ and the normal component $\tilde{\mathbf{x}}$.
3. The normal component is orthogonal to every vector in the subspace S. The converse is also true. Thus, if $\mathbf{x} - \mathbf{a}$ is orthogonal to every vector in subspace S and vector $\mathbf{a}$ is an element of subspace S, vector $\mathbf{a}$ is the orthogonal projection of vector $\mathbf{x}$ on subspace S. The projection of a vector on a subspace is unique.
4. The norm of vector $\mathbf{x}$ is larger than or equal to the norm of the projection $\hat{\mathbf{x}}$. This can readily be shown by considering property 2. It follows that

$$\begin{aligned}\|\mathbf{x}\|^2 &= (\hat{\mathbf{x}} + \tilde{\mathbf{x}}, \hat{\mathbf{x}} + \tilde{\mathbf{x}})\\ &= (\hat{\mathbf{x}}, \hat{\mathbf{x}}) + 2(\hat{\mathbf{x}}, \tilde{\mathbf{x}}) + (\tilde{\mathbf{x}}, \tilde{\mathbf{x}})\\ &= (\hat{\mathbf{x}}, \hat{\mathbf{x}}) + (\tilde{\mathbf{x}}, \tilde{\mathbf{x}})\end{aligned}$$

Hence

$$\|\mathbf{x}\| \geq \|\hat{\mathbf{x}}\| \tag{2.2-35}$$

The third step follows from the orthogonality of $\hat{\mathbf{x}}$ and $\tilde{\mathbf{x}}$.

5. For any vector $\mathbf{a}$ in subspace S, the norm of $\mathbf{x} - \hat{\mathbf{x}}$ is less than or equal to the norm of $\mathbf{x} - \mathbf{a}$; that is,

$$\|\mathbf{x} - \hat{\mathbf{x}}\| \leq \|\mathbf{x} - \mathbf{a}\| \tag{2.2-36}$$

This property can be proved by noting that, for any vector $\mathbf{a}$ in subspace S, the vector $\hat{\mathbf{x}} - \mathbf{a}$ is also in S, since the projection $\hat{\mathbf{x}}$ is an element of subspace S. Thus

$$\begin{aligned} \|\mathbf{x} - \mathbf{a}\|^2 &= \|(\mathbf{x} - \hat{\mathbf{x}}) + (\hat{\mathbf{x}} - \mathbf{a})\|^2 \\ &= \|\tilde{\mathbf{x}} + (\hat{\mathbf{x}} - \mathbf{a})\|^2 \\ &= (\tilde{\mathbf{x}}, \tilde{\mathbf{x}}) + 2(\tilde{\mathbf{x}}, \hat{\mathbf{x}} - \mathbf{a}) + (\hat{\mathbf{x}} - \mathbf{a}, \hat{\mathbf{x}} - \mathbf{a}) \\ &= (\tilde{\mathbf{x}}, \tilde{\mathbf{x}}) + (\hat{\mathbf{x}} - \mathbf{a}, \hat{\mathbf{x}} - \mathbf{a}) \\ &\geq \|\mathbf{x} - \hat{\mathbf{x}}\|^2 \end{aligned}$$

The equality sign is satisfied when $\hat{\mathbf{x}} = \mathbf{a}$.

2.3 EIGENVALUE PROBLEMS AND QUADRATIC FORMS

Of frequent occurrence in modern control engineering is the problem of determining those values of a scalar parameter λ for which there exist nontrivial solutions to the set of homogeneous equations

$$\begin{aligned} a_{11}x_1 + a_{12}x_2 + \cdots + a_{1n}x_n &= \lambda x_1 \\ a_{21}x_1 + a_{22}x_2 + \cdots + a_{2n}x_n &= \lambda x_2 \\ \cdots\cdots\cdots\cdots\cdots\cdots\cdots\cdots \\ a_{n1}x_1 + a_{n2}x_2 + \cdots + a_{nn}x_n &= \lambda x_n \end{aligned} \tag{2.3-1}$$

Such a problem is known as an *eigenvalue problem*. Values of λ for which nontrivial solutions exist are called eigenvalues of the problem or of the matrix $\mathbf{A} = [a_{ik}]$. The corresponding vector solutions are known as eigenvectors of the problem or of the matrix $\mathbf{A}$. A column made up of the elements of an eigenvector is often referred to as a modal column. In vector notation, Eq. (2.3-1) may be written as

$$\mathbf{A}\mathbf{x} = \lambda\mathbf{x} \tag{2.3-2}$$

where

$$\mathbf{A} = \begin{bmatrix} a_{11} & a_{12} & \cdots & a_{1n} \\ a_{21} & a_{22} & \cdots & a_{2n} \\ \cdots & \cdots & \cdots & \cdots \\ a_{n1} & a_{n2} & \cdots & a_{nn} \end{bmatrix} \tag{2.3-3}$$

and

$$\mathbf{x} = \begin{bmatrix} x_1 \\ x_2 \\ \cdot \\ \cdot \\ \cdot \\ x_n \end{bmatrix} \tag{2.3-4}$$

Shifting the left-hand member of Eq. (2.3-2) to the right yields

$$(\mathbf{A} - \lambda\mathbf{I})\mathbf{x} = \mathbf{0} \tag{2.3-5}$$

This problem possesses nontrivial solutions if and only if the determinant of the coefficient matrix $[\mathbf{A} - \lambda\mathbf{I}]$ vanishes; that is,

$$|\mathbf{A} - \lambda\mathbf{I}| = \begin{vmatrix} a_{11} - \lambda & a_{12} & \cdots & a_{1n} \\ a_{21} & a_{22} - \lambda & \cdots & a_{2n} \\ \cdots & \cdots & \cdots & \cdots \\ a_{n1} & a_{n2} & \cdots & a_{nn} - \lambda \end{vmatrix} = 0 \tag{2.3-6}$$

Expansion of the determinant gives the characteristic equation in λ. The n solutions $\lambda_1, \lambda_2, \ldots, \lambda_n$ are the eigenvalues of the matrix $\mathbf{A}$. Corresponding to each such value λ_k, the vector solutions of the equation are the eigenvectors of the matrix $\mathbf{A}$. Clearly, the determinant $|\mathbf{A} - \lambda\mathbf{I}|$ of Eq. (2.3-6) expands into an nth-order polynomial,

$$f(\lambda) = |\mathbf{A} - \lambda\mathbf{I}| = (-\lambda)^n + b_{n-1}(-\lambda)^{n-1} + \cdots + b_1(-\lambda) + b_0 \tag{2.3-7}$$

The function $f(\lambda)$ is called the characteristic function or eigenfunction for $\mathbf{A}$.

In many practical considerations, $\mathbf{A}$ in Eq. (2.3-5) is a symmetric matrix. A matrix $\mathbf{A}$ is said to be symmetric if it is characterized by the condition that

$$a_{ij} = a_{ji} \tag{2.3-8}$$

It can be shown that the eigenvectors of a symmetric matrix possess the following fundamental properties:

1. Two eigenvectors of a real symmetric matrix corresponding to different eigenvalues are orthogonal.
2. All eigenvalues of a real symmetric matrix are real.
3. The eigenvectors of an nth-order symmetric matrix $\mathbf{A}$ generate an n-dimensional vector space.
4. There exists at least one orthonormal set of eigenvectors of $\mathbf{A}$ which generates the n-dimensional vector space. By an orthonormal set of vectors is meant a set of orthogonal vectors which are normalized by the condition $(\mathbf{x}_i, \mathbf{x}_i) = 1$.
5. If an eigenvalue λ_i has multiplicity r, the eigenvectors corresponding to λ_i generate a subspace of dimension r.
6. For an eigenvalue λ_i with multiplicity r, there are exactly r linearly independent eigenvectors with eigenvalue λ_i in any set of n orthonormal eigenvectors of $\mathbf{A}$.
7. If one or more eigenvalues have multiplicity $r \geq 2$, there are an infinite number of different sets of orthonormal eigenvectors of $\mathbf{A}$ which generate the n-dimensional vector space, corresponding to the different ways of selecting orthonormal sets to generate the subspaces with dimension $r \geq 2$.

Now consider the nonhomogeneous equation

$$(\mathbf{A} - \lambda\mathbf{I})\mathbf{x} = \mathbf{c} \tag{2.3-9}$$

where $\mathbf{A}$ is a real symmetric matrix. If Eq. (2.3-9) has a solution, it can be expressed as a linear combination of the eigenvectors of $\mathbf{A}$. Assume that $\mathbf{e}_1, \mathbf{e}_2, \ldots, \mathbf{e}_n$ are the normalized eigenvectors. These are unit vectors normalized to $(\mathbf{x}, \mathbf{x}) = 1$. Then one has

$$\mathbf{A}\mathbf{e}_1 = \lambda_1\mathbf{e}_1 \qquad \mathbf{A}\mathbf{e}_2 = \lambda_2\mathbf{e}_2 \qquad \cdots \qquad \mathbf{A}\mathbf{e}_n = \lambda_n\mathbf{e}_n \tag{2.3-10}$$

The solution can be assumed to be of the form

$$\mathbf{x} = \sum_{j=1}^{n} a_j\mathbf{e}_j \tag{2.3-11}$$

where the parameters a_j are to be determined. Substituting Eq. (2.3-11) into Eq. (2.3-9) and using Eqs. (2.3-10) leads to

$$\sum_{j=1}^{n} (\lambda_j - \lambda)a_j\mathbf{e}_j = \mathbf{c} \tag{2.3-12}$$

From this equation the parameters a_j are determined by forming the scalar product of any $\mathbf{e}_i$ into both members of Eq. (2.3-12). Since $(\mathbf{e}_i, \mathbf{e}_j) = \delta_{ij}$, the ith coefficient a_i must then satisfy the equation

$$(\lambda_i - \lambda)a_i = (\mathbf{e}_i, \mathbf{c}) \qquad i = 1, 2, \ldots, n \tag{2.3-13}$$

Hence, if λ is not an eigenvalue,

$$\mathbf{x} = \sum_{j=1}^{n} \frac{(\mathbf{e}_j, \mathbf{c})}{\lambda_j - \lambda}\mathbf{e}_j \tag{2.3-14}$$

forms the unique solution to Eq. (2.3-9).

Quadratic Forms

A quadratic form in n variables $x_1, x_2, \ldots, x_n$ is an expression in which each term contains either the square of a variable or the product of two different variables:

$$\begin{aligned} Q(x_k) &= \sum_{i=1}^{n}\sum_{j=1}^{n} a_{ij}x_ix_j \\ &= a_{11}x_1x_1 + a_{12}x_1x_2 + \cdots + a_{1n}x_1x_n \\ &\quad + a_{21}x_2x_1 + a_{22}x_2x_2 + \cdots + a_{2n}x_2x_n \\ &\quad + \cdots \\ &\quad + a_{n1}x_nx_1 + a_{n2}x_nx_2 + \cdots + a_{nn}x_nx_n \end{aligned} \tag{2.3-15}$$

This expression determines a unique value of $Q(x_k)$ for any set of x_k. By writing

$$\mathbf{x} = \begin{bmatrix} x_1 \\ x_2 \\ \cdot \\ \cdot \\ \cdot \\ x_n \end{bmatrix}$$

and $$\mathbf{A} = [a_{ij}]$$

Eq. (2.3-15) can be put into the matrix form

$$\begin{aligned} Q(\mathbf{x}) &= \sum_{i=1}^{n} x_i \sum_{i=1}^{n} a_{ij}x_j \\ &= \sum_{i=1}^{n} x_i(\mathbf{Ax})_i \\ &= \mathbf{x}'\mathbf{Ax} \end{aligned} \tag{2.3-16}$$

where $\mathbf{A}$ is said to be the matrix associated with the n-dimensional quadratic form. In the derivation of Eq. (2.3-16), $(\mathbf{Ax})_i$ denotes the ith row of $\mathbf{Ax}$. For example, the quadratic form $Q(\mathbf{x}) = ax_1^2 + 2bx_1x_2 + cx_2^2$ can be written in the form

$$x_1(ax_1 + bx_2) + x_2(bx_1 + cx_2)$$

Hence, if the vector $\mathbf{x}$ and the matrix $\mathbf{A}$ are defined by

$$\mathbf{x} = \begin{bmatrix} x_1 \\ x_2 \end{bmatrix} \quad \text{and} \quad \mathbf{A} = \begin{bmatrix} a & b \\ b & c \end{bmatrix}$$

then it follows that $Q(\mathbf{x}) = \mathbf{x}'\mathbf{Ax}$.

In Eq. (2.3-15) it is observed that a_{ij} and a_{ji} are both coefficients of x_ix_j when $i \neq j$. Thus the coefficient of x_ix_j is $a_{ij} + a_{ji}$ for $i \neq j$. By defining new coefficients,

$$b_{ij} = b_{ji} = \frac{a_{ij} + a_{ji}}{2} \tag{2.3-17}$$

the matrix associated with a quadratic form is converted into a symmetric matrix. Hence the matrix $\mathbf{A}$ associated with the quadratic form $\mathbf{x}'\mathbf{Ax}$ can be assumed to be symmetric.

The quadratic form $\mathbf{x}'\mathbf{Ax}$ is said to be positive-definite if it is positive for all $\mathbf{x}$ except $\mathbf{x} = \mathbf{0}$. For example, the quadratic form

$$Q(\mathbf{x}, \mathbf{I}) = \mathbf{x}'\mathbf{x} = \sum_{i=1}^{n} x_i^2 \tag{2.3-18}$$

is positive-definite. The quadratic form $\mathbf{x}'\mathbf{A}\mathbf{x}$ is said to be positive-semidefinite if it is nonnegative for all $\mathbf{x}$ and there exist points $\mathbf{x} \neq \mathbf{0}$ for which $\mathbf{x}'\mathbf{A}\mathbf{x} = 0$. The quadratic form $\mathbf{x}'\mathbf{A}\mathbf{x}$ is said to be negative-definite if it is negative for all $\mathbf{x}$ except $\mathbf{x} = \mathbf{0}$. The quadratic form is said to be negative-semidefinite if it is nonpositive for all $\mathbf{x}$ and there exist points $\mathbf{x} \neq \mathbf{0}$ for which $\mathbf{x}'\mathbf{A}\mathbf{x} = 0$. If a quadratic form $\mathbf{x}'\mathbf{A}\mathbf{x}$ is positive for some $\mathbf{x}$ and negative for others, it is said to be indefinite.

The quadratic form $\mathbf{x}'\mathbf{A}\mathbf{x}$ is positive-definite if and only if all eigenvalues of $\mathbf{A}$ are positive. The quadratic form $\mathbf{x}'\mathbf{A}\mathbf{x}$ is positive-semidefinite if and only if all eigenvalues of $\mathbf{A}$ are nonnegative and at least one of the eigenvalues vanishes. The quadratic form $\mathbf{x}'\mathbf{A}\mathbf{x}$ is indefinite if and only if the matrix $\mathbf{A}$ has both positive and negative eigenvalues. Similar statements can be made for negative-definite and negative-semidefinite quadratic forms. If one knows the eigenvalues of $\mathbf{A}$, one can immediately determine whether the quadratic form is positive -definite, semidefinite, etc. A positive-definite form remains positive-definite when expressed in terms of a new set of variables provided that the transformation of the variables is nonsingular. If matrices $\mathbf{A} = [a_{ij}]$ and $\mathbf{B} = [b_{ij}]$ are positive-definite, the matrix $\mathbf{C} = [a_{ij}b_{ij}]$ is also positive-definite.

It can be shown that a necessary and sufficient condition for the quadratic form $\mathbf{x}'\mathbf{A}\mathbf{x}$ or the symmetric matrix $\mathbf{A}$ to be positive-definite is that the naturally ordered principal minors of $\mathbf{A}$ are all positive; that is,

$$a_{11} > 0 \qquad \begin{vmatrix} a_{11} & a_{12} \\ a_{21} & a_{22} \end{vmatrix} > 0 \qquad \begin{vmatrix} a_{11} & a_{12} & a_{13} \\ a_{21} & a_{22} & a_{23} \\ a_{31} & a_{32} & a_{33} \end{vmatrix} > 0 \qquad \cdots \qquad |\mathbf{A}| > 0 \tag{2.3-19}$$

This property provides a simple procedure for determining whether the quadratic form is positive-definite. For example, the quadratic form $4x_1^2 + 5x_1x_2 + 3x_2^2$ is positive-definite, since it can be written as

$$[x_1, x_2] \begin{bmatrix} 4 & 2 \\ 3 & 3 \end{bmatrix} \begin{bmatrix} x_1 \\ x_2 \end{bmatrix}$$

and the principal minors of $\mathbf{A}$ are

$$4 > 0 \qquad \text{and} \qquad \begin{vmatrix} 4 & 2 \\ 3 & 3 \end{vmatrix} = 6 > 0$$

The criteria for positive and negative definiteness in terms of eigenvalues are sometimes not useful in applications, because the numerical determination of the eigenvalues of a matrix of large dimension is a very difficult task. Any direct attempt based upon a straightforward expansion of the determinant $|\mathbf{A} - \lambda\mathbf{I}|$ is destined for failure because of the extraordinarily large number of terms appearing in the expansion of a determinant. On the other hand, the determinantal criterion for positive-definiteness, as given in Eq. (2.3-19), provides computational simplicity.

Reduction to Diagonal Form

1. Symmetric Matrices with Distinct Eigenvalues. Let $\lambda_1, \lambda_2, \ldots, \lambda_n$ be the distinct eigenvalues of symmetric matrix $\mathbf{A}$ and $\mathbf{x}_1, \mathbf{x}_2, \ldots, \mathbf{x}_n$ be the corresponding set of eigenvectors which are normalized by the condition that

$$(\mathbf{x}_i, \mathbf{x}_i) = 1$$

Consider a matrix $\mathbf{T}$ given by

$$\mathbf{T} = (\mathbf{x}_1, \mathbf{x}_2, \ldots, \mathbf{x}_n) \tag{2.3-20}$$

which is formed by using the eigenvectors $\mathbf{x}_i$ as columns. The transpose of matrix $\mathbf{T}$ is given by

$$\mathbf{T}' = \begin{bmatrix} \mathbf{x}_1' \\ \mathbf{x}_2' \\ \cdot \\ \cdot \\ \cdot \\ \mathbf{x}_n' \end{bmatrix} \tag{2.3-21}$$

In view of the orthogonality of eigenvectors corresponding to distinct eigenvalues of a symmetric matrix, this is true:

$$\mathbf{T}'\mathbf{T} = [\mathbf{x}_i'\mathbf{x}_j] = [\delta_{ij}] = \mathbf{I} \tag{2.3-22}$$

Thus the matrix $\mathbf{T}$ is an orthogonal matrix.

Making use of the relationships

$$\mathbf{AT} = (\mathbf{Ax}_1, \mathbf{Ax}_2, \ldots, \mathbf{Ax}_n)$$

and

$$\mathbf{Ax}_i = \lambda_i\mathbf{x}_i$$

then

$$\mathbf{AT} = (\lambda_1\mathbf{x}_1, \lambda_2\mathbf{x}_2, \ldots, \lambda_n\mathbf{x}_n) \tag{2.3-23}$$

It follows from Eqs. (2.3-21) and (2.3-23) that

$$\mathbf{T}'\mathbf{AT} = [\lambda_i\mathbf{x}_i'\mathbf{x}_j] = [\lambda_i\delta_{ij}] \tag{2.3-24}$$

Upon expansion, Eq. (2.3-24) may be expressed as

$$\mathbf{\Lambda} = \mathbf{T}'\mathbf{AT} \tag{2.3-25}$$

$$\mathbf{\Lambda} = \begin{bmatrix} \lambda_1 & 0 & \cdots & 0 \\ 0 & \lambda_2 & \cdots & 0 \\ \cdot & \cdot & \cdots & \cdot \\ 0 & 0 & \cdots & \lambda_n \end{bmatrix} \tag{2.3-26}$$

A matrix of this type is referred to as a diagonal matrix. Premultiplying

Eq. (2.3-25) by **T** and postmultiplying Eq. (2.3-25) by **T**′ yields

$$\mathbf{A} = \mathbf{T\Lambda T}' \tag{2.3-27}$$

Thus a symmetric matrix may be expressed in terms of a diagonal matrix. It is noted that both matrix **A** and diagonal matrix **T′AT** have the same eigenvalues.

A quadratic form

$$Q(\mathbf{x}) = \mathbf{x}'\mathbf{A}\mathbf{x} \tag{2.3-28}$$

can be reduced to the *canonical form.* By letting

$$\mathbf{x} = \mathbf{T}\mathbf{y} \tag{2.3-29}$$

where the matrix **T** is given by Eq. (2.3-20), Eq. (2.3-28) reduces to

$$\begin{aligned} Q(\mathbf{x}) &= (\mathbf{Ty})'\mathbf{ATy} \\ &= \mathbf{y}'\mathbf{T}'\mathbf{ATy} \\ &= \mathbf{y}'\mathbf{\Lambda y} \end{aligned} \tag{2.3-30}$$

This representation is referred to as the canonical form. Upon expansion, Eq. (2.3-30) yields

$$\sum_{i=1}^{n} \sum_{j=1}^{n} a_{ij}x_i x_j = \sum_{i=1}^{n} \lambda_i y_i^2 \tag{2.3-31}$$

Since the matrix **T** is orthogonal, Eq. (2.3-29) implies that

$$\mathbf{T}'\mathbf{x} = \mathbf{T}'\mathbf{T}\mathbf{y} = \mathbf{y} \tag{2.3-32}$$

Thus, to each value of **x** there corresponds precisely one value of **y**, and conversely.

2. General Symmetric Matrices. The diagonalization of a symmetric matrix is not limited to matrices with distinct eigenvalues. Any real symmetric matrix may be transformed into diagonal form by means of an orthogonal transformation. The validity of this statement can be demonstrated by considering a second-order symmetric matrix,

$$\mathbf{A} = \begin{bmatrix} a_{11} & a_{12} \\ a_{21} & a_{22} \end{bmatrix} = \begin{bmatrix} \mathbf{a}_1 \\ \mathbf{a}_2 \end{bmatrix} \tag{2.3-33}$$

where

$$\mathbf{a}_1 = (a_{11}, a_{12}) \tag{2.3-34a}$$

$$\mathbf{a}_2 = (a_{21}, a_{22}) \tag{2.3-34b}$$

Let λ_1 and λ_2 be the eigenvalues of **A**, and $\mathbf{x}_1$ and $\mathbf{x}_2$ be the corresponding eigenvectors. $\mathbf{x}_1$ and $\mathbf{x}_2$ are defined by

$$\mathbf{x}_1 = \begin{bmatrix} x_{11} \\ x_{21} \end{bmatrix} \quad \text{and} \quad \mathbf{x}_2 = \begin{bmatrix} x_{12} \\ x_{22} \end{bmatrix} \tag{2.3-35}$$

Then

$$\mathbf{A}\mathbf{x}_1 = \lambda_1 \mathbf{x}_1 \tag{2.3-36}$$

and

$$\begin{bmatrix} a_{11}x_{11} + a_{12}x_{21} \\ a_{21}x_{11} + a_{22}x_{21} \end{bmatrix} = \lambda_1 \begin{bmatrix} x_{11} \\ x_{21} \end{bmatrix} \tag{2.3-37}$$

Since the orthogonal matrix **T** is given by

$$\mathbf{T} = [\mathbf{x}_1, \mathbf{x}_2] = \begin{bmatrix} x_{11} & x_{12} \\ x_{21} & x_{22} \end{bmatrix} \tag{2.3-38}$$

and

$$\mathbf{T}' = \begin{bmatrix} x_{11} & x_{21} \\ x_{12} & x_{22} \end{bmatrix} \tag{2.3-39}$$

the transformed matrix **T'AT** is

$$\mathbf{T'AT} = \mathbf{T}' \begin{bmatrix} a_{11}x_{11} + a_{12}x_{21} & a_{11}x_{12} + a_{12}x_{22} \\ a_{21}x_{11} + a_{22}x_{21} & a_{21}x_{12} + a_{22}x_{22} \end{bmatrix} \tag{2.3-40}$$

$$\mathbf{T'AT} = \mathbf{T}' \begin{bmatrix} \lambda_1 x_{11} & (\mathbf{a}_1, \mathbf{x}_1) \\ \lambda_1 x_{21} & (\mathbf{a}_2, \mathbf{x}_2) \end{bmatrix} \tag{2.3-41}$$

In the above reduction, use is made of Eqs. (2.3-34), (2.3-35), and (2.3-37). When the multiplication is carried out, Eq. (2.3-41) reduces to

$$\mathbf{T'AT} = \begin{bmatrix} \lambda_1 & b_{12} \\ 0 & b_{22} \end{bmatrix} \tag{2.3-42}$$

where the parameters b_{12} and b_{22} are to be determined. Since matrix **A** is symmetrical and

$$(\mathbf{T'AT})' = \mathbf{T'A'(T')'} = \mathbf{T'AT} \tag{2.3-43}$$

the transformed matrix is symmetric and

$$b_{12} = 0$$

Since the eigenvalues of matrix **A** are identical with the eigenvalues of **T'AT**, b_{22} must be the eigenvalue λ_2 of matrix **A**. Hence

$$\mathbf{T'AT} = \begin{bmatrix} \lambda_1 & 0 \\ 0 & \lambda_2 \end{bmatrix} \tag{2.3-44}$$

In this way the proof of the n-dimensional case can be carried out by induction.

3. General Matrices with Distinct Eigenvalues. It can be shown that, if the eigenvalues of matrix **A** are distinct, matrix **A** can be transformed into a diagonal matrix

$$\mathbf{T}^{-1}\mathbf{AT} = \begin{bmatrix} \lambda_1 & 0 & \cdots & 0 \\ 0 & \lambda_2 & \cdots & 0 \\ \cdots & \cdots & \cdots & \cdots \\ 0 & 0 & \cdots & \lambda_n \end{bmatrix} \tag{2.3-45}$$

where $\lambda_1, \lambda_2, \ldots, \lambda_n$ are the eigenvalues of matrix **A**, and matrix **T** can be formed by using the corresponding eigenvectors as columns. It is noted that, if the matrix **A** is symmetric, $\mathbf{T'T} = \mathbf{I}$ and Eq. (2.3-45) reduces to Eq. (2.3-25).

However, there are matrices which cannot be reduced to a diagonal form by means of a nonsingular matrix. For example, n-dimensional matrices which do not possess n linearly independent eigenvectors cannot be diagonalized. For an arbitrary square matrix, it is always possible to transform the matrix into the Jordan canonical form

$$\mathbf{T}^{-1}\mathbf{A}\mathbf{T} = \begin{bmatrix} \mathbf{L}_{k_1}(\lambda_1) & 0 & \cdots & 0 \\ 0 & \mathbf{L}_{k_2}(\lambda_2) & \cdots & 0 \\ \cdots & \cdots & \cdots & \cdots \\ 0 & 0 & \cdots & \mathbf{L}_{k_r}(\lambda_r) \end{bmatrix} \tag{2.3-46}$$

with $k_1 + k_2 + \cdots + k_r = n$, where λ_i are the eigenvalues of matrix $\mathbf{A}$, not necessarily distinct, and $\mathbf{L}_{k_i}(\lambda_i)$ is a $k_i \times k_i$ matrix of the form

$$\mathbf{L}_{k_i}(\lambda_i) = \begin{bmatrix} \lambda_i & 1 & 0 & \cdots & \cdots & 0 \\ 0 & \lambda_i & 1 & \cdots & \cdots & 0 \\ \cdots & \cdots & \cdots & \cdots & \cdots & \cdots \\ \cdots & \cdots & \cdots & \cdots & \lambda_i & 1 \\ 0 & 0 & \cdots & \cdots & \cdots & \lambda_i \end{bmatrix} \tag{2.3-47}$$

with $L_1(\lambda) = \lambda$.

The transformation defined by

$$\mathbf{\Lambda} = \mathbf{T}^{-1}\mathbf{A}\mathbf{T}$$

is referred to as a similarity transformation. Matrix $\mathbf{A}$ is said to be similar to the matrix $\mathbf{\Lambda}$. Similar matrices have the same set of eigenvalues and the same characteristic functions. A similarity transformation can be shown to convert any square matrix to the Jordan canonical form

$$\begin{bmatrix} \lambda_1 & \alpha_1 & 0 & 0 & \cdots & 0 \\ 0 & \lambda_2 & \alpha_2 & 0 & \cdots & 0 \\ 0 & 0 & \lambda_3 & \alpha_3 & \cdots & 0 \\ \cdots & \cdots & \cdots & \cdots & \cdots & \cdots \\ 0 & 0 & 0 & \cdots & \cdots & \alpha_{n-1} \\ 0 & 0 & 0 & 0 & \cdots & \lambda_n \end{bmatrix}$$

where the α_1 are either 1 or 0. Hence every square matrix is similar to the Jordan canonical matrix. When the eigenvalues are all distinct or when the matrix $\mathbf{A}$ is symmetric, the Jordan canonical matrix reduces to a diagonal matrix.

Cayley-Hamilton Theorem

This theorem reveals a very interesting and useful property of the characteristic polynomial. It states that every matrix satisfies its own *characteristic equation.*

Let $\lambda_1, \lambda_2, \ldots, \lambda_n$ be the eigenvalues of the matrix **A**. The characteristic equation of A is given by

$$f(\lambda) = (\lambda - \lambda_1)(\lambda - \lambda_2) \cdots (\lambda - \lambda_n) = 0 \tag{2.3-48}$$

Then the Cayley-Hamilton theorem implies that

$$f(\mathbf{A}) = (\mathbf{A} - \lambda_1\mathbf{I})(\mathbf{A} - \lambda_2\mathbf{I}) \cdots (\mathbf{A} - \lambda_n\mathbf{I}) = 0 \tag{2.3-49}$$

This theorem is also applicable when there are repeated roots of the characteristic equation. Let the characteristic equation have r repeated roots at $\lambda = \lambda_i$. Then the characteristic polynomial can be written as

$$f(\lambda) = (\lambda - \lambda_i)^r p(\lambda) \tag{2.3-50}$$

The modified characteristic equation is then given by

$$(\lambda - \lambda_i)p(\lambda) = 0 \tag{2.3-51}$$

which is often referred to as the *minimal equation* for λ. It can be shown that every matrix **A** satisfies its own minimal equation; that is, the minimal polynomial for **A** is equal to zero:

$$(\mathbf{A} - \lambda_i\mathbf{I})p(\mathbf{A}) = 0 \tag{2.3-52}$$

Thus the Cayley-Hamilton theorem can be restated as follows: The characteristic polynomial for **A** is divisible by the minimal polynomial for **A**. For example, consider the matrix

$$\mathbf{A} = \begin{bmatrix} 7 & 4 & -1 \\ 4 & 7 & -1 \\ -4 & -4 & 4 \end{bmatrix}$$

The corresponding characteristic equation is

$$(\lambda - 3)^2(\lambda - 12) = 0$$

Then it is found that the minimal polynomial for **A** is

$$(\mathbf{A} - 3\mathbf{I})(\mathbf{A} - 12\mathbf{I}) = \begin{bmatrix} 4 & 4 & -1 \\ 4 & 4 & -1 \\ -4 & -4 & 1 \end{bmatrix} \begin{bmatrix} -5 & 4 & -1 \\ 4 & -5 & -1 \\ -4 & -4 & -8 \end{bmatrix}$$

which is equal to zero. Hence

$$f(\mathbf{A}) = (\mathbf{A} - 3\mathbf{I})^2(\mathbf{A} - 12\mathbf{I}) = 0$$

This equation follows from the Cayley-Hamilton theorem.

Differentiation of a Quadratic Form

In view of the fact that the optimum design of control systems often involves the differentiation of quadratic forms when the optimum performance of the system is characterized by a quadratic performance index, the differentiation of a quadratic form is briefly reviewed.

1. Differentiation with Respect to a Scalar. Let

$$Q(x_k) = \mathbf{x}'\mathbf{A}\mathbf{x} = \sum_{i=1}^{n} \sum_{j=1}^{n} a_{ij}x_i x_j \tag{2.3-53}$$

Then differentiating $Q(x_k)$ with respect to x_k yields

$$\begin{aligned}
\frac{dQ(x_k)}{dx_k} &= \frac{d}{dx_k}\left[a_{kk}x_k^2 + x_k\left(\sum_{\substack{i=1\\ i\neq k}}^{n} a_{ki}x_i + \sum_{\substack{j=1\\ j\neq k}}^{n} a_{jk}x_j\right)\right] \\
&= 2a_{kk}x_k + \sum_{\substack{i=1\\ i\neq k}}^{n} a_{ki}x_i + \sum_{\substack{j=1\\ j\neq k}}^{n} a_{jk}x_j \\
&= \sum_{i=1}^{n} a_{ki}x_i + \sum_{j=1}^{n} a_{jk}x_j \\
&= \sum_{i=1}^{n} (a_{ki} + a_{ik})x_i
\end{aligned}$$

Hence the derivative may be expressed in matrix form as

$$\frac{dQ(x_k)}{dx_k} = (\mathbf{A}\mathbf{x})_k + (\mathbf{A}'\mathbf{x})_k \tag{2.3-54}$$

That is, the derivative of $Q(x_k)$ with respect to x_k is equal to the sum of the kth row of the column vectors $\mathbf{Ax}$ and $\mathbf{A'x}$. It follows from Eq. (2.3-54) that, when $\mathbf{A} = \mathbf{I}$,

$$\frac{d(\mathbf{x}'\mathbf{x})}{dx_k} = 2x_k \tag{2.3-55}$$

2. Differentiation with Respect to a Vector Variable. Let the vector $\mathbf{x}$ be given by

$$\mathbf{x} = \begin{bmatrix} x_1 \\ x_2 \\ \cdot \\ \cdot \\ \cdot \\ x_n \end{bmatrix} \tag{2.3-56}$$

and the differentiation operator $\nabla_{\mathbf{x}}$ be defined by

$$\nabla_{\mathbf{x}} = \frac{d}{d\mathbf{x}} = \begin{bmatrix} \frac{\partial}{\partial x_1} \\ \frac{\partial}{\partial x_2} \\ \cdot \\ \cdot \\ \cdot \\ \frac{\partial}{\partial x_n} \end{bmatrix} \tag{2.3-57}$$

Since $Q(\mathbf{x}) = \mathbf{x}'\mathbf{A}\mathbf{x}$,

$$\nabla_{\mathbf{x}}Q(\mathbf{x}) = \frac{dQ(\mathbf{x})}{d\mathbf{x}} = \begin{bmatrix} \frac{\partial}{\partial x_1} \\ \frac{\partial}{\partial x_2} \\ \cdot \\ \cdot \\ \cdot \\ \frac{\partial}{\partial x_n} \end{bmatrix} \left(\sum_{i=1}^{n} \sum_{j=1}^{n} a_{ij}x_ix_j \right) \tag{2.3-58}$$

Making use of Eq. (2.3-54), the derivative reduces to

$$\frac{dQ(\mathbf{x})}{d\mathbf{x}} = \begin{bmatrix} (\mathbf{Ax})_1 \\ (\mathbf{Ax})_2 \\ \cdot \\ \cdot \\ \cdot \\ (\mathbf{Ax})_n \end{bmatrix} + \begin{bmatrix} (\mathbf{A'x})_1 \\ (\mathbf{A'x})_2 \\ \cdot \\ \cdot \\ \cdot \\ (\mathbf{A'x})_n \end{bmatrix}$$

$$= \mathbf{Ax} + \mathbf{A'x} \tag{2.3-59}$$

Thus the differentiation of a quadratic form with respect to the vector variable yields the sum of two column vectors. In the special case of $\mathbf{A} = \mathbf{I}$, it follows from Eq. (2.3-59) that

$$\frac{d(\mathbf{x}'\mathbf{x})}{d\mathbf{x}} = 2\mathbf{x} \tag{2.3-60}$$

Sylvester Expansion Theorem

This theorem finds useful application in evaluating functions expressed as infinite power series of the matrix $\mathbf{A}$. Let $\lambda_1, \lambda_2, \ldots, \lambda_n$ be the n distinct eigenvalues of the $n \times n$ matrix $\mathbf{A}$. The theorem states that the function

$$f(\mathbf{A}) = \sum_{k=1}^{\infty} c_k\mathbf{A}^k \tag{2.3-61}$$

is equivalent to

$$f(\mathbf{A}) = \sum_{i=1}^{n} f(\lambda_i)\mathbf{F}(\lambda_i) \tag{2.3-62}$$

where

$$\mathbf{F}(\lambda_i) = \prod_{\substack{j=1 \\ j \neq i}}^{n} \left[\frac{\mathbf{A} - \lambda_j \mathbf{I}}{\lambda_i - \lambda_j}\right] \tag{2.3-63}$$

It is important to note that $\mathbf{F}(\lambda_i)$ is independent of the type of function $f(\mathbf{A})$. Some of the important properties of $\mathbf{F}(\lambda_i)$ are summarized as follows:

(1) $$\mathbf{F}(\lambda_i)\mathbf{F}(\lambda_j) = 0 \qquad \text{for } i \neq j$$

This property follows from the Cayley-Hamilton theorem, since

$$\mathbf{F}(\lambda_i)\mathbf{F}(\lambda_j) = \prod_{\substack{k=1 \\ k \neq i}}^{n} \frac{\mathbf{A} - \lambda_k \mathbf{I}}{\lambda_i - \lambda_k} \prod_{\substack{m=1 \\ m \neq j}}^{n} \frac{\mathbf{A} - \lambda_m \mathbf{I}}{\lambda_j - \lambda_m}$$

$$= \prod_{k=1}^{n} [\mathbf{A} - \lambda_k \mathbf{I}] \mathbf{\Phi}(\mathbf{A}, \lambda_m)$$

(2) $$[\mathbf{F}(\lambda_i)]^r = \mathbf{F}(\lambda_i)$$

(3) $$\sum_{i=1}^{n} \mathbf{F}(\lambda_i) = \mathbf{I}$$

As an illustration, consider the function

$$f(\mathbf{A}) = e^{\mathbf{A}t}$$

where the matrix $\mathbf{A}$ is given by

$$\mathbf{A} = \begin{bmatrix} 1 & -3 \\ 1 & -1 \end{bmatrix}$$

The characteristic equation of $\mathbf{A}$ is given by

$$\begin{vmatrix} \lambda - 1 & 3 \\ -1 & \lambda + 1 \end{vmatrix} = 0$$

which may be reduced to

$$\lambda^2 + 2 = 0$$

The eigenvalues of $\mathbf{A}$ are $\lambda_1 = j\sqrt{2}$ and $\lambda_2 = -j\sqrt{2}$.

Applying the Sylvester expansion theorem yields

$$f(\mathbf{A}) = e^{\mathbf{A}t} = \sum_{i=1}^{2} f(\lambda_i)\mathbf{F}(\lambda_i)$$

Since

$$f(\lambda_1) = e^{j\sqrt{2}t} \qquad \text{and} \qquad f(\lambda_2) = e^{-j\sqrt{2}t}$$

$$\mathbf{F}(\lambda_1) = \frac{\mathbf{A} + j\sqrt{2}\,\mathbf{I}}{j2\sqrt{2}} \qquad \text{and} \qquad \mathbf{F}(\lambda_2) = \frac{\mathbf{A} - j\sqrt{2}\,\mathbf{I}}{-j2\sqrt{2}}$$

$$\begin{aligned}
f(\mathbf{A}) &= \frac{e^{j\sqrt{2}t}[\mathbf{A} + j\sqrt{2}\,\mathbf{I}] - e^{-j\sqrt{2}t}[\mathbf{A} - j\sqrt{2}\,\mathbf{I}]}{j2\sqrt{2}} \\
&= \frac{1}{j2\sqrt{2}}\{j\sqrt{2}\,(e^{j\sqrt{2}t} + e^{-j\sqrt{2}t})\mathbf{I} + (e^{j\sqrt{2}t} - e^{-j\sqrt{2}t})\mathbf{A}\} \\
&= (\cos\sqrt{2}\,t)\mathbf{I} + \left(\frac{1}{\sqrt{2}}\sin\sqrt{2}\,t\right)\mathbf{A} \\
&= \begin{bmatrix} \cos\sqrt{2}\,t + \dfrac{1}{\sqrt{2}}\sin\sqrt{2}\,t & -\dfrac{3}{\sqrt{2}}\sin\sqrt{2}\,t \\ \dfrac{1}{\sqrt{2}}\sin\sqrt{2}\,t & \cos\sqrt{2}\,t - \dfrac{1}{\sqrt{2}}\sin\sqrt{2}\,t \end{bmatrix}
\end{aligned}$$

This result can readily be checked for formal evaluation by use of the Laplace transforms.

2.4 VECTOR–MATRIX DIFFERENTIAL EQUATIONS

An important class of control processes which have received a great deal of attention is the linear multivariable systems subject to additive disturbances. The dynamic characterization of such a control process is usually described by the following differential equation in vector-matrix notation:

$$\dot{\mathbf{x}}(t) = \mathbf{A}(t)\mathbf{x}(t) + \mathbf{D}(t)\mathbf{m}(t) + \mathbf{n}(t) \tag{2.4-1}$$

where $\mathbf{A}(t)$ = coefficient matrix of the process
$\mathbf{D}(t)$ = driving matrix
$\mathbf{x}(t)$ = state vector of the process
$\mathbf{m}(t)$ = control vector
$\mathbf{n}(t)$ = disturbance vector

If the control process is of nth order, the coefficient matrix $\mathbf{A}(t)$ is an $n \times n$ square matrix. The process described by Eq. (2.4-1) is said to be linear and nonstationary. If the coefficient matrix of the process and the driving matrix are time-invariant, the process is linear and stationary. When the matrices **A** and **D** are functions of random parameters of the process, it is said to be a linear random-parameter system. The analysis and design of control systems usually requires a solution of Eq. (2.4-1) with an associated set of initial conditions.

a. Stationary Case

In the case of linear stationary processes, the coefficient matrix and the driving matrix are time-invariant, and Eq. (2.4-1) reduces to

$$\dot{\mathbf{x}}(t) = \mathbf{A}\mathbf{x}(t) + \mathbf{D}\mathbf{m}(t) + \mathbf{n}(t) \tag{2.4-2}$$

This equation is first solved with the forcing term $\mathbf{m}(t)$ equal to zero and the process subject to no disturbance. The solution is then extended to the case with forcing term and disturbance.

1. Force-free Motion. Under this situation, Eq. (2.4-2) simplifies to

$$\dot{\mathbf{x}}(t) = \mathbf{A}\mathbf{x}(t) \tag{2.4-3}$$

It is assumed that the process starts to move at time t_0 from the initial state $\mathbf{x}_0$. The solution to Eq. (2.4-3) can be derived in a manner analogous to the scalar case. The analogy suggests that the solution of Eq. (2.4-3) is

$$\mathbf{x}(t) = [\exp \mathbf{A}(t - t_0)]\mathbf{x}_0 \tag{2.4-4}$$

where

$$\exp \mathbf{A}t = \sum_{k=0}^{\infty} \mathbf{A}_k \frac{t_k}{k!} \tag{2.4-5}$$

This series can be shown to converge absolutely and uniformly in any finite interval of the time axis. The function

$$\boldsymbol{\phi}(t - t_0) = \exp \mathbf{A}(t - t_0) \tag{2.4-6}$$

is often referred to as the transition matrix of the process. Use of Eq. (2.4-6) reduces Eq. (2.4-4) to

$$\mathbf{x}(t) = \boldsymbol{\phi}(t - t_0)\mathbf{x}_0 \tag{2.4-7}$$

It is noted that the transition matrix describes the behavior of the process under the force-free situation.

2. Forced Motion. When the multivariable process is subject to the forcing term $\mathbf{m}(t)$ and additive disturbance $\mathbf{n}(t)$, the process dynamics is characterized by Eq. (2.4-2). The solution to this equation can be assumed to be of a form similar to Eq. (2.4-7). Thus

$$\mathbf{x}(t) = \boldsymbol{\phi}(t - t_0)\mathbf{C}_1(t) \tag{2.4-8}$$

where a time-varying vector $\mathbf{C}_1(t)$ takes the place of the constant initial-state vector $\mathbf{x}_0$ for the force-free case. Differentiation of Eq. (2.4-8) with respect to t results in

$$\dot{\mathbf{x}}(t) = \mathbf{A}\mathbf{x}(t) + \boldsymbol{\phi}(t - t_0)\dot{\mathbf{C}}_1(t) \tag{2.4-9}$$

If Eq. (2.4-8) is the solution to Eq. (2.4-2), then the quantities at the right of both Eqs. (2.4-2) and (2.4-9) must be equal. This leads to

$$\mathbf{D}\mathbf{m}(t) + \mathbf{n}(t) = \boldsymbol{\phi}(t - t_0)\dot{\mathbf{C}}_1(t) \tag{2.4-10}$$

Solving for $\mathbf{C}_1(t)$ yields

$$\mathbf{C}_1(t) = \int_{t_0}^{t} \boldsymbol{\phi}^{-1}(\tau - t_0)[\mathbf{Dm}(\tau) + \mathbf{n}(\tau)]\, d\tau + \mathbf{C}_2 \tag{2.4-11}$$

In view of Eq. (2.4-11) and the definition of transition matrix, Eq. (2.4-8) becomes

$$\mathbf{x}(t) = \boldsymbol{\phi}(t - t_0)\mathbf{C}_2 + \int_{t_0}^{t} \boldsymbol{\phi}(t - \tau)[\mathbf{Dm}(\tau) + \mathbf{n}(\tau)]\, d\tau \tag{2.4-12}$$

At $t = t_0$, $\boldsymbol{\phi}(t - t_0) = I$ and $\mathbf{C}_2 = \mathbf{x}(t_0)$. Hence the solution to Eq. (2.4-2) is

$$\mathbf{x}(t) = \boldsymbol{\phi}(t - t_0)\mathbf{x}(t_0) + \int_{t_0}^{t} \boldsymbol{\phi}(t - \tau)[\mathbf{Dm}(\tau) + \mathbf{n}(\tau)]\, d\tau \tag{2.4-13}$$

b. Nonstationary Case

The dynamics of a linear nonstationary process is characterized by Eq. (2.4-1). It should be noted that, in this situation, the analogy to the scalar case generally leads to a wrong guess. The solution of the homogeneous equation

$$\dot{\mathbf{x}}(t) = \mathbf{A}(t)\mathbf{x}(t) \tag{2.4-14}$$

by analogy to the scalar case would be

$$\mathbf{x}(t) = \left[\exp \int_{t_0}^{t} \mathbf{A}(\tau)\, d\tau\right] \mathbf{C}_1 \tag{2.4-15}$$

In fact, this is true only when $\mathbf{A}(t)$ and $\int_{t_0}^{t} \mathbf{A}(\tau)\, d\tau$ commute for all t.

Now let $\boldsymbol{\phi}(t, t_0)$ be the matrix solution of the homogeneous equation

$$\dot{\mathbf{X}}(t) = \mathbf{A}(t)\mathbf{X}(t) \tag{2.4-16}$$

with initial condition $\mathbf{X}(t_0) = \mathbf{I}$. $\boldsymbol{\phi}(t, t_0)$ is the transition matrix of the time-varying system. At $t = t_0$, $\boldsymbol{\phi}(t, t_0) = \mathbf{I}$. The solution to the inhomogeneous equation may be determined by use of Lagrange's method of variation of parameters. Assume that the solution to Eq. (2.4-1) is

$$\mathbf{x}(t) = \boldsymbol{\phi}(t, t_0)\mathbf{C}_1(t) \tag{2.4-17}$$

Differentiating,

$$\begin{aligned} \dot{\mathbf{x}}(t) &= \dot{\boldsymbol{\phi}}(t, t_0)\mathbf{C}_1(t) + \boldsymbol{\phi}(t, t_0)\dot{\mathbf{C}}_1(t) \\ &= \mathbf{A}(t)\boldsymbol{\phi}(t, t_0)\mathbf{C}_1(t) + \boldsymbol{\phi}(t, t_0)\dot{\mathbf{C}}_1(t) \\ &= \mathbf{A}(t)\mathbf{x}(t) + \boldsymbol{\phi}(t, t_0)\dot{\mathbf{C}}_1(t) \end{aligned} \tag{2.4-18}$$

Comparing Eq. (2.4-1) with Eq. (2.4-18) yields

$$\boldsymbol{\phi}(t, t_0)\dot{\mathbf{C}}_1(t) = \mathbf{D}(t)\mathbf{m}(t) + \mathbf{n}(t) \tag{2.4-19}$$

Solving for $\mathbf{C}_1(t)$,

$$\mathbf{C}_1(t) = \int_{t_0}^{t} \boldsymbol{\phi}^{-1}(\tau, t_0)[\mathbf{D}(\tau)\mathbf{m}(\tau) + \mathbf{n}(\tau)]\, d\tau + \mathbf{C}_2 \tag{2.4-20}$$

Thus

$$\mathbf{x}(t) = \boldsymbol{\phi}(t, t_0)\mathbf{C}_2 + \int_{t_0}^{t} \boldsymbol{\phi}(t, \tau)[\mathbf{D}(\tau)\mathbf{m}(\tau) + \mathbf{n}(\tau)]\, d\tau \qquad (2.4\text{-}21)$$

Since at $t = t_0$, $\boldsymbol{\phi}(t, t_0) = \mathbf{I}$, $\mathbf{C}_2 = \mathbf{x}(t_0)$, the general solution to the multivariable control process described by Eq. (2.4-1) is given by

$$\mathbf{x}(t) = \boldsymbol{\phi}(t, t_0)\mathbf{x}(t_0) + \int_{t_0}^{t} \boldsymbol{\phi}(t, \tau)[\mathbf{D}(\tau)\mathbf{m}(\tau) + \mathbf{n}(\tau)]\, d\tau \qquad (2.4\text{-}22)$$

It may be noted that, in the case of time-varying systems, the transition matrix cannot be expressed as a simple exponential form. In general, there is no formula for $\boldsymbol{\phi}(t, t_0)$, although it may be expressed as an infinite series of successive integrals.

Canonical Form and Vandermonde Matrix

The analysis and optimum synthesis of control systems sometimes require the transformation of the state differential equation which characterizes the system into a canonical form. Such a transformation will lead to great simplification in analysis and synthesis. The dynamic characterization of a linear control process is usually described by the state differential equation in vector-matrix notation:

$$\dot{\mathbf{x}}(t) = \mathbf{A}\mathbf{x}(t) + \mathbf{d}m \qquad (2.4\text{-}23)$$

where $\mathbf{x}$ = state vector of the process
m = control signal
$\mathbf{A}$ = coefficient matrix as previously defined
$\mathbf{d}$ = driving matrix given by

$$\mathbf{d} = (0 \quad 0 \quad 0 \quad \cdots \quad 0 \quad 0 \quad d)' \qquad (2.4\text{-}24)$$

Consider an nth-order control process. The matrix $\mathbf{d}$ is an $n \times 1$ column matrix with all the elements equal to zero except the last one. Let the eigenvalues of $\mathbf{A}$ be $\lambda_1, \lambda_2, \ldots, \lambda_n$, which are distinct. By the linear transformation

$$\mathbf{X} = \mathbf{T}\mathbf{y} \qquad (2.4\text{-}25)$$

Eq. (2.4-23) can be reduced to the *canonical form*

$$\dot{\mathbf{y}}(t) = \boldsymbol{\Lambda}\mathbf{y}(t) + \mathbf{T}^{-1}\mathbf{d}m \qquad (2.4\text{-}26)$$

where $\mathbf{y}$ is referred to as the canonical state vector which represents the n canonical state variables, the matrix $\boldsymbol{\Lambda}$ is the diagonal matrix in λ_i, and the matrix $\mathbf{T}$ is an $n \times n$ matrix formed by using the eigenvectors $\mathbf{x}_i$ as columns.

It can be shown that

$$\mathbf{\Lambda} = \mathbf{T}^{-1}\mathbf{A}\mathbf{T} = \begin{bmatrix} \lambda_1 & 0 & \cdots & 0 \\ 0 & \lambda_2 & \cdots & 0 \\ \cdots & \cdots & \cdots & \cdots \\ 0 & 0 & \cdots & \lambda_n \end{bmatrix} \tag{2.4-27}$$

that the matrix **T** can be expressed in terms of eigenvalues as a Vandermonde matrix

$$\mathbf{T} = \begin{bmatrix} 1 & 1 & \cdots & 1 & \cdots & 1 \\ \lambda_1 & \lambda_2 & \cdots & \lambda_i & \cdots & \lambda_n \\ \lambda_1^2 & \lambda_2^2 & \cdots & \lambda_i^2 & \cdots & \lambda_n^2 \\ \cdots & \cdots & \cdots & \cdots & \cdots & \cdots \\ \lambda_1^{n-1} & \lambda_2^{n-1} & \cdots & \lambda_i^{n-1} & \cdots & \lambda_n^{n-1} \end{bmatrix} \tag{2.4-28}$$

and that the transition matrix for the canonical system is a diagonal matrix given by

$$\boldsymbol{\phi}_c(t) = e^{\mathbf{\Lambda}t} = \begin{bmatrix} e^{\lambda_1 t} & 0 & \cdots & 0 \\ 0 & e^{\lambda_2 t} & \cdots & 0 \\ \cdots & \cdots & \cdots & \cdots \\ 0 & 0 & \cdots & e^{\lambda_n t} \end{bmatrix} \tag{2.4-29}$$

The Vandermonde matrix **T** defined in Eq. (2.4-28) is invertible, since the eigenvalues λ_i are assumed to be distinct. This can readily be proved by contradiction. If the matrix **T** cannot be inverted, then the row vectors of **T** are not linearly independent. Consequently, there would exist a linear combination of rows which is identical with a zero row vector; that is,

$$b_1\lambda_i^{n-1} + b_2\lambda_i^{n-2} + \cdots + b_{n-1}\lambda_i + b_n = 0 \tag{2.4-30}$$

where $i = 1, 2, \ldots, n$. Since an $(n - 1)$st-degree polynomial cannot have n distinct roots, the above assumption leads to a contradiction. Hence the matrix **T** is invertible.

The inverse of the Vandermonde matrix can readily be determined by making use of the Lagrange interpolation formula

$$f(z) = \sum_{i=1}^{n} f(\lambda_i)P_i(z) \tag{2.4-31}$$

where

$$P_i(z) = \prod_{\substack{j=1 \\ j\neq i}}^{n} \frac{z - \lambda_j}{\lambda_i - \lambda_j} \tag{2.4-32}$$

is a polynomial having the property that $P_i(\lambda_j)$ is a Kronecker δ function. The polynomials $P_1, P_2, \ldots, P_n$ are linearly independent and form a basis of vector space V of dimension n. Now, by letting

$$f(z) = z^k \tag{2.4-33}$$

Eq. (2.4-31) reduces to

$$z^k = \sum_{i=1}^{n} (\lambda_i)^k P_i(z) \qquad k = 0, 1, \ldots, n-1 \tag{2.4-34}$$

In matrix notations,

$$\mathbf{Z} = \mathbf{TP} \tag{2.4-35}$$

where $$\mathbf{Z} = (1 \quad z \quad z^2 \quad \cdots \quad z^i \quad \cdots \quad z^{n-1})' \tag{2.4-36}$$

and $$\mathbf{P} = (P_0 \quad P_1 \quad P_2 \quad \cdots \quad P_i \quad \cdots \quad P_{n-1})' \tag{2.4-37}$$

Thus the matrix $\mathbf{P}$ is given by

$$\mathbf{P} = \mathbf{T}^{-1}\mathbf{Z} \tag{2.4-38}$$

By defining $\mathbf{T}^{-1}$ as

$$\mathbf{T}^{-1} = \begin{bmatrix} \alpha_{11} & \alpha_{12} & \cdots & \alpha_{1n} \\ \alpha_{21} & \alpha_{22} & \cdots & \alpha_{2n} \\ \cdots & \cdots & \cdots & \cdots \\ \alpha_{i1} & \alpha_{i2} & \cdots & \alpha_{in} \\ \alpha_{n1} & \alpha_{n2} & \cdots & \alpha_{nn} \end{bmatrix} \tag{2.4-39}$$

expanding Eq. (2.4-38) yields

$$P_i(z) = \sum_{j=1}^{n} \alpha_{ij} z^{j-1} \qquad i = 1, 2, \ldots, n \tag{2.4-40}$$

Therefore the element α_{ij} of the inverse Vandermonde matrix is given by the coefficient of the z^{j-1} term of the polynomial defined in Eq. (2.4-32). The elements of the ith row of $\mathbf{T}^{-1}$ are the coefficients of the polynomial, Eq. (2.4-32), expressed in ascending powers of z.

Furthermore, it is easy to show that the elements of the column matrix $\mathbf{T}^{-1}\mathbf{d}$ are the residues at the n poles of $d/\Delta(\lambda)$, where

$$\Delta(\lambda) = \det\,[\lambda\mathbf{I} - \mathbf{A}] \tag{2.4-41}$$

From Eqs. (2.4-24) and (2.4-39),

$$\mathbf{T}^{-1}\mathbf{d} = [d\lambda_{1n} \quad d\lambda_{2n} \quad \cdots \quad d\lambda_{in} \quad \cdots \quad d\lambda_{nn}]' \tag{2.4-42}$$

Thus the element $d\lambda_{in}$ of this column matrix is equal to the coefficient of the highest power of λ in the polynomial $dP_i(\lambda)$; that is,

$$d\alpha_{in} = \prod_{\substack{j=1 \\ j\neq i}}^{n} \frac{d}{\lambda_i - \lambda_j} = \left.\frac{d(\lambda - \lambda_i)}{\Delta(\lambda)}\right|_{\lambda=\lambda_i} \tag{2.4-43}$$

which is the residue at the ith pole of $d/\Delta(\lambda)$.

2.5 GENERALIZED COORDINATES

Lagrangian Equations of Motion

Consider the simple system shown in Fig. 2.5-1. The frictional forces are assumed to be negligible. The kinetic energy of the moving mass M is

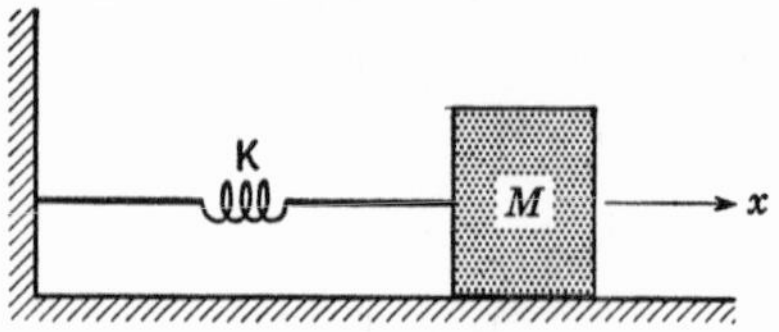

Fig. 2.5-1 A simple mechanical system.

given by

$$T = \tfrac{1}{2}M\dot{x}^2 \tag{2.5-1}$$

The potential energy in the spring is

$$V = \int_0^x Kx\,dx = \tfrac{1}{2}Kx^2 \tag{2.5-2}$$

Applying Newton's second law of motion, the equation of performance is

$$M\ddot{x} + Kx = 0 \tag{2.5-3}$$

Differentiating Eq. (2.5-1) with respect to $\dot{x}$ yields

$$\frac{\partial T}{\partial \dot{x}} = M\dot{x} \tag{2.5-4}$$

The time derivative of Eq. (2.5-4) is

$$\frac{d}{dt}\left(\frac{\partial T}{\partial \dot{x}}\right) = M\ddot{x} \tag{2.5-5}$$

Differentiating Eq. (2.5-2) with respect to x,

$$\frac{\partial V}{\partial x} = Kx \tag{2.5-6}$$

Adding Eq. (2.5-5) to Eq. (2.5-6) and using Eq. (2.5-3) yields

$$\frac{d}{dt}\left(\frac{\partial T}{\partial \dot{x}}\right) + \frac{\partial V}{\partial x} = 0 \tag{2.5-7}$$

This is a special case of Lagrange's equations of motion for dissipationless systems,

$$\frac{d}{dt}\left(\frac{\partial T}{\partial \dot{q}_i}\right) - \frac{\partial T}{\partial q_i} + \frac{\partial V}{\partial q_i} = 0 \tag{2.5-8}$$

In Eq. (2.5-8), the q_i are referred to as the generalized coordinates, where $i = 1, 2, \ldots, n$, for systems with n degrees of freedom.

By defining

$$L = L(\dot{q}_i, q_i) = T(\dot{q}_i, q_i) - V(q_i) \tag{2.5-9}$$

as the *Lagrangian* of the system, Lagrange's equation for conservative systems with no external force may be expressed as

$$\frac{d}{dt}\left(\frac{\partial L}{\partial \dot{q}_i}\right) - \frac{\partial L}{\partial q_i} = 0 \tag{2.5-10}$$

It is to be noted that, in changing to generalized coordinates, the systems for which D'Alembert's principle holds are still being dealt with. The Lagrangian equation of motion can be derived from Hamilton's variational principle. The principle states that, for any dynamic system under the influence of the conservative forces starting from any reasonable initial conditions, the system will move so as to minimize the time average of the difference between kinetic and potential energies. In mathematical notation,

$$\delta \int_{t_1}^{t_2} (T - V)\, dt = 0 \qquad \text{or} \qquad \int_{t_1}^{t_2} \delta L\, dt = 0$$

From application of Hamilton's variational principle to the Lagrangian of Eq. (2.5-9) is derived

$$\delta L = \sum_i \frac{\partial L}{\partial \dot{q}_i}\,\delta \dot{q}_i + \sum_i \frac{\partial L}{\partial q_i}\,\delta q_i \tag{2.5-11}$$

with the initial conditions that $\delta q_i = 0$ at $t = t_1$ and $t = t_2$, and

$$\begin{aligned}\int_{t_1}^{t_2} \delta L\, dt &= \int_{t_1}^{t_2} \sum_i \frac{\partial L}{\partial \dot{q}_i}\,\delta \dot{q}_i\, dt + \int_{t_1}^{t_2} \sum_i \frac{\partial L}{\partial q_i}\,\delta q_i\, dt \\ &= \sum_i \frac{\partial L}{\partial \dot{q}_i}\,\delta q_i \Big|_{t_1}^{t_2} - \int_{t_1}^{t_2} \sum_i \frac{d}{dt}\left(\frac{\partial L}{\partial \dot{q}_i}\right)\delta q_i\, dt + \int_{t_1}^{t_2} \sum_i \frac{\partial L}{\partial q_i}\,\delta q_i\, dt \\ &= \int_{t_1}^{t_2} \sum_i \left[\frac{\partial L}{\partial q_i} - \frac{d}{dt}\left(\frac{\partial L}{\partial \dot{q}_i}\right)\right]\delta q_i\, dt = 0 \end{aligned} \tag{2.5-12}$$

In the above derivation use is made of the fact that $\delta \dot{q}_i$ and δq_i are not independent of one another, and $\dot{q}_i$ are the time derivatives of q_i. Since there are as many q_i as there are degrees of freedom, and as the δq_i are independent of time, Eq. (2.5-12) can be satisfied only if the quantity in the brackets is equal to zero. This condition leads to Lagrange's equation of motion given in Eq. (2.5-10). It is noted that the derivation of Lagrange's equation is independent of the choice of coordinates. Converting from one set of generalized coordinates to another, the transformed equation still remains invariant in form.

For systems with dissipation but no external force, it can be shown that Lagrange's equation is

$$\frac{d}{dt}\left(\frac{\partial L}{\partial \dot{q}_i}\right) - \frac{\partial L}{\partial q_i} + \frac{\partial F}{\partial \dot{q}_i} = 0 \tag{2.5-13}$$

where F is termed the Rayleigh dissipation function. If the system undergoes a small motion, the work done against frictional forces is

$$\sum_i R_i \dot{q}_i \,\Delta q_i$$

friction force prop. to velocity

where R_i are the friction constants and $R_i \dot{q}_i$ are the forces to overcome friction. The power dissipated owing to frictional forces is then given by

$\frac{\Delta q_i}{\Delta t} = \dot{q}_i \quad \frac{\dot{q}_i}{\Delta t \to 0}$

$$\sum_i R_i \dot{q}_i^2$$

The Rayleigh dissipation function F is defined by

$$F = \tfrac{1}{2} \sum_i R_i \dot{q}_i^2 \tag{2.5-14}$$

Hence

$$\frac{\partial F}{\partial \dot{q}_i} = \sum_i R_i \dot{q}_i \tag{2.5-15}$$

When the system is subject to external forces, the Lagrangian equations of motion become

$$\frac{d}{dt}\left(\frac{\partial T}{\partial \dot{q}_i}\right) - \frac{\partial T}{\partial q_i} = Q_i \tag{2.5-16}$$

where Q_i denotes generalized forces. If the forces are conservative,

$$Q_i = -\frac{\partial V}{\partial q_i} \tag{2.5-17}$$

$V = V(q_1, q_2, \ldots, q_n)$ is the potential energy which does not contain $\dot{q}_i, \dot{q}_2, \ldots, \dot{q}_n$. In vector notation, Lagrange's equation may be expressed as

$$\frac{d}{dt}\left(\frac{\partial T}{\partial \dot{\mathbf{q}}}\right) - \frac{\partial T}{\partial \mathbf{q}} = \mathbf{Q} \tag{2.5-18}$$

Hamiltonian Equations of Motion

Let p_i denote the components of the generalized momentum of the system, corresponding to q_i. Then

$$p_i = \frac{\partial T}{\partial \dot{q}_i} \tag{2.5-19}$$

$T = \tfrac{1}{2} M \dot{x}^2$
Kin. energy

$\frac{\partial T}{\partial \dot{x}} = M\dot{x}$
Momentum

The kinetic energy of the system is often written as a function of the generalized velocities and the generalized coordinates:

$$T = T(\dot{q}_1, \dot{q}_2, \ldots, \dot{q}_n; q_1, q_2, \ldots, q_n) \qquad (2.5\text{-}20a)$$

or

$$T_{\dot{\mathbf{q}}} = T_{\dot{\mathbf{q}}}(\dot{\mathbf{q}}, \mathbf{q}) \qquad (2.5\text{-}20b)$$

This is referred to as the Lagrangian expression for kinetic energy. On the other hand, the kinetic energy can also be expressed in terms of generalized momenta and generalized coordinates. Thus

$$T = T(p_1, p_2, \ldots, p_n; q_1, q_2, \ldots, q_n) \qquad (2.5\text{-}21a)$$

or

$$T_{\mathbf{p}} = T_{\mathbf{p}}(\mathbf{p}, \mathbf{q}) \qquad (2.5\text{-}21b)$$

This is referred to as the hamiltonian expression for kinetic energy. Of course, by definition,

$$T_{\dot{q}} \approx T_p \qquad (2.5\text{-}22)$$

From Eq. (2.5-22) may be derived, upon differentiation with respect to q_i,

$$\frac{\partial T_p}{\partial q_i} = \frac{\partial T_{\dot{q}}}{\partial \dot{q}_1}\frac{\partial \dot{q}_1}{\partial q_i} + \frac{\partial T_{\dot{q}}}{\partial \dot{q}_2}\frac{\partial \dot{q}_2}{\partial q_i} + \cdots + \frac{\partial T_{\dot{q}}}{\partial q_i} + \cdots + \frac{\partial T_{\dot{q}}}{\partial \dot{q}_n}\frac{\partial \dot{q}_n}{\partial q_i} \qquad (2.5\text{-}23)$$

In view of Eq. (2.5-19),

$$\frac{\partial T_p}{\partial q_i} = p_1 \frac{\partial \dot{q}_1}{\partial q_i} + p_2 \frac{\partial \dot{q}_2}{\partial q_i} + \cdots + \frac{\partial T_{\dot{q}}}{\partial q_i} + \cdots + p_n \frac{\partial \dot{q}_n}{\partial q_i} \qquad (2.5\text{-}24)$$

By Euler's theorem,

$$2T_{\dot{q}} = \dot{q}_1 \frac{\partial T_{\dot{q}}}{\partial \dot{q}_1} + \dot{q}_2 \frac{\partial T_{\dot{q}}}{\partial \dot{q}_2} + \cdots + \dot{q}_n \frac{\partial T_{\dot{q}}}{\partial \dot{q}_n} \qquad (2.5\text{-}25)$$

which reduces to

$$2T_{\dot{q}} = p_1\dot{q}_1 + p_2\dot{q}_2 + \cdots + p_n\dot{q}_n = (\mathbf{p}, \dot{\mathbf{q}}) \qquad (2.5\text{-}26)$$

Since $T_{\dot{q}}$ is equivalent to T_p by definition,

$$2T_p = p_1\dot{q}_1 + p_2\dot{q}_2 + \cdots + p_n\dot{q}_n \qquad (2.5\text{-}27)$$

Taking the partial derivative with respect to q_i,

$$2\frac{\partial T_p}{\partial q_i} = p_1 \frac{\partial \dot{q}_1}{\partial q_i} + p_2 \frac{\partial \dot{q}_2}{\partial q_i} + \cdots + p_n \frac{\partial \dot{q}_n}{\partial q_i} \qquad (2.5\text{-}28)$$

Subtracting Eq. (2.5-24) from Eq. (2.5-28) yields

$$\frac{\partial T_p}{\partial q_i} = -\frac{\partial T_{\dot{q}}}{\partial q_i} \qquad (2.5\text{-}29)$$

Now taking the partial derivative of Eq. (2.5-22) with respect to p_i,

$$\frac{\partial T_p}{\partial p_i} = \frac{\partial T_{\dot{q}}}{\partial \dot{q}_1}\frac{\partial \dot{q}_1}{\partial p_i} + \frac{\partial T_{\dot{q}}}{\partial \dot{q}_2}\frac{\partial \dot{q}_2}{\partial p_i} + \cdots + \frac{\partial T_{\dot{q}}}{\partial \dot{q}_n}\frac{\partial \dot{q}_n}{\partial p_i} \qquad (2.5\text{-}30)$$

which may be written as

$$\frac{\partial T_p}{\partial p_i} = p_1 \frac{\partial \dot{q}_1}{\partial p_i} + p_2 \frac{\partial \dot{q}_2}{\partial p_i} + \cdots + p_n \frac{\partial \dot{q}_n}{\partial p_i} \tag{2.5-31}$$

Taking the partial derivative of Eq. (2.5-27) with respect to p_i,

$$2 \frac{\partial T_p}{\partial p_i} = p_1 \frac{\partial \dot{q}_1}{\partial p_i} + p_2 \frac{\partial \dot{q}_2}{\partial p_i} + \cdots + \dot{q}_i + \cdots + p_n \frac{\partial \dot{q}_n}{\partial p_i} \tag{2.5-32}$$

Subtraction of Eq. (2.5-31) from Eq. (2.5-32) yields

$$\frac{\partial T_p}{\partial p_i} = \dot{q}_i \tag{2.5-33}$$

By making use of Eqs. (2.5-29) and (2.5-33), Lagrange's equations of motion given by Eq. (2.5-16) are reduced to

$$\dot{p}_i + \frac{\partial T_p}{\partial q_i} = Q_i \tag{2.5-34}$$

$$\dot{q}_i = \frac{\partial T_p}{\partial p_i} \tag{2.5-35}$$

where $i = 1, 2, \ldots, n$. These two sets of equations are known as the *hamiltonian equations* of motion.

In the case of conservative systems, the generalized forces are given by

$$Q_i = -\frac{\partial V}{\partial q_i} \tag{2.5-36}$$

where V is the potential energy $V(q_1, q_2, \ldots, q_n)$, not containing $\dot{q}_1, \dot{q}_2, \ldots, \dot{q}_n$. The Lagrangian equation may be written as

$$\frac{d}{dt}\left(\frac{\partial T_{\dot{q}}}{\partial \dot{q}_i}\right) = \frac{\partial T_{\dot{q}}}{\partial q_i} - \frac{\partial V}{\partial q_i} \tag{2.5-37}$$

Since the Lagrangian is defined as

$$L(\dot{q}_i, q_i) = T_{\dot{q}}(\dot{q}_i, q_i) - V(q_i) \tag{2.5-38}$$

the partial derivatives of the Lagrangian are

$$\frac{\partial L}{\partial \dot{q}_i} = \frac{\partial T_{\dot{q}}}{\partial \dot{q}_i} \tag{2.5-39}$$

and

$$\frac{\partial L}{\partial q_i} = \frac{\partial T_{\dot{q}}}{\partial q_i} - \frac{\partial V}{\partial q_i} \tag{2.5-40}$$

When the system is conservative, a function of the coordinates and momenta which remains constant throughout the motion of the system is the total energy, the sum of kinetic and potential energy. When this is expressed in terms of the coordinates q and the momenta p, it is referred to as the hamiltonian function H for the system. Thus

$$H = T_p + V = H(\mathbf{p}, \mathbf{q}) \qquad (2.5\text{-}41)$$

Then it follows from Eq. (2.5-41), upon differentiation, that

$$\frac{\partial H}{\partial q_i} = \frac{\partial T_p}{\partial q_i} + \frac{\partial V}{\partial q_i} \qquad (2.5\text{-}42)$$

and

$$\frac{\partial H}{\partial p_i} = \frac{\partial T_p}{\partial p_i} \qquad (2.5\text{-}43)$$

Substitution of Eqs. (2.5-36), (2.5-42), and (2.5-43) into Eqs. (2.5-34) and (2.5-35) leads to

$$\frac{dp_i}{dt} = -\frac{\partial H}{\partial q_i} \qquad (2.5\text{-}44)$$

$$\frac{dq_i}{dt} = \frac{\partial H}{\partial p_i} \qquad (2.5\text{-}45)$$

These two sets of equations are known as the *hamiltonian canonical equations.*

It is not difficult to see that the hamiltonian function of the p's and q's is independent of time. The time derivative of H is

$$\frac{dH}{dt} = \sum_{i=1}^{n} \left(\frac{\partial H}{\partial p_i} \frac{dp_i}{dt} + \frac{\partial H}{\partial q_i} \frac{dq_i}{dt} \right)$$

which is zero according to Eqs. (2.5-44) and (2.5-45) unless H depends explicitly on the time. Thus any hamiltonian for which the canonical equations hold is an invariant of the motion for the system. For conservative systems the total change of H with time is zero. In some cases, where H may depend explicitly on the time, the variation of H with t due to changes of the p's and q's is still zero, but the total change dH/dt is equal to the explicit change $\partial H/\partial t$, which is equal to $-\partial L/\partial t$.

In many cases it is impossible to solve the equations of motion given by Eqs. (2.5-44) and (2.5-45). One way to simplify the equations is by a transformation from the set of variables p_i and q_i to another set of variables α_i and β_i such that the transformed equations of motion are simpler in the new variables. The transformations which will generate the new equations of motion still in the canonical form are called *canonical transformations.* Thus, if

$$p_i = p_i(\boldsymbol{\alpha}, \boldsymbol{\beta}) \qquad q_i = q_i(\boldsymbol{\alpha}, \boldsymbol{\beta}) \qquad (2.5\text{-}46)$$

is a canonical transformation from the $\mathbf{p}$, $\mathbf{q}$ set to an $\boldsymbol{\alpha}$, $\boldsymbol{\beta}$ set, the equations of motion in the $\boldsymbol{\alpha}$, $\boldsymbol{\beta}$ set will be

$$\frac{d\alpha_i}{dt} = -\frac{\partial \bar{H}}{\partial \beta_i} \qquad \frac{d\beta_i}{dt} = \frac{\partial \bar{H}}{\partial \alpha_i} \qquad (2.5\text{-}47)$$

where $\bar{H}$ is the hamiltonian expressed in the $\boldsymbol{\alpha}$, $\boldsymbol{\beta}$ set. The transformation

$$p_i = \frac{\partial S}{\partial q_i} \qquad \beta_i = \frac{\partial S}{\partial \alpha_i} \tag{2.5-48}$$

changes the hamiltonian $H(\mathbf{p}, \mathbf{q})$ into $\bar{H}(\boldsymbol{\alpha})$, which does not contain the β_i, where the function S is referred to as the generating function $S(\boldsymbol{\alpha}, \mathbf{q})$. This transformation converts the equations of motion into

$$\frac{d\alpha_i}{dt} = -\frac{\partial \bar{H}}{\partial \beta_i} = 0 \tag{2.5-49}$$

$$\frac{d\beta_i}{dt} = \frac{\partial \bar{H}}{\partial \alpha_i} = \text{const} \tag{2.5-50}$$

The first set of equations implies that the α_i are constant. The second set of equations follows from the fact that $\bar{H}$ is a function of α_i only, and the α_i are constant. Clearly, the set of equations (2.5-49) and (2.5-50) is much simpler than Eqs. (2.5-44) and (2.5-45). The solution is readily obtained if the generating function $S(\boldsymbol{\alpha}, \mathbf{q})$ can be determined. Thus the present task becomes the determination of $S(\boldsymbol{\alpha}, \mathbf{q})$ which satisfies the partial differential equation

$$H\left(\frac{\partial S}{\partial q_i}, q_i\right) = \bar{H}(\alpha_i) \tag{2.5-51}$$

The right-hand quantity of Eq. (2.5-51) represents the total energy of the system. Since $\beta_i = \partial S/\partial \alpha_i$,

$$\frac{\partial \beta_i}{\partial t} = \frac{\partial}{\partial t}\left(\frac{\partial S}{\partial \alpha_i}\right) \tag{2.5-52}$$

Combining Eqs. (2.5-50) and (2.5-52) yields

$$\frac{\partial H}{\partial t} = -\frac{d\alpha_i}{dt}\frac{\partial^2 S}{\partial \alpha_i\,\partial t} = -\frac{d}{dt}\left(\frac{\partial S}{\partial t}\right) \tag{2.5-53}$$

Hence

$$H = -\frac{\partial S}{\partial t} \tag{2.5-54}$$

Equation (2.5-54) is known as the *Hamilton-Jacobi equation.* The theories discussed above will be applied to the design of optimum control systems.

2.6 CONCLUSION

The material presented in this chapter serves merely as an introduction to some of the mathematical foundations for the study of modern approaches to control-system design. Many important phases of the subject, such as measure theory, Hilbert transforms, Banah space, semigroup theory, statistics, and probability, have not been included. However, the mathematics associated with linear algebra, vector differential equations, and generalized coordinates has been emphasized in order to acquaint the engineer with some of the powerful tools available for his use. While the transform theory has formed the basis for the classical approaches to control-system design, the fundamental principles in linear algebra play an important role in modern control theory.

References

For comprehensive and scholarly treatments of set theory and finite-dimension vector spaces, it will be advantageous to see the work of Gantmaker,[66] Hadley,[73] Halmos,[74] and Hoffman and Kunze.[79]

References for Sec. 3 are Bellman,[21] Gantmaker,[66] and Pipes.[126]

Suggested references for Sec. 4 are Coddington and Levinson[45] and Pipes.[126]

For Sec. 5 an excellent reference is Goldstein.[70]

3

STATE–SPACE METHODS OF ANALYSIS

Most problems encountered in scientific and engineering investigations fall into one of the following two categories: *analysis* problems, where it is necessary to predict the behavior of a specified system, and *synthesis* problems, where it is essential to construct a system with specified behavior. There are two major approaches to the treatment of both the analysis and synthesis of linear control systems. The commonly used block-diagram approach involves in essence the determination of the transfer characteristics of the system components and the overall transfer characteristics. The designer's task is to select the controller which will satisfy both static and dynamic performance specifications. The second approach is based primarily upon the characterization of a system by a number of simple first-order differential equations describing the state variables of the systems, with the initial conditions given by the state-transition equations. The state variables may be likened to the generalized coordinates in classical mechanics. This approach is often carried out with a state-variable diagram and is referred to as the state-space approach, which forms the core of modern control theory. This chapter is concerned with the analysis of control systems by state-space methods.

3.1 STATE-SPACE CONCEPT

State-space techniques in control and information systems developed rapidly during the past several years. Although the introduction of these techniques into the control field is relatively new, the basic concepts underlying these techniques have long been used in classical dynamics, quantum mechanics, finite-state machines, ordinary differential equations, and other fields. The idea of *state* as a basic concept in the representation of systems

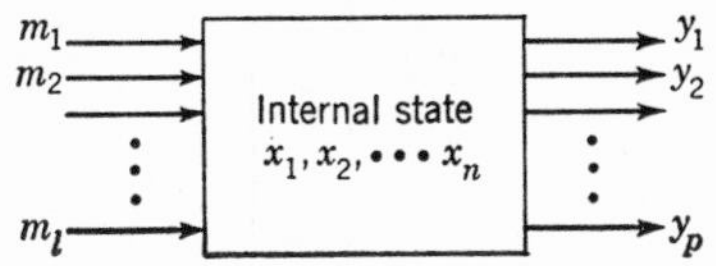

Fig. 3.1-1 State-variable representation of a system.

was first introduced in 1936 by A. M. Turing. Later, the concept was employed by C. E. Shannon in his basic work on information theory. The wide application of the state-space concept in the control field was initiated in the forties by the Russian scientists M. A. Aizerman, A. A. Fel'dbaum, A. M. Letov, A. I. Lur'e, and others. In the United States the introduction of the concept of state and related techniques into the optimum design of linear as well as nonlinear systems is due primarily to R. Bellman. In addition, there are numerous, more recent contributions to the application of state-space techniques to automatic control, among which the basic work of R. E. Kalman has played a prominent role in advancing the state of the art in this rapidly growing field.

From the point of view of system analysis and synthesis, it is convenient to classify the variables which characterize or are associated with the system into (1) *input*, or *excitation*, *variables*, m_i, which represent the stimuli generated by systems other than the one under investigation and which influence the system behavior; (2) *output*, or *response*, *variables*, y_j, which describe those aspects of system behavior that are of interest to the investigator; and (3) *state*, or *intermediate*, *variables*, x_k, which characterize the dynamic behavior of the system under investigation. Schematically, a system can be depicted by a black box with a number of accessible terminals, as shown in Fig. 3.1-1. The input terminals represent a set of input, or excitation, variables, m_i; the output terminals describe a set of output, or response, variables, y_j. The intermediate, or state, variables, x_k, are embedded inside the box and are thus inaccessible. The m_i, y_j, and x_k are assumed to be time functions, with $m_i(t)$, $y_j(t)$, and $x_k(t)$ denoting, respectively, the values of m_i, y_j, and x_k at time t. For convenience, the set of input variables is represented by an *input vector*

$$\mathbf{m} = \begin{bmatrix} m_1 \\ m_2 \\ \cdot \\ \cdot \\ \cdot \\ m_l \end{bmatrix} \tag{3.1-1}$$

the set of output variables is described by an *output vector*

$$\mathbf{y} = \begin{bmatrix} y_1 \\ y_2 \\ \cdot \\ \cdot \\ \cdot \\ y_p \end{bmatrix} \tag{3.1-2}$$

and the set of state variables is represented by a *state vector*

$$\mathbf{x} = \begin{bmatrix} x_1 \\ x_2 \\ \cdot \\ \cdot \\ \cdot \\ x_n \end{bmatrix} \tag{3.1-3}$$

In view of the vector-space concept discussed in Chap. 2, the set of all possible values which the input vector $\mathbf{m}$ can assume at time t forms the *input space* of the system. Similarly, the set of all possible values which the output vector $\mathbf{y}$ can assume at time t forms the *output space* of the system, and the set of all possible values which the state vector $\mathbf{x}$ can assume at time t forms the *state space* of the system.

At any instant t, the state of the system is a function of the initial state $\mathbf{x}(t_0)$ and the input vector $\mathbf{m}(t_0, t)$; that is,

$$\mathbf{x}(t) = \mathbf{F}[\mathbf{x}(t_0); \mathbf{m}(t_0, t)] \tag{3.1-4}$$

where $\mathbf{F}$ is a single-valued function of its arguments. The output vector at time t is also a function of $\mathbf{x}(t_0)$ and $\mathbf{m}(t_0, t)$ and may be written as

$$\mathbf{y}(t) = \boldsymbol{\psi}[\mathbf{x}(t_0); \mathbf{m}(t_0, t)] \tag{3.1-5}$$

Equations (3.1-4) and (3.1-5) are often referred to as the state equations of the system. For systems which can be described by differential equations, Eqs. (3.1-4) and (3.1-5) take the following general form:

$$\dot{\mathbf{x}}(t) = \mathbf{F}[\mathbf{x}(t); \mathbf{m}(t)] \tag{3.1-6}$$
$$\mathbf{y}(t) = \boldsymbol{\psi}[\mathbf{x}(t); \mathbf{m}(t)] \tag{3.1-7}$$

When the system is a finite automaton, the state equations characterizing the system are

$$\mathbf{x}(n) = \mathbf{F}[\mathbf{x}(n-1), \mathbf{m}(n-1)] \tag{3.1-8}$$
$$\mathbf{y}(n) = \boldsymbol{\psi}[\mathbf{x}(n), \mathbf{m}(n)] \tag{3.1-9}$$

If the system is describable by linear differential equations, the state equations of the system may be reduced to

$$\dot{\mathbf{x}}(t) = \mathbf{A}(t)\mathbf{x}(t) + \mathbf{D}(t)\mathbf{m}(t) \tag{3.1-10}$$
$$\mathbf{y}(t) = \mathcal{B}(t)\mathbf{x}(t) + \mathbf{G}(t)\mathbf{m}(t) \tag{3.1-11}$$

where $\mathbf{A}(t)$ is the coefficient matrix, $\mathbf{D}(t)$ is the driving matrix, $\mathcal{B}(t)$ is the output matrix, and $\mathbf{G}(t)$ is the transmission matrix of the system.

For a linear random-parameter system, the state equation may be expressed as

$$\dot{\mathbf{x}}(t) = \mathbf{A}(\mathbf{r})\mathbf{x}(t) + \mathbf{D}(\mathbf{r})\mathbf{m}(t) \tag{3.1-12}$$

where matrices $\mathbf{A}$ and $\mathbf{D}$ are functions of the vector of random variables $\mathbf{r}$. The characterization of systems by state equations forms the starting point of modern control theory.

3.2 SYSTEM CHARACTERIZATION BY STATE VARIABLES

A linear stationary system or process can be described by a set of first-order linear differential equations with constant coefficients, which may be expressed in vector-matrix form as

$$\frac{d\mathbf{v}(t)}{dt} = \mathbf{A}\mathbf{v}(t) \tag{3.2-1}$$

where $\mathbf{v}(t)$ is a column vector for the input variables m_i and the state variables x_k,

$$\mathbf{v} = \begin{bmatrix} \mathbf{m} \\ \mathbf{x} \end{bmatrix} \tag{3.2-2}$$

and $\mathbf{A}$ is a coefficient matrix. If the input variables are treated as state variables of the overall system, vector $\mathbf{v}$ may be considered as the state vector of the overall system.

As an illustration, consider a second-order system characterized by

$$\ddot{x}(t) + a\dot{x}(t) + bx(t) = m(t) \tag{3.2-3}$$

To convert this ordinary differential equation into vector-matrix form, let

$$x_1 = x \qquad \text{and} \qquad x_2 = \dot{x}_1 \tag{3.2-4}$$

Then one obtains

$$\dot{x}_1 = x_2 \tag{3.2-5a}$$
$$\dot{x}_2 = m - bx_1 - ax_2 \tag{3.2-5b}$$

First consider the case $\mathbf{m} = 0$. By defining

$$\mathbf{x} = \begin{bmatrix} x_1 \\ x_2 \end{bmatrix} \tag{3.2-6}$$

$$\mathbf{A} = \begin{bmatrix} 0 & 1 \\ -b & -a \end{bmatrix} \tag{3.2-7}$$

Eqs. (3.2-5) may be written as

$$\frac{d\mathbf{x}}{dt} = \mathbf{Ax} \tag{3.2-8}$$

Next, it is assumed that the input signal m is a step function. Then one has

$$\dot{m} = 0 \tag{3.2-9a}$$
$$\dot{x}_1 = x_2 \tag{3.2-9b}$$
$$\dot{x}_2 = m - bx_1 - ax_2 \tag{3.2-9c}$$

By defining

$$\mathbf{v} = \begin{bmatrix} \mathbf{m} \\ \mathbf{x} \end{bmatrix} = \begin{bmatrix} m \\ x_1 \\ x_2 \end{bmatrix} \tag{3.2-10}$$

$$\mathbf{A} = \begin{bmatrix} 0 & 0 & 0 \\ 0 & 0 & 1 \\ 1 & -b & -a \end{bmatrix} \tag{3.2-11}$$

Eqs. (3.2-9) reduce to

$$\frac{d\mathbf{v}}{dt} = \mathbf{Av} \tag{3.2-12}$$

where $\mathbf{A}$ represents the coefficient matrix of the overall system. When the input signal m is an arbitrary signal, the overall system can be characterized by Eq. (3.2-12) as long as m is described as input state variables. The input description by state variables is discussed in the next section.

Now let the initial conditions for Eq. (3.2-1) be $\mathbf{v}(0^+)$. Taking the Laplace transform of both sides of Eq. (3.2-1),

$$s\mathbf{V}(s) - \mathbf{v}(0^+) = \mathbf{AV}(s) \tag{3.2-13}$$

Rearranging,

$$[s\mathbf{I} - \mathbf{A}]\mathbf{V}(s) = \mathbf{v}(0^+) \tag{3.2-14}$$

Hence the Laplace transform of the state vector $\mathbf{v}(t)$ is

$$\mathbf{V}(s) = [s\mathbf{I} - \mathbf{A}]^{-1}\mathbf{v}(0^+) \tag{3.2-15}$$

where $\mathbf{I}$ is the unity matrix.

Taking the inverse Laplace transform of Eq. (3.2-15) yields

$$\mathbf{v}(t) = \mathcal{L}^{-1}\{[s\mathbf{I} - \mathbf{A}]^{-1}\}\mathbf{v}(0^+) \tag{3.2-16}$$

Defining

$$\mathbf{\Phi}(t) = \mathcal{L}^{-1}\{[s\mathbf{I} - \mathbf{A}]^{-1}\} \tag{3.2-17}$$

Eq. (3.2-16) reduces to

$$\mathbf{v}(t) = \mathbf{\Phi}(t)\mathbf{v}(0^+) \tag{3.2-18}$$

The function $\mathbf{\Phi}(t)$ is referred to as the overall transition matrix of the system.

As discussed in Sec. 2.4, the solution to Eq. (3.2-1) may be written as

$$\mathbf{v}(t) = e^{\mathbf{A}t}\mathbf{v}(0^+) \tag{3.2-19}$$

Comparing Eqs. (3.2-18) and (3.2-19) leads to

$$\mathbf{\Phi}(t) = e^{\mathbf{A}t} \tag{3.2-20a}$$

$$\mathbf{\Phi}(t) = \mathcal{L}^{-1}\{[s\mathbf{I} - \mathbf{A}]^{-1}\} \tag{3.2-20b}$$

which provide two ways of evaluating the transition matrix. If Eq. (3.2-20*a*) is employed to determine $\mathbf{\Phi}(t)$, the Sylvester expansion theorem discussed in Sec. 2.3 may be used to advantage.

Referring to the above illustrative example, it is found that

$$[s\mathbf{I} - \mathbf{A}] = \begin{bmatrix} s & -1 \\ b & s + a \end{bmatrix} \tag{3.2-21}$$

Then

$$\mathbf{\Phi}(s) = [s\mathbf{I} - \mathbf{A}]^{-1} = \frac{1}{s(s + a) + b}\begin{bmatrix} s + a & 1 \\ -b & s \end{bmatrix} \tag{3.2-22}$$

When the eigenvalues of matrix **A** are real and distinct,

$$\lambda_1 = \frac{a}{2} + \frac{1}{2}\sqrt{a^2 - 4b} \qquad \lambda_2 = \frac{a}{2} - \frac{1}{2}\sqrt{a^2 - 4b}$$

with $a^2 > 4b$. The transition matrix $\mathbf{\Phi}(t)$ is given by

$$\mathbf{\Phi}(t) = \frac{1}{\sqrt{a^2 - 4b}}\begin{bmatrix} (\lambda_1 - a)e^{-\lambda_1 t} - (\lambda_2 - a)e^{-\lambda_2 t} & e^{-\lambda_2 t} - e^{-\lambda_1 t} \\ b(e^{-\lambda_1 t} - e^{-\lambda_2 t}) & \lambda_1 e^{-\lambda_1 t} - \lambda_2 e^{-\lambda_2 t} \end{bmatrix} \tag{3.2-23}$$

When the eigenvalues of matrix **A** are complex, the transition matrix $\mathbf{\Phi}(t)$ is found to be

$$\mathbf{\Phi}(t) = \begin{bmatrix} e^{-at/2}\left(\cos\omega_0 t + \dfrac{a}{2\omega_0}\sin\omega_0 t\right) & \dfrac{1}{\omega_0}e^{-at/2}\sin\omega_0 t \\ -\dfrac{b}{\omega_0}e^{-at/2}\sin\omega_0 t & e^{-at/2}\left(\cos\omega_0 t - \dfrac{a}{2\omega_0}\sin\omega_0 t\right) \end{bmatrix} \tag{3.2-24}$$

where

$$\omega_0 = \sqrt{b - \frac{a^2}{4}}$$

The determination of $\boldsymbol{\Phi}(t)$ by use of the Sylvester expansion theorem is illustrated in Sec. 2.3. Other methods of evaluating the transition matrix are discussed in succeeding sections.

An alternative way of defining state variables makes use of the state-variable diagram. A state-variable diagram is made up of integrators, amplifiers, and summing devices. The outputs of the integrators denote the state variables. The state-variable diagram describes the relationships among the state variables and provides physical interpretations of the state variables. Consider the running example. The state-variable diagram may be derived directly from the given differential equation characterizing the system or from its Laplace transform. Taking the Laplace transform of both sides of Eq. (3.2-3) and rearranging,

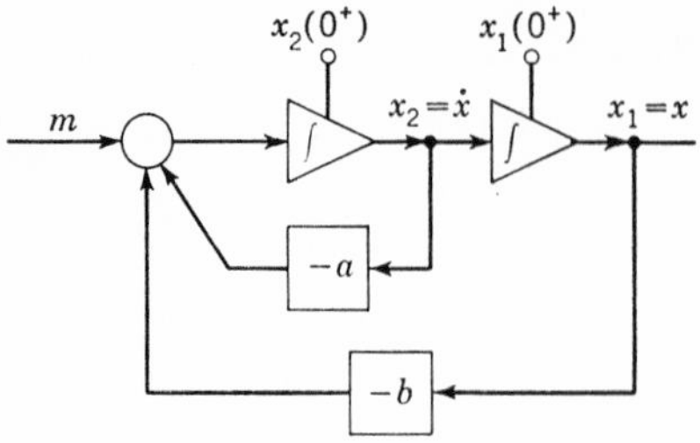

Fig. 3.2-1 State-variable diagram for a second-order system.

$$(s^2 + as + b)X(s) = M(s) + (s + a)x(0^+) + a\dot{x}(0^+) \tag{3.2-25}$$

Hence

$$X(s) = \frac{s^{-2}M(s)}{1 + as^{-1} + bs^{-2}} + \frac{s^{-1}(1 + as^{-1})x(0^+)}{1 + as^{-1} + bs^{-2}} + \frac{s^{-2}\dot{x}(0^+)}{1 + as^{-1} + bs^{-2}} \tag{3.2-26}$$

The state-variable diagram follows immediately from Eq. (3.2-26), and is depicted in Fig. 3.2-1. The output $x = x_1$ consists of three parts which are due to $m(t)$, $x_1(0^+)$, and $x_2(0^+)$, respectively. From the diagram it is observed that the output due to $x_1(0^+)$ is

$$\frac{s^{-1}(1 + as^{-1})x_1(0^+)}{1 + as^{-1} + bs^{-2}}$$

and the output due to $x_2(0^+)$ is

$$\frac{x_2(0^+)}{1 + as^{-1} + bs^{-2}}$$

a. State-variable Diagram for Continuous Systems

For continuous systems the state-variable diagram is the same as the analog-computer simulation diagram. The state-variable diagram may be derived from the overall transfer function of the system in three different ways: (1) direct programming, (2) parallel programming, and (3) iterative programming. To illustrate the various ways of deriving the state-variable diagram, consider the system with overall transfer function

$$\frac{Y(s)}{M(s)} = \frac{s^2 + 3s + 2}{s(s^2 + 7s + 12)} \tag{3.2-27}$$

1. Direct Programming. Equation (3.2-27) may be written as

$$\frac{Y(s)}{M(s)} = \frac{s^{-1} + 3s^{-2} + 2s^{-3}}{1 + 7s^{-1} + 12s^{-2}}$$

or

$$Y(s) = (s^{-1} + 3s^{-2} + 2s^{-3})E(s) \tag{3.2-28}$$

where

$$E(s) = \frac{M(s)}{1 + 7s^{-1} + 12s^{-2}}$$

Transposing,

$$E(s) = M(s) - 7s^{-1}E(s) - 12s^{-2}E(s) \tag{3.2-29}$$

The state-variable diagram follows from Eqs. (3.2-28) and (3.2-29) and is shown in Fig. 3.2-2. The state variables are x_1, x_2, and x_3. The differential

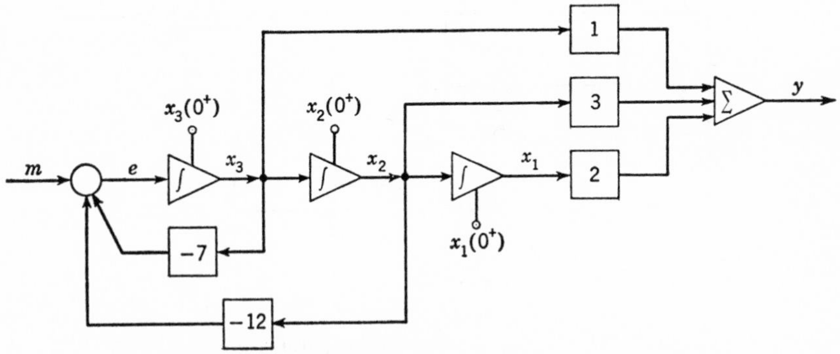

Fig. 3.2-2 State-variable diagram for direct programming.

equations for the state variables are readily obtained by inspection of the diagram. Assuming a step-function input, one has

$$\dot{m} = 0$$
$$\dot{x}_1 = x_2$$
$$\dot{x}_2 = x_3$$
$$\dot{x}_3 = m - 12x_2 - 7x_3$$

Thus

$$\mathbf{v} = \begin{bmatrix} m \\ x_1 \\ x_2 \\ x_3 \end{bmatrix}$$

and

$$\mathbf{A} = \begin{bmatrix} 0 & 0 & 0 & 0 \\ 0 & 0 & 1 & 0 \\ 0 & 0 & 0 & 1 \\ 1 & 0 & -12 & -7 \end{bmatrix}$$

The output $y(t)$ is given by a linear combination of the state variables:

$$y(t) = 2x_1(t) + 3x_2(t) + x_3(t)$$

2. Parallel Programming. Equation (3.2-27) is first expressed in partial-fraction form,

$$\frac{Y(s)}{M(s)} = \frac{1}{6s} - \frac{2}{3(s+3)} + \frac{3}{2(s+4)} \tag{3.2-30}$$

The state-variable diagram follows immediately, and is depicted in Fig. 3.2-3.

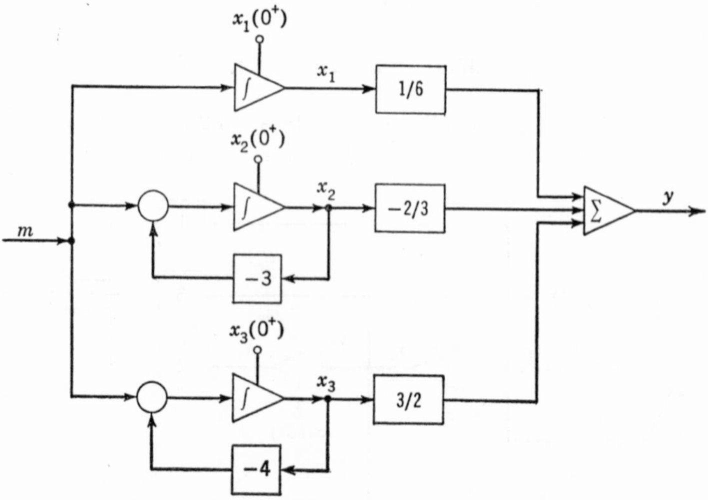

Fig. 3.2-3 State-variable diagram for parallel programming.

The set of first-order differential equations is now given by

$$\begin{aligned} \dot{m} &= 0 \\ \dot{x}_1 &= m \\ \dot{x}_2 &= m - 3x_2 \\ \dot{x}_3 &= m - 4x_3 \end{aligned}$$

Here again the input m is assumed to be a step function. The coefficient matrix $\mathbf{A}$ is

$$\mathbf{A} = \begin{bmatrix} 0 & 0 & 0 & 0 \\ 1 & 0 & 0 & 0 \\ 1 & 0 & -3 & 0 \\ 1 & 0 & 0 & -4 \end{bmatrix}$$

and the output $y(t)$ is the linear combination of state variables,

$$y(t) = \tfrac{1}{6}x_1(t) - \tfrac{2}{3}x_2(t) + \tfrac{3}{2}x_3(t)$$

3. Iterative Programming. Equation (3.2-27) is put into the factored form, and the state-variable diagram can readily be derived from this equation, shown in Fig. 3.2-4. Assuming a step-function input, the state

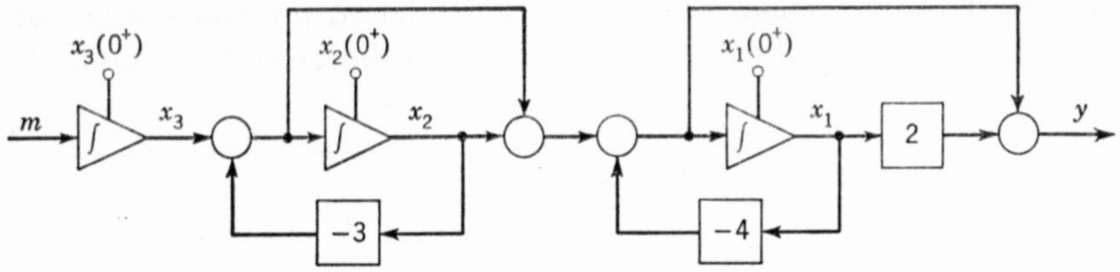

Fig. 3.2-4 State-variable diagram for iterative programming.

variables are defined by

$$\begin{aligned} \dot{m} &= 0 \\ \dot{x}_1 &= -4x_1 + x_2 + x_3 \\ \dot{x}_2 &= -3x_2 + x_3 \\ \dot{x}_3 &= m \end{aligned}$$

The coefficient matrix is

$$\mathbf{A} = \begin{bmatrix} 0 & 0 & 0 & 0 \\ 0 & -4 & 1 & 1 \\ 0 & 0 & -3 & 1 \\ 1 & 0 & 0 & 0 \end{bmatrix}$$

and the output $y(t)$ is given by

$$y(t) = -2x_1(t) - 2x_2(t) + x_3(t)$$

The foregoing discussion also illustrates the characterization of a system by different sets of state variables.

b. State-variable Diagram for Discrete Systems

For discrete systems the state-variable diagram is almost the same as the computer simulation diagram, which may be derived from the pulse-transfer function of the system in three different ways:[136] (1) direct programming,

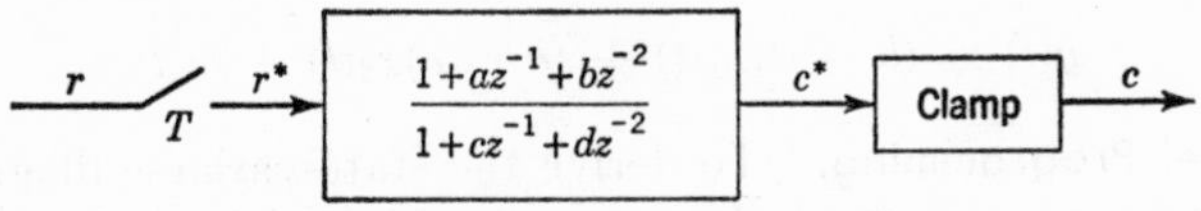

Fig. 3.2-5 Block diagram of a simple discrete-data system.

(2) parallel programming, and (3) iterative programming. The state-variable diagram is made up of samplers, clamp-delay elements, summing devices, and amplifiers or potentiometers. To illustrate the various ways of deriving the state-variable diagram, consider the discrete system characterized by the pulse-transfer function

$$D(z) = \frac{1 + az^{-1} + bz^{-2}}{1 + cz^{-1} + dz^{-2}} \tag{3.2-31}$$

and the block diagram is shown in Fig. 3.2-5.

1. Direct Programming. Following the standard procedure, the state-variable diagram for this system is derived as shown in Fig. 3.2-6. The

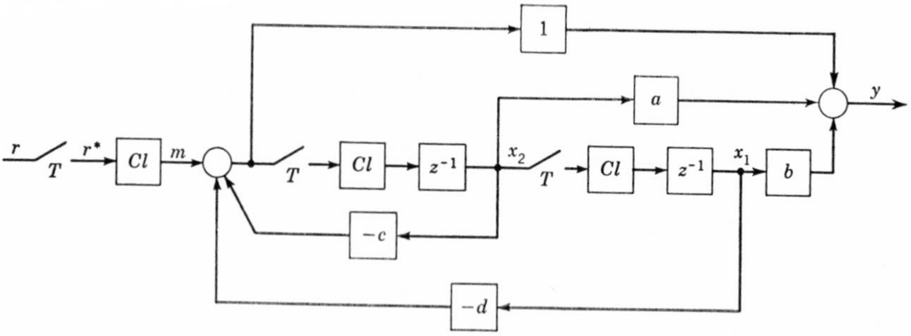

Fig. 3.2-6 State-variable diagram for direct programming.

plant state variables are x_1 and x_2, which are the output of the clamp-delay element. Inspection of the state-variable diagram reveals that the state differential equations are

$$\dot{x}_1 = 0$$
$$\dot{x}_2 = 0$$

and the state-transition equations are

$$\begin{aligned} x_1(nT^+) &= x_1(\overline{n+1}\,T) = x_2(nT) \\ x_2(nT^+) &= -dx_1(nT) - cx_2n(T) + m(nT) \\ m(nT^+) &= r(nT) \end{aligned}$$

The state-transition equations describe the transition of state variables and excitation variables at sampling instants and provide the initial conditions during each transition of the state variables. The output signal $y(t)$ is a linear combination of the state variables x_1 and x_2 and the excitation variable m; thus

$$y(t) = (b - d)x_1(t) + (a - c)x_2(t) + m(t)$$

2. Parallel Programming. To derive the state-variable diagram by the parallel-programming method, the pulse-transfer function is decomposed into partial fractions. Thus Eq. (3.2-31) is written as

$$D(z) = \frac{1 + \alpha_1 z^{-1}}{1 + \beta_1 z^{-1}} + \frac{1 + \alpha_2 z^{-1}}{1 + \beta_2 z^{-1}} \tag{3.2-32}$$

where α_1, α_2, β_1, and β_2 are known functions of a, b, c, and d. The state-variable diagram follows immediately from Eq. (3.2-32), and is depicted in Fig. 3.2-7. The state differential equations are simply

$$\dot{x}_1 = 0$$
$$\dot{x}_2 = 0$$

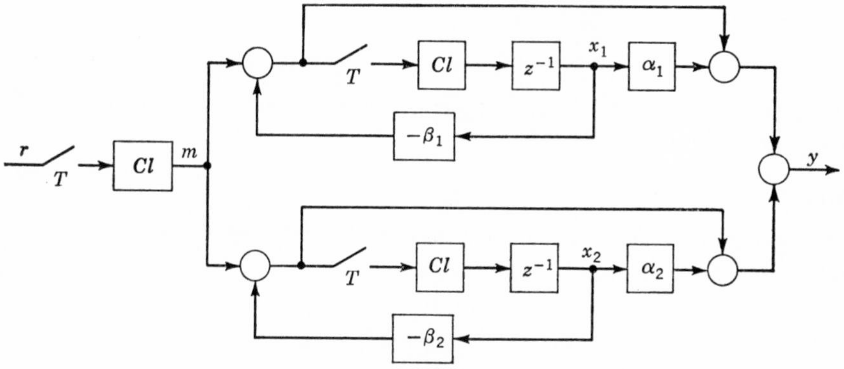

Fig. 3.2-7 State-variable diagram for parallel programming.

and the state-transition equations are

$$\begin{aligned} x_1(nT^+) &= -\beta_1 x_1(nT) + m(nT) \\ x_2(nT^+) &= -\beta_2 x_2(nT) + m(nT) \\ m(nT^+) &= r(nT) \end{aligned}$$

The output $y(t)$ is readily obtained by inspection of the state-variable diagram,

$$y(t) = \alpha_1 x_1(t) + \alpha_2 x_2(t) + 2m(t)$$

which is a linear combination of the state variables and the excitation variable.

3. Iterative Programming. The pulse-transfer function is first expressed in factored form,

$$D(z) = \frac{(1 + \alpha z^{-1})(1 + \beta z^{-1})}{(1 + \gamma z^{-1})(1 + \delta z^{-1})} \tag{3.2-33}$$

The state-variable diagram follows immediately, and is shown in Fig. 3.2-8.

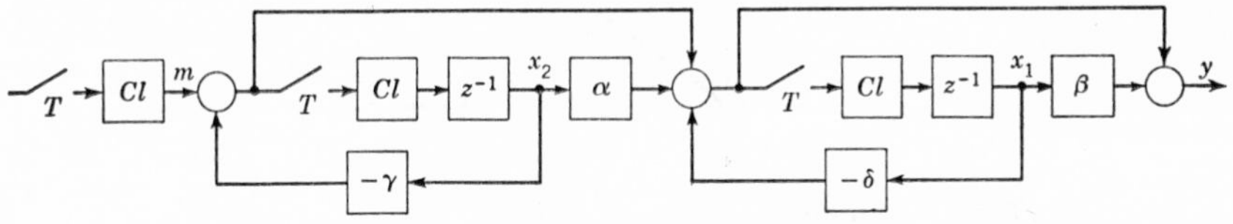

Fig. 3.2-8 State-variable diagram for iterative programming.

Examination of the diagram indicates that the state differential equations are

$$\begin{aligned} \dot{x}_1 &= 0 \\ \dot{x}_2 &= 0 \end{aligned}$$

and the state-transition equations are

$$\begin{aligned} x_1(nT^+) &= -\delta x_1(nT) + (\alpha - \delta)x_2(nT) + m(nT) \\ x_2(nT^+) &= -\gamma x_2(nT) + m(nT) \\ m(nT^+) &= r(nT) \end{aligned}$$

The output $y(t)$ is found to be

$$y(t) = (\beta - \delta)x_1(t) + (\alpha - \gamma)x_2(t) + m(t)$$

which is likewise a linear combination of the excitation variable and the state variables.

Example 3.2-1 A Linear Interpolation System

Consider the linear interpolation system shown in Fig. 3.2-9. Derive the state-variable diagram, the state differential equations, and the state-transition equations.

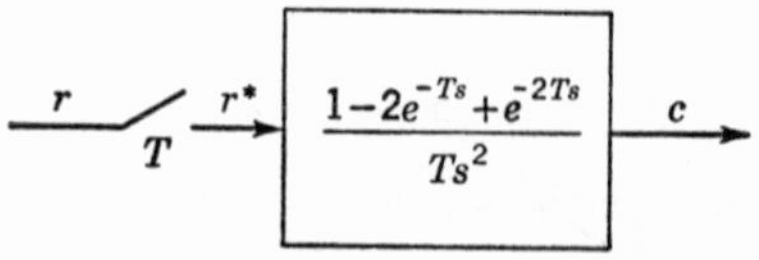

Fig. 3.2-9 A linear interpolation system.

Taking the inverse Laplace transform of the transfer function

$$G(s) = \frac{1 - 2e^{-Ts} + e^{-2Ts}}{Ts^2}$$

gives the impulse response

$$g(t) = \frac{t}{T}u(t) - 2\left(\frac{t}{T} - 1\right)u(t - T) + \left(\frac{t}{T} - 2\right)u(t - 2T)$$

where $u(t)$ denotes the unit-step function. The waveform of the impulse response is illustrated in Fig. 3.2-10. The output of this interpolation system can be determined by superimposing the impulse responses due to the impulsive inputs at the successive sampling instants. Figure 3.2-11 illus-

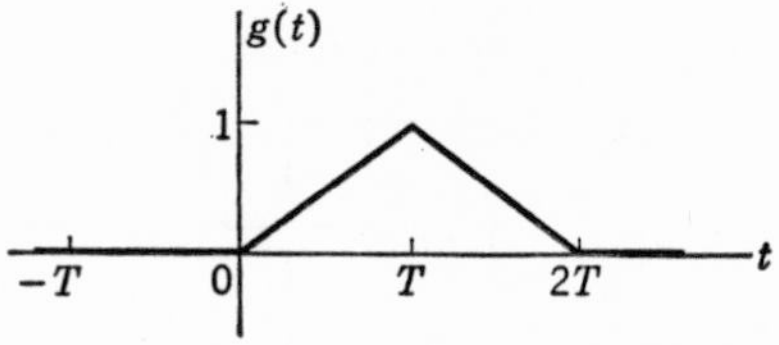

Fig. 3.2-10 Impulse response of the linear interpolation system.

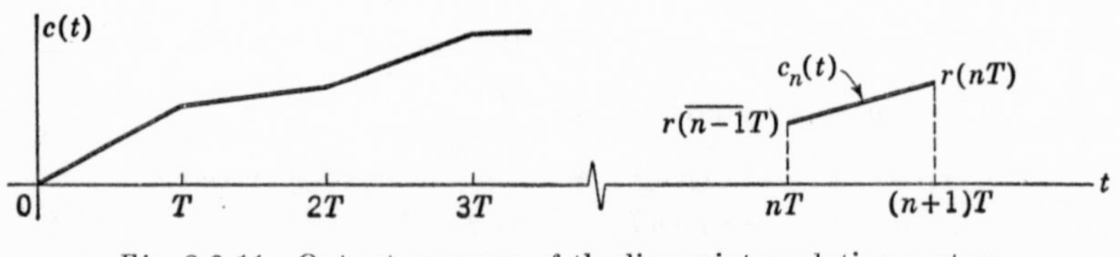

Fig. 3.2-11 Output response of the linear interpolation system.

trates the waveform of the output. Thus, during the interval

$$0 < t - nT \leq nT \qquad \text{or} \qquad nT < t \leq (n+1)T$$

the output of the interpolation system $c_n(t)$ is given by

$$c_n(t) = r(\overline{n-1}\,T) + \frac{1}{T}\{r(nT) - r(\overline{n-1}\,T)\}(t - nT)$$

which describes the recursion formula, or generating function, for this linear interpolator.

The state-variable diagram describing this system can be readily derived from the above generating function and is shown in Fig. 3.2-12. The state

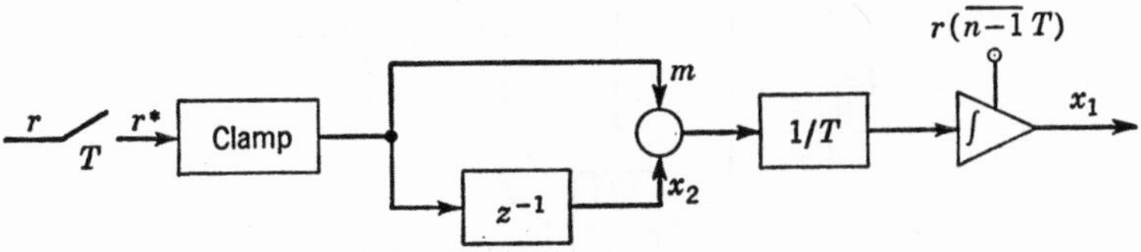

Fig. 3.2-12 State-variable diagram of the linear interpolation system.

variables x_1 and x_2 are the output of the integrator and the clamp-delay element, respectively. Examination of the state-variable diagram reveals that the state differential equations are

$$\dot{x}_1 = \frac{1}{T}(m - x_2)$$
$$\dot{x}_2 = 0$$

where m is the driving, or excitation, signal. The state-transition equations that specify the initial conditions during each transition of the state variables are found to be

$$x_1(nT^+) = x_1(nT) = r(\overline{n-1}\,T)$$
$$x_2(nT^+) = m(nT)$$
$$m(nT^+) = r(nT)$$

Example 3.2-2 State-variable Characterization of a Stirred-tank Chemical Reactor

To illustrate the characterization by state variables of a real system encountered in practice, the stirred-tank reactor in a chemical process is here considered.[71] The simplified schematic diagram of a stirred-tank chemical reactor is shown in Fig. 3.2-13. In the reactor, two reactions take place: $C_1 \rightarrow C_2$ at a rate r_1, and $C_2 \rightarrow C_3$ at a rate r_2. It is assumed that:

1. The components C_1, C_2, and C_3 have the same specific heat and density.
2. There is no change of molecular weight of the components.
3. The reaction $C_1 \rightarrow C_2$ is exothermic, and reaction $C_2 \rightarrow C_3$ is endothermic, with heats of reaction equal to H_1 and H_2, respectively.

The reaction rates are given by

$$r_1 = w_1 e^{\alpha_1 - \beta_1/x_3}$$

and

$$r_2 = w_2 e^{\alpha_2 - \beta_2/x_3}$$

where w_1 and w_2 are weight fractions of components C_1 and C_2, respectively, x_3 is the reactor temperature, and α_1, α_2, β_1, β_2 are constants. Let the flow rates of C_1 and C_2 be f_1 and f_2, their temperatures be T_1 and T_2, the rate of heat transfer from the reactor be m, and the weight fraction of component

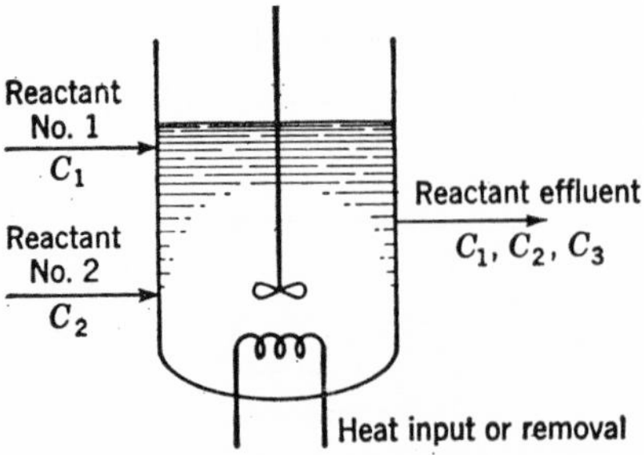

Fig. 3.2-13 A stirred-tank chemical reactor.

C_3 be w_3. The three weight fractions are related by $w_1 + w_2 + w_3 = 1$. In this problem, f_1, f_2, T_1, and T_2 are assumed to be uncontrolled but deterministic disturbances, and the rate of reactor heat transfer m is the control input. Defining the state variables by $x_1 = w_1$, $x_2 = w_3$, and $x_3 =$ reactor temperature and applying the principles of heat and material balances yields the state differential equations

$$\begin{aligned}
\dot{x}_1 &= f_1 - (f_1 + f_2 - e^{\alpha_1 - \beta_1/x_3})x_1 \\
\dot{x}_2 &= (1 - x_1 - x_2)e^{\alpha_2 - \beta_2/x_3} - (f_1 + f_2)x_2 \\
\dot{x}_3 &= H_1 x_1 e^{\alpha_1 - \beta_1/x_3} + H_2(1 - x_1 - x_2)e^{\alpha_2 - \beta_2/x_3} \\
&\qquad + f_1(T_1 - x_3) + f_2(T_2 - x_3) + m
\end{aligned}$$

which characterize the dynamics of the stirred-tank reactor. It is to be noted that these differential equations are nonlinear and cannot be expressed in a simple vector-matrix notation as defined in Eq. (3.2-1).

Choice of State Variables

The characterization of a control system by state-variable diagram is not unique. There are several different ways of describing the system, depending upon the nature of the state variables chosen. Different ways of choosing the state variables of the system generally lead to quite different configurations of the state-variable diagrams. As an illustration, consider the aircraft landing system discussed in Sec. 1.3. The landing of an aircraft consists of several phases of operation.[54] During the first phase the aircraft is guided toward the airport with approximately the correct heading by

RDF (radio direction-finding) equipment. The second phase begins within a few miles of the airport, during which radio contact is made with the radio beam of the instrument landing system. Following this beam, the pilot guides the aircraft along a glide-path angle of approximately $-3°$ toward the runway. At an altitude of about 100 ft, the flare-out phase of the landing begins. During the final phase of the landing, the radio beam of the instrument landing system is no longer effective for guiding the aircraft because of electromagnetic disturbances. The $-3°$ glide-path angle becomes undesirable from the viewpoint of safety and comfort. The pilot must guide the aircraft along the desired flare path by making visual contact with the ground. The linearized short-period equation of motion of the aircraft is found to be

$$\frac{d^3\theta(t)}{dt^3} + 2\zeta\omega_0 \frac{d^2\theta(t)}{dt^2} + \omega_0{}^2 \frac{d\theta(t)}{dt} = KT_0\omega_0{}^2 \frac{d\theta(t)}{dt} + K\omega_0{}^2\delta(t) \qquad (3.2\text{-}34)$$

The pitch angle θ and the altitude h are related by the differential equation

$$T_0 \frac{d^2h(t)}{dt^2} + \frac{dh(t)}{dt} = V\theta(t) \qquad (3.2\text{-}35)$$

In Eqs. (3.2-34) and (3.2-35), all the symbols are as defined in Sec. 1.3 and will not be repeated here. By combining Eqs. (3.2-34) and (3.2-35) and taking the Laplace transform, the transfer function relating the elevator deflection δ to the altitude h is obtained:

$$h(s) = \frac{KV}{s^2\left(1 + \dfrac{2\zeta}{\omega_0}s + \dfrac{1}{\omega_0{}^2}s^2\right)}(s) \qquad (3.2\text{-}36)$$

From this the state-variable diagram describing the aircraft system is readily

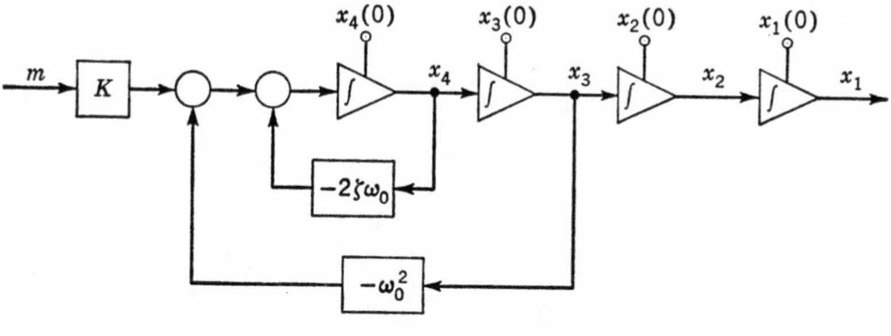

Fig. 3.2-14 A state-variable diagram describing the aircraft.

derived and is shown in Fig. 3.2-14. In this characterization, the state variables chosen are

$$x_1 = h \qquad x_2 = \frac{dh}{dt} \qquad x_3 = \frac{d^2h}{dt^2} \qquad x_4 = \frac{d^3h}{dt^3} \qquad (3.2\text{-}37)$$

It is shown in Sec. 1.3 that, by proper substitution, the above aircraft differential equations may be converted into the following set of first-order differential equations:

$$\begin{aligned} \dot{x}_1 &= x_2 \\ \dot{x}_2 &= x_3 \\ \dot{x}_3 &= x_4 \\ \dot{x}_4 &= -\omega_0^2 x_3 - 2\zeta\omega_0 x_4 + Km \end{aligned} \tag{3.2-38}$$

The state-variable diagram can also be derived from this set of differential equations. In this representation of the aircraft system, the altitude and its three time derivatives are chosen as the state variables, even though both d^2h/dt^2 and d^3h/dt^3 are not readily measurable.

Another way of characterizing the aircraft system by a state-variable diagram is to choose the altitude, the altitude rate, the pitch angle, and the pitch rate as the state variables. These quantities are readily measurable with radar altimeter and gyros. Combining Eqs. (3.2-34) and (3.2-35) by eliminating θ yields

$$\frac{d^4h(t)}{dt^4} + 2\zeta\omega_0 \frac{d^3h(t)}{dt^3} + \omega_0^2 \frac{d^2h(t)}{dt^2} = KV\omega_0^2\delta(t) \tag{3.2-39}$$

It follows from Eq. (3.2-35) that

$$T_0 \frac{d^2h(t)}{dt^2} = V\theta(t) - \frac{dh(t)}{dt} \tag{3.2-40}$$

Differentiating Eq. (3.2-40) with respect to t gives

$$T_0 \frac{d^3h(t)}{dt^3} = V \frac{d\theta(t)}{dt} - \frac{d^2h(t)}{dt^2} \tag{3.2-41}$$

Differentiating Eq. (3.2-41) with respect to t,

$$T_0 \frac{d^4h(t)}{dt^4} = V \frac{d^2\theta(t)}{dt^2} - \frac{d^3h(t)}{dt^3} \tag{3.2-42}$$

Combining Eqs. (3.2-39) and (3.2-42),

$$\begin{aligned} \frac{d^2\theta(t)}{dt^2} - \frac{1 - 2\zeta\omega_0T_0}{T_0}\frac{d\theta(t)}{dt} + \frac{1 - 2\zeta\omega_0T_0 + \omega_0^2T_0^2}{T_0^2}\theta(t) \\ - \frac{1 - 2\zeta\omega_0T_0 + \omega_0^2T_0^2}{VT_0^2}\frac{dh(t)}{dt} = K\omega_0^2T_0\delta(t) \end{aligned} \tag{3.2-43}$$

Let the state variables be defined by

$$x_1 = h \qquad x_2 = \frac{dh}{dt} \qquad x_3 = \theta \qquad x_4 = \frac{d\theta}{dt} \tag{3.2-44}$$

and the elevator deflection δ be replaced by m. Then, from Eq. (3.2-44),

$$\dot{x}_1 = x_2 \tag{3.2-45a}$$

from Eqs. (3.2-40) and (3.2-44),

$$\dot{x}_2 = a_{22}x_2 + a_{23}x_3 \tag{3.2-45b}$$
$$\dot{x}_3 = x_4 \tag{3.2-45c}$$

and from Eqs. (3.2-43) and (3.2-44),

$$\dot{x}_4 = a_{42}x_2 + a_{43}x_3 + a_{44}x_4 + K_0m \tag{3.2-45d}$$

where

$$K_0 = K\omega_0{}^2T_0$$
$$a_{22} = -\frac{1}{T_0} \qquad a_{23} = \frac{V}{T_0}$$
$$a_{42} = \frac{1}{VT_0{}^2} - \frac{2\zeta\omega_0}{VT_0} + \frac{\omega_0{}^2}{V}$$
$$a_{43} = \frac{1}{T_0{}^2} + \frac{2\zeta\omega_0}{T_0} - \omega_0{}^2$$
$$a_{44} = \frac{1}{T_0} - 2\zeta\omega_0$$

The state-variable diagram of the aircraft system is readily derived from Eqs. (3.2-45) and is shown in Fig. 3.2-15. It may be observed that this

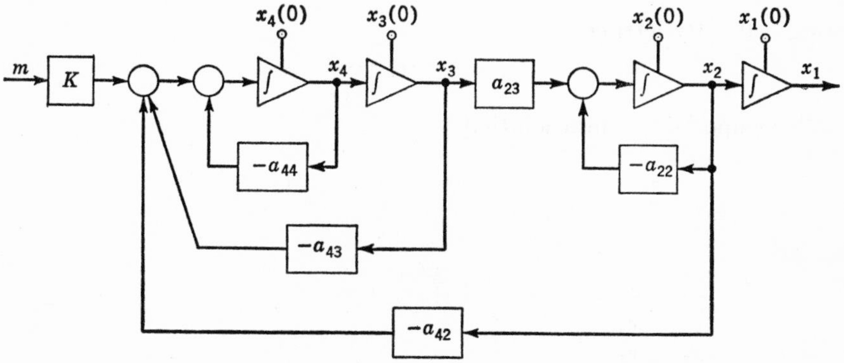

Fig. 3.2-15 A state-variable diagram describing the aircraft.

state-variable diagram is quite different from that of Fig. 3.2-14. However, in this state-variable diagram, all the state variables are measurable. As will be discussed in later chapters of this book, in the design of optimum control systems it is extremely desirable that all the state variables be accessible for measurement and observation. Consequently, in the choice of state-variable characterization of a system, it is important to choose measurable quantities as state variables.

This section only demonstrates how the state-variable diagrams, the state differential equations, and the state-transition equations of control systems are derived; the use of the state differential equations and the state-transition equations in the analysis of discrete systems will be discussed in Sec. 3.5. The design of control systems by means of state-transition techniques is the subject matter of the succeeding chapters.

3.3 INPUT DESCRIPTION BY STATE VARIABLES

The preceding section discusses the state variables and the state-variable diagrams which are used to characterize a process or plant. In order to unify the state-variable characterization of a system subject to inputs and disturbances, the state variables and state-variable diagrams should also be used to characterize the input signals. An input-signal, or excitation, variable may be considered as the output of an input-function generator or a system generating the input signal, which can then be described by state variables and a state-variable diagram. The state-variable characterization of a few commonly encountered input signals is discussed in this section.[68]

a. Polynomial Input

A polynomial input can be expressed as

$$r = r_0 + r_1 t + r_2 t^2 + \cdots + r_{n-1} t^{n-1} \tag{3.3-1}$$

with $t \geq 0$. By letting

$$r = x_1$$

it follows upon differentiation that

$$\begin{aligned} \dot{x}_1 &= r_1 + 2r_2 t + \cdots + (n-1) r_{n-1} t^{n-2} \\ &= x_2 \end{aligned}$$

Similarly,

$$\begin{aligned} \dot{x}_2 &= 2r_2 + 6r_3 t + \cdots + (n-1)(n-2) r_{n-1} t^{n-3} \\ &= x_3 \\ \dot{x}_3 &= x_4 \\ &\cdots\cdots \\ \dot{x}_i &= x_{i+1} \\ &\cdots\cdots \\ \dot{x}_{n-1} &= x_n \\ \dot{x}_n &= 0 \end{aligned}$$

Here the x_i, $i = 1, 2, \ldots, n$, are referred to as the input state variables. The above state differential equations point out that a polynomial input can be generated by a series of integrators connected in cascade as shown in Fig.

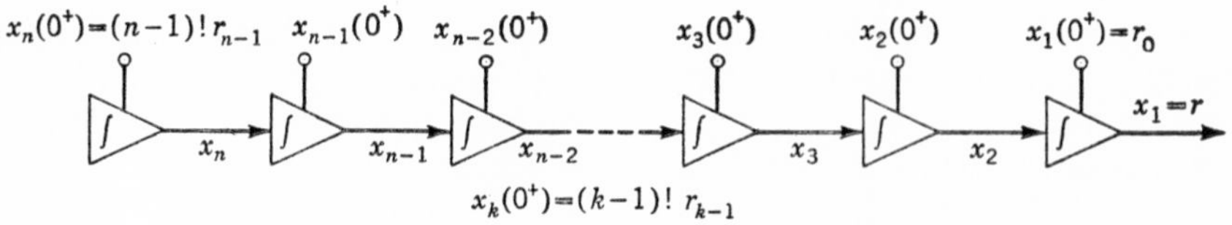

Fig. 3.3-1 State-variable diagram for a polynomial input.

3.3-1. The initial conditions on the integrators are

$$
\begin{aligned}
x_1(0) &= r_0 \\
x_2(0) &= r_1 \\
&\cdots\cdots \\
x_n(0) &= r_{n-1}(n-1)!
\end{aligned}
$$

which are the coefficients of the polynomial representing the input multiplied by an appropriate constant. The output from the system described by the state-variable diagram forms the given input signal.

b. Step-function Input

Let the input be given by

$$r = r_0 u(t) \tag{3.3-2}$$

where $u(t)$ denotes the unit-step function. Defining state variable x_1 as

$$r = x_1$$

then

$$\dot{x}_1 = 0$$

with the initial condition $x_1(0) = r$. The state-variable diagram is shown in Fig. 3.3-2.

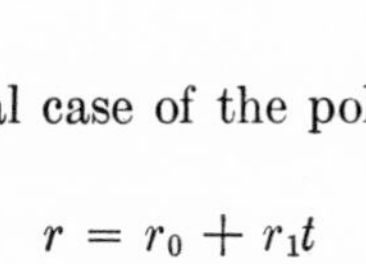

Fig. 3.3-2 State-variable diagram for a step-function input.

c. Ramp-function Input

A ramp function is a special case of the polynomial function and can be written as

$$r = r_0 + r_1 t \tag{3.3-3}$$

with $t \geq 0$. By letting

$$r = x_1$$

the state differential equations are

$$
\begin{aligned}
\dot{x}_1 &= r_1 = x_2 \\
\dot{x}_2 &= 0
\end{aligned}
$$

with the initial conditions $x_1(0) = r_0$ and $x_2(0) = r_1$. The state-variable diagram is depicted in Fig. 3.3-3.

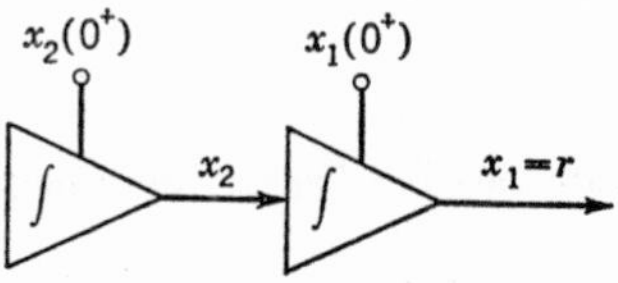

Fig. 3.3-3 State-variable diagram for a ramp-function input.

d. Exponential Input

An exponential input is given by

$$r = r_0 e^{at} \qquad \text{for } t \geq 0 \tag{3.3-4}$$

Let $\qquad r = x_1$

Then $\qquad \dot{x}_1 = ar_0 e^{at} = ar = ax_1$

with the initial condition $x_1(0) = r(0) = r_0$. The state-variable diagram follows immediately from the above equation, and is shown in Fig. 3.3-4.

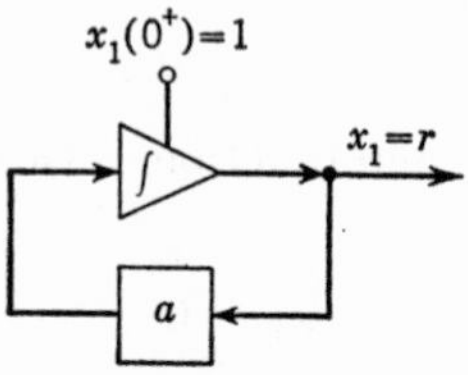

Fig. 3.3-4 State-variable diagram for an exponential input.

The state-variable diagram may be derived in an alternative way. Taking the Laplace transform of Eq. (3.3-4) yields

$$R(s) = \frac{r_0}{s - a}$$

Rearranging, $\qquad R(s) = \frac{r_0}{s} + \frac{a}{s} R(s)$

from which the state-variable diagram follows.

e. Sinusoidal Input

The solution to the harmonic equation

$$\ddot{x}_1 + \omega^2 x_1 = 0 \qquad t \geq 0 \tag{3.3-5}$$

yields a sinusoidal signal. This equation may be decomposed into

$$\dot{x}_1 = \omega x_2 \tag{3.3-6a}$$
$$\dot{x}_2 = -\omega x_1 \tag{3.3-6b}$$

The initial conditions are $x_1(0)$ and $x_2(0)$. Equations (3.3-6) form the state differential equations of the system generating the sinusoidal input signal.

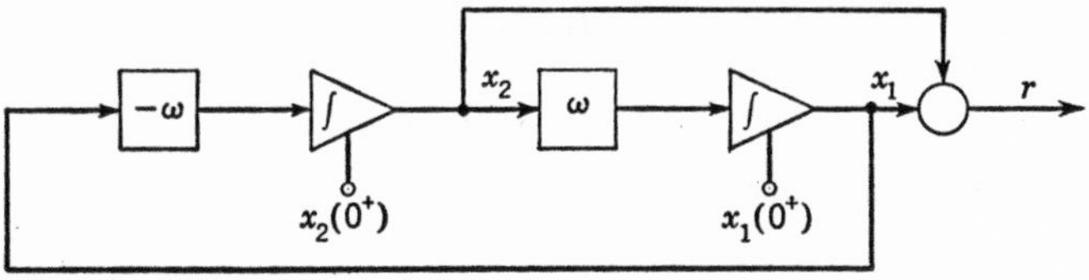

Fig. 3.3-5 State-variable diagram for a sinusoidal input.

The state-variable diagram follows from Eqs. (3.3-6) and is shown in Fig. 3.3-5. It is observed that the signal r is given by

$$r = x_1(0) \cos \omega t + x_2(0) \sin \omega t \tag{3.3-7}$$

f. Sawtooth Input

Referring to the sawtooth waveform shown in Fig. 3.3-6, it is noted that, during the interval

$$nT < t < (n + 1)T$$

the sawtooth wave is described by

$$r(t) = \frac{t - nT}{T} \tag{3.3-8}$$

The sawtooth input may be considered as the combination of a number of finite ramp inputs which are successively delayed. Consequently, the state-variable diagram of a sawtooth generator bears some resemblance to that

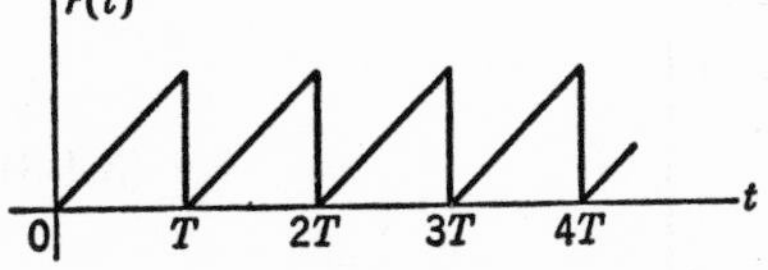

Fig. 3.3-6 Sawtooth waveform.

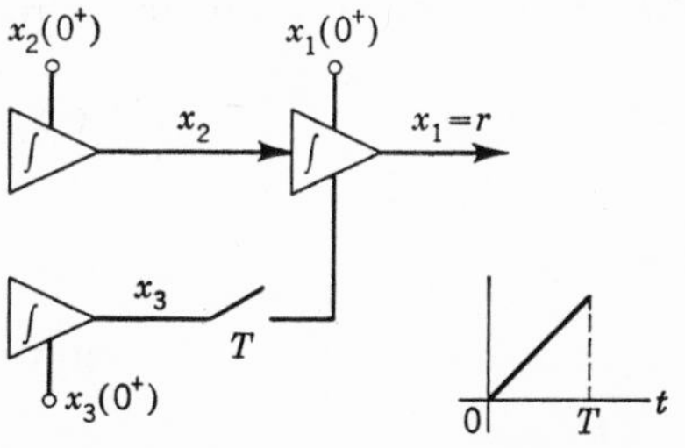

Fig. 3.3-7 State-variable diagram for a sawtooth input.

of the ramp function, except that sampling is introduced to start the ramp function every T sec. The state-variable diagram is depicted in Fig. 3.3-7. It is observed that, at the sampling instants, the switch is closed and

$x_1(nT) = x_3(0) = 0$. The initial conditions on the integrators are

$$x_1(0) = 0$$
$$x_2(0) = \frac{1}{T}$$
$$x_3(0) = 0$$

The state differential equations are

$$\dot{x}_1 = x_2$$
$$\dot{x}_2 = 0$$
$$\dot{x}_3 = 0$$

and the state-transition equations are

$$x_1(nT^+) = x_3(nT)$$
$$x_2(nT^+) = x_2(nT)$$
$$x_3(nT^+) = x_3(nT)$$

3.4 TRANSITION MATRIX

When the process and the inputs, or excitation, variables are represented by a state-variable diagram, the transition matrix[45] of the system may be derived by inspection of the state-variable diagram. Denoting the process state variables by a column vector $\mathbf{x}$, the input state variables by column vector $\mathbf{m}$, and the state variables of the overall system by column vector $\mathbf{v}$, the state differential equation of a linear multivariable, stationary process subject to inputs $\mathbf{m}$ is given by

$$\frac{d\mathbf{v}(\lambda)}{d\lambda} = \mathbf{A}\mathbf{v}(\lambda) \tag{3.4-1}$$

where $\mathbf{A}$ is the coefficient matrix of the overall system, and the state vectors $\mathbf{v}(\lambda)$, $\mathbf{m}(\lambda)$, and $\mathbf{x}(\lambda)$ are given, respectively, by

$$\mathbf{v}(\lambda) = \begin{bmatrix} \mathbf{m}(\lambda) \\ \mathbf{x}(\lambda) \end{bmatrix} \tag{3.4-2}$$

$$\mathbf{m}(\lambda) = \begin{bmatrix} m_1(\lambda) \\ m_2(\lambda) \\ \cdot \\ \cdot \\ \cdot \\ m_j(\lambda) \end{bmatrix} \tag{3.4-3}$$

and

$$\mathbf{x}(\lambda) = \begin{bmatrix} x_1(\lambda) \\ x_2(\lambda) \\ \cdot \\ \cdot \\ \cdot \\ x_r(\lambda) \end{bmatrix} \tag{3.4-4}$$

It is assumed that the process is of the rth order and the input signals can be described by j state variables. The solution to Eq. (3.4-1) is found to be

$$\mathbf{v}(\lambda) = \mathbf{\Phi}(\lambda)\mathbf{v}(0^+) \tag{3.4-5}$$

where

$$\mathbf{v}(0^+) = \begin{bmatrix} \mathbf{m}(0^+) \\ \mathbf{x}(0^+) \end{bmatrix} \tag{3.4-6}$$

$$\mathbf{m}(0^+) = \begin{bmatrix} m_1(0^+) \\ m_2(0^+) \\ \cdot \\ \cdot \\ \cdot \\ m_j(0^+) \end{bmatrix} \tag{3.4-7}$$

and

$$\mathbf{x}(0^+) = \begin{bmatrix} x_1(0^+) \\ x_2(0^+) \\ \cdot \\ \cdot \\ \cdot \\ x_r(0^+) \end{bmatrix} \tag{3.4-8}$$

The transition matrix $\mathbf{\Phi}(\lambda)$ is given by

$$\mathbf{\Phi}(\lambda) = \begin{bmatrix} a_{11}(\lambda) & a_{12}(\lambda) & \cdots & a_{1n}(\lambda) \\ a_{21}(\lambda) & a_{22}(\lambda) & \cdots & a_{2n}(\lambda) \\ \cdots & \cdots & \cdots & \cdots \\ a_{j1}(\lambda) & a_{j2}(\lambda) & \cdots & a_{jn}(\lambda) \\ a_{(j+1)1}(\lambda) & a_{(j+1)2}(\lambda) & \cdots & a_{(j+1)n}(\lambda) \\ \cdots & \cdots & \cdots & \cdots \\ a_{n1}(\lambda) & a_{n2}(\lambda) & \cdots & a_{nn}(\lambda) \end{bmatrix} \tag{3.4-9}$$

with $j + r = n$, where the $a_{ij}(\lambda)$ are to be determined. $\mathbf{\Phi}(\lambda)$ is the overall transition matrix, since it covers both the process state variables and the input state variables. When the initial conditions are specified, the time functions describing the state variables can readily be determined.

The transition matrix may be determined from the step-function responses of the system. Substituting Eq. (3.4-9) into Eq. (3.4-5) and expanding yields

$$\begin{aligned} m_i(\lambda) &= a_{i1}(\lambda)m_1(0^+) + a_{i2}(\lambda)m_2(0^+) + \cdots + a_{ij}(\lambda)m_j(0^+) \\ &\quad + a_{i(j+1)}(\lambda)x_1(0^+) + a_{i(j+2)}(\lambda)x_2(0^+) + \cdots + a_{in}(\lambda)x_r(0^+) \end{aligned} \tag{3.4-10}$$

$$\begin{aligned} x_k(\lambda) &= a_{k1}(\lambda)m_1(0^+) + a_{k2}(\lambda)m_2(0^+) + \cdots + a_{kj}(\lambda)m_j(0^+) \\ &\quad + a_{k(j+1)}(\lambda)x_1(0^+) + a_{k(j+2)}(\lambda)x_2(0^+) + \cdots + a_{kn}(\lambda)x_r(0^+) \end{aligned} \tag{3.4-11}$$

The elements a_{ik} are either constants or functions of λ, which describe the corresponding unit-step response. When

$$m_1(0^+) = 1$$
$$m_2(0^+) = m_3(0^+) = \cdots = m_j(0^+)$$
$$= x_1(0^+) = x_2(0^+) = \cdots = x_r(0^+) = 0$$

Eq. (3.4-10) leads to

$$a_{i1}(\lambda) = m_i(\lambda)$$

Thus $a_{i1}(\lambda)$ is the unit-step response measured at m_i of the state-variable diagram with input $m_1(0^+) = 1$ and initial conditions on the other integrators equal to zero. Similarly, $a_{i(j+1)}(\lambda)$ is the unit-step response measured at m_i of the state-variable diagram with input $x_1(0^+) = 1$ and initial conditions on the other integrators equal to zero.

When

$$m_1(0^+) = 1$$
$$m_2(0^+) = m_3(0^+) = \cdots = m_j(0^+)$$
$$= x_1(0^+) = x_2(0^+) = \cdots = x_r(0^+) = 0$$

Eq. (3.4-11) reduces to

$$a_{k1}(\lambda) = x_k(\lambda)$$

Thus $a_{k1}(\lambda)$ is the unit-step response measured at x_k of the state-variable diagram with input $m_1(0^+) = 1$ and initial conditions on the other integrators equal to zero. In like manner, $a_{k(j+1)}(\lambda)$ is the unit-step response measured at x_k of the state-variable diagram with input $x_1(0^+) = 1$ and initial conditions on the other integrators equal to zero. It is noted that the first subscript of a_{ik} indicates where the response is measured and the second subscript designates where the input is applied. In many situations the functions $a_{ik}(\lambda)$ may be determined by inspection of the state-variable diagram of the system. Thus the above analysis provides a simplified method for the determination of the transition matrix.

The foregoing discussion reveals that the elements of the square matrix $\mathbf{\Phi}(\lambda)$ are given by the respective unit-step responses. The $\mathbf{\Phi}(\lambda)$ matrix describes the transient behavior of the system subject to a specified change of the states, and is referred to as the transition matrix. It should be pointed out that the argument λ of $\mathbf{\Phi}(\lambda)$ is equal to t for the analysis of continuous systems, and λ is equal to $t - nT$ for $0 < \lambda \leq T$ in the case of discrete systems. Several examples are given below to illustrate the evaluation of a transition matrix by inspection of the state-variable diagram.

Example 3.4-1 A Simple First-order System

Consider a system characterized by the following differential equation,

$$\dot{x}(t) + ax(t) = am(t)$$

with initial condition $x(0^+)$. Determine the transition matrix of the system.

Taking the Laplace transform of both sides of the above differential equation,

$$sX(s) - x(0^+) + aX(s) = aM(s)$$

Rearranging, $$X(s) = \frac{a}{s+a} M(s) + \frac{1}{s+a} x(0^+)$$

Assuming the excitation variable $m(t)$ to be a unit-step function, the state-variable diagram of the system is derived from the above equation, as shown

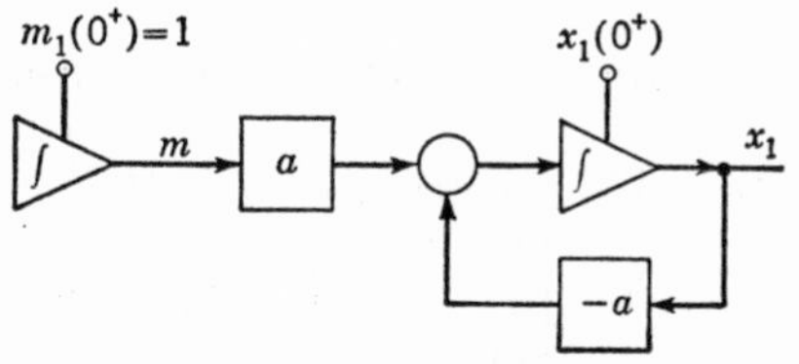

Fig. 3.4-1 State-variable diagram for a first-order system subject to a unit-step-function input.

in Fig. 3.4-1. Inspection of this diagram reveals that

$$a_{11}(t) = 1$$
$$a_{21}(t) = \mathcal{L}^{-1}\left\{\frac{a}{s(s+a)}\right\} = 1 - e^{-at}$$
$$a_{12}(t) = 0$$
$$a_{22}(t) = \mathcal{L}^{-1}\left\{\frac{a}{s+a}\right\} = ae^{-at}$$

Thus the overall transition matrix is

$$\mathbf{\Phi}(t) = \begin{bmatrix} 1 & 0 \\ 1 - e^{-at} & ae^{-at} \end{bmatrix}$$

It follows from the state differential equation

$$\frac{d\mathbf{v}(t)}{dt} = \mathbf{\Phi}(t)\mathbf{v}(t)$$

that
$$m_1(t) = 1$$
$$\begin{aligned} x_1(t) &= x(t) \\ &= (1 - e^{-at})m_1(0^+) + ae^{-at}x_1(0^+) \\ &= (1 - e^{-at})u(t) + x(0^+)e^{-at} \end{aligned}$$

Example 3.4-2 A Second-order System

Consider a system characterized by

$$\ddot{x}(t) + \dot{x}(t) = m(t)$$

with $m(t)$ a unit-step function and initial conditions $x(0^+)$, $\dot{x}(0^+)$. Determine the transition matrix.

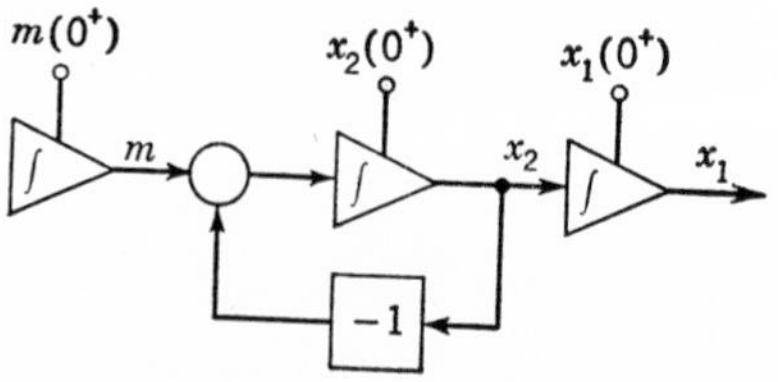

Fig. 3.4-2 State-variable diagram for a second-order system subject to a unit-step function input.

The state-variable diagram is shown in Fig. 3.4-2, from which it is obtained that

$$a_{11}(t) = 1 \qquad a_{12}(t) = a_{13}(t) = 0$$

$$a_{21}(t) = \mathcal{L}^{-1}\left\{\frac{1}{s}\frac{1}{s+1}\frac{1}{s}\right\} = t - 1 + e^{-t}$$

$$a_{22}(t) = \mathcal{L}^{-1}\left\{\frac{1}{s}\right\} = 1$$

$$a_{23}(t) = \mathcal{L}^{-1}\left\{\frac{1}{s}\frac{s}{s+1}\frac{1}{s}\right\} = 1 - e^{-t}$$

$$a_{31}(t) = \mathcal{L}^{-1}\left\{\frac{1}{s}\frac{1}{s+1}\right\} = 1 - e^{-t}$$

$$a_{32}(t) = 0$$

$$a_{33}(t) = \mathcal{L}^{-1}\left\{\frac{1}{s}\frac{s}{s+1}\right\} = e^{-t}$$

Thus the overall transition matrix is

$$\mathbf{\Phi}(t) = \begin{bmatrix} 1 & 0 & 0 \\ t - 1 + e^{-t} & 1 & 1 - e^{-t} \\ 1 - e^{-t} & 0 & e^{-t} \end{bmatrix}$$

Since the state vector is

$$\mathbf{v}(t) = \begin{bmatrix} m_1(t) \\ x_1(t) \\ x_2(t) \end{bmatrix}$$

and the initial-condition vector is

$$\mathbf{v}(0^+) = \begin{bmatrix} m_1(0^+) \\ x_1(0^+) \\ x_2(0^+) \end{bmatrix}$$

the step-function response of the system is given by

$$x_1(t) = (t - 1 + e^{-t})u(t) + x(0^+) + \dot{x}(0^+)(1 - e^{-t})$$

Example 3.4-3 A Simple System Subject to a Sawtooth Input

Given a system subject to a sawtooth input and characterized by

$$\dot{x}(t) + ax(t) = am(t)$$

with initial condition $x(0^+)$. The waveform of the input signal $m(t)$ is shown in Fig. 3.4-3. Determine the overall transition matrix.

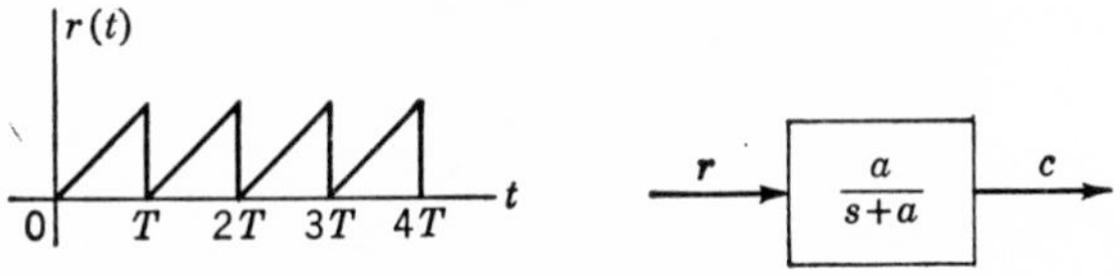

Fig. 3.4-3 A simple first-order system subject to a sawtooth input.

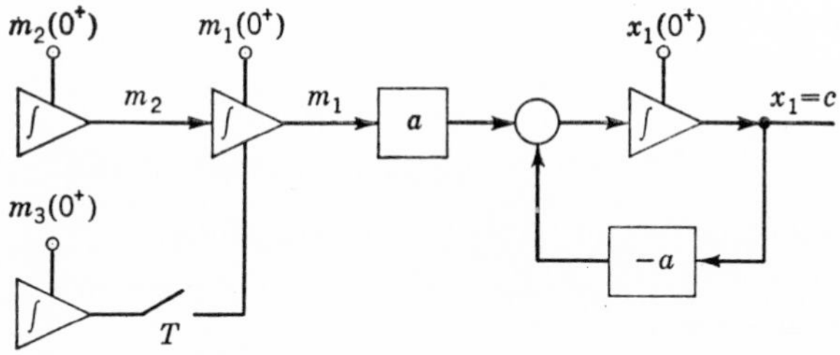

Fig. 3.4-4 State-variable diagram for a system subject to a sawtooth input.

From the state-variable diagram depicted in Fig. 3.4-4, it is found that

$$a_{11}(t) = 1 \qquad a_{12}(t) = \mathcal{L}^{-1}\left\{\frac{1}{s^2}\right\} = t$$

$$\begin{aligned} a_{13}(t) &= 0 & a_{14}(t) &= 0 \\ a_{21}(t) &= 0 & a_{22}(t) &= 1 \\ a_{23}(t) &= 0 & a_{24}(t) &= 0 \\ a_{31}(t) &= 0 & a_{32}(t) &= 0 \\ a_{33}(t) &= 1 & a_{34}(t) &= 0 \end{aligned}$$

$$a_{41}(t) = \mathcal{L}^{-1}\left\{\frac{a}{s(s+a)}\right\} = 1 - e^{-at}$$

$$a_{42}(t) = \mathcal{L}^{-1}\left\{\frac{a}{s^2(s+a)}\right\} = t - \frac{1}{a}(1 - e^{-at})$$

$$a_{43}(t) = 0$$

$$a_{44}(t) = \mathcal{L}^{-1}\left\{\frac{1}{s}\frac{s}{s+a}\right\} = e^{-at}$$

Hence the overall transition matrix is

$$\mathbf{\Phi}(t) = \begin{bmatrix} 1 & t & 0 & 0 \\ 0 & 1 & 0 & 0 \\ 0 & 0 & 1 & 0 \\ 1 - e^{-at} & t - \frac{1}{a}(1 - e^{-at}) & 0 & e^{-at} \end{bmatrix}$$

Since the state vector is expressed as

$$\mathbf{v}(t) = \begin{bmatrix} m_1(t) \\ m_2(t) \\ m_3(t) \\ x_1(t) \end{bmatrix}$$

the response of the specified system is given by

$$x_1(t) = (1 - e^{-at})\, m_1(0^+) + \left[t - \frac{1}{a}(1 - e^{-at})\right] m_2(0^+) + x_1(0^+)\, e^{-at}$$
$$= \frac{t}{T} - \frac{1}{aT}(1 - e^{-at}) + x(0^+)\, e^{-at}$$

3.5 STATE-TRANSITION ANALYSIS OF DISCRETE-DATA SYSTEMS

A linear, stationary discrete-data system can be described by a set of first-order linear differential equations with constant coefficients which may be expressed in vector form as[147]

$$\frac{d\mathbf{v}(\lambda)}{d\lambda} = \mathbf{A}\mathbf{v}(\lambda) \tag{3.5-1}$$

where $\lambda = t - nT$, and $0 < \lambda \leq T$. The state vector $\mathbf{v}$ consists of the input state vector $\mathbf{m}$ and the process state vector $\mathbf{x}$. Equation (3.5-1), which characterizes the discrete-data system during a sampling period, is referred to as the state differential equation of the system. The initial conditions for the state differential equation may be given in vector form as

$$\mathbf{v}(nT^+) = \mathbf{B}\mathbf{v}(nT) \tag{3.5-2}$$

This equation, which describes the transition of the state variables of the system of the sampling instants, is often referred to as the state-transition equation. Both $\mathbf{A}$ and $\mathbf{B}$ are square matrices, and can be written down by inspection of the state-variable diagram of the system.

Taking the Laplace transform of Eq. (3.5-1) gives

$$s\mathbf{V}(s) = \mathbf{A}\mathbf{V}(s) + \mathbf{v}(0^+) \tag{3.5-3}$$

Rearranging,

$$\mathbf{V}(s) = [s\mathbf{I} - \mathbf{A}]^{-1}\mathbf{v}(0^+) \tag{3.5-4}$$

Taking the inverse transform of Eq. (3.5-4) yields the solution to the state differential equation as

$$\mathbf{v}(\lambda) = \mathbf{\Phi}(\lambda)\mathbf{v}(0^+) \tag{3.5-5}$$

where the overall transition matrix is given by

$$\mathbf{\Phi}(\lambda) = \mathcal{L}^{-1}[s\mathbf{I} - \mathbf{A}]^{-1} \tag{3.5-6}$$

In terms of t, Eq. (3.5-5) becomes

$$\mathbf{v}(t) = \mathbf{\Phi}(t - nT)\mathbf{v}(nT^+) \tag{3.5-7}$$

which describes the behavior of the system during the interval

$$nT < t \leq (n + 1)T \tag{3.5-8}$$

Consequently, at the sampling instant $t = (n + 1)T$,

$$\mathbf{v}(\overline{n + 1}\ T) = \mathbf{\Phi}(T)\mathbf{v}(nT^+) \tag{3.5-9}$$

In view of the relationship given in Eq. (3.5-2), the state vector $\mathbf{v}$ may be expressed as

$$\mathbf{v}(t) = \mathbf{\Phi}(t - nT)\mathbf{B}\mathbf{v}(nT) \tag{3.5-10}$$

and

$$\mathbf{v}(\overline{n + 1}\ T) = \mathbf{\Phi}(T)\mathbf{B}\mathbf{v}(nT) \tag{3.5-11}$$

This is a recursion equation from which the successive values of the state variables at the sampling instants can be computed. It is to be noted that, in the case of continuous systems, the $\mathbf{B}$ matrix is a unity matrix, and $\lambda = t$.

By defining

$$\mathbf{H}(t - nT) = \mathbf{\Phi}(t - nT)\mathbf{B} \tag{3.5-12}$$

Eq. (3.5-10) may be written as

$$\mathbf{v}(t) = \mathbf{H}(t - nT)\mathbf{v}(nT) \tag{3.5-13}$$

This equation determines the state variables of the system at any instant of time during the interval $nT < t \leq (n + 1)T$. Then, at $t = (n + 1)T$,

$$\mathbf{v}(\overline{n + 1}\ T) = \mathbf{H}(T)\mathbf{v}(nT) \tag{3.5-14}$$

By assigning successive values for n, Eq. (3.5-14) leads to the following series of equations:

$$\begin{array}{ll}
n = 0 & \mathbf{v}(T) = \mathbf{H}(T)\mathbf{v}(0) \\
n = 1 & \mathbf{v}(2T) = \mathbf{H}(T)\mathbf{v}(T) \\
n = 2 & \mathbf{v}(3T) = \mathbf{H}(T)\mathbf{v}(2T) \\
\cdots & \cdots\cdots\cdots \\
n = k - 1 & \mathbf{v}(kT) = \mathbf{H}(T)\mathbf{v}(\overline{k - 1}\ T) \\
\cdots & \cdots\cdots\cdots \\
n = n - 1 & \mathbf{v}(nT) = \mathbf{H}(T)\mathbf{v}(\overline{n - 1}\ T)
\end{array} \tag{3.5-15}$$

Combining these equations and simplifying yields

$$\mathbf{v}(nT) = \mathbf{H}^n(T)\mathbf{v}(0) \tag{3.5-16}$$

Since the z transform is defined by[136]

$$\mathbf{V}(z) = \sum_{n=0}^{\infty} \mathbf{v}(nT)z^{-n} \tag{3.5-17}$$

combining Eqs. (3.5-16) and (3.5-17) yields the z transform as

$$\mathbf{V}(z) = \sum_{n=0}^{\infty} [\mathbf{H}(T)z^{-1}]^n\mathbf{v}(0) \tag{3.5-18}$$

In view of the relationship

$$\sum_{n=0}^{\infty} [\mathbf{H}(T)z^{-1}]^n = [\mathbf{I} - z^{-1}\mathbf{H}(T)]^{-1} \tag{3.5-19}$$

the z transform for the state vector of the discrete-data system is given by

$$\mathbf{V}(z) = [\mathbf{I} - z^{-1}\mathbf{H}(T)]^{-1}\mathbf{v}(0) \tag{3.5-20}$$

Clearly, the inverse transform of Eq. (3.5-20) yields the state vector as

$$\mathbf{v}(nT) = \mathfrak{z}^{-1}[\mathbf{I} - z^{-1}\mathbf{H}(T)]^{-1}\mathbf{v}(0) \tag{3.5-21}$$

This is a general solution from which the state variables of the system at successive sampling instants can be computed once the overall transition matrix and the **B** matrix of the system are determined and the initial-state variables are known. Equation (3.5-21) provides a unified, systematic way of analyzing the dynamic performance of discrete-data systems.

Stability Considerations

Let the $\mathbf{H}(T)$ matrix be partitioned according to the dimensions of vectors **m** and **x**:

$$\mathbf{H}(T) = \begin{bmatrix} \boldsymbol{\alpha}(T) & \mathbf{0} \\ \boldsymbol{\gamma}(T) & \boldsymbol{\beta}(T) \end{bmatrix} \tag{3.5-22}$$

where $\boldsymbol{\alpha}(T)$ is a square matrix. Then

$$\begin{aligned} \mathbf{I} - z^{-1}\mathbf{H}(T) &= \begin{bmatrix} \mathbf{I} & \mathbf{0} \\ \mathbf{0} & \mathbf{I} \end{bmatrix} - z^{-1}\begin{bmatrix} \boldsymbol{\alpha}(T) & \mathbf{0} \\ \boldsymbol{\gamma}(T) & \boldsymbol{\beta}(T) \end{bmatrix} \\ &= \begin{bmatrix} \mathbf{I} - z^{-1}\boldsymbol{\alpha}(T) & \mathbf{0} \\ -z^{-1}\boldsymbol{\gamma}(T) & \mathbf{I} - z^{-1}\boldsymbol{\beta}(T) \end{bmatrix} \end{aligned} \tag{3.5-23}$$

Since, by definition,

$$\mathbf{V}(z) = \begin{bmatrix} \mathbf{M}(z) \\ \mathbf{X}(z) \end{bmatrix} \quad \text{and} \quad \mathbf{v}(0) = \begin{bmatrix} \mathbf{m}(0) \\ \mathbf{x}(0) \end{bmatrix}$$

Eq. (3.5-20) may be written as

$$\begin{bmatrix} \mathbf{M}(z) \\ \mathbf{X}(z) \end{bmatrix} = \begin{bmatrix} [\mathbf{I} - z^{-1}\boldsymbol{\alpha}(T)]^{-1} & \mathbf{0} \\ z^{-1}[\mathbf{I} - z^{-1}\boldsymbol{\beta}(T)]^{-1}\boldsymbol{\gamma}(T)[\mathbf{I} - z^{-1}\boldsymbol{\alpha}(T)]^{-1} & [\mathbf{I} - z^{-1}\boldsymbol{\beta}(T)]^{-1} \end{bmatrix}\begin{bmatrix} \mathbf{m}(0) \\ \mathbf{x}(0) \end{bmatrix} \tag{3.5-24}$$

In deriving the above equation, use is made of Eq. (3.5-23). Hence the z transforms for the input state vector and the process state vector are given, respectively, by

$$\mathbf{M}(z) = [\mathbf{I} - z^{-1}\boldsymbol{\alpha}(T)]^{-1}\mathbf{m}(0) \tag{3.5-25}$$

and

$$\mathbf{X}(z) = z^{-1}[\mathbf{I} - z^{-1}\boldsymbol{\beta}(T)]^{-1}\boldsymbol{\gamma}(T)\mathbf{M}(z) + [\mathbf{I} - z^{-1}\boldsymbol{\beta}(T)]^{-1}\mathbf{x}(0) \tag{3.5-26}$$

In Eq. (3.5-26), the first term on the right-hand side is due to the input state vector **M** and the second term is due to the initial conditions of the system. The second term is zero for systems which are initially at rest. The sequences of the input state variables and the process state variables are readily obtained by taking the inverse transform of Eqs. (3.5-25) and (3.5-26), respectively.

With the system initially at quiescence, the process state vector is given in z transform by

$$\mathbf{X}(z) = z^{-1}[\mathbf{I} - z^{-1}\boldsymbol{\beta}(T)]^{-1}\boldsymbol{\gamma}(T)\mathbf{M}(z) \qquad (3.5\text{-}27)$$

The characteristic equation of the system is

$$\det[\mathbf{I} - z^{-1}\boldsymbol{\beta}(T)] = 0 \qquad (3.5\text{-}28)$$

Hence, for stability, the roots of Eq. (3.5-28) must lie inside the unit circle of the z plane.[136]

In view of Eq. (3.5-22), the state vector given by Eq. (3.5-13) may be expressed as

$$\begin{bmatrix} \mathbf{m}(t) \\ \mathbf{x}(t) \end{bmatrix} = \begin{bmatrix} \boldsymbol{\alpha}(t - nT) & 0 \\ \boldsymbol{\gamma}(t - nT) & \boldsymbol{\beta}(t - nT) \end{bmatrix} \begin{bmatrix} \mathbf{m}(nT) \\ \mathbf{x}(nT) \end{bmatrix} \qquad (3.5\text{-}29)$$

Consequently, during the interval $nT < t \leq (n + 1)T$, the process state vector is given by

$$\mathbf{x}(t) = \boldsymbol{\gamma}(t - nT)\mathbf{m}(nT) + \boldsymbol{\beta}(t - nT)\mathbf{x}(nT) \qquad (3.5\text{-}30)$$

where the values of $\mathbf{m}(nT)$ and $\mathbf{x}(nT)$ can readily be determined from Eqs. (3.5-25) and (3.5-26). By letting $n = 0, 1, 2, \ldots$, Eq. (3.5-30) yields the time functions for the process state variables.

To illustrate the application of the method discussed above to the analysis of discrete-data systems, the following numerical examples are worked out.

Example 3.5-1 Open-loop System

The block diagram of a simple sampled-data system is shown in Fig. 3.5-1. The input is a unit-step function, and the sampling period is T sec. Determine the output response of the system.

From the state-variable diagram shown in Fig. 3.5-2, the following state

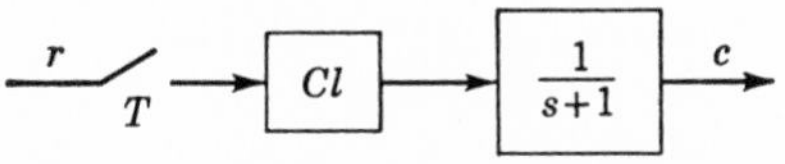

Fig. 3.5-1 A simple sampled-data system.

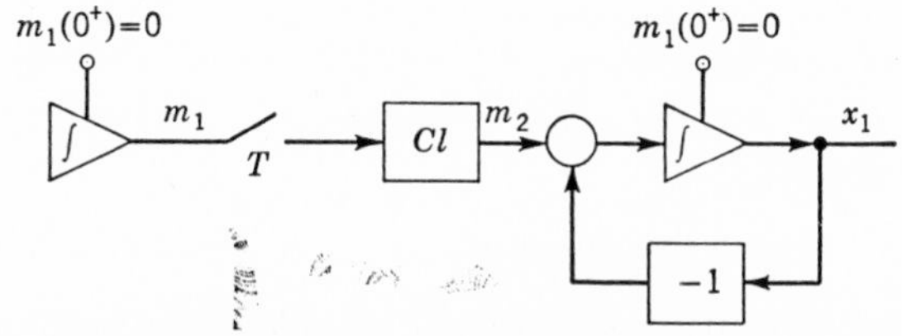

Fig. 3.5-2 State-variable diagram for the simple sampled-data system.

differential equations can be derived,

$$\begin{aligned} \dot{m}_1 &= 0 \\ \dot{m}_2 &= 0 \\ \dot{x}_1 &= m_2 - x_1 \end{aligned}$$

and the state-transition equations are

$$\begin{aligned} m_1(nT^+) &= m_1(nT) \\ m_2(nT^+) &= m_1(nT) \\ x_1(nT^+) &= x_1(nT) \end{aligned}$$

Hence the **A** and **B** matrices are

$$\mathbf{A} = \begin{bmatrix} 0 & 0 & 0 \\ 0 & 0 & 0 \\ 0 & 1 & -1 \end{bmatrix} \qquad \mathbf{B} = \begin{bmatrix} 1 & 0 & 0 \\ 1 & 0 & 0 \\ 0 & 0 & 1 \end{bmatrix}$$

The transition matrix is found to be

$$\mathbf{\Phi}(t) = \begin{bmatrix} 1 & 0 & 0 \\ 0 & 1 & 0 \\ 0 & 1 - e^{-t} & e^{-t} \end{bmatrix}$$

Thus the $\mathbf{H}(T)$ matrix is given by

$$\mathbf{H}(T) = \mathbf{\Phi}(T)\mathbf{B} = \begin{bmatrix} 1 & 0 & 0 \\ 1 & 0 & 0 \\ 1 - e^{-T} & 0 & e^{-T} \end{bmatrix}$$

and

$$\boldsymbol{\alpha}(T) = \begin{bmatrix} 1 & 0 \\ 1 & 0 \end{bmatrix} \qquad \boldsymbol{\beta}(T) = e^{-T}$$

$$\boldsymbol{\gamma}(T) = [1 - e^{-T} \quad 0]$$

$$\mathbf{I} - z^{-1}\boldsymbol{\alpha}(T) = \begin{bmatrix} 1 - z^{-1} & 0 \\ -z^{-1} & 1 \end{bmatrix}$$

$$\mathbf{I} - z^{-1}\boldsymbol{\beta}(T) = 1 - z^{-1}e^{-T}$$

Since

$$\mathbf{X}(z) = z^{-1}[\mathbf{I} - z^{-1}\boldsymbol{\beta}(T)]^{-1}\boldsymbol{\gamma}(T)[\mathbf{I} - z^{-1}\boldsymbol{\alpha}(T)]^{-1}\mathbf{m}(0)$$

by substitution,

$$\mathbf{X}(z) = \frac{z(1 - e^{-T})}{(z - 1)(z - e^{-T})}$$

Clearly, this example is so simple that the solution can be obtained quickly by the classical method. Nothing is gained by use of the unified approach. However, the main purpose of this example is to illustrate the analysis discussed in this section.

Example 3.5-2 Closed-loop System

Determine the output response of the sampled-data system shown in Fig. 3.5-3. The system is subject to a unit-step input.

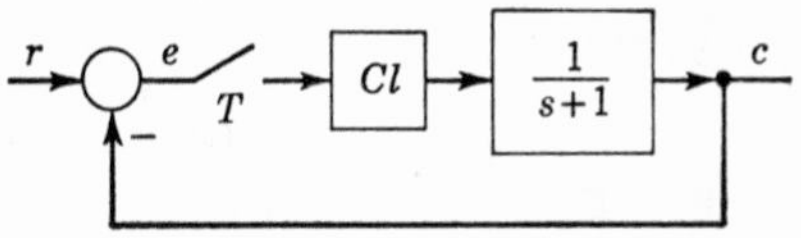

Fig. 3.5-3 A simple feedback sampled-data system.

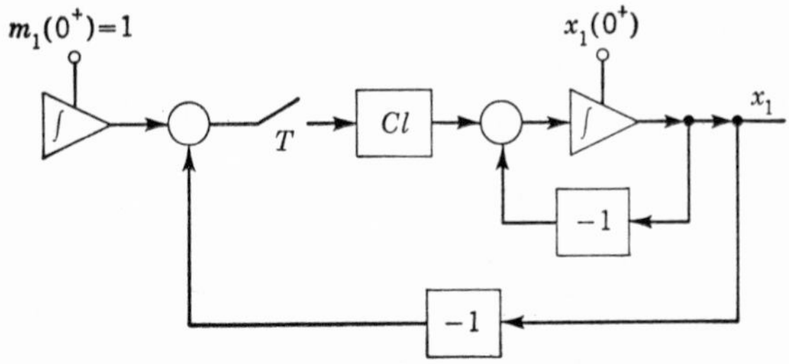

Fig. 3.5-4 State-variable diagram for the feedback sampled-data system.

The state-variable diagram of the system is depicted in Fig. 3.5-4. It is found from the diagram that the state differential equations are

$$\begin{aligned} \dot{m}_1 &= 0 \\ \dot{m}_2 &= 0 \\ \dot{x}_1 &= m_2 - x_1 \end{aligned}$$

and the state-transition equations are

$$\begin{aligned} m_1(nT^+) &= m_1(nT) \\ m_2(nT^+) &= m_1(nT) - x_1(nT) \\ x_1(nT^+) &= x_1(nT) \end{aligned}$$

Thus the **A** and **B** matrices are

$$\mathbf{A} = \begin{bmatrix} 0 & 0 & 0 \\ 0 & 0 & 0 \\ 0 & 1 & -1 \end{bmatrix} \qquad \mathbf{B} = \begin{bmatrix} 1 & 0 & 0 \\ 1 & 0 & -1 \\ 0 & 0 & 1 \end{bmatrix}$$

As an illustration, the overall transition matrix is derived by a different method. By reference to the state-variable diagram,

$$\begin{aligned} m_1(\lambda) &= 1 = m_1(0^+) \\ m_2(\lambda) &= m_1(\lambda) - x_1(\lambda) = m_2(0^+) \end{aligned}$$

and

$$\dot{x}_1(\lambda) = m_1(0^+) - x_1(\lambda)$$

The preceding differential equation has the solution

$$x_1(\lambda) = (1 - e^{-\lambda})m_2(0^+) + e^{-\lambda}x_1(0^+)$$

Hence the overall transition matrix is

$$\mathbf{\Phi}(\lambda) = \begin{bmatrix} 1 & 0 & 0 \\ 0 & 1 & 0 \\ 0 & 1 - e^{-\lambda} & e^{-\lambda} \end{bmatrix}$$

The $\mathbf{H}(T)$ matrix is computed as

$$\mathbf{H}(T) = \mathbf{\Phi}(T)\mathbf{B} = \begin{bmatrix} 1 & 0 & 0 \\ 1 & 0 & -1 \\ 1 - e^{-T} & 0 & -1 + 2e^{-T} \end{bmatrix}$$

$\mathbf{H}(T)$ is partitioned in such a way that

$$\alpha(T) = 1 \qquad \beta(T) = \begin{bmatrix} 0 & -1 \\ 0 & -1 + 2e^{-T} \end{bmatrix} \qquad \gamma(T) = \begin{bmatrix} 1 \\ 1 - e^{-T} \end{bmatrix}$$

Consequently,

$$[\mathbf{I} - z^{-1}\beta(T)]^{-1} = \frac{1}{1 - z^{-1}(2e^{-T} - 1)} \begin{bmatrix} 1 - z^{-1}(2e^{-T} - 1) & 1 + z^{-1} \\ 0 & 1 \end{bmatrix}$$

$$[\mathbf{I} - z^{-1}\alpha(T)]^{-1} = \frac{1}{1 - z^{-1}}$$

If $x_1(0^+) = 0$, it follows from Eqs. (3.5-25) and (3.5-26), by proper substitution, that

$$\begin{bmatrix} M_2(z) \\ X_1(z) \end{bmatrix} = \frac{z}{(z-1)(z - 2e^{-T} + 1)} \begin{bmatrix} 1 - z^{-1}(2e^{-T} - 1) + (1 + z^{-1})(1 - e^{-T}) \\ 1 - e^{-T} \end{bmatrix}$$

Hence

$$X_1(z) = \frac{z(1 - e^{-T})}{(z-1)(z - 2e^{-T} + 1)}$$

By the classical method,

$$G(z) = \mathfrak{z}\left\{\frac{1 - e^{-Ts}}{s(s+1)}\right\} = \frac{1 - e^{-T}}{z - e^{-T}}$$

$$R(z) = \frac{z}{z - 1}$$

and

$$C(z) = \frac{G(z)}{1 + G(z)} R(z) = \frac{z(1 - e^{-T})}{(z-1)(z - 2e^{-T} + 1)}$$

which checks the result given above.

If the initial condition on the system is

$$x_1(0^+) = c_0$$

the proper substitution into Eqs. (3.5-25) and (3.5-26) leads to

$$\begin{bmatrix} M_2(z) \\ X_1(z) \end{bmatrix} = \frac{z}{(z-1)(z - 2e^{-T} + 1)} \begin{bmatrix} 1 - z^{-1}(2e^{-T} - 1) + (1 + z^{-1})(1 - e^{-T}) \\ 1 - e^{-T} \end{bmatrix} + \frac{z}{z - 2e^{-T} + 1} \begin{bmatrix} c_0(1 + z^{-1}) \\ c_0 \end{bmatrix}$$

Hence

$$X_1(z) = \frac{z(1 - e^{-T})}{(z-1)(z - 2e^{-T} + 1)} + \frac{c_0 z}{z - 2e^{-T} + 1}$$

The foregoing rather simple numerical examples appear to give the impression that analysis of discrete-data systems by the state-transition method would lead to a more complicated solution than analysis by the classical method. However, these simple examples have been selected merely for the purpose of illustrating the method of analysis presented in this section. It is felt that the best way to demonstrate a method and to clarify its presentation is by illustration of simple examples. More sophisticated application of the state-transition method to complicated problems is discussed in the following section. It will be seen that the unified, general approach surpasses the classical method in the analysis of complex systems and in optimum synthesis, discussed in the latter part of the book.

3.6 NONCONVENTIONAL SAMPLING SYSTEMS

The preceding section is concerned with the analysis of basic sampled-data systems by the state-transition method. For simple sampled-data problems, the classical z-transform approach appears less complicated than the state-transition analysis, although the latter is a more general method and a more powerful tool. This section extends the analysis presented in the previous section to more complicated discrete-data control problems. This includes variable-rate, multirate, nonsynchronized, pulse-width-modulated, pulse-frequency-modulated, and finite-width discrete-data systems.[136] These systems are identified as nonconventional discrete-data systems.

Assume that the basic sampling period of the nonconventional discrete-data system is T sec. The basic sampling period is subdivided into a number of intervals. The subdivision of the basic sampling period determines whether the discrete-data system is of cyclic-variable-rate, multirate, nonsynchronized, pulse-width-modulated, pulse-frequency-modulated, or finite-pulse-width type. In Fig. 3.6-1, the basic sampling period is subdivided into k intervals which are not all equal. Classification of the nonconventional sampling problems is based on the nature of the subintervals.

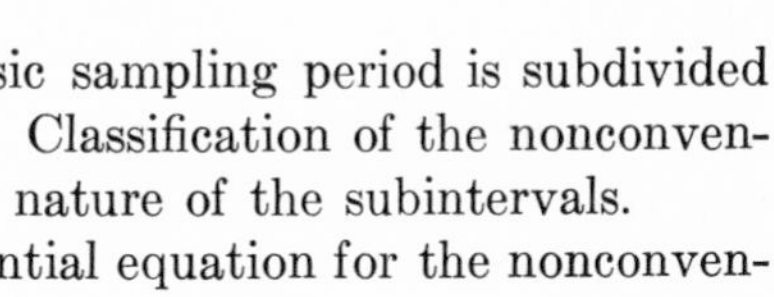

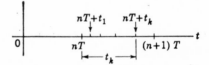

Fig. 3.6-1 Time scale for nonconventional sampling system.

During a subinterval τ, the state differential equation for the nonconventional discrete-data system is given by

$$\frac{d\mathbf{v}(\lambda)}{d\lambda} = \mathbf{A}\mathbf{v}(\lambda) \tag{3.6-1}$$

where λ lies in the interval $0 < \lambda \leq \tau$. The general solution to Eq. (3.6-1) has been found to be

$$\mathbf{v}(\lambda) = \mathbf{\Phi}(\lambda)\mathbf{B}\mathbf{v}(0) = \mathbf{H}(\lambda)\mathbf{v}(0) \tag{3.6-2}$$

During the subinterval

$$nT < t \leq nT + t_1$$
$$0 < t - nT \leq t_1$$

the initial conditions are $\mathbf{v}(nT^+)$ and the solution to Eq. (3.6-1) is

$$\mathbf{v}(\lambda) = \mathbf{\Phi}_0(\lambda)\mathbf{v}(0^+) \tag{3.6-3}$$

with the state-transition equation given by

$$\mathbf{v}(nT^+) = \mathbf{B}_0\mathbf{v}(nT) \tag{3.6-4}$$

where $\mathbf{\Phi}_0(\lambda)$ is the transition matrix during this subinterval.

Since $\lambda = t - nT$, Eq. (3.6-3) reduces to

$$\mathbf{v}(t) = \mathbf{\Phi}_0(t - nT)\mathbf{v}(nT^+) \tag{3.6-5}$$

By defining

$$\mathbf{H}_0(t - nT) = \mathbf{\Phi}_0(t - nT)\mathbf{B}_0 \tag{3.6-6}$$

the state vector $\mathbf{v}(t)$ may be written as

$$\mathbf{v}(t) = \mathbf{H}_0(t - nT)\mathbf{v}(nT) \tag{3.6-7}$$

For the sake of convenience in later development, Eq. (3.6-7) is put in the form

$$\mathbf{v}(t) = \boldsymbol{\psi}_0(t - nT)\mathbf{v}(nT) \tag{3.6-8}$$

and by definition,

$$\boldsymbol{\psi}_0(t - nT) = \mathbf{H}_0(t - nT) \tag{3.6-9}$$

During the subinterval

$$nT + t_1 < t \leq nT + t_2$$
$$t_1 < t - nT \leq t_2$$

the initial conditions are given by the vector $\mathbf{v}(nT + t_1^+)$, and the solution to Eq. (3.6-1) is

$$\mathbf{v}(\lambda) = \mathbf{\Phi}_1(\lambda)\mathbf{v}(0^+) \tag{3.6-10}$$

with the state-transition equation

$$\mathbf{v}(nT + t_1^+) = \mathbf{B}_1\mathbf{v}(nT + t_1) \tag{3.6-11}$$

where $\mathbf{\Phi}_1(\lambda)$ is the transition matrix during this subinterval. It can be seen that the transition matrices and the **B** matrices may be different during different subintervals. Since $\lambda = t - (nT + t_1)$, Eq. (3.6-10) becomes

$$\begin{aligned}\mathbf{v}(t) &= \mathbf{\Phi}_1(t - nT - t_1)\mathbf{v}(nT + t_1^+)\\ &= \mathbf{H}_1(t - nT - t_1)\mathbf{v}(nT + t_1)\end{aligned} \tag{3.6-12}$$

where

$$\mathbf{H}_1(t - nT - t_1) = \mathbf{\Phi}_1(t - nT - t_1)\mathbf{B}_1 \tag{3.6-13}$$

Equation (3.6-5) gives the value of $\mathbf{v}(nT + t_1)$ as

$$\mathbf{v}(nT + t_1) = \mathbf{H}_0(t_1)\mathbf{v}(nT) \tag{3.6-14}$$

Hence

$$\mathbf{v}(t) = \mathbf{H}_1(t - nT - t_1)\mathbf{H}_0(t_1)\mathbf{v}(nT) \tag{3.6-15}$$

By defining

$$\boldsymbol{\psi}_1(t - nT) = \mathbf{H}_1(t - nT - t_1)\mathbf{H}_0(t_1) \tag{3.6-16}$$

Eq. (3.6-15) may be written as

$$\mathbf{v}(t) = \boldsymbol{\psi}_1(t - nT)\mathbf{v}(nT) \tag{3.6-17}$$

During the subinterval

$$nT + t_2 < t \leq nT + t_3$$
$$t_2 < t - nT \leq t_3$$

the initial-condition vector is $\mathbf{v}(nT + t_2^+)$, and the solution to Eq. (3.6-1) is given by

$$\mathbf{v}(\lambda) = \boldsymbol{\Phi}_2(\lambda)\mathbf{v}(0^+) \tag{3.6-18}$$

with the state-transition equation

$$\mathbf{v}(nT + t_2^+) = \mathbf{B}_2\mathbf{v}(nT + t_2) \tag{3.6-19}$$

where $\boldsymbol{\Phi}_2(\lambda)$ is the transition matrix during this subinterval. Since $\lambda = t - (nT + t_2)$,

$$\begin{aligned} \mathbf{v}(t) &= \boldsymbol{\Phi}_2(t - nT - t_2)\mathbf{v}(nT + t_2^+) \\ &= \mathbf{H}_2(t - nT - t_2)\mathbf{v}(nT + t_2) \end{aligned} \tag{3.6-20}$$

where

$$\mathbf{H}_2(t - nT - t_2) = \boldsymbol{\Phi}_2(t - nT - t_2)\mathbf{B}_2 \tag{3.6-21}$$

It follows from Eq. (3.6-15) that

$$\mathbf{v}(nT + t_2) = \mathbf{H}_1(t_2 - t_1)\mathbf{H}_0(t_1)\mathbf{v}(nT) \tag{3.6-22}$$

Hence

$$\mathbf{v}(t) = \mathbf{H}_2(t - nT - t_2)\mathbf{H}_1(t_2 - t_1)\mathbf{H}_0(t_1)\mathbf{v}(nT) \tag{3.6-23}$$

which may be expressed as

$$\mathbf{v}(t) = \boldsymbol{\psi}_2(t - nT)\mathbf{v}(nT) \tag{3.6-24}$$

by defining

$$\boldsymbol{\psi}_2(t - nT) = \mathbf{H}_2(t - nT - t_2)\mathbf{H}_1(t_2 - t_1)\mathbf{H}_0(t_1) \tag{3.6-25}$$

During the subinterval

$$nT + t_3 < t \leq nT + t_4$$

the initial-condition vector is $\mathbf{v}(nT + t_3^+)$ and the state-transition equation is

$$\mathbf{v}(nT + t_3^+) = \mathbf{B}_3\mathbf{v}(nT + t_3) \tag{3.6-26}$$

In like manner, the solution to Eq. (3.6-1) is found to be

$$\mathbf{v}(t) = \boldsymbol{\psi}_3(t - nT)\mathbf{v}(nT) \tag{3.6-27}$$

where

$$\boldsymbol{\psi}_3(t - nT) = \mathbf{H}_3(t - nT - t_3)\mathbf{H}_2(t_3 - t_2)\mathbf{H}_1(t_2 - t_1)\mathbf{H}_0(t_1) \tag{3.6-28}$$

and

$$\mathbf{H}_3(t - nT - t_3) = \boldsymbol{\Phi}_3(t - nT - t_3)\mathbf{B}_3 \tag{3.6-29}$$

During the subinterval

$$nT + t_i < t \leq nT + t_{i+1}$$

it can readily be shown that the solution to Eq. (3.6-1) is

$$\mathbf{v}(t) = \boldsymbol{\psi}_i(t - nT)\mathbf{v}(nT) \tag{3.6-30}$$

where

$$\boldsymbol{\psi}_i(t - nT) = \mathbf{H}_i(t - nT - t_i)\mathbf{H}_{i-1}(t_i - t_{i-1}) \cdots \mathbf{H}_1(t_2 - t_1)\mathbf{H}_0(t_1) \tag{3.6-31}$$

which is generally different for different subintervals within the basic sampling period. Hence, by letting $t_{i+1} = t_1, t_2, \ldots, t_k, T$, and $n = 0, 1, 2, \ldots$, Eq. (3.6-30) describes the complete response of the system. The application of the analysis discussed above is best illustrated by examples. In view of the recursive nature of this approach, the procedure of analysis is ideal for programming on a digital computer. With the advent of high-speed digital computers, the mathematical thinking and engineering analysis and design have been greatly affected. The computational feasibility is one of the important merits of this new approach.

Example 3.6-1 Multirate Sampled-data System

Consider the multirate sampled-data system shown in Fig. 3.6-2. The sampling period of the low-speed sampler is 1 sec. The high-speed sampler

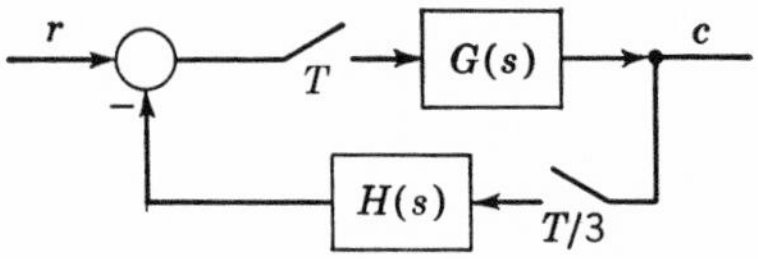

Fig. 3.6-2 A multirate sampled-data system.

operates three times faster. Zero-order holds are used in both the forward circuit and the feedback circuit. The transfer functions are

$$G(s) = \frac{1 - e^{-Ts}}{s} \frac{0.5}{s + 1}$$

and

$$H(s) = \frac{1 - e^{-Ts/3}}{s} \frac{1}{s}$$

Determine the system response to a unit-step-function input.

The state-variable diagram is depicted in Fig. 3.6-3. The state vector is defined by

$$\mathbf{v}(\lambda) = \begin{bmatrix} m_1(\lambda) \\ x_1(\lambda) \\ x_2(\lambda) \\ x_3(\lambda) \\ x_4(\lambda) \end{bmatrix}$$

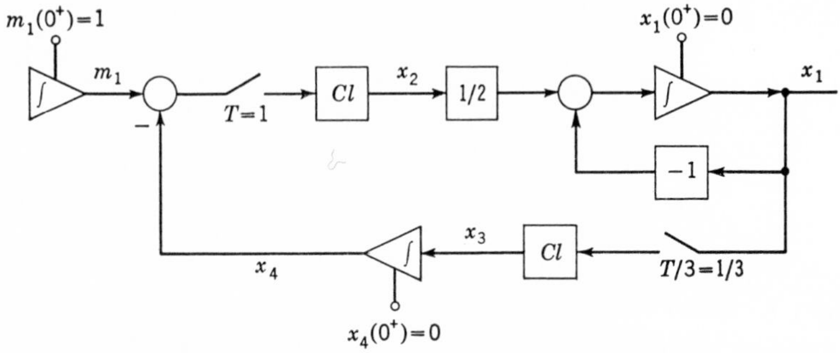

Fig. 3.6-3 State-variable diagram for the multirate sampled-data system.

and the initial-condition vector is

$$\mathbf{v}(0^+) = \begin{bmatrix} 1 \\ 0 \\ 0 \\ 0 \\ 0 \end{bmatrix}$$

From the state-variable diagram it is found that, during the first subinterval,

$$\mathbf{A}_0 = \begin{bmatrix} 0 & 0 & 0 & 0 & 0 \\ 0 & -1 & 0.5 & 0 & 0 \\ 0 & 0 & 0 & 0 & 0 \\ 0 & 0 & 0 & 1 & 0 \\ 0 & 0 & 0 & 0 & 0 \end{bmatrix}$$

$$\mathbf{B}_0 = \begin{bmatrix} 1 & 0 & 0 & 0 & 0 \\ 0 & 1 & 0 & 0 & 0 \\ 1 & 0 & 0 & 0 & -1 \\ 0 & 1 & 0 & 0 & 0 \\ 0 & 0 & 0 & 0 & 1 \end{bmatrix}$$

$$\mathbf{\Phi}_0(\lambda) = \begin{bmatrix} 1 & 0 & 0 & 0 & 0 \\ 0 & e^{-\lambda} & 0.5(1 - e^{-\lambda}) & 0 & 0 \\ 0 & 0 & 1 & 0 & 0 \\ 0 & 0 & 0 & 1 & 0 \\ 0 & 0 & 0 & \lambda & 1 \end{bmatrix}$$

$$\mathbf{H}_0(\lambda) = \begin{bmatrix} 1 & 0 & 0 & 0 & 0 \\ 0.5(1 - e^{-\lambda}) & e^{-\lambda} & 0 & 0 & -0.5(1 - e^{-\lambda}) \\ 1 & 0 & 0 & 0 & -1 \\ 0 & 1 & 0 & 0 & 0 \\ 0 & \lambda & 0 & 0 & 1 \end{bmatrix}$$

Thus, for $nT < t \leq nT + T/3$,

$$\mathbf{v}(t) = \psi_0(t - nT)\mathbf{v}(nT)$$
$$\psi_0(t - nT) = \mathbf{H}_0(t - nT)$$

During the second and third subintervals,

$$\mathbf{A}_1 = \mathbf{A}_2 = \mathbf{A}_0$$

$$\mathbf{B}_1 = \mathbf{B}_2 = \begin{bmatrix} 1 & 0 & 0 & 0 & 0 \\ 0 & 1 & 0 & 0 & 0 \\ 0 & 0 & 1 & 0 & 0 \\ 0 & 1 & 0 & 0 & 0 \\ 0 & 0 & 0 & 0 & 1 \end{bmatrix}$$

$$\mathbf{\Phi}_1(\lambda) = \mathbf{\Phi}_2(\lambda) = \mathbf{\Phi}_0(\lambda)$$

$$\mathbf{H}_1(\lambda) = \mathbf{H}_2(\lambda) = \begin{bmatrix} 1 & 0 & 0 & 0 & 0 \\ 0 & e^{-\lambda} & 0.5(1 - e^{-\lambda}) & 0 & 0 \\ 0 & 0 & 1 & 0 & 0 \\ 0 & 1 & 0 & 0 & 0 \\ 0 & \lambda & 0 & 0 & 1 \end{bmatrix}$$

For $nT + T/3 < t \leq nT + 2T/3$,

$$\mathbf{v}(t) = \boldsymbol{\psi}_1(t - nT)\mathbf{v}(nT)$$

$$\boldsymbol{\psi}_1(t - nT) = \mathbf{H}_1\left(t - nT - \frac{T}{3}\right)\mathbf{H}_0\left(\frac{T}{3}\right)$$

For $nT + 2T/3 < t \leq (n + 1)T$,

$$\mathbf{v}(t) = \boldsymbol{\psi}_2(t - nT)\mathbf{v}(nT)$$

$$\boldsymbol{\psi}_2(t - nT) = \mathbf{H}_2\left(t - nT - \frac{2T}{3}\right)\mathbf{H}_1\left(\frac{T}{3}\right)\mathbf{H}_0\left(\frac{T}{3}\right)$$

With $T = 1$ sec, the following matrices are determined:

$$\boldsymbol{\psi}_0\left(\frac{T}{3}\right) = \mathbf{H}_0\left(\frac{T}{3}\right) = \begin{bmatrix} 1 & 0 & 0 & 0 & 0 \\ 0.14 & 0.72 & 0 & 0 & -0.14 \\ 1 & 0 & 0 & 0 & -1 \\ 0 & 1 & 0 & 0 & 0 \\ 0 & 0.33 & 0 & 0 & 0 \end{bmatrix}$$

$$\boldsymbol{\psi}_1\left(\frac{T}{3}\right) = \mathbf{H}_1\left(\frac{T}{3}\right)\mathbf{H}_0\left(\frac{T}{3}\right) = \begin{bmatrix} 1 & 0 & 0 & 0 & 0 \\ 0.24 & 0.52 & 0 & 0 & -0.24 \\ 1 & 0 & 0 & 0 & -1 \\ 0.14 & 0.72 & 0 & 0 & -0.14 \\ 0.046 & 0.57 & 0 & 0 & 0.954 \end{bmatrix}$$

$$\boldsymbol{\psi}_2\left(\frac{T}{3}\right) = \mathbf{H}_2\left(\frac{T}{3}\right)\mathbf{H}_1\left(\frac{T}{3}\right)\mathbf{H}_0\left(\frac{T}{3}\right) = \begin{bmatrix} 1 & 0 & 0 & 0 & 0 \\ 0.31 & 0.36 & 0 & 0 & -0.31 \\ 1 & 0 & 0 & 0 & -1 \\ 0.24 & 0.52 & 0 & 0 & -0.24 \\ 0.13 & 0.74 & 0 & 0 & 0.874 \end{bmatrix}$$

Since
$$\mathbf{v}(0) = \begin{bmatrix} 1 \\ 0 \\ 0 \\ 0 \\ 0 \end{bmatrix}$$

the following state vectors are obtained:

$$\mathbf{v}(\tfrac{1}{3}) = \psi_0(\tfrac{1}{3})\mathbf{v}(0) = \begin{bmatrix} 1 \\ 0.14 \\ 1 \\ 0 \\ 0 \end{bmatrix} \qquad \mathbf{v}(\tfrac{2}{3}) = \psi_1(\tfrac{1}{3})\mathbf{v}(0) = \begin{bmatrix} 1 \\ 0.24 \\ 1 \\ 0.14 \\ 0.046 \end{bmatrix}$$

$$\mathbf{v}(1) = \psi_2(\tfrac{1}{3})\mathbf{v}(0) = \begin{bmatrix} 1 \\ 0.31 \\ 1 \\ 0.24 \\ 0.13 \end{bmatrix} \qquad \mathbf{v}(1\tfrac{1}{3}) = \psi_0(\tfrac{1}{3})\mathbf{v}(1) = \begin{bmatrix} 1 \\ 0.24 \\ 1 \\ 0.14 \\ 0.046 \end{bmatrix}$$

$$\mathbf{v}(1\tfrac{2}{3}) = \psi_1(\tfrac{1}{3})\mathbf{v}(1) = \begin{bmatrix} 1 \\ 0.35 \\ 0.954 \\ 0.30 \\ 0.23 \end{bmatrix} \qquad \mathbf{v}(2) = \psi_2(\tfrac{1}{3})\mathbf{v}(1) = \begin{bmatrix} 1 \\ 0.38 \\ 0.87 \\ 0.37 \\ 0.46 \end{bmatrix}$$

$$\mathbf{v}(2\tfrac{1}{3}) = \psi_0(\tfrac{1}{3})\mathbf{v}(2) = \begin{bmatrix} 1 \\ 0.30 \\ 0.954 \\ 0.24 \\ 0.12 \end{bmatrix} \qquad \mathbf{v}(2\tfrac{2}{3}) = \psi_1(\tfrac{1}{3})\mathbf{v}(2) = \begin{bmatrix} 1 \\ 0.36 \\ 0.77 \\ 0.36 \\ 0.46 \end{bmatrix}$$

$$\mathbf{v}(3) = \psi_2(\tfrac{1}{3})\mathbf{v}(2) = \begin{bmatrix} 1 \\ 0.31 \\ 0.53 \\ 0.33 \\ 0.82 \end{bmatrix} \qquad \mathbf{v}(3\tfrac{1}{3}) = \psi_0(\tfrac{1}{3})\mathbf{v}(3) = \begin{bmatrix} 1 \\ 0.35 \\ 0.88 \\ 0.30 \\ 0.22 \end{bmatrix}$$

$$\mathbf{v}(3\tfrac{2}{3}) = \psi_1(\tfrac{1}{3})\mathbf{v}(3) = \begin{bmatrix} 1 \\ 0.31 \\ 0.54 \\ 0.33 \\ 0.25 \end{bmatrix} \qquad \mathbf{v}(4) = \psi_2(\tfrac{1}{3})\mathbf{v}(3) = \begin{bmatrix} 1 \\ 0.20 \\ 0.26 \\ 0.25 \\ 1.05 \end{bmatrix}$$

The output sequence in response to a unit-step-function input is

$$0,\ 0.14,\ 0.24 \qquad 0.31,\ 0.24,\ 0.35 \qquad 0.38,\ 0.30,\ 0.36 \qquad 0.31,\ \ldots$$

which occur at $k/3$ sec, $k = 0, 1, 2, \ldots$, respectively.

Example 3.6-2 Variable-rate Sampled-data System

Consider the cyclic variable-rate error-sampled feedback system shown in Fig. 3.6-4. The sampler operates at the instants $t = 0, T/4; T, 5T/4; \ldots;$

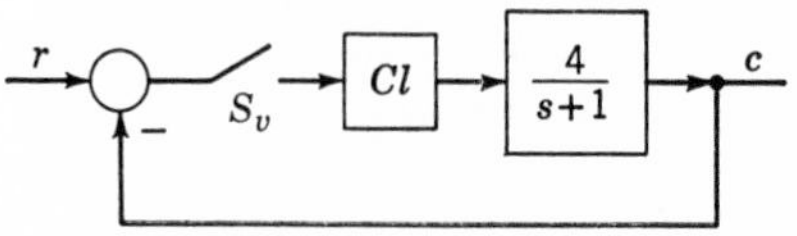

Fig. 3.6-4 A variable-rate sampled-data system.

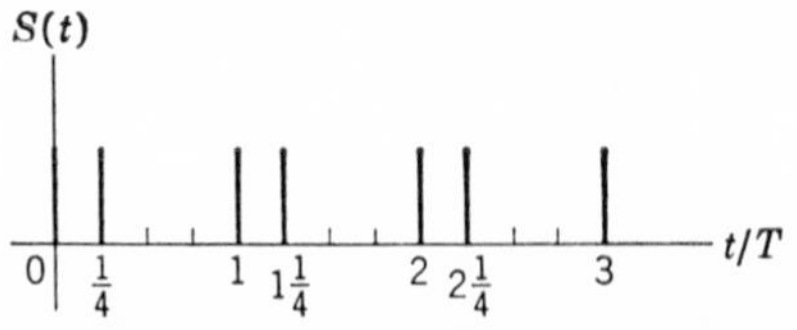

Fig. 3.6-5 The sampling function of the variable-rate sampler.

kT, $(k + \frac{1}{4})T; \ldots;$ as shown in Fig. 3.6-5. The basic sampling period is 1 sec. A zero-order hold is used as the smoothing device. The transfer function of the controlled plant is

$$G(s) = \frac{4}{s+1}$$

Determine the transient response of the system to a unit-step-function input.

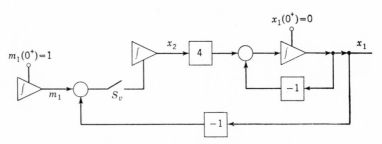

Fig. 3.6-6 State-variable diagram for the variable-rate sampled-data system.

The state-variable diagram is plotted in Fig. 3.6-6. Let the state vector of the system be

$$\mathbf{v} = \begin{bmatrix} m_1 \\ x_1 \\ x_2 \end{bmatrix}$$

The analysis is initiated with the determination of the following matrices by examination of the state-variable diagram:

$$\mathbf{A}_0 = \mathbf{A}_1 = \begin{bmatrix} 0 & 0 & 0 \\ 0 & -1 & 4 \\ 0 & 0 & 0 \end{bmatrix}$$

$$\mathbf{B}_0 = \mathbf{B}_1 = \begin{bmatrix} 1 & 0 & 0 \\ 0 & 1 & 0 \\ 1 & -1 & 0 \end{bmatrix}$$

$$\mathbf{\Phi}_0(\lambda) = \mathbf{\Phi}_1(\lambda) = \begin{bmatrix} 1 & 0 & 0 \\ 0 & e^{-\lambda} & 4(1 - e^{-\lambda}) \\ 0 & 0 & 1 \end{bmatrix}$$

$$\mathbf{H}_0(\lambda) = \mathbf{H}_1(\lambda) = \mathbf{\Phi}_0(\lambda)\mathbf{B}_0 = \begin{bmatrix} 1 & 0 & 0 \\ 4(1 - e^{-\lambda}) & 5e^{-\lambda} - 4 & 0 \\ 1 & -1 & 0 \end{bmatrix}$$

The second step in the analysis is to determine $x_1(nT)$. During the interval

$$\frac{T}{4} < t - nT \leq T$$

$$\mathbf{v}(t) = \boldsymbol{\psi}_1(t - nT)\mathbf{v}(nT)$$

where

$$\boldsymbol{\psi}_1(t - nT) = \mathbf{H}_1\left(t - nT - \frac{T}{4}\right)\mathbf{H}_0\left(\frac{T}{4}\right)$$

$$= \begin{bmatrix} 1 & 0 & 0 \\ \begin{matrix} -12 + 16e^{-(t-n-\frac{1}{4})} \\ \quad - 20e^{-(t-n)} + 16e^{-\frac{1}{4}} \end{matrix} & \begin{matrix} 16 - 20e^{-(t-n-\frac{1}{4})} \\ \quad + 25e^{-(t-n)} - 20e^{-\frac{1}{4}} \end{matrix} & 0 \\ -3 + 4e^{-\frac{1}{4}} & -5e^{-\frac{1}{4}} + 4 & 0 \end{bmatrix}$$

Thus

$$m_1(t) = m_1(n) = 1$$

$$x_1(t) = [-12 + 16e^{-(t-n-\frac{1}{4})} - 20e^{-(t-n)} + 16e^{-\frac{1}{4}}]m_1(n) + [16 - 20e^{-(t-n-\frac{1}{4})} + 25e^{-(t-n)} - 20e^{-\frac{1}{4}}]x_1(n)$$

For $n = 0$,

$$x_1(1) = -12 + 16e^{-\frac{3}{4}} - 20e^{-1} + 16e^{-\frac{1}{4}} = 0.661$$

For $n = 1$,

$$x_1(2) = 0.661 + (16 - 20e^{-\frac{3}{4}} + 25e^{-1} - 20^{-\frac{1}{4}})0.661 = 0.661 + 0.174 \times 0.661 = 0.776$$

For $n = 2$,

$$x_1(3) = 0.661 + 0.174 \times 0.776 = 0.796$$

For $n = 3$,

$$x_1(4) = 0.661 + 0.174 \times 0.796 = 0.800$$

For $n = 4$,

$$x_1(5) = 0.661 + 0.174 \times 0.800 = 0.801$$

For $n = 5$,

$$x_1(6) = 0.661 + 0.174 \times 0.801 = 0.802$$

During the interval

$$0 < t - nT \leq \frac{T}{4}$$

$$\mathbf{v}(t) = \boldsymbol{\psi}_0(t - nT)\mathbf{v}(nT)$$

where
$$\boldsymbol{\psi}_0(t - nT) = \mathbf{H}_0(t - nT)$$
$$= \begin{bmatrix} 1 & 0 & 0 \\ 4 - 4e^{-(t-nT)} & 5e^{-(t-nT)} - 4 & 0 \\ 1 & -1 & 0 \end{bmatrix}$$

Thus
$$x_1(t) = [4 - 4e^{-(t-n)}]m_1(n) + [5e^{-(t-n)} - 4]x_1(n)$$
$$m_1(t) = m_1(n) = 1$$

For $n = 0$,

$$x_1(\tfrac{1}{4}) = 4 - 4e^{-\frac{1}{4}} = 0.888$$

For $n = 1$,

$$x_1(1\tfrac{1}{4}) = 4(1 - e^{-\frac{1}{4}}) + (5e^{-\frac{1}{4}} - 4)0.661$$
$$= 0.818$$

For $n = 2$,

$$x_1(2\tfrac{1}{4}) = 4(1 - e^{-\frac{1}{4}}) + (5e^{-\frac{1}{4}} - 4)0.776$$
$$= 0.804$$

At the instants $t = nT + T/2$,

$$x_1(n + \tfrac{1}{2}) = (-12 + 32e^{-\frac{1}{4}} - 20e^{-\frac{1}{2}}) + (16 - 40e^{-\frac{1}{4}} + 25e^{-\frac{1}{2}})x_1(n)$$
$$= 0.791 + 0.011x_1(n)$$

Hence

$$x_1(\tfrac{1}{2}) = 0.791$$
$$x_1(1\tfrac{1}{2}) = 0.791 + 0.011 \times 0.661 = 0.798$$
$$x_1(2\tfrac{1}{2}) = 0.791 + 0.011 \times 0.776 = 0.799$$
$$x_1(3\tfrac{1}{2}) = 0.791 + 0.011 \times 0.799 = 0.800$$

At the instants $t = nT + 3T/4$,

$$x_1(n + \tfrac{3}{4}) = (-12 + 16e^{-\frac{1}{2}} - 20e^{-\frac{3}{4}} + 16e^{-\frac{1}{4}})$$
$$+ (16 - 20e^{-\frac{1}{2}} + 25e^{-\frac{3}{4}} + 25e^{-\frac{1}{4}} - 20e^{-\frac{1}{4}})x_1(n)$$
$$= 0.718 + 0.102x_1(n)$$

Thus
$$x_1(\tfrac{3}{4}) = 0.718$$
$$x_1(1\tfrac{3}{4}) = 0.718 + 0.102 \times 0.661 = 0.785$$
$$x_1(2\tfrac{3}{4}) = 0.718 + 0.102 \times 0.776 = 0.797$$
$$x_1(3\tfrac{3}{4}) = 0.718 + 0.102 \times 0.796 = 0.799$$

The unit-step-function response is plotted in Fig. 3.6-7. This result checks with the solution obtained by the classical z-transform method as illustrated in Ref. 136.

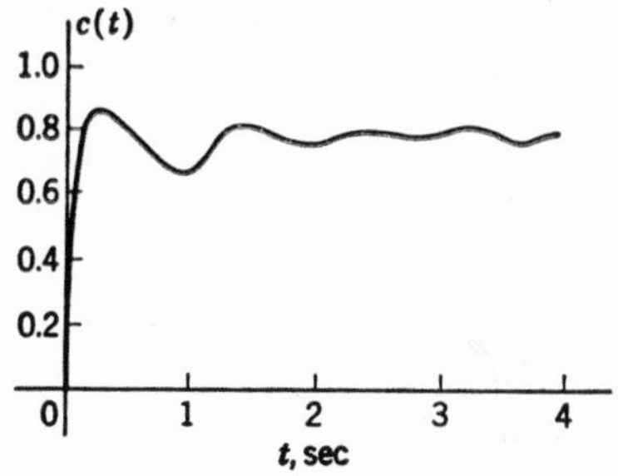

Fig. 3.6-7 The unit-step-function response of the system of Example 3.6-2.

Example 3.6-3 Finite-width Sampled-data System

Consider the finite-width sampled-data system shown in Fig. 3.6-8. The control process is characterized by the transfer function

$$G(s) = \frac{5}{s(s+5)}$$

Zero initial conditions are assumed. The sampling period T is 1 sec, and the sampling duration τ is 0.2 sec. Determine the output of the system in response to a unit-step-function input.

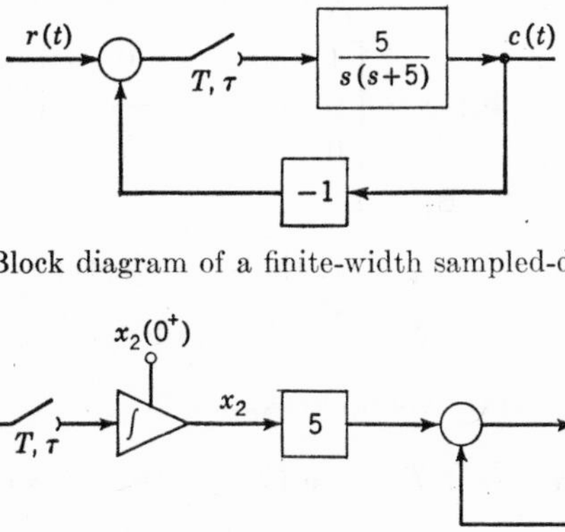

Fig. 3.6-8 Block diagram of a finite-width sampled-data system.

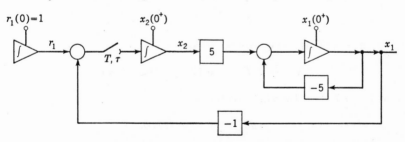

Fig. 3.6-9 State-variable diagram of the finite-width sampled-data system.

The state-variable diagram of this system is depicted in Fig. 3.6-9, from which the transition matrices during various intervals can readily be determined. The state vector $\mathbf{v}$ is defined as

$$\mathbf{v} = \begin{bmatrix} r_1 \\ x_1 \\ x_2 \end{bmatrix}$$

During the interval $0 < t - nT \leq \tau$, the overall transition matrix $\mathbf{\Phi}_0(\lambda)$ is found to be

$$\mathbf{\Phi}_0(\lambda) =$$

$$\begin{bmatrix} 1 & 0 & 0 \\ 1 + \frac{b}{\sqrt{5}} e^{-a\lambda} - \frac{a}{\sqrt{5}} e^{-b\lambda} & \frac{a}{\sqrt{5}} e^{-a\lambda} - \frac{b}{\sqrt{5}} e^{-b\lambda} & \sqrt{5}\,(e^{-b\lambda} - e^{-a\lambda}) \\ 1 + \frac{(b-1)e^{-a\lambda}}{\sqrt{5}} - \frac{(a-1)e^{-b\lambda}}{\sqrt{5}} & \frac{1}{\sqrt{5}}(e^{-a\lambda} - e^{-b\lambda}) & \frac{1}{\sqrt{5}}(ae^{-b\lambda} - be^{-a\lambda}) \end{bmatrix}$$

where $a = 3.618$ and $b = 1.3819$ are the roots of

$$s^2 + 5s + 5 = 0$$

By inspection of the state-variable diagram,

$$\mathbf{B}_0 = \mathbf{I}$$

Hence

$$\mathbf{H}_0(\lambda) = \mathbf{\Phi}_0(\lambda)$$

and for $nT < t \leq nT + \tau$, the state vector is given by

$$\mathbf{v}(t) = \mathbf{\Phi}_0(t - nT)\mathbf{v}(nT)$$

During the interval $\tau < t - nT \leq T$, reference to the state-variable diagram derives the overall transition matrix $\mathbf{\Phi}_1(\lambda)$ and the matrix $\mathbf{B}_1$:

$$\mathbf{\Phi}_1(\lambda) = \begin{bmatrix} 1 & 0 & 0 \\ 0 & e^{-5\lambda} & 1 - e^{-5\lambda} \\ 0 & 0 & 1 \end{bmatrix}$$

$$\mathbf{B}_1 = \mathbf{I}$$

Thus, for $nT + \tau < t \leq (n+1)T$, the state vector is given by

$$\mathbf{v}(t) = \mathbf{\Phi}_1(t - nT - \tau)\mathbf{\Phi}_0(\tau)\mathbf{v}(nT)$$

At $t = (n+1)T$, the state vector becomes

$$\mathbf{v}(\overline{n+1}\ T) = \mathbf{\Phi}_1(T - \tau)\mathbf{\Phi}_0(\tau)\mathbf{v}(nT)$$

and at $t = nT + \tau$, the state vector is

$$\mathbf{v}(nT + \tau) = \mathbf{\Phi}_0(\tau)\mathbf{v}(nT)$$

Repeated application of these two recurrence relationships yields the response of the system.

Using the values $\tau = 0.2$ sec and $T = 1$ sec, the transition matrices $\mathbf{\Phi}_0(\tau)$ and $\mathbf{\Phi}_1(T - \tau)$ are obtained:

$$\mathbf{\Phi}_0(\tau) = \begin{bmatrix} 1 & 0 & 0 \\ 0.0742 & 0.3212 & 0.6093 \\ 0.1963 & -0.1219 & 0.9258 \end{bmatrix}$$

and
$$\mathbf{\Phi}_1(T - \tau) = \begin{bmatrix} 1 & 0 & 0 \\ 0 & 0.0183 & 0.9817 \\ 0 & 0 & 1 \end{bmatrix}$$

Hence, by letting $n = 0, 1, 2, \ldots$, the state vectors $\mathbf{v}(\tau)$, $\mathbf{v}(T)$, $\mathbf{v}(T + \tau)$, $\mathbf{v}(2T)$, . . . can readily be evaluated. For $n = 0$, it is found that

$$\mathbf{v}(\tau) = \mathbf{\Phi}_0(\tau)\mathbf{v}(0) = \begin{bmatrix} 1 \\ 0.0742 \\ 0.1963 \end{bmatrix}$$

and
$$\mathbf{v}(T) = \mathbf{\Phi}_1(T - \tau)\mathbf{\Phi}_0(\tau)\mathbf{v}(0) = \begin{bmatrix} 1 \\ 0.1951 \\ 0.1960 \end{bmatrix}$$

since the initial vector is given by

$$\mathbf{v}(0) = \begin{bmatrix} 1 \\ 0 \\ 0 \end{bmatrix}$$

For $n = 1$, it is found that

$$\mathbf{v}(T + \tau) = \mathbf{\Phi}_0(\tau)\mathbf{v}(T) = \begin{bmatrix} 1 \\ 0.2565 \\ 0.3543 \end{bmatrix}$$

$$\mathbf{v}(2T) = \mathbf{\Phi}_1(T - \tau)\mathbf{\Phi}_0(\tau)\mathbf{v}(T) = \begin{bmatrix} 1 \\ 0.3546 \\ 0.3543 \end{bmatrix}$$

Similarly,

$$\mathbf{v}(2T + \tau) = \begin{bmatrix} 1 \\ 0.4040 \\ 0.4810 \end{bmatrix} \qquad \mathbf{v}(3T) = \begin{bmatrix} 1 \\ 0.4807 \\ 0.4811 \end{bmatrix}$$

$$\mathbf{v}(3T + \tau) = \begin{bmatrix} 1 \\ 0.5217 \\ 0.5831 \end{bmatrix} \qquad \mathbf{v}(4T) = \begin{bmatrix} 1 \\ 0.5830 \\ 0.5831 \end{bmatrix}$$

$$\mathbf{v}(4T + \tau) = \begin{bmatrix} 1 \\ 0.6167 \\ 0.6651 \end{bmatrix} \qquad \mathbf{v}(5T) = \begin{bmatrix} 1 \\ 0.6652 \\ 0.6651 \end{bmatrix}$$

$$\mathbf{v}(5T + \tau) = \begin{bmatrix} 1 \\ 0.6931 \\ 0.7310 \end{bmatrix} \qquad \mathbf{v}(6T) = \begin{bmatrix} 1 \\ 0.7320 \\ 0.7310 \end{bmatrix}$$

$$\mathbf{v}(6T + \tau) = \begin{bmatrix} 1 \\ 0.7545 \\ 0.7839 \end{bmatrix} \qquad \mathbf{v}(7T) = \begin{bmatrix} 1 \\ 0.7844 \\ 0.7839 \end{bmatrix}$$

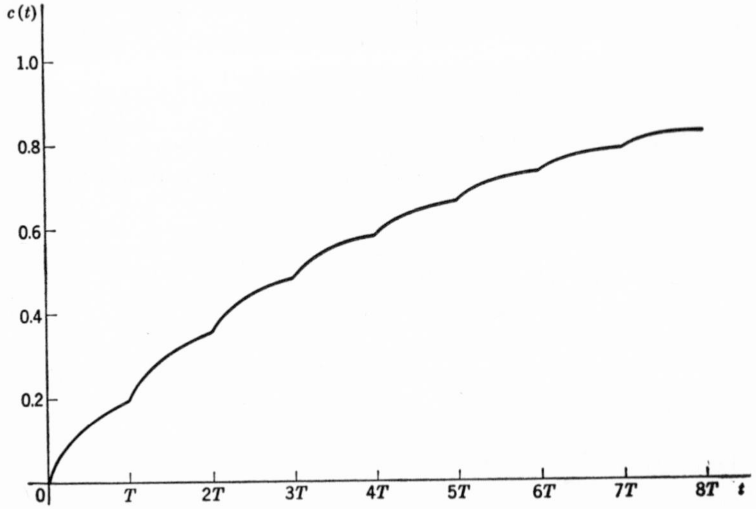

Fig. 3.6-10 Step-function response of the finite-width system.

The step-function response $c(t) = x_1(t)$ is plotted in Fig. 3.6-10. It is well known that the exact analysis of finite-width sampled-data feedback control systems by classical transform techniques is extremely complicated and tedious, if not unwieldy. However, as illustrated in this example, the exact analysis of such problems can be readily carried out by the state-transition method in a straightforward and systematic manner.

The technique described in this section also provides a very powerful tool for the study of pulse-width-modulated feedback control systems. The application of this technique to the analysis of this type of control problem is illustrated by an example.

Example 3.6-4 Pulse-width-modulated Control System

One of the operating methods of an electrohydraulic servo is the pulse-width-modulated mode in which the input signal to a spool wave is given in the form of pulse-width-modulated waves. Consider the pulse-width-

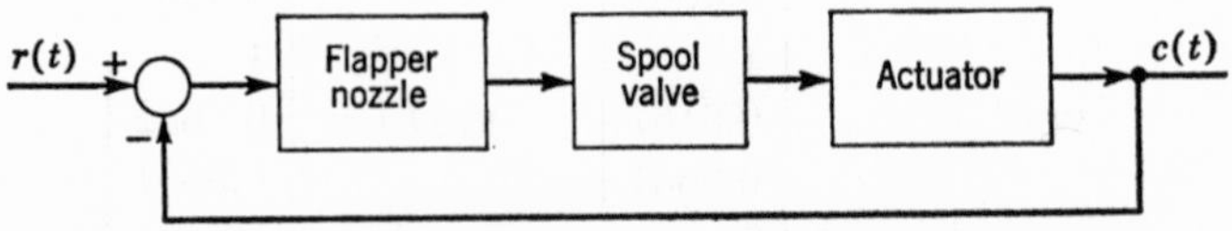

Fig. 3.6-11 Block diagram of an electrohydraulic servo.

modulated feedback control system shown in Fig. 3.6-11. The transfer function of the spool valve and actuator is

$$G(s) = \frac{1}{s(s + 0.5)}$$

Zero initial conditions are assumed. The pulse-width modulator possesses the following properties: the sampling period is 1 sec; the magnitude of the pulse is equal to unity; and the width of the pulse is equal to the value of the corresponding sample. Determine the output of the system in response to a unit-step-function input.

The state-variable diagram of this system is shown in Fig. 3.6-12, in which the pulse-width modulator is represented by a nonlinear sampling device

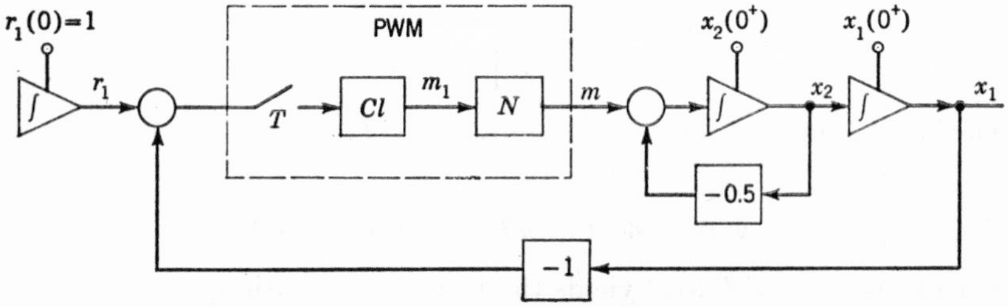

Fig. 3.6-12 State-variable diagram for the PWM system.

such that, during the nth sampling interval,

$$\begin{aligned} \tau_n &= |m_1(nT^+)| \qquad \text{for} \qquad |m_1(nT^+)| < 1 \\ \tau_n &= T \qquad \text{for} \qquad |m_1(nT^+)| \geq 1 \end{aligned}$$

where τ_n denotes the width of the pulse of control signal m during the nth sampling period. The state vector $\mathbf{v}$ and the initial-condition vector $\mathbf{v}(0)$ are given by

$$\mathbf{v} = \begin{bmatrix} r_1 \\ x_1 \\ x_2 \\ m_1 \end{bmatrix} \qquad \text{and} \qquad \mathbf{v}(0) = \begin{bmatrix} 1 \\ 0 \\ 0 \\ 0 \end{bmatrix}$$

During the interval $nT < t \leq nT + \tau_n$, where τ_n is as defined above, the pulse height is

$$\begin{aligned} m &= +1 \qquad \text{for} \qquad m_1(nT^+) > 0 \\ m &= -1 \qquad \text{for} \qquad m_1(nT^+) < 0 \end{aligned}$$

and the state vector $\mathbf{v}(t)$ is

$$\mathbf{v}(t) = \mathbf{\Phi}_0(t - nT)\mathbf{B}_0\mathbf{v}(nT)$$

Letting $t = nT + \tau_n$ yields the transition equation

$$\mathbf{v}(nT + \tau_n) = \mathbf{\Phi}_0(\tau_n)\mathbf{B}_0\mathbf{v}(nT)$$

The transition matrix $\mathbf{\Phi}_0$ and the coefficient matrix $\mathbf{B}_0$ can be derived by examination of the state-variable diagram.

$$\Phi_0(\lambda) = \begin{bmatrix} 1 & 0 & 0 & 0 \\ 0 & 1 & 2(1 - e^{-\lambda/2}) & \dfrac{2}{|m_1(nT^+)|}(\lambda - 2 + 2e^{-\lambda/2}) \\ 0 & 0 & e^{-\lambda/2} & \dfrac{2}{|m_1(nT^+)|}(1 - e^{-\lambda/2}) \\ 0 & 0 & 0 & 1 \end{bmatrix}$$

$$\mathbf{B}_0 = \begin{bmatrix} 1 & 0 & 0 & 0 \\ 0 & 1 & 0 & 0 \\ 0 & 0 & 1 & 0 \\ 1 & -1 & 0 & 0 \end{bmatrix}$$

During the interval $nT + \tau_n < t \leq (n + 1)T$,

$$m = 0$$

and
$$\mathbf{v}(t) = \Phi_1(t - nT - \tau_n)\mathbf{v}(nT + \tau_n)$$

Substituting $(n + 1)T$ for t yields the transition equation

$$\mathbf{v}(\overline{n + 1}\ T) = \Phi_1(T - \tau_n)\mathbf{v}(nT + \tau_n)$$

The transition matrix Φ_1 is determined from the state-variable diagram:

$$\Phi_1(\lambda) = \begin{bmatrix} 1 & 0 & 0 & 0 \\ 0 & 1 & 2(1 - e^{-\lambda/2}) & 0 \\ 0 & 0 & e^{-\lambda/2} & 0 \\ 0 & 0 & 0 & 1 \end{bmatrix}$$

For $n = 0$, $m_1(0^+) = 1$, $\tau_0 = 1$, and

$$\Phi_0(\tau_0) = \begin{bmatrix} 1 & 0 & 0 & 0 \\ 0 & 1 & 0.787 & 0.426 \\ 0 & 0 & 0.607 & 0.787 \\ 0 & 0 & 0 & 1 \end{bmatrix}$$

Hence
$$\mathbf{v}(\tau_0) = \mathbf{v}(T) = \Phi_0(\tau_0)\mathbf{B}_0\mathbf{v}(0) = \begin{bmatrix} 1 \\ 0.426 \\ 0.787 \\ 1 \end{bmatrix}$$

and
$$\mathbf{v}(T^+) = \begin{bmatrix} 1 \\ 0.426 \\ 0.787 \\ 0.574 \end{bmatrix}$$

Since $m_1(\tau_0^+) = m_1(T^+) = 0.574$, $\tau_1 = 0.574$. For $n = 1$,

$$\Phi_0(\tau_1) = \begin{bmatrix} 1 & 0 & 0 & 0 \\ 0 & 1 & 0.5 & 0.258 \\ 0 & 0 & 0.75 & 0.872 \\ 0 & 0 & 0 & 1 \end{bmatrix}$$

$$\mathbf{v}(T+\tau_1) = \mathbf{\Phi}_0(\tau_1)\mathbf{v}(T^+) = \begin{bmatrix} 1 \\ 0.968 \\ 1.091 \\ 0.574 \end{bmatrix}$$

$$\mathbf{\Phi}_1(T-\tau_1) = \mathbf{\Phi}_1(0.426) = \begin{bmatrix} 1 & 0 & 0 & 0 \\ 0 & 1 & 0.384 & 0 \\ 0 & 0 & 0.808 & 0 \\ 0 & 0 & 0 & 1 \end{bmatrix}$$

$$\mathbf{v}(2T) = \mathbf{\Phi}_1(T-\tau_1)\mathbf{v}(T+\tau_1) = \begin{bmatrix} 1 \\ 1.386 \\ 0.881 \\ 0.574 \end{bmatrix}$$

and

$$\mathbf{v}(2T^+) = \begin{bmatrix} 1 \\ 1.386 \\ 0.881 \\ -0.386 \end{bmatrix}$$

Since $m_1(2T^+) = -0.386$, $\tau_2 = 0.386$. For $n = 2$,

$$\mathbf{\Phi}_0(\tau_2) = \begin{bmatrix} 1 & 0 & 0 & 0 \\ 0 & 1 & 0.352 & 0.176 \\ 0 & 0 & 0.824 & 0.912 \\ 0 & 0 & 0 & 1 \end{bmatrix}$$

which gives

$$\mathbf{v}(2T+\tau_2) = \mathbf{\Phi}_0(\tau_2)\mathbf{v}(2T^+) = \begin{bmatrix} 1 \\ 1.628 \\ 0.373 \\ -0.386 \end{bmatrix}$$

$$\mathbf{\Phi}_1(T-\tau_2) = \mathbf{\Phi}_1(0.614) = \begin{bmatrix} 1 & 0 & 0 & 0 \\ 0 & 1 & 0.531 & 0 \\ 0 & 0 & 0.735 & 0 \\ 0 & 0 & 0 & 1 \end{bmatrix}$$

which gives

$$\mathbf{v}(3T) = \mathbf{\Phi}_1(T-\tau_2)\mathbf{v}(2T+\tau_2) = \begin{bmatrix} 1 \\ 1.825 \\ 0.274 \\ -0.386 \end{bmatrix}$$

and

$$\mathbf{v}(3T^+) = \begin{bmatrix} 1 \\ 1.825 \\ 0.274 \\ -0.825 \end{bmatrix}$$

Since $m_1(3T^+) = -0.825$, $\tau_3 = 0.825$. For $n = 3$,

$$\mathbf{\Phi}_0(\tau_3) = \begin{bmatrix} 1 & 0 & 0 & 0 \\ 0 & 1 & 0.678 & 0.356 \\ 0 & 0 & 0.661 & 0.833 \\ 0 & 0 & 0 & 1 \end{bmatrix}$$

which gives

$$\mathbf{v}(3T + \tau_3) = \mathbf{\Phi}_0(\tau_3)\mathbf{v}(3T^+) = \begin{bmatrix} 1 \\ 1.716 \\ -0.497 \\ -0.825 \end{bmatrix}$$

$$\mathbf{\Phi}_1(T - \tau_3) = \begin{bmatrix} 1 & 0 & 0 & 0 \\ 0 & 1 & 0.168 & 0 \\ 0 & 0 & 0.916 & 0 \\ 0 & 0 & 0 & 1 \end{bmatrix}$$

which gives

$$\mathbf{v}(4T) = \mathbf{\Phi}_1(T - \tau_3)\mathbf{v}(3T + \tau_3) = \begin{bmatrix} 1 \\ 1.633 \\ -0.455 \\ -0.825 \end{bmatrix}$$

and

$$\mathbf{v}(4T^+) = \begin{bmatrix} 1 \\ 1.633 \\ -0.455 \\ -0.633 \end{bmatrix}$$

Since $m_1(4T^+) = -0.633$, $\tau_4 = 0.633$. Continuing in similar fashion, the values of the state vector at other instants can be determined:

$$\mathbf{v}(4T + \tau_4) = \begin{bmatrix} 1 \\ 1.200 \\ -0.875 \\ -0.633 \end{bmatrix} \qquad \mathbf{v}(5T) = \begin{bmatrix} 1 \\ 0.899 \\ -0.728 \\ -0.633 \end{bmatrix}$$

$$\mathbf{v}(5T + \tau_5) = \begin{bmatrix} 1 \\ 0.829 \\ -0.594 \\ 0.101 \end{bmatrix} \qquad \mathbf{v}(6T) = \begin{bmatrix} 1 \\ 0.397 \\ -0.379 \\ 0.101 \end{bmatrix} \qquad \cdots$$

The output response and the output waveform of the pulse-width modulator are plotted in Fig. 3.6-13. These values check with those calculated by using the laborious and painstaking classical method.

This illustrative example provides further evidence that the modern approach developed in this section is far superior to the conventional techniques available in the literature.

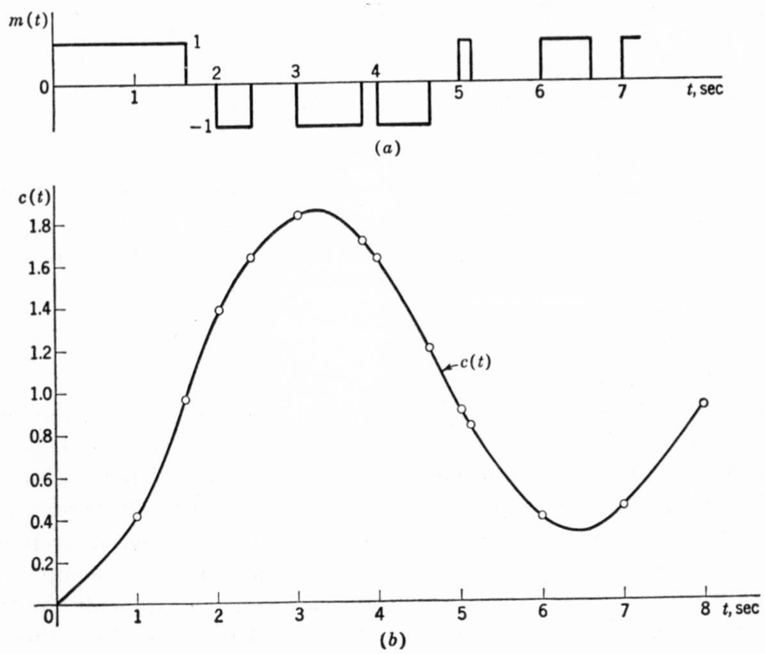

Fig. 3.6-13 (*a*) Control-signal waveform; (*b*) step-function response of the PWM system.

3.7 CONCLUSION

In this chapter an attempt has been made to present the analysis of control systems by state-space methods. At any instant t, the state vector $\mathbf{x}(t)$ and the output vector $\mathbf{y}(t)$ of a system are functions of the initial-state variables and the input variables:

$$\mathbf{x}(t) = \mathbf{F}[\mathbf{x}(t_0); \mathbf{m}(t_0, t)]$$
$$\mathbf{y}(t) = \boldsymbol{\psi}[\mathbf{x}(t_0); \mathbf{m}(t_0, t)]$$

These equations are referred to as the state equations of the system. For a linear system, the state equations may be reduced to

$$\dot{\mathbf{x}}(t) = \mathbf{A}(t)\mathbf{x}(t) + \mathbf{D}(t)\mathbf{m}(t)$$
$$\mathbf{y}(t) = \mathcal{B}(t)\mathbf{x}(t) + \mathbf{G}(t)\mathbf{m}(t)$$

The characterization of systems by state equations forms the starting point of modern control theory.

A linear stationary system can be described by the vector-matrix differential equation

$$\dot{\mathbf{v}}(t) = \mathbf{A}\mathbf{v}(t)$$

where $\mathbf{v}(t)$ represents a column vector for the input variables and the state variables. The solution to this equation is

$$\mathbf{v}(t) = \mathbf{\Phi}(t)\mathbf{v}(0^+)$$

where the overall transition matrix $\mathbf{\Phi}(t)$ is given by

$$\mathbf{\Phi}(t) = e^{\mathbf{A}t} = \mathcal{L}^{-1}\{[s\mathbf{I} - \mathbf{A}]^{-1}\}$$

The transition matrix may be determined by use of the Sylvester expansion theorem, by means of inverse Laplace transformation, or by inspection of the state-variable diagram. The three different ways of deriving the state-variable diagram from the overall transfer function of a system are:

1. Direct programming
2. Parallel programming
3. Iterative programming

In order to unify the state-variable characterization of a system, the inputs and disturbances are also characterized by the state variables. This leads to the state-variable-diagram representation of the augmented system.

Although the state-transition method does not seem to offer any advantage over the classical method in the analysis of conventional discrete-data systems, it provides a systematic, unified approach to solving complicated, nonconventional sampling problems which are generally difficult to attack by the classical method. It has been shown that the general solution to a nonconventional discrete-data system is given by

$$\mathbf{v}(t) = \boldsymbol{\psi}_i(t - nT)\mathbf{v}(nT)$$

where

$$\boldsymbol{\psi}_i(t - nT) = \mathbf{H}_i(t - nT - t_i)\mathbf{H}_{i-1}(t_i - t_{i-1}) \cdots \mathbf{H}_1(t_2 - t_1)\mathbf{H}_0(t_1)$$
$$\mathbf{H}_i(t - nT - t_i) = \mathbf{\Phi}_i(t - nT - t_i)\mathbf{B}_i$$

Examples are given to illustrate the analysis of multirate, variable-rate, finite-width, and pulse-width-modulated control systems by the state-transition method. One of the important advantages of this approach is that the analysis procedure is of a recursive nature and thus can readily be programmed on a digital computer to yield a quick, accurate solution.

It should be emphasized that the characterization of a control system by state-variable diagram is not unique. The system may be described in several different ways, depending upon the nature of the state variable selected. Different ways of choosing the state variables of the system generally lead to quite different configurations of the state-variable diagrams. In the choice of state-variable characterization of a system, it is important to choose measurable quantities as state variables.

References

Suggested references are Bellman,[22] Coddington and Levinson,[45] Gilbert,[68] Kalman and Bertram,[91] Kalman and Koepcke,[93] Kipiniak,[94] Tou,[136,138,139,142] and Tou and Vadhanaphuti.[147]

4

SYSTEM DESIGN BY STATE–TRANSITION METHOD

In the preceding chapter the state-transition method is used in the analysis of continuous and discrete-data control systems. It can be observed that, for simple problems, the classical transform methods tend to yield a solution more rapidly than the state-space approach. However, for complicated problems the state-space approach provides a unified and systematic solution which can readily be programmed on a digital computer. The real advantages and usefulness of the state-space approach will not be fully appreciated until the applications of this approach to system design are discussed. Classical methods of system design present severe limitations and difficulties when applied to the optimum design of high-order and multivariable processes and systems subject to control-signal saturation. In fact, their applications are limited to idealized and relatively simple feedback control systems. On the other hand, the state-space approach facilitates the solution of a large class of more realistic control problems which can only with difficulty be treated by conventional means. This chapter is concerned with the design of control systems by the state-transition method.

4.1 DIGITAL CONTROL OF LINEAR SYSTEMS FOR DEADBEAT PERFORMANCE

By deadbeat performance is meant that a system responds to a stepwise input in the quickest manner without overshoot. Since deadbeat operation often necessitates instant transfer of energy, it is extremely difficult to design a linear continuous system with deadbeat performance. Such a feature can, however, be realized by the introduction of a nonlinear element, such as a relay, into the system or by making use of a digital controller. This section is devoted to the design for deadbeat performance by the latter means.

Consider the feedback system shown in Fig. 4.1-1. The system is subject to a step-function input. The control process is assumed to be linear and

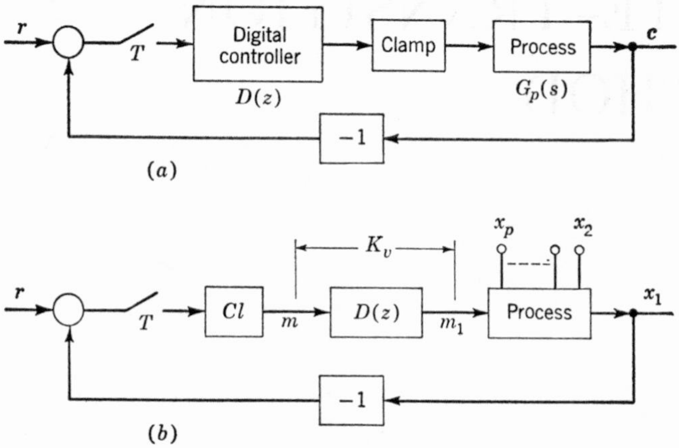

Fig. 4.1-1 A digital control system.

of the pth order, which can be described by p state variables. The transfer function of the control process is described by the state-variable-diagram representation. The state vector of the system is given by

$$\mathbf{v} = \begin{bmatrix} r_1 \\ \mathbf{x} \\ m \end{bmatrix} \tag{4.1-1}$$

where r_1 denotes the input state variable, $\mathbf{x}$ is the process state vector

$$\mathbf{x} = \begin{bmatrix} x_1 \\ x_2 \\ \cdot \\ \cdot \\ \cdot \\ x_p \end{bmatrix} \tag{4.1-2}$$

and m stands for the control signal. The design problem requires the determination of the control signal m and the digital controller $D(z)$ such that the system will respond with deadbeat performance.

Variable-gain Approach[147]

The desired digital controller may be treated as a variable-gain element K_v, which will have different values during different sampling periods. The input to the variable-gain element K_v is the control signal m, and the output is assumed to be m_1. At any sampling instant $t = nT^+$, the input and output of the variable-gain element are related through a constant multiplying factor K_n; that is,

$$m_1(nT^+) = K_n m(nT^+) \tag{4.1-3}$$

where K_n is the gain constant of the variable-gain element during the $(n + 1)$st sampling period.

Based upon the above argument, the transition matrix $\mathbf{\Phi}$ of the system is expressed as a function of the variable gain K_n and has different values at different sampling instants. It has been shown in Sec. 3.5 that the state-transition equations for the linear system are given by

$$\mathbf{v}(nT^+) = \mathbf{B}\mathbf{v}(nT) \tag{4.1-4}$$

$$\mathbf{v}(\overline{n + 1}\ T) = \mathbf{\Phi}(T)\mathbf{v}(nT^+) \tag{4.1-5}$$

$$\mathbf{v}(\overline{n + 1}\ T) = \mathbf{\Phi}(T)\mathbf{B}\mathbf{v}(nT) \tag{4.1-6}$$

Thus, for $n = 0$,

$$\mathbf{v}(0^+) = \mathbf{B}\mathbf{v}(0) \tag{4.1-7}$$

and at $t = T$,

$$\mathbf{v}(T) = \mathbf{\Phi}_0(T)\mathbf{B}\mathbf{v}(0) \tag{4.1-8}$$

where $\mathbf{v}(0)$ is the given initial-state vector. Since the transition matrix $\mathbf{\Phi}_0(T)$ is a function of the gain constant K_0 of the variable-gain element during the first sampling period, the state vector $\mathbf{v}(T)$ at $t = T$ is also a function of K_0. Once $\mathbf{v}(T)$ is determined from Eq (4.1-8) in terms of K_0, the state vector $\mathbf{v}(T^+)$ can readily be found from the state-variable diagram of the system or by use of Eq. (4.1-4). It follows from Eq. (4.1-5) that the state vector $\mathbf{v}(2T)$ is given by

$$\mathbf{v}(2T) = \mathbf{\Phi}_1(T)\mathbf{v}(T^+) \tag{4.1-9}$$

where the transition matrix $\mathbf{\Phi}_1(T)$ is a function of the gain constant K_1 of the variable-gain element during the second sampling period, and the state vector $\mathbf{v}(T^+)$ is a function of K_0. Thus the state vector $\mathbf{v}(2T)$ is a function of both K_0 and K_1. Once $\mathbf{v}(2T)$ is found, the state vector $\mathbf{v}(2T^+)$ follows from Eq. (4.1-4), or can be determined by inspection of the state-variable diagram of the system. The state vector $\mathbf{v}(2T^+)$ is also a function of both K_0 and K_1.

In like manner, at $t = kT$, the state vector is given by

$$\mathbf{v}(kT) = \mathbf{\Phi}_{k-1}(T)\mathbf{v}(\overline{k-1}\;T^+) \tag{4.1-10}$$

where the transition matrix $\mathbf{\Phi}_{k-1}(T)$ is a function of the gain constant K_{k-1} of the variable-gain element during the kth sampling period, and the state vector $\mathbf{v}(\overline{k-1}\;T^+)$ is a function of the gain constants $K_0, K_1, K_2, \ldots, K_{k-2}$. Hence the state vector $\mathbf{v}(kT)$ is a function of the gain constants $K_0, K_1, K_2, \ldots, K_{k-2}$, and K_{k-1}.

The pulse-transfer function $D(z)$ of the digital controller may be expressed in terms of the various gain constants K_j of the variable-gain element as follows: Starting with

$$m(0^+) = r_1(0^+) \tag{4.1-11}$$

then

$$m_1(0^+) = K_0 m(0^+) = K_0 r_1(0^+) \tag{4.1-12}$$

Similarly,

$$m_1(T^+) = K_1 m(T^+) \tag{4.1-13}$$

where $m(T^+)$ is obtained from

$$\mathbf{v}(T^+) = \mathbf{B}\mathbf{v}(T) = \mathbf{B}\mathbf{\Phi}_0(T)\mathbf{v}(0^+) \tag{4.1-14}$$

since, as defined in Eq. (4.1-1), $m(T^+)$ is an element of $\mathbf{v}(T^+)$. Similarly,

$$m_1(2T^+) = K_2 m(2T^+) \tag{4.1-15}$$

where $m(2T^+)$ is derived from

$$\mathbf{v}(2T^+) = \mathbf{B}\mathbf{\Phi}_1(T)\mathbf{v}(T^+) \tag{4.1-16a}$$

$$\mathbf{v}(2T^+) = \mathbf{B}\mathbf{\Phi}_1(T)\mathbf{B}\mathbf{\Phi}_0(T)\mathbf{v}(0^+) \tag{4.1-16b}$$

In general,

$$m_1(jT^+) = K_j m(jT^+) \tag{4.1-17}$$

where $m(jT^+)$ is determined from

$$\mathbf{v}(jT^+) = \mathbf{B}\mathbf{\Phi}_{j-1}(T)\mathbf{v}(\overline{j-1}\;T^+) \tag{4.1-18a}$$

$$\mathbf{v}(jT^+) = \mathbf{B}\mathbf{\Phi}_{j-1}(T)\mathbf{B}\mathbf{\Phi}_{j-2}(T) \cdots \mathbf{B}\mathbf{\Phi}_0(T)\mathbf{v}(0^+) \tag{4.1-18b}$$

Since the z transform for the control sequence $m(jT^+)$ is

$$M(z) = \sum_{j=0}^{n} m(jT^+)z^{-j} \tag{4.1-19}$$

and the z transform for the sequence $m_1(T^+)$ is given by

$$M_1(z) = \sum_{j=0}^{n} K_j m(jT^+) z^{-j} \tag{4.1-20}$$

the pulse-transfer function $D(z)$ is the ratio

$$D(z) = \frac{M_1(z)}{M(z)} = \frac{\sum_{j=0}^{n} K_j m(jT^+) z^{-j}}{\sum_{j=0}^{n} m(jT^+) z^{-j}} \tag{4.1-21}$$

Consequently, the design problem reduces to the determination of the various gain constants K_j of the variable-gain element. Once the gain constants K_j are found, the desired digital controller is determined.

The gain constants K_j are evaluated from the performance specifications. To obtain deadbeat performance, the following conditions must be satisfied. The output response is always less than the input signal for $t < pT$, where T is the sampling period. The system error is zero for $t \geq pT$. These conditions are satisfied if

$$x_1(pT) = r_1(pT) \tag{4.1-22}$$
$$x_2(pT) = x_3(pT) = \cdots = x_p(pT) = 0 \tag{4.1-23}$$

where p denotes the order of the control process, and the state variables $x_2(pT)$, $x_3(pT)$, . . . , $x_p(pT)$ are functions of the gain constants K_0, K_1, K_2, . . . , K_{p-1}, which are derived from Eq. (4.1-10). Equation (4.1-23) implies that the inputs to the various integrators are equal to zero for $t \geq pT$. The successive gain constants K_j can be determined by solving Eqs. (4.1-22) and (4.1-23). To clarify the above discussions, this method of design is best illustrated by numerical examples.

Example 4.1-1 Control Process with Integration

Consider the system shown in Fig. 4.1-2. The sampling period is assumed to be 1 sec. The transfer function of the control process is

$$G_p(s) = \frac{10}{s(s+1)}$$

The performance specifications are that (1) the system can have no ripple and zero error in the steady state of the step-function response, and (2) the

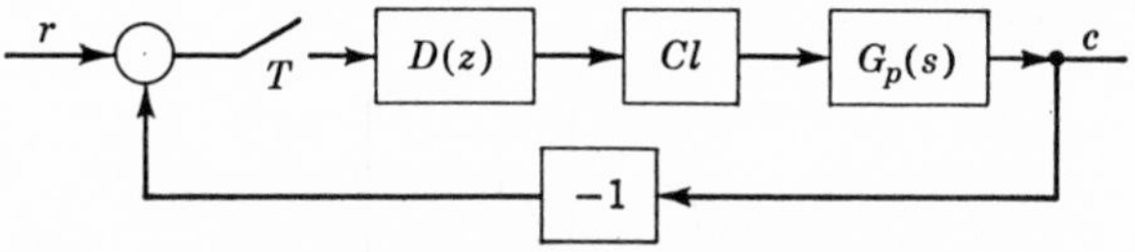

Fig. 4.1-2 Block diagram of the illustrative example.

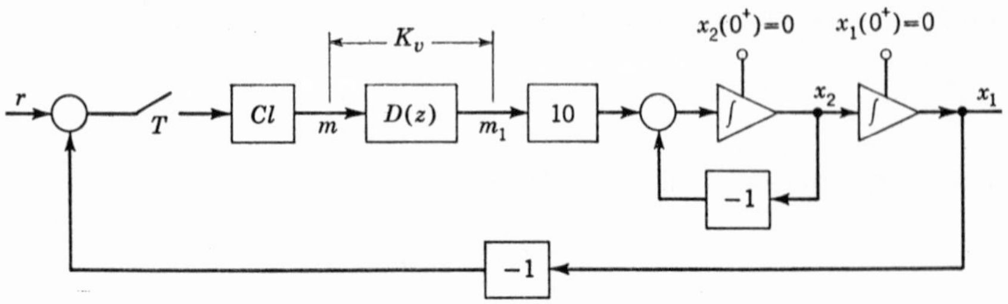

Fig. 4.1-3 State-variable diagram of the illustrative example.

transient must decay to zero in the shortest possible time. Design a digital controller to meet these requirements.

A state-variable diagram of the system with the digital controller represented by a variable-gain element K_v is depicted in Fig. 4.1-3. With the state vector of the system defined as

$$\mathbf{v} = \begin{bmatrix} r_1 \\ x_1 \\ x_2 \\ m \end{bmatrix}$$

the transition matrix $\mathbf{\Phi}(T)$ and the $\mathbf{B}$ matrix are found to be, respectively,

$$\mathbf{\Phi}_n(T) = \begin{bmatrix} 1 & 0 & 0 & 0 \\ 0 & 1 & 0.632 & 3.68K_n \\ 0 & 0 & 0.368 & 6.32K_n \\ 0 & 0 & 0 & 1 \end{bmatrix}$$

and

$$\mathbf{B} = \begin{bmatrix} 1 & 0 & 0 & 0 \\ 0 & 1 & 0 & 0 \\ 0 & 0 & 1 & 0 \\ 1 & -1 & 0 & 0 \end{bmatrix}$$

The initial-state vector $\mathbf{v}(0)$ is

$$\mathbf{v}(0) = \begin{bmatrix} 1 \\ 0 \\ 0 \\ 0 \end{bmatrix}$$

For $n = 0$ and at $t = T$, Eq. (4.1-8) yields

$$\mathbf{v}(T) = \begin{bmatrix} 1 \\ 3.68K_0 \\ 6.32K_0 \\ 1 \end{bmatrix}$$

and inspection of the state-variable diagram gives

$$\mathbf{v}(T^+) = \begin{bmatrix} 1 \\ 3.68K_0 \\ 6.32K_0 \\ 1 - 3.68K_0 \end{bmatrix}$$

This expression can also be obtained analytically by use of Eq. (4.1-4).
Similarly, for $n = 1$ and at $t = 2T$, Eq. (4.1-9) yields

$$\mathbf{v}(2T) = \begin{bmatrix} 1 \\ 7.68K_0 + 3.68(1 - 3.68K_0)K_1 \\ 2.32K_0 + 6.32(1 - 3.68K_0)K_1 \\ 1 - 3.68K_0 \end{bmatrix}$$

which points out that this second-order system settles in two sampling periods. Hence, for the specified performance, the following conditions must be fulfilled:

$$x_1(2T) = 7.68K_0 + 3.68(1 - 3.68K_0)K_1 = 1$$
$$x_2(2T) = 2.32K_0 + 6.32(1 - 3.68K_0)K_1 = 0$$

The solution to these two simultaneous equations is

$$K_0 = 0.158 \qquad \text{and} \qquad K_1 = -0.138$$

Thus

$$m(T^+) = 1 - 3.68K_0 = 0.418$$
$$m_1(0^+) = K_0m(0^+) = 0.158$$
$$m_1(T^+) = K_1m(T^+) = -0.0578$$

and the pulse-transfer function of the desired digital controller is given by

$$D(z) = \frac{0.158(1 - 0.368z^{-1})}{1 + 0.418z^{-1}}$$

Example 4.1-2 Control Process with No Integration

Consider the system shown in Fig. 4.1-2. The sampling period is assumed to be 1 sec. The transfer function of the control process is

$$G_p(s) = \frac{10}{(s + 1)(s + 2)}$$

Design a digital controller so as to enable the system to respond to a unit-step input with deadbeat performance.

Since the given control process does not involve integration, the design may be carried out either by introducing integration or without introducing integration, as illustrated in the following paragraphs.

a. Introducing Integration. The transfer function of the control process may be written as

$$G_p(s) = \frac{10s}{s(s+1)(s+2)}$$

With this form of the transfer function, a state-variable diagram of the sys-

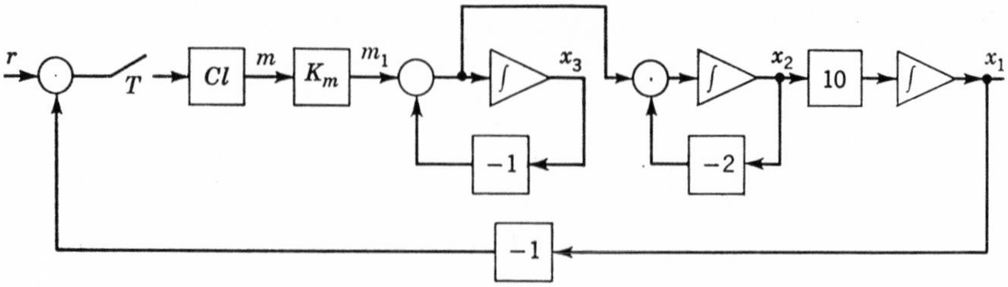

Fig. 4.1-4 State-variable diagram of the illustrative example.

tem is shown in Fig. 4.1-4, where $D(z)$ is replaced by the variable-gain element K_n. The state vector $\mathbf{v}$ is defined as

$$\mathbf{v} = \begin{bmatrix} r \\ x_1 \\ x_2 \\ x_3 \\ m \end{bmatrix}$$

Then the initial-state vectors are

$$\mathbf{v}(0) = \begin{bmatrix} 1 \\ 0 \\ 0 \\ 0 \\ 0 \end{bmatrix} \quad \text{and} \quad \mathbf{v}(0^+) = \begin{bmatrix} 1 \\ 0 \\ 0 \\ 0 \\ 1 \end{bmatrix}$$

The transition matrix is found to be

$$\mathbf{\Phi}(\lambda) = \begin{bmatrix} 1 & 0 & 0 & 0 & 0 \\ 0 & 1 & 5(1 - e^{-2\lambda}) & -5 + 10e^{-\lambda} - 5e^{-2\lambda} & (5 - 10e^{-\lambda} + 5e^{-2\lambda})K_n \\ 0 & 0 & e^{-2\lambda} & -e^{-\lambda} + e^{-2\lambda} & (e^{-\lambda} - e^{-2\lambda})K_n \\ 0 & 0 & 0 & e^{-\lambda} & (1 - e^{-\lambda})K_n \\ 0 & 0 & 0 & 0 & 1 \end{bmatrix}$$

Since $T = 1$ sec,

$$\mathbf{\Phi}_n(T) = \mathbf{\Phi}(K_n) = \begin{bmatrix} 1 & 0 & 0 & 0 & 0 \\ 0 & 1 & 4.325 & -1.997 & 1.997K_n \\ 0 & 0 & 0.135 & -0.233 & 0.233K_n \\ 0 & 0 & 0 & 0.368 & 0.632K_n \\ 0 & 0 & 0 & 0 & 1 \end{bmatrix}$$

From the state-transition equations

$$\begin{aligned}\mathbf{v}(\overline{n+1}\,T) &= \mathbf{\Phi}(K_n)\mathbf{v}(nT^+)\\ \mathbf{v}(nT^+) &= \mathbf{B\Phi}(K_{n-1})\mathbf{B\Phi}(K_{n-2})\cdots\mathbf{B\Phi}(K_0)\mathbf{v}(0^+)\end{aligned}$$

For $n = 0$,

$$\mathbf{v}(T) = \mathbf{\Phi}(K_0)\mathbf{v}(0^+) = \begin{bmatrix} 1 \\ 1.997K_0 \\ 0.233K_0 \\ 0.632K_0 \\ 1 \end{bmatrix}$$

and

$$\mathbf{v}(T^+) = \mathbf{Bv}(T) = \begin{bmatrix} 1 \\ 1.997K_0 \\ 0.233K_0 \\ 0.632K_0 \\ 1 - 1.997K_0 \end{bmatrix}$$

For $n = 1$,

$$\mathbf{v}(2T) = \mathbf{\Phi}(K_1)\mathbf{v}(T^+) = \begin{bmatrix} 1 \\ 1.747K_0 + 1.997(1 - 1.997K_0)K_1 \\ -0.1165K_0 + 0.233(1 - 1.997K_0)K_1 \\ 0.232K_0 + 0.632(1 - 1.997K_0)K_1 \\ 1 - 1.997K_0 \end{bmatrix}$$

Since the system is of second order, the response can be made to settle in two sampling periods. To obtain deadbeat performance, the following conditions must be satisfied:

$$\begin{aligned}x_1(2T) &= 1.747K_0 + 1.997(1 - 1.997K_0)K_1 = 1\\ x_2(2T) &= -0.1165K_0 + 0.233(1 - 1.997K_0)K_1 = 0\end{aligned}$$

Solving for K_0 and K_1 yields

$$K_0 = 0.366 \qquad \text{and} \qquad K_1 = 0.678$$

Hence

$$\begin{aligned}m_1(0^+) &= K_0 m(0^+) = 0.366\\ m(T^+) &= 1 - 1.997K_0 = 0.267\\ m_1(T^+) &= K_1 m(T^+) = 0.181\end{aligned}$$

and

$$x_3(2T) = 0.232K_0 + 0.632(1 - 1.997K_0)K_1 = 0.2$$

It can be noted that deadbeat performance requires zero input to the third integrator for $t \geq 2T$. To satisfy this requirement on the third integrator, the output of the variable-gain element K_n must be maintained at 0.2 after the second sampling period. Thus the z transform of the output sequence from K_n may be written as

$$M_1(z) = 0.366 + 0.181z^{-1} + 0.2z^{-2} + 0.2z^{-3} + \cdots$$

which reduces to

$$M_1(z) = \frac{0.366 - 0.185z^{-1} + 0.019z^{-2}}{1 - z^{-1}}$$

Since the z transform of the input to K_n is

$$M(z) = 1 + 0.267z^{-1}$$

the pulse-transfer function of the desired digital controller is given by

$$D(z) = \frac{0.366 - 0.185z^{-1} + 0.019z^{-2}}{(1 - z^{-1})(1 + 0.267z^{-1})}$$

b. Without Introducing Integration. Since the transfer function of the control process is

$$G_p(s) = \frac{10}{(s + 1)(s + 2)}$$

a state-variable diagram of the system is shown in Fig. 4.1-5 with $D(z)$

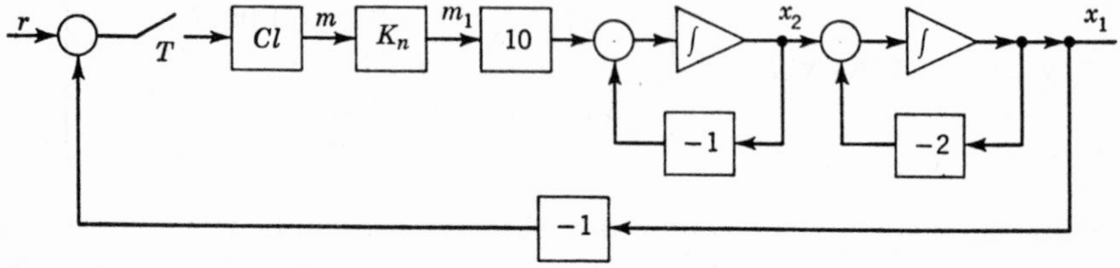

Fig. 4.1-5 State-variable diagram of the illustrative example.

replaced by the variable-gain element K_n. The state vector $\mathbf{v}$ is defined as

$$\mathbf{v} = \begin{bmatrix} r \\ x_1 \\ x_2 \\ m \end{bmatrix}$$

The initial-state vectors are

$$\mathbf{v}(0) = \begin{bmatrix} 1 \\ 0 \\ 0 \\ 0 \end{bmatrix} \qquad \text{and} \qquad \mathbf{v}(0^+) = \begin{bmatrix} 1 \\ 0 \\ 0 \\ 1 \end{bmatrix}$$

The transition matrix is then given by

$$\mathbf{\Phi}(\lambda) = \begin{bmatrix} 1 & 0 & 0 & 0 \\ 0 & e^{-2\lambda} & e^{-\lambda} - e^{-2\lambda} & 5(1 - 2e^{-\lambda} + e^{-2\lambda})K_n \\ 0 & 0 & 0 & 10(1 - e^{-\lambda})K_n \\ 0 & 0 & 0 & 1 \end{bmatrix}$$

and

$$\mathbf{\Phi}_n(T) = \mathbf{\Phi}(K_n) = \begin{bmatrix} 1 & 0 & 0 & 0 \\ 0 & 0.135 & 0.233 & 2K_n \\ 0 & 0 & 0.368 & 6.32K_n \\ 0 & 0 & 0 & 1 \end{bmatrix}$$

Since

$$\mathbf{v}(\overline{n+1}\,T) = \mathbf{\Phi}(K_n)\mathbf{v}(nT^+)$$

for $n = 0$,

$$\mathbf{v}(T) = \mathbf{\Phi}(K_0)\mathbf{v}(0^+) = \begin{bmatrix} 1 \\ 2K_0 \\ 6.32K_0 \\ 1 \end{bmatrix}$$

Referring to the state-variable diagram, it is found that

$$\mathbf{v}(T^+) = \begin{bmatrix} 1 \\ 2K_0 \\ 6.32K_0 \\ 1 - 2K_0 \end{bmatrix}$$

For $n = 1$,

$$\mathbf{v}(2T) = \mathbf{\Phi}(K_1)\mathbf{v}(T^+) = \begin{bmatrix} 1 \\ 0.174K_0 + 2(1 - 2K_0)K_1 \\ 0.233K_0 + 6.32(1 - 2K_0)K_1 \\ 1 - 2K_0 \end{bmatrix}$$

Since the given system is a second-order system, the response can be made to settle in two sampling periods. In order to have zero steady-state error, the following conditions must be satisfied:

1. $x_1(2T) = 1$.
2. The inputs to all integrators are zero for $t \geq 2T$. From the state-variable diagram may be obtained

$$x_1(2T) = 1$$
$$x_2(2T) = 2$$

and $m_1(nT^+) = m(nT^+)K_n = 0.2$ for $n > 2$; that is, after the end of the second sampling instant, the output from the variable-gain element K_n is always equal to 0.2. Consequently,

$$0.174K_0 + 2(1 - 2K_0)K_1 = 1$$
$$0.233K_0 + 6.32(1 - 2K_0)K_1 = 2$$

Solving for K_0 and K_1,

$$K_0 = 0.366 \qquad \text{and} \qquad K_1 = 0.678$$

Thus

$$x_1(T) = 2K_0 = 0.732$$
$$m(T^+) = 1 - 2K_0 = 0.267$$
$$m_1(0^+) = K_0 m(0^+) = 0.366$$
$$m_1(T^+) = K_1 m(T^+) = 0.181$$

The input signal to K_n has the z transform

$$M(z) = 1 + 0.267z^{-1}$$

and the z transform of the output signal from K_n is

$$\begin{aligned} M_1(z) &= 0.366 + 0.181z^{-1} + 0.2z^{-2} + 0.2z^{-3} + \cdots \\ &= \frac{0.366 - 0.185z^{-1} + 0.019z^{-2}}{1 - z^{-1}} \end{aligned}$$

Therefore the pulse-transfer function of the desired digital controller is given by

$$D(z) = \frac{0.366 - 0.185z^{-1} + 0.019z^{-2}}{(1 - z^{-1})(1 + 0.267z^{-1})}$$

which agrees with the pulse-transfer function derived previously.

c. Design of Digital Controller by Use of the Classical Method. The desired digital controller to meet the deadbeat-performance requirement can also be designed by applying the classical method. For the sake of comparison, detailed design procedures by the classical method are worked out as follows:

The transfer function of the clamp is

$$G_h(s) = \frac{1 - e^{-Ts}}{s}$$

Then

$$G(s) = G_h(s)G_p(s) = \frac{10(1 - e^{-s})}{s(s + 1)(s + 2)}$$

since $T = 1$ sec. The corresponding z transform is

$$G(z) = \frac{2z^{-1}(1 + 0.365z^{-1})}{(1 - 0.368z^{-1})(1 - 0.135z^{-1})}$$

Following the method of Ref. 136, let

$$\begin{aligned} 1 - W_e(z) &= b_0z^{-1}(1 + 0.365z^{-1}) \\ W_e(z) &= (1 - z^{-1})(1 + a_1z^{-1}) \end{aligned}$$

Then

$$1 - W_e(z) = (1 - a_1)z^{-1} + a_1z^{-2}$$

Equating the corresponding coefficients yields

$$\begin{aligned} b_0 &= 1 - a_1 \\ a_1 &= 0.365b_0 \end{aligned}$$

Hence

$$a_1 = 0.267 \qquad \text{and} \qquad b_0 = 0.733$$

Then

$$\begin{aligned} 1 - W_e(z) &= 0.733z^{-1}(1 + 0.365z^{-1}) \\ W_e(z) &= (1 - z^{-1})(1 + 0.267z^{-1}) \end{aligned}$$

Since

$$D(z) = \frac{1 - W_e(z)}{G(z)W_e(z)}$$

by substitution,

$$D(z) = \frac{0.366 - 0.185z^{-1} + 0.019z^{-1}}{(1 - z^{-1})(1 + 0.267z^{-1})}$$

which checks the result obtained above.

The modified z transform of the system output is given by

$$C(z, m) = G_e(z)G(z, m)R(z)$$

where

$$G_e(z) = \frac{1 - W_e(z)}{G(z)} = 0.366(1 - 0.368z^{-1})(1 - 0.135z^{-1})$$

$$G(z, m) = 5z^{-1}\left[\frac{(1 - 0.503z^{-1} + 0.049z^{-2}) - 2e^{-m}(1 - 1.135z^{-1} + 0.135z^{-2})}{(1 - 0.368z^{-1})(1 - 0.135z^{-1})} + \frac{e^{-2m}(1 - 1.368z^{-1} + 0.368z^{-2})}{(1 - 0.368z^{-1})(1 - 0.135z^{-1})}\right]$$

$$R(z) = \frac{1}{1 - z} - 1$$

Thus

$$C(z, m) = \frac{1.83z^{-1}}{1 - z^{-1}}[(1 - 0.503z^{-1} + 0.049z^{-2}) - 2e^{-m}(1 - 1.35z^{-1} + 0.135z^{-2}) + e^{-2m}(1 - 1.368z^{-1} + 0.368z^{-2})]$$

$$C(z, 1) = \frac{0.733(1 + 0.368z^{-1})}{1 - z^{-1}} = 0.732z^{-1} + z^{-2} + z^{-3} + \cdots$$

$$C(z, \tfrac{1}{2}) = \frac{0.286z^{-1} + 0.682z^{-2} + 0.036z^{-3}}{1 - z^{-1}} = 0.286z^{-1} + 0.968z^{-2} + z^{-3} + z^{-4} + \cdots$$

$$C(z, \tfrac{1}{4}) = \frac{0.086z^{-1} + 0.79z^{-2} + 0.114z^{-3}}{1 - z^{-1}} = 0.086z^{-1} + 0.876z^{-2} + z^{-3} + z^{-4} + \cdots$$

The above output transforms make it evident that the system response to a unit-step input settles to two sampling periods without overshoot and steady-state error.

The foregoing example points out that the design of linear systems for deadbeat performance can be readily executed by the classical method, although the state-transition approach generally leads to a unified and systematic solution and may provide some insight into the dynamics of the system. The state-transition method becomes more advantageous than the classical transform method in system design when nonlinearities and initial conditions are not disregarded. In the presence of a nonlinear element the classical method would fail. On the other hand, the state-transition approach remains a powerful design technique even when the system contains nonlinearity. In the following section, the variable-gain concept is extended to the design of optimum control for nonlinear discrete-data systems.

4.2 OPTIMUM CONTROL OF NONLINEAR DISCRETE-DATA SYSTEMS

The design of optimum control for a system is based on criteria defining optimum performance. However, choice of such criteria is rather subjective and generally depends upon the particular requirements of each application. For instance, a control system may be designed on the basis of transient behavior in response to a step-function input, or it may be optimized on the basis of minimum rms error. Consequently, no optimum control is universally applicable. A control system which is optimized on the basis of one criterion may fail to give an optimum performance when measured by another standard of merit. This section is concerned with optimum control

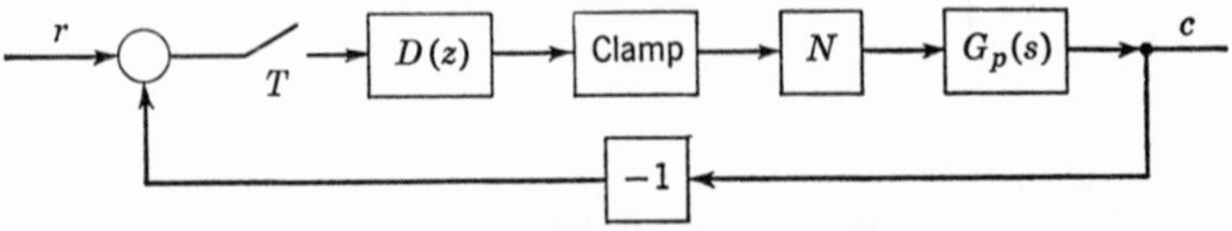

Fig. 4.2-1 A nonlinear discrete-data system.

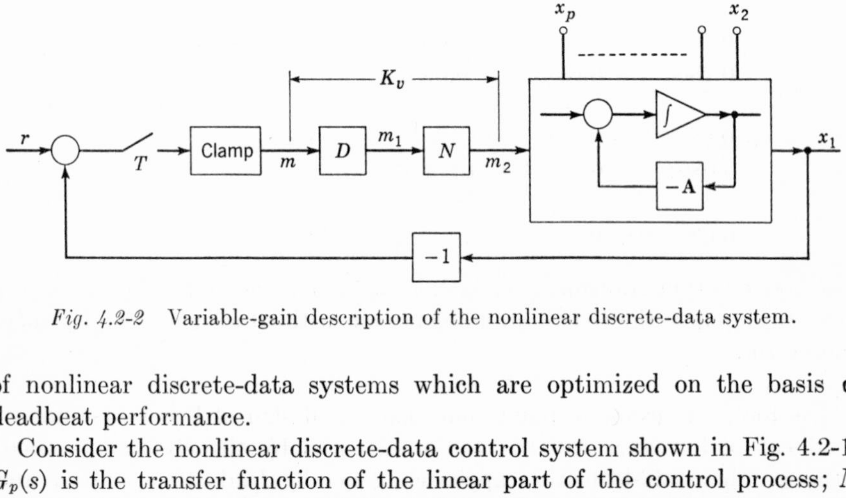

Fig. 4.2-2 Variable-gain description of the nonlinear discrete-data system.

of nonlinear discrete-data systems which are optimized on the basis of deadbeat performance.

Consider the nonlinear discrete-data control system shown in Fig. 4.2-1. $G_p(s)$ is the transfer function of the linear part of the control process; N denotes the transfer characteristic of the nonlinear element in the process; and $D(z)$ represents the pulse-transfer function of the digital controller which is to be determined. A zero-order hold, or clamp, is used as a data-smoothing device. This nonlinear system is designed for performing with deadbeat response to a step-function input.

The block diagram is redrawn as shown in Fig. 4.2-2, with the position of the controller D and the clamp interchanged and the control process described by its state-variable-diagram representation. Let the output signal from the clamp be m, which is the clamped error signal. The state vector of the feedback system is given by

$$\mathbf{v} = \begin{bmatrix} r_1 \\ \mathbf{x} \\ m \end{bmatrix} \tag{4.2-1}$$

where

$$\mathbf{x} = \begin{bmatrix} x_1 \\ x_2 \\ \cdot \\ \cdot \\ \cdot \\ x_p \end{bmatrix} \tag{4.2-2}$$

is the vector for the state variables of the process, which is assumed to be of the pth order and is described by p state variables, $x_1, x_2, \ldots, x_p$. The symbol x_1 also represents the output of the control system. The input to the system, r_1, is assumed to be a step function.

Variable-gain Concept

The desired digital controller and the system nonlinear element may be treated as an element of variable gain K_v, referred to as the *D-N* combination. The variable gain K_v has different values during different sampling periods; it is also dependent upon the characteristic of the nonlinear element N. The input to the *D-N* combination is m, and the output is m_2. At any sampling instant $t = nT^+$, m_2 and m are related by a constant K_n; that is,

$$m_2(nT^+) = K_n m(nT^+) \tag{4.2-3}$$

where K_n is the gain constant of the *D-N* combination during the $(n + 1)$st sampling period.

Based upon the above argument, the transition matrix $\mathbf{\Phi}$ of the system is expressed as a function of the variable gain K_v and has different values at different sampling instants. From Eqs. (4.1-4) and (4.1-5), it can be obtained that, at $n = 0$,

$$\mathbf{v}(0^+) = \mathbf{B}\mathbf{v}(0) \tag{4.2-4}$$

$$\mathbf{v}(T) = \mathbf{\Phi}_0(T)\mathbf{v}(0^+) \tag{4.2-5}$$

The transition matrix $\mathbf{\Phi}_0(T)$ is a function of K_0, and Eq. (4.2-5) may be written as

$$\mathbf{v}(T) = \mathbf{\Phi}(K_0)\mathbf{v}(0^+) \tag{4.2-6}$$

Since both $\mathbf{B}$ and $\mathbf{v}(0)$ are known, $\mathbf{v}(0^+)$ is defined, and

$$m(0^+) = r_1(0^+) \tag{4.2-7}$$

If $m(0^+)$ exceeds the saturation limit of the nonlinear element, K_0 should be taken as the maximum allowable value of the variable gain K_v during the first sampling period. Thus

$$K_0 = \frac{m_2(0^+)}{r_1(0^+)} \tag{4.2-8}$$

where $m_2(0^+)$ is given by the saturation limit of the nonlinear element.

At $n = 1$,

$$\mathbf{v}(T^+) = \mathbf{B}\mathbf{v}(T) \tag{4.2-9}$$

from which the value of $m(T^+)$ can be computed, and

$$\mathbf{v}(2T) = \mathbf{\Phi}_1(T)\mathbf{v}(T^+) \tag{4.2-10}$$

where the transition matrix $\mathbf{\Phi}_1(T)$ is a function of K_1. Equation (4.2-10) can also be written as

$$\mathbf{v}(2T) = \mathbf{\Phi}(K_1)\mathbf{v}(T^+) \tag{4.2-11}$$

If $m(T^+)$ is greater than the saturation limit of the nonlinear element, K_1 should be taken as the maximum allowable value of K_v during the second sampling period. It should be noted that, in order to realize deadbeat performance, $m_2(T^+)$ must be as large as possible. Thus $m_2(T^+)$ should be equal to the saturation limit. K_1 is then given by

$$K_1 = \frac{m_2(T^+)}{m(T^+)} \tag{4.2-12}$$

At $n = 2$,

$$\mathbf{v}(2T^+) = \mathbf{B}\mathbf{v}(2T) \tag{4.2-13}$$

and

$$\mathbf{v}(3T) = \mathbf{\Phi}_2(T)\mathbf{v}(2T^+) \tag{4.2-14}$$

Equation (4.2-14) can be written as

$$\mathbf{v}(3T) = \mathbf{\Phi}(K_2)\mathbf{v}(2T^+) \tag{4.2-15}$$

Now, if $m(2T^+)$ still exceeds the saturation limit of the nonlinear element, K_2 may be determined in similar fashion. However, if $m(2T^+)$ is less than the saturation limit, the determination of K_2 calls for other conditions for deadbeat performance. The system error is zero for $t \geq kT$, if

$$x_1(kT) = r_1(kT) \tag{4.2-16}$$

and

$$x_2(kT) = x_3(kT) = \cdots = x_p(kT) = 0 \tag{4.2-17}$$

where $x_1(kT), x_2(kT), \ldots, x_p(kT)$ are functions of the successive constants of the variable gain K_v and can be derived from the state vector

$$\mathbf{v}(kT) = \mathbf{\Phi}_{k-1}(T)\mathbf{v}(\overline{k-1}\,T^+) \tag{4.2-18a}$$

or

$$\mathbf{v}(kT) = \mathbf{\Phi}(K_{k-1})\mathbf{v}(\overline{k-1}\,T^+) \tag{4.2-18b}$$

Hence, the successive values for K_v can be obtained by solving Eqs. (4.2-16) and (4.2-17).

Now the input and output signals of the *D-N* combination are completely determined. The z transforms of these two signals are

$$M(z) = m(0^+) + m(T^+)z^{-1} + \cdots + m(kT^+)z^{-k} \tag{4.2-19}$$

$$M_2(z) = K_0m(0^+) + K_1m(T^+)z^{-1} + \cdots + K_km(kT^+)z^{-k} \tag{4.2-20}$$

The z transform of the input signal to the nonlinear element follows from Eq. (4.2-20) and may be written as

$$M_1(z) = a_0 + a_1z^{-1} + \cdots + a_kz^{-k} \tag{4.2-21}$$

Since a_j and $K_jm(jT^+)$ are the input and output of the nonlinear element, the coefficients a_j can be determined either analytically or graphically from the characteristic curve of the nonlinearity. Hence the desired digital controller for deadbeat performance is characterized by the pulse-transfer function

$$D(z) = \frac{\sum_{j=0}^{k} a_jz^{-j}}{\sum_{j=0}^{k} m(jT^+)z^{-j}} \tag{4.2-22}$$

From the foregoing discussions it is seen that the settling time of the control system depends upon the order of the process as well as the characteristic of the nonlinear element. The presence of saturation or limiting may cause a longer settling time. Suppose that a pth-order nonlinear system can be brought to the steady state without overshoot in $p + q$ sampling periods. The value of q is determined by the characteristic of the nonlinear element and should be made as small as possible in the design for minimum-time control. This optimum-design problem requires the evaluation of the $p + q$ gain constants taken by the variable-gain element. If the first q values of the control signal m exceed the saturation limit of the nonlinear element, the successive gain constants $K_0, K_1, \ldots, K_{q-1}$ should take the maximum allowable values, and the first q values of $m_2(kT^+)$ should be equal to the saturation limit. If the remaining p values of the control signal are less than the saturation limit, the values of the gain constants K_q through K_{p+q-1} are determined so as to satisfy the conditions for deadbeat performance. When the control signal $m(jT^+)$ exceeds the saturation limit, the input signal to the nonlinear element $m_1(jT^+)$ may either exceed or stay within the saturation limit. In the former case, the gain constant K_j will assume the maximum allowable value. If the assumption that $m_1(jT^+)$ stays within the saturation limit does not hold, the computed values of the gain constants will turn out to be imaginary or complex, which is physically unrealizable. When the control signal $m(jT^+)$ does not exceed the saturation limit, the input signal to the nonlinear element $m_1(jT^+)$ again may either exceed or stay within the saturation limit. To attain minimum-time control, $m_1(jT^+)$ is usually assumed to lie within the saturation limit. If this assumption is not valid, however, the calculated values of the gain constants will be either imaginary or complex and the gain constant K_j will take the maximum allowable value.

Synthesis Procedure

Based upon the technique developed above, the synthesis of nonlinear discrete-data control systems can be carried out systematically in four major steps, which are summarized as follows:

1. Draw the state-variable diagram of the system, with the desired digital controller D and the nonlinear element N represented by a variable-gain element K_v, and determine the transition matrix and the **B** matrix of the system by inspection of the state-variable diagram.

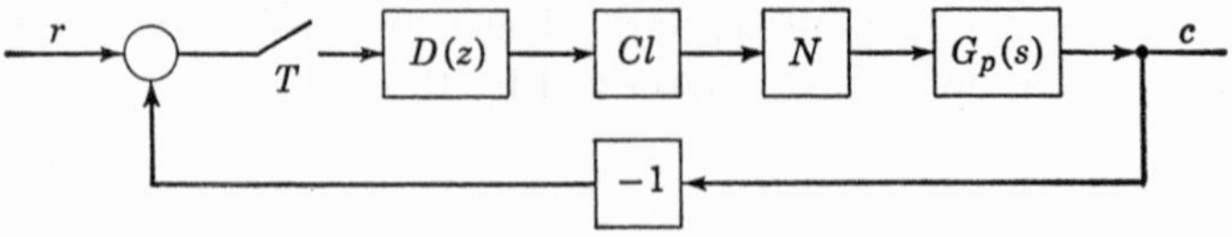

Fig. 4.2-3 Block diagram of the illustrative example.

2. Evaluate the input signal to the D-N combination from the transition matrix and the **B** matrix by using the following equations:

$$\mathbf{v}(nT^+) = \mathbf{B}\mathbf{v}(nT)$$
$$\mathbf{v}(\overline{n+1})\,T = \mathbf{\Phi}(K_n)\mathbf{v}(nT^+)$$

3. Compute the gain constants K_n and the output signal of the D-N combination from the results of step 2, and evaluate the input signal to the nonlinear element, analytically or graphically.

4. Determine the pulse-transfer function of the desired digital controller by use of Eq. (4.2-22).

It is to be noted that this synthesis procedure can also be applied to the design of digital controllers for multirate, variable-rate, and finite-pulse-width sampled-data control systems containing nonlinear elements. The development of the synthesis technique as outlined above is best illustrated by the following numerical examples.

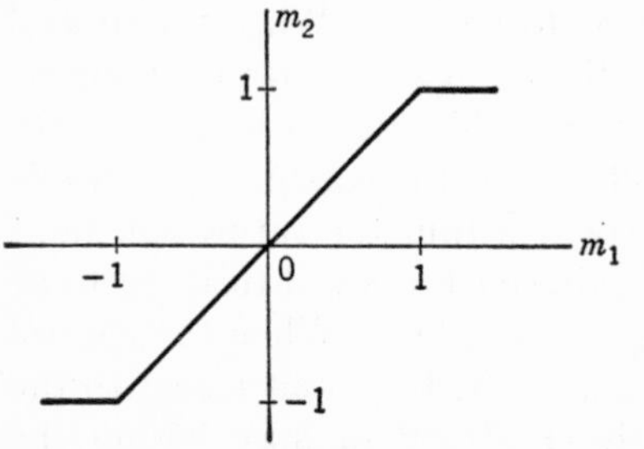

Fig. 4.2-4 Idealized saturation curve.

Example 4.2-1 Saturation Nonlinearity

Consider the nonlinear feedback system shown in Fig. 4.2-3. The transfer function of the control process is

$$G_p(s) = \frac{1}{s(s+1)}$$

The sampling period is 1 sec, and the input is a step function of two units. The nonlinear characteristic curve is depicted in Fig. 4.2-4. Design a digital controller for this system to exhibit deadbeat performance. Zero initial conditions are assumed.

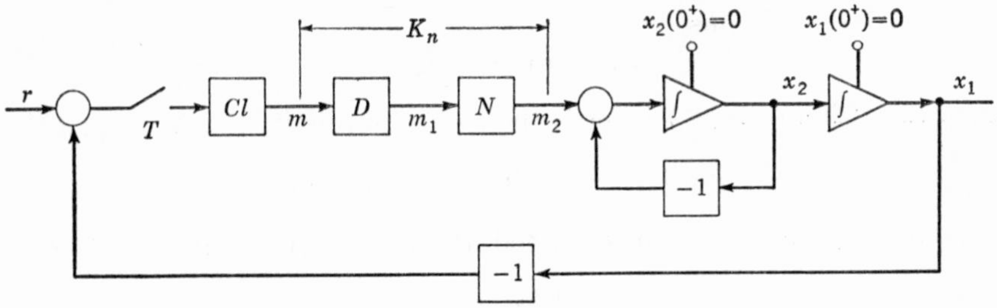

Fig. 4.2-5 State-variable diagram of the illustrative example.

The state-variable diagram of this system is drawn in Fig. 4.2-5. The transition matrix and the **B** matrix are found by examination of the state-variable diagram:

$$\mathbf{\Phi}_n(\lambda) = \begin{bmatrix} 1 & 0 & 0 & 0 \\ 0 & 1 & 1-e^{-\lambda} & (\lambda - 1 + e^{-\lambda})K_n \\ 0 & 0 & e^{-\lambda} & (1-e^{-\lambda})K_n \\ 0 & 0 & 0 & 1 \end{bmatrix}$$

$$\mathbf{B} = \begin{bmatrix} 1 & 0 & 0 & 0 \\ 0 & 1 & 0 & 0 \\ 0 & 0 & 1 & 0 \\ 1 & -1 & 0 & 0 \end{bmatrix}$$

The state vector is given by

$$\mathbf{v} = \begin{bmatrix} r \\ x_1 \\ x_2 \\ m \end{bmatrix}$$

and the initial-state vector is

$$\mathbf{v}(0) = \begin{bmatrix} 2 \\ 0 \\ 0 \\ 0 \end{bmatrix}$$

Since $T = 1$ sec,

$$\mathbf{\Phi}_n(T) = \mathbf{\Phi}(K_n) = \begin{bmatrix} 1 & 0 & 0 & 0 \\ 0 & 1 & 0.632 & 0.368K_n \\ 0 & 0 & 0.368 & 0.632K_n \\ 0 & 0 & 0 & 1 \end{bmatrix}$$

For $n = 0$,

$$\mathbf{v}(0^+) = \mathbf{B}\mathbf{v}(0) = \begin{bmatrix} 2 \\ 0 \\ 0 \\ 2 \end{bmatrix}$$

from which one obtains

$$m(0^+) = 2$$

Since the value of $m(0^+)$ exceeds the saturation limit, which is equal to 1

$$m_2(0^+) = 1 \qquad \text{and} \qquad K_0 = 0.5$$

Thus, during the first sampling period, the transition matrix is

$$\mathbf{\Phi}(K_0) = \begin{bmatrix} 1 & 0 & 0 & 0 \\ 0 & 1 & 0.632 & 0.184 \\ 0 & 0 & 0.368 & 0.316 \\ 0 & 0 & 0 & 0 \end{bmatrix}$$

The state vector at $t = T$ is

$$\mathbf{v}(T) = \mathbf{\Phi}(K_0)\mathbf{v}(0^+) = \begin{bmatrix} 2 \\ 0.368 \\ 0.632 \\ 2 \end{bmatrix}$$

and

$$\mathbf{v}(T^+) = \mathbf{B}\mathbf{v}(T) = \begin{bmatrix} 2 \\ 0.368 \\ 0.632 \\ 1.632 \end{bmatrix}$$

which gives

$$m(T^+) = 1.632$$

Since the value of $m(T^+)$ is larger than the saturation limit,

$$m_2(T^+) = 1 \qquad \text{and} \qquad K_1 = 0.612$$

Hence, during the second sampling period, the transition matrix is

$$\mathbf{\Phi}(K_1) = \begin{bmatrix} 1 & 0 & 0 & 0 \\ 0 & 1 & 0.632 & 0.225 \\ 0 & 0 & 0.368 & 0.387 \\ 0 & 0 & 0 & 1 \end{bmatrix}$$

For $n = 1$,

$$\mathbf{v}(2T) = \mathbf{\Phi}(K_1)\mathbf{v}(T^+) = \begin{bmatrix} 2 \\ 1.135 \\ 0.864 \\ 1.632 \end{bmatrix}$$

$$\mathbf{v}(2T^+) = \mathbf{B}\mathbf{v}(2T) = \begin{bmatrix} 2 \\ 1.135 \\ 0.864 \\ 0.865 \end{bmatrix}$$

$$m(2T^+) = 0.865$$

Since the values of $m(2T^+)$ are now less than 1, gain constant K_2 must be determined from the other conditions for deadbeat performance.

For $n = 2$,

$$\mathbf{v}(3T) = \mathbf{\Phi}(K_2)\mathbf{v}(2T^+) = \begin{bmatrix} 2 \\ 1.681 + 0.318K_2 \\ 0.318 + 0.547K_2 \\ 0.87 \end{bmatrix}$$

and

$$\mathbf{v}(3T^+) = \mathbf{B}\mathbf{v}(3T) = \begin{bmatrix} 2 \\ 1.681 + 0.318K_2 \\ 0.318 + 0.547K_2 \\ 0.319 - 0.318K_2 \end{bmatrix}$$

Similarly, for $n = 3$,

$$\mathbf{v}(4T) = \mathbf{\Phi}(K_3)\mathbf{v}(3T^+) = \begin{bmatrix} 2 \\ 1.882 + 0.664K_2 + 0.117(1 - K_2)K_3 \\ 0.117 + 0.201K_2 + 0.201(1 - K_2)K_3 \\ 0.319 - 0.318K_2 \end{bmatrix}$$

Then the conditions for deadbeat performance are

$$1.882 + 0.664K_2 + 0.117(1 - K_2)K_3 = 2.0$$
$$0.117 + 0.201K_2 + 0.201(1 - K_2)K_3 = 0$$

Solving for K_2 and K_3,

$$K_2 = 0.341 \qquad \text{and} \qquad K_3 = -1.40$$

Hence

$$m(3T^+) = 0.319 - 0.319K_2 = 0.210$$
$$M(z) = 2 + 1.632z^{-1} + 0.865z^{-2} + 0.210z^{-3}$$
$$M_2(z) = 1 + z^{-1} + 0.295z^{-2} - 0.296z^{-3}$$

Since the saturation curve is linear between the saturation limits,

$$M_1(z) = M_2(z)$$

Therefore

$$D(z) = \frac{0.5(1 + z^{-1} - 0.295z^{-2} - 0.296z^{-3})}{1 + 0.816z^{-1} + 0.433z^{-2} + 0.105z^{-3}}$$

and the output response settles in four sampling periods. It can readily be shown that, in the absence of nonlinearity, the compensated system could be made to settle in two sampling periods in response to a step-function input, as shown in Fig. 4.2-6. The longer settling time is caused by the saturation effect of the nonlinear element.

Now, if the saturation curve is not linear between the saturation limits, as shown in Fig. 4.2-7, the input and output of the D-N combination remain unchanged as long as the more realistic curve has the same saturation limits as the idealized curve of Fig. 4.2-4. But the input to the nonlinear element is changed to

$$M_1(z) = 1 + z^{-1} + 0.1z^{-2} - 0.1z^{-3}$$

which may be determined graphically from the saturation curve of Fig. 4.2-7. Therefore, in this case, the desired pulse-transfer function is

$$D(z) = \frac{0.5(1 + z^{-1} + -0.1z^{-2} - 0.1z^{-3})}{1 + 0.816z^{-1} + 0.433z^{-2} + 0.105z^{-3}}$$

The output of the compensated system in response to the specified

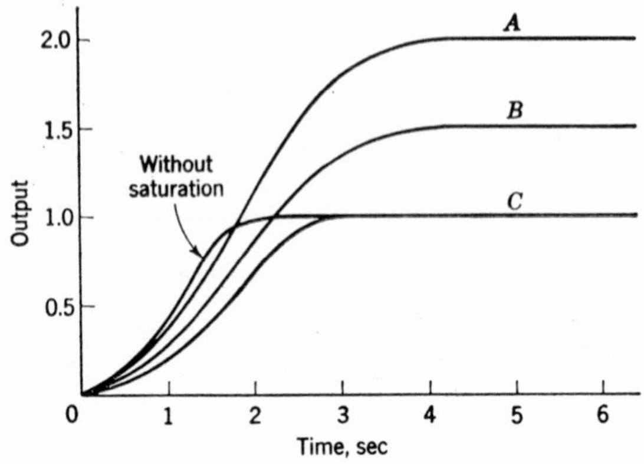

Fig. 4.2-6 Step-function response of Example 4.2-1. Step inputs: (*A*) 2.0; (*B*) 1.5; (*C*) 1.0.

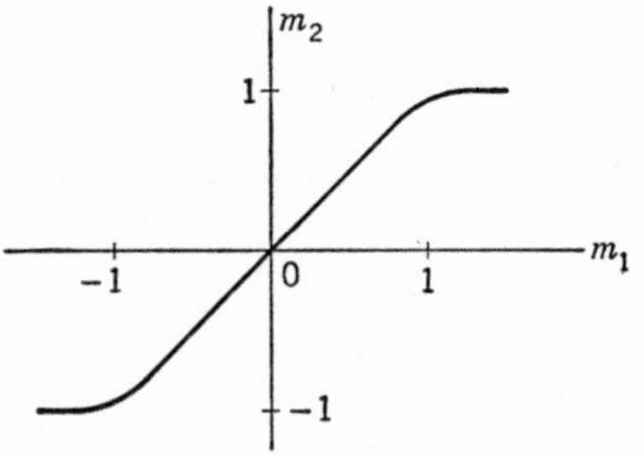

Fig. 4.2-7 Saturation curve.

step-function input is the same as the system with idealized saturation nonlinearity. It can be seen that the deadbeat response depends upon the magnitude of the step input and the saturation limit. However, the nonlinear characteristic between the saturation limits has no influence upon the output of the compensated system.

With reference to the running example, if the input is a unit-step function, it can be shown that the response will settle in three sampling periods. The initial-state vector is now given by

$$\mathbf{v}(0) = \begin{bmatrix} 1 \\ 0 \\ 0 \\ 0 \end{bmatrix}$$

Thus
$$\mathbf{v}(0^+) = \begin{bmatrix} 1 \\ 0 \\ 0 \\ 1 \end{bmatrix}$$

$$\mathbf{v}(T) = \mathbf{\Phi}(K_0)\mathbf{v}(0^+) = \begin{bmatrix} 1 \\ 0.368 \\ 0.632 \\ 1 \end{bmatrix}$$

$$\mathbf{v}(T^+) = \mathbf{B}\mathbf{v}(T) = \begin{bmatrix} 1 \\ 0.368 \\ 0.632 \\ 0.632 \end{bmatrix}$$

$$m(0^+) = 1 \qquad \text{and} \qquad m(T^+) = 0.632$$

Since $m(0^+)$ is limited by saturation effect,

$$m_2(0^+) = 1 \qquad \text{and} \qquad K_0 = 1$$

It can be shown that, if the saturation effect were ignored, the value of $m_2(0^+)$ would be 1.58. This would violate the assumption that the maximum allowable value of $m_2(0^+)$ is 1.

Since the value of $m(T^+)$ is less than the saturation limit, the gain constants K_1 and K_2 should be determined from other conditions for deadbeat performance. To proceed as before, compute

$$\mathbf{v}(2T) = \mathbf{\Phi}(K_1)\mathbf{v}(T^+) = \begin{bmatrix} 1 \\ 0.7674 + 0.233K_1 \\ 0.233 + 0.399K_1 \\ 0.632 \end{bmatrix}$$

$$\mathbf{v}(2T^+) = \mathbf{B}\mathbf{v}(2T) = \begin{bmatrix} 1 \\ 0.7674 + 0.233K_1 \\ 0.233 + 0.399K_1 \\ 0.233 - 0.233K_1 \end{bmatrix}$$

$$\mathbf{v}(3T) = \mathbf{\Phi}(K_2)\mathbf{v}(2T^+) = \begin{bmatrix} 1 \\ 0.914 + 0.485K_1 + 0.0857(1 - K_1)K_2 \\ 0.0857 + 0.147K_1 + 0.147(1 - K_1)K_2 \\ 0.233(1 - K_1) \end{bmatrix}$$

Then the conditions for deadbeat performance are

$$0.914 + 0.485K_1 + 0.0857(1 - K_1)K_2 = 1.0$$
$$0.0857 + 0.147K_1 + 0.147(1 - K_1)K_2 = 0$$

Solving for K_1 and K_2 gives

$$K_1 = 0.34 \quad \text{and} \quad K_2 = -1.401$$

Hence

$$m(2T^+) = 0.233 - 0.233K_1 = 0.154$$
$$M(z) = 1 + 0.632z^{-1} + 0.154z^{-2}$$
$$M_2(z) = 1 + 0.215z^{-1} - 0.2157z^{-2}$$

Therefore

$$D(z) = \frac{1 + 0.215z^{-1} - 0.2157z^{-2}}{1 + 0.632z^{-1} + 0.154z^{-2}}$$

and the unit-step response settles in three sampling periods.

The above illustrative example points out that the minimum settling time for deadbeat performance is determined by the size of the step-function input. It can be shown that, when $r(t) \leq 0.631u(t)$, the system response can be made to settle in two sampling periods and the saturation effect becomes immaterial. Let the input function be

$$r(t) = Ru(t)$$

Then

$$\mathbf{v}(0^+) = \begin{bmatrix} R \\ 0 \\ 0 \\ R \end{bmatrix}$$

and

$$\mathbf{v}(T) = \mathbf{\Phi}(K_0)\mathbf{v}(0^+) = \begin{bmatrix} R \\ 0.368K_0R \\ 0.632K_0R \\ R \end{bmatrix}$$

$$\mathbf{v}(T^+) = \begin{bmatrix} R \\ 0.368K_0R \\ 0.632K_0R \\ R(1 - 0.386K_0) \end{bmatrix}$$

$$\mathbf{v}(2T) = \mathbf{\Phi}(K_1)\mathbf{v}(T^+) = \begin{bmatrix} R \\ 0.767K_0R + 0.368(1 - 0.368K_0)K_1R \\ 0.233K_0R + 0.632(1 - 0.368K_0)K_1R \\ (1 - 0.368K_0)R \end{bmatrix}$$

If the response settles in two sampling periods,

$$0.767K_0 + 0.368(1 - 0.368K_0)K_1 = 1$$
$$0.233K_0 + 0.632(1 - 0.368K_0)K_1 = 0$$

Solving for K_0 and K_1 yields

$$K_0 = 1.585 \quad \text{and} \quad K_1 = -1.40$$

Since the nonlinear element saturates for $m_2 \geq 1.0$,

$$m(0^+)K_0 = 1.585m(0^+) = 1$$

or

$$m(0^+) = 0.631$$

Since $m(0^+) = R$, the system deadbeats in two sampling periods when $R \leq 0.631$. Several step-function responses are plotted in Fig. 4.2-6 for comparison.

Example 4.2-2 Asymmetrical Nonlinearity

Consider the control system of the previous example, except that the nonlinear characteristic is asymmetrical as shown in Fig. 4.2-8 and the system is subject to a unit-step input. Design a digital controller for the system to meet the deadbeat-performance requirement.

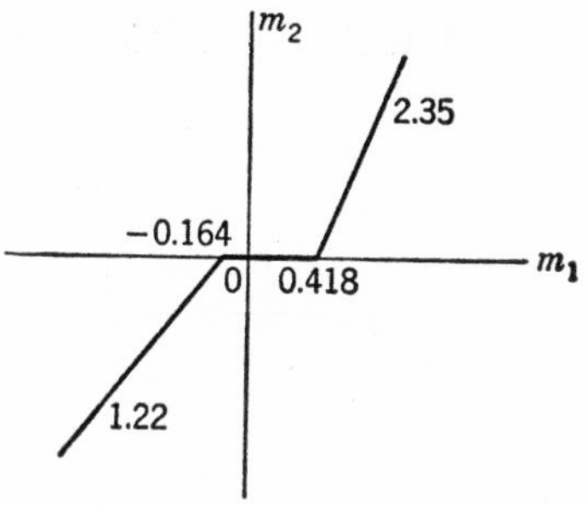

Fig. 4.2-8 Asymmetrical nonlinearity.

The initial-state vector is now given by

$$\mathbf{v}(0) = \begin{bmatrix} 1 \\ 0 \\ 0 \\ 0 \end{bmatrix}$$

The transition matrix $\mathbf{\Phi}_n(\lambda)$ and the $\mathbf{B}$ matrix have been found in Example 4.2-1. For $n = 0$,

$$\mathbf{v}(0^+) = \mathbf{B}\mathbf{v}(0) = \begin{bmatrix} 1 \\ 0 \\ 0 \\ 1 \end{bmatrix}$$

which gives

$$m(0^+) = 1$$

Since

$$\mathbf{\Phi}_0(T) = \mathbf{\Phi}(K_0) = \begin{bmatrix} 1 & 0 & 0 & 0 \\ 0 & 1 & 0.632 & 0.368K_0 \\ 0 & 0 & 0.368 & 0.632K_0 \\ 0 & 0 & 0 & 1 \end{bmatrix}$$

then $$\mathbf{v}(T) = \mathbf{\Phi}(K_0)\mathbf{v}(0^+) = \begin{bmatrix} 1 \\ 0.368K_0 \\ 0.632K_0 \\ 1 \end{bmatrix}$$

and $$\mathbf{v}(T^+) = \mathbf{B}\mathbf{v}(T) = \begin{bmatrix} 1 \\ 0.358K_0 \\ 0.632K_0 \\ 1 - 0.368K_0 \end{bmatrix}$$

In like manner, for $n = 1$,

$$\mathbf{v}(2T) = \mathbf{\Phi}(K_1)\mathbf{v}(T^+) = \begin{bmatrix} 1 \\ 0.768K_0 + 0.368(1 - 0.368K_0)K_1 \\ 0.232K_0 + 0.632(1 - 0.368K_0)K_1 \\ 1 - 0.368K_0 \end{bmatrix}$$

For the system to respond with deadbeat performance, the following

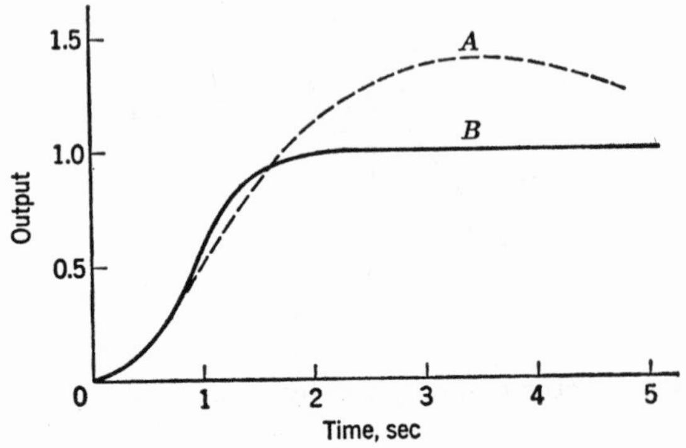

Fig. 4.2-9 Step-function response of Example 4.2-2. (*A*) Uncompensated; (*B*) compensated.

conditions must be fulfilled:

$$x_1(2T) = 0.768K_0 + 0.368(1 - 0.368K_0)K_1 = 1$$
$$x_2(2T) = 0.232K_0 + 0.632(1 - 0.368K_0)K_1 = 0$$

Solving these two simultaneous equations yields

$$K_0 = 1.58 \qquad \text{and} \qquad K_1 = 1.38$$

Thus, $$m(T^+) = 1 - 0.368K_0 = 0.418$$

and the input and output of the *D-N* combination are

$$M(z) = 1 + 0.418z^{-1}$$
$$M_2(z) = 1.58 - 0.577z^{-1}$$

By making use of Fig. 4.2-8, the z transform of the input to the nonlinear element is found to be

$$M_1(z) = 1.902 - 0.636z^{-1}$$

Hence the pulse-transfer function of the desired digital controller is given by

$$D(z) = \frac{1.092(1 - 0.582z^{-1})}{1 + 0.418z^{-1}}$$

The output response to a unit-step input of the compensated system is plotted in Fig. 4.2-9, which reaches steady state without overshoot in two sampling periods.

4.3 FURTHER CONSIDERATIONS OF TRANSITION MATRIX

The preceding two sections present the design of the optimum control for linear and nonlinear systems. The optimum control is carried out by incorporating a digital controller in the forward path of the control loop. A basic assumption is made that the initial conditions of the system are set at zero. The system is required to respond to stepwise inputs in the quickest manner without overshoot. In the following sections, discussion is centered upon optimum control of linear systems with arbitrary initial conditions. System design of this sort is often initiated with a vector-matrix differential equation with explicit forcing function, such as

$$\dot{\mathbf{x}}(t) = \mathbf{A}(t)\mathbf{x}(t) + \mathbf{D}(t)\mathbf{m}(t)$$

which characterizes the dynamics of the control process. In the above equation, $\mathbf{x}$ is the state vector of the control process or plant and $\mathbf{m}$ denotes the control vector. If the control process is of nth order and is subject to r control inputs, the state vector $\mathbf{x}$ is an $n \times 1$ column vector, the control vector $\mathbf{m}$ is an $r \times 1$ column vector, the coefficient matrix $\mathbf{A}$ is an $n \times n$ square matrix, and the driving matrix $\mathbf{D}$ is an $n \times r$ matrix. Although this type of equation has been studied in Sec. 2.4, further investigation is undertaken here so as to clarify several important physical concepts and to derive some recurrence relationships which are useful in optimum design.

Review of the Solution of First-order Ordinary Linear Differential Equation

Consider a first-order linear differential equation

$$\dot{x}(t) = ax(t) + bm(t) \tag{4.3-1}$$

where a and b are constants and $m(t)$ is a forcing function. By well-known techniques, the solution is found to be

$$\begin{aligned} x(t) &= K_0e^{at} + e^{at}\int_{t_0}^{t} e^{-a\tau}bm(\tau)\,d\tau \\ &= K_0e^{at} + \int_{t_0}^{t} be^{a(t-\tau)}m(\tau)\,d\tau \end{aligned} \tag{4.3-2}$$

With the initial condition given by $x(t) = x(t_0^+) = x_0$ and defining

$$g(t) = e^{at} \tag{4.3-3}$$

Eq. (4.3-2) may be expressed as

$$x(t) = g(t - t_0)x(t_0^+) + \int_{t_0}^{t} g(t - \tau)bm(\tau)\, d\tau \tag{4.3-4}$$

where $g(t)$ is referred to as the unit-impulse response of the system. The solution $x(t)$ consists of two parts:

1. The transient part

$$x_0 g(t - t_0)$$

which accounts for the impulse response. The impulse response is the output of the system in response to an impulse input of strength x_0 occurring at $t = t_0^+$.

2. The steady-state part

$$\int_{t_0}^{t} g(t - \tau)bm(\tau)\, d\tau$$

which represents the output response. The output response is defined as the output of the system when the forcing function is the input; hence it is given by the convolution integral of the unit-impulse response and the forcing function.

When the forcing function is a step function,

$$\begin{aligned} m(t) &= m(t_0^+)u(t - t_0) \\ &= m(t_0^+) \qquad \text{for } t > t_0 \end{aligned}$$

the solution to Eq. (4.3-1) becomes

$$x(t) = g(t - t_0)x(t_0^+) + \int_{t_0}^{t} g(t - \tau)bm(t_0^+)\, d\tau \tag{4.3-5a}$$

$$x(t) = \underbrace{i(t - t_0)}_{\text{impulse response}} + \underbrace{h(t - t_0)m(t_0^+)}_{\text{step response}} \tag{4.3-5b}$$

where $h(t)$ is the unit-step response and is defined by

$$h(t) = \int_0^t g(t - t)b\, d\tau \tag{4.3-6}$$

If the forcing function $m(t)$ is the output of a sampler hold with sampling period equal to T, then at $t = T$,

$$x(T) = g(T - t_0)x(t_0^+) + \int_{t_0}^{T} g(t - \tau)bm(\tau)\, d\tau \tag{4.3-7}$$

where $0 \le t_0 \le T$. Since, during the first sampling period,

$$m(\tau) = m(t_0^+) \tag{4.3-8}$$

$$x(T) = g(T - t_0)x(t_0^+) + \int_{t_0}^{T} g(t - \tau)bm(t_0^+)\, d\tau \tag{4.3-9}$$

In view of Eq. (4.3-6),

$$x(T) = g(T - t_0)x(t_0^+) + h(T - t_0)m(t_0^+) \tag{4.3-10}$$

For $t_0 = 0$,

$$x(T) = g(T)x(0^+) + h(T)m(0^+) \tag{4.3-11}$$

Solution of Vector-matrix Differential Equations

Consider the vector-matrix differential equation with explicit forcing function

$$\dot{\mathbf{x}}(t) = \mathbf{A}\mathbf{x}(t) + \mathbf{D}\mathbf{m}(t) \tag{4.3-12}$$

where $\mathbf{A}$ is defined as the coefficient matrix of the control process or plant, and $\mathbf{D}$ is referred to as the driving matrix. By analogy to the scalar case, the solution to Eq. (4.3-12) is

$$\mathbf{x}(t) = e^{\mathbf{A}(t-t_0)}\mathbf{x}(t_0) + \int_{t_0}^{t} e^{\mathbf{A}(t-\tau)}\mathbf{D}\mathbf{m}(\tau)\, d\tau \tag{4.3-13}$$

with the initial condition given by $\mathbf{x}(t_0)$.

By defining

$$\boldsymbol{\phi}(t) = e^{\mathbf{A}t} \tag{4.3-14}$$

as the transition matrix of the control process or plant, the solution may be written as

$$\mathbf{x}(t) = \boldsymbol{\phi}(t - t_0)\mathbf{x}(t_0) + \int_{t_0}^{t} \boldsymbol{\phi}(t - \tau)\mathbf{D}\mathbf{m}(\tau)\, d\tau \tag{4.3-15}$$

which consists of the transient part, or the state-impulse response,

$$\boldsymbol{\phi}(t - t_0)\mathbf{x}(t_0) \tag{4.3-16}$$

and the steady-state part, or the output response,

$$\int_{t_0}^{t} \boldsymbol{\phi}(t - \tau)\mathbf{D}\mathbf{m}(\tau)\, d\tau \tag{4.3-17}$$

The transition matrix is analogous to the unit-impulse response of a first-order system. Thus the transition matrix describes the transient behavior of a high-order system. The output response is the output of the high-order system when the forcing function is the input. It is given by the vector convolution integral of the transition matrix and the forcing function.

In the case of sampled-data systems, $\mathbf{m}(t)$ is the output of a sampler hold, and thus

$$\mathbf{m}(t) = \mathbf{m}(nT^+) \qquad \text{for } nT < t \leq (n + 1)T \tag{4.3-18}$$

Then, during the interval $nT < t \leq (n + 1)T$, the state vector is

$$\mathbf{x}(t) = \boldsymbol{\phi}(t - nT)\mathbf{x}(nT^+) + \int_{nT^+}^{t} \boldsymbol{\phi}(t - \tau)\mathbf{D}\mathbf{m}(nT^+)\, d\tau \tag{4.3-19}$$

During the interval $t_0 < t \leq T$, $t_0 \geq 0$,

$$\mathbf{x}(t) = \boldsymbol{\phi}(t - t_0)\mathbf{x}(t_0^+) + \int_{t_0}^{t} \boldsymbol{\phi}(t - \tau)\mathbf{D}\mathbf{m}(t_0^+)\, d\tau \tag{4.3-20}$$

Define

$$\mathbf{h}(t) = \int_0^t \boldsymbol{\phi}(u)\mathbf{D}\, du \tag{4.3-21}$$

Then

$$\mathbf{h}(t) = \int_0^t \boldsymbol{\phi}(t - \tau)\mathbf{D}\, d\tau \tag{4.3-22}$$

and

$$\mathbf{h}(t - t_0) = \int_{t_0}^t \boldsymbol{\phi}(t - \tau)\mathbf{D}\, d\tau \tag{4.3-23}$$

The state vector for $t_0 < t \leq T$, $t_0 \geq 0$, can be expressed as

$$\mathbf{x}(t) = \boldsymbol{\phi}(t - t_0)\mathbf{x}(t_0^+) + \mathbf{h}(t - t_0)\mathbf{m}(t_0^+) \tag{4.3-24}$$

At $t = T$,

$$\mathbf{x}(T) = \boldsymbol{\phi}(T - t_0)\mathbf{x}(t_0^+) + \mathbf{h}(T - t_0)\mathbf{m}(t_0^+) \tag{4.3-25}$$

and for $t_0 = 0$,

$$\mathbf{x}(T) = \boldsymbol{\phi}(T)\mathbf{x}(0^+) + \mathbf{h}(T)\mathbf{m}(0^+) \tag{4.3-26}$$

It is to be noted that Eqs. (4.3-24), (4.3-25), and (4.3-26) are analogous to Eqs. (4.3-5), (4.3-10), and (4.3-11), respectively.

Using Eq. (4.3-21), the state vector during the interval $nT < t \leq (n + 1)T$ may be written as

$$\mathbf{x}(t) = \boldsymbol{\phi}(t - nT)\mathbf{x}(nT) + \mathbf{h}(t - nT)\mathbf{m}(nT) \tag{4.3-27}$$

which leads to the transition equation

$$\mathbf{x}(\overline{n + 1}\, T) = \boldsymbol{\phi}(T)\mathbf{x}(nT) + \mathbf{h}(T)\mathbf{m}(nT) \tag{4.3-28}$$

where

$$\boldsymbol{\phi}(T) = e^{\mathbf{A}T} \tag{4.3-29}$$

is the plant transition matrix and

$$\mathbf{h}(T) = \int_0^T \boldsymbol{\phi}(T)\mathbf{D}\, d\tau \tag{4.3-30}$$

is referred to as the control transition matrix.

With the forcing function set equal to zero, the transition equation of the system becomes

$$\mathbf{x}(\overline{n + 1}\, T) = \boldsymbol{\phi}(T)\mathbf{x}(nT) \tag{4.3-31}$$

which implies that the state vectors of the plant or control process at two consecutive sampling instants are related through premultiplication by the matrix $\boldsymbol{\phi}(T)$. Hence $\boldsymbol{\phi}(T)$ is referred to as the plant transition matrix. In like manner, the state vector for the driving function at sampling instants may be expressed as

$$\mathbf{m}(\overline{n + 1}\, T) = \mathbf{R}(T)\mathbf{m}(nT) \tag{4.3-32}$$

where the matrix $\mathbf{R}(T)$ relates the control input vectors at two consecutive sampling instants and is defined as the input, or driving, transition matrix.

When the input, or driving, state vector is combined with the plant state vector to form state vector

$$\mathbf{v}(t) = \begin{bmatrix} \mathbf{m}(t) \\ \mathbf{x}(t) \end{bmatrix} \tag{4.3-33}$$

Eq. (4.3-28) may be expressed as

$$\mathbf{v}(\overline{n+1}\,T) = \mathbf{\Phi}(T)\mathbf{v}(nT) \tag{4.3-34}$$

where

$$\mathbf{\Phi}(T) = \begin{bmatrix} \mathbf{R}(T) & 0 \\ \mathbf{h}(T) & \mathbf{\phi}(T) \end{bmatrix} \tag{4.3-35}$$

is referred to as the overall transition matrix of the system.

Example 4.3-1

Consider the system shown in Fig. 4.3-1. Determine the plant transition matrix $\mathbf{\phi}(T)$ and the control transition matrix $\mathbf{h}(T)$.

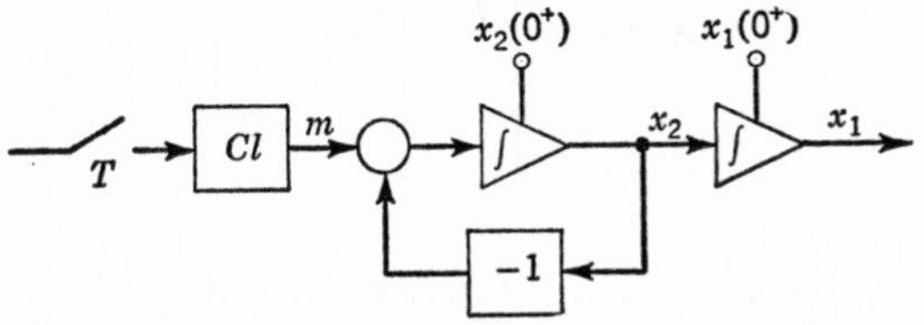

Fig. 4.3-1 A second-order process.

Two different ways of computing $\mathbf{\phi}(T)$ and $\mathbf{h}(T)$ are illustrated below:

1. The vector-matrix equation for the given system is

$$\dot{\mathbf{x}}(t) = \mathbf{A}\mathbf{x}(t) + \mathbf{D}m(t)$$

where the matrices $\mathbf{A}$ and $\mathbf{D}$ are

$$\mathbf{A} = \begin{bmatrix} 0 & 1 \\ 0 & -1 \end{bmatrix} \quad \text{and} \quad \mathbf{D} = \begin{bmatrix} 0 \\ 1 \end{bmatrix}$$

which are determined by inspection of the state-variable diagram. The plant transition matrix $\mathbf{\phi}(T)$ is given by

$$\mathbf{\phi}(T) = e^{\mathbf{A}T} = \begin{bmatrix} 1 & 1 - e^{-T} \\ 0 & e^{-T} \end{bmatrix}$$

which can also be found from the state-variable diagram. Using Eq. (4.3-30),

$$\mathbf{h}(T) = \int_0^T \begin{bmatrix} 1 & 1 - e^{-\tau} \\ 0 & e^{-\tau} \end{bmatrix} \begin{bmatrix} 0 \\ 1 \end{bmatrix} d\tau = \int_0^T \begin{bmatrix} 1 - e^{-\tau} \\ e^{-\tau} \end{bmatrix} d\tau$$

$$= \begin{bmatrix} T - 1 + e^{-T} \\ 1 - e^{-T} \end{bmatrix}$$

2. Both $\phi(T)$ and $\mathbf{h}(T)$ can be found by inspection, once the overall transition matrix $\mathbf{\Phi}(T)$ is determined. Examination of the state-variable diagram yields the transition matrix

$$\mathbf{\Phi}(\lambda) = \begin{bmatrix} 1 & 0 & 0 \\ \lambda - 1 + e^{-\lambda} & 1 & 1 - e^{-\lambda} \\ 1 - e^{-\lambda} & 0 & e^{-\lambda} \end{bmatrix}$$

where $nT < \lambda \leq (n + 1)T$. Thus

$$\mathbf{\Phi}(T) = \begin{bmatrix} 1 & 0 & 0 \\ T - 1 + e^{-T} & 1 & 1 - e^{-T} \\ 1 - e^{-T} & 0 & e^{-T} \end{bmatrix}$$

In view of Eq. (4.3-35), it follows from the above expression that

$$\mathbf{h}(T) = \begin{bmatrix} T - 1 + e^{-T} \\ 1 - e^{-T} \end{bmatrix}$$

and

$$\phi(T) = \begin{bmatrix} 1 & 1 - e^{-T} \\ 0 & e^{-T} \end{bmatrix}$$

Some Properties of the Transition Matrix $\phi(T)$

The transition matrix $\phi(T)$ possesses several interesting properties which find much use in the design of optimum control systems. These properties are summarized below:

1. $\phi(0)$ is a unity matrix.

2. $\phi(kT) = [\phi(T)]^k$.
   Since, by definition, $\phi(kT) = e^{\mathbf{A}Tk} = (e^{\mathbf{A}T})^k$, then

$$\phi(kT) = [\phi(T)]^k$$

3. $\phi(-kT) = [\phi(kT)]^{-1}$.
   Since $\phi(-kT) = e^{-\mathbf{A}kT} = (e^{\mathbf{A}kT})^{-1}$, then $\phi(-kT) = [\phi(kT)]^{-1}$.

4. $\phi(\overline{j + k}\,T - \tau) = \phi(jT)\phi(kT - \tau) = \phi(jT - \tau)\phi(kT)$.
   Since $\phi(\overline{j + k}\,T - \tau) = e^{\mathbf{A}jT}e^{\mathbf{A}(kT-\tau)}$, then

$$\phi(\overline{j + k}\,T - \tau) = \phi(jT)\phi(kT - \tau)$$

5. $\phi(kT)\mathbf{h}(-kT) = -\mathbf{h}(kT)$.
   The overall transition matrix is

$$\mathbf{\Phi}(kT) = \begin{bmatrix} 1 & 0 \\ \mathbf{h}(kT) & \phi(kT) \end{bmatrix}$$

Replacing k by $-k$,

$$\mathbf{\Phi}(-kT) = \begin{bmatrix} 1 & 0 \\ \mathbf{h}(-kT) & \boldsymbol{\phi}(-kT) \end{bmatrix}$$

Since
$$\mathbf{\Phi}(kT)\mathbf{\Phi}(-kT) = \mathbf{\Phi}(0) = \mathbf{I}$$

$$\begin{bmatrix} 1 & 0 \\ \mathbf{h}(kT) + \boldsymbol{\phi}(kT)\mathbf{h}(-kT) & \boldsymbol{\phi}(kT)\boldsymbol{\phi}(-kT) \end{bmatrix} = \mathbf{I}$$

Hence
$$\mathbf{h}(kT) + \boldsymbol{\phi}(kT)\mathbf{h}(-kT) = \mathbf{0}$$

which gives property 5, upon transposing.

6. $\boldsymbol{\phi}(jT)\mathbf{h}(kT) + \mathbf{h}(jT) = \mathbf{h}(\overline{j+k}\,T)$.
   Since

$$\mathbf{h}(\overline{j+k}\,T) = \int_0^{(j+k)T} \boldsymbol{\phi}(\overline{j+k}\,T - \tau)\mathbf{D}\,d\tau$$
$$= \int_0^{kT} \boldsymbol{\phi}(\overline{j+k}\,T - \tau)\mathbf{D}\,d\tau + \int_{kT}^{(j+k)T} \boldsymbol{\phi}(\overline{j+k}\,T - \tau)\mathbf{D}\,d\tau$$

using property 4,

$$\mathbf{h}(\overline{j+k}\,T) = \boldsymbol{\phi}(jT)\int_0^{kT} \boldsymbol{\phi}(kT - \tau)\mathbf{D}\,d\tau + \int_{kT}^{(j+k)T} \boldsymbol{\phi}(\overline{j+k}\,T - \tau)\mathbf{D}\,d\tau$$

In view of Eq. (4.3-23),

$$\mathbf{h}(\overline{j+k}\,T) = \boldsymbol{\phi}(jT)\mathbf{h}(kT) + \mathbf{h}(jT)$$

which proves the property.

4.4 CONCEPT OF CONTROLLABILITY AND OBSERVABILITY

A process or plant is said to be completely controllable[88] if it is possible to take the process from some initial state $\mathbf{x}(t_0)$ to a desired equilibrium state $\mathbf{x}(t_1)$ in a finite time interval $t_1 - t_0$. In other words, a process is completely controllable if there exists a control signal $\mathbf{m}(t)$, defined over a finite interval $t_0 \leq t \leq t_1$, which moves the process from initial state $\mathbf{x}(t_0)$ to a desired equilibrium state $\mathbf{x}(t_1)$ in time interval $t_1 - t_0$. This phenomenon has previously been identified as deadbeat response, or finite-transition-time response.

A necessary and sufficient condition for complete controllability in the discrete-time case may be stated as follows: An nth-order linear discrete-time process is completely controllable if and only if the vectors

$$\begin{aligned} \mathbf{s}_1 &= \boldsymbol{\phi}(-T)\mathbf{h}(T) \\ \mathbf{s}_2 &= \boldsymbol{\phi}(-2T)\mathbf{h}(T) \\ &\cdots\cdots\cdots\cdots \\ \mathbf{s}_n &= \boldsymbol{\phi}(-nT)\mathbf{h}(T) \end{aligned} \tag{4.4-1}$$

are linearly independent.[140]

These vectors arise in the following manner: The control process is assumed to be subject to a single control signal and is characterized by

$$\dot{\mathbf{x}}(t) = \mathbf{A}\mathbf{x}(t) + \mathbf{d}m(t) \tag{4.4-2}$$

The assumption of single control signal is made for the sake of simplicity in interpretation. The transition equation describing the process is

$$\mathbf{x}(\overline{k+1}\,T) = \boldsymbol{\phi}(T)\mathbf{x}(kT) + \mathbf{h}(T)m(kT) \tag{4.4-3}$$

where $\boldsymbol{\phi}(T)$ is the transition matrix of the process and

$$\mathbf{h}(T) = \int_0^T \boldsymbol{\phi}(\tau)\mathbf{d}\,d\tau \tag{4.4-4}$$

For $k = 0$, Eq. (4.4-3) yields

$$\mathbf{x}(T) = \boldsymbol{\phi}(T)\mathbf{x}(0) + \mathbf{h}(T)m(0) \tag{4.4-5}$$

Thus, if it is assumed that $\mathbf{x}(T) = \mathbf{0}$, the initial state $\mathbf{x}(0)$ from which this equilibrium condition can be reached in one sampling period is

$$\mathbf{x}(0) = -\boldsymbol{\phi}(-T)\mathbf{h}(T)m(0) = -m(0)\mathbf{s}_1 \tag{4.4-6}$$

If the value of $m(0)$ is not bounded, all initial states $\mathbf{x}(0)$ lying along vector $\mathbf{s}_1$ can be taken to $\mathbf{x}(T) = \mathbf{0}$ in one sampling period. When the control signal $m(0)$ is bounded, the region of such initial states does not include the entire line through vector $\mathbf{s}_1$.

For $k = 1$, Eq. (4.4-3) yields

$$\mathbf{x}(2T) = \boldsymbol{\phi}(T)\mathbf{x}(T) + \mathbf{h}(T)m(T) \tag{4.4-7}$$

Using Eq. (4.4-5) and properties of transition matrix,

$$\mathbf{x}(2T) = \boldsymbol{\phi}(2T)\mathbf{x}(0) + \boldsymbol{\phi}(T)\mathbf{h}(T)m(0) + \mathbf{h}(T)m(T) \tag{4.4-8}$$

If it is assumed that $\mathbf{x}(2T) = \mathbf{0}$, the initial state $\mathbf{x}(0)$ from which this equilibrium condition can be reached in two sampling periods is

$$\mathbf{x}(0) = -m(0)\mathbf{s}_1 - m(T)\mathbf{s}_2 \tag{4.4-9}$$

where the vectors

$$\mathbf{s}_1 = \boldsymbol{\phi}(-T)\mathbf{h}(T) \qquad \text{and} \qquad \mathbf{s}_2 = \boldsymbol{\phi}(-2T)\mathbf{h}(T)$$

are linearly independent. If the values of the control signal, $m(0)$ and $m(T)$, are not bounded, all initial states $\mathbf{x}(0)$ lying in the plane containing vectors $\mathbf{s}_1$ and $\mathbf{s}_2$ can be taken to the equilibrium states $\mathbf{x}(2T) = 0$ in two sampling periods. However, when either $m(0)$ or $m(T)$ or both are bounded, the region of such initial states does not include the entire plane containing basis vectors $\mathbf{s}_1$ and $\mathbf{s}_2$.

In like manner, for $k = n$, the initial-state vector $\mathbf{x}(0)$ may be expressed as

$$\mathbf{x}(0) = -m(0)\mathbf{s}_1 - m(T)\mathbf{s}_2 - \cdots - m(\overline{i-1}\,T)\mathbf{s}_i - \cdots - m(\overline{n-1}\,T)\mathbf{s}_n \tag{4.4-10}$$

where the n vectors

$$\mathbf{s}_i = \boldsymbol{\phi}(-iT)\mathbf{h}(T) \qquad i = 1, 2, \ldots, n \tag{4.4-11}$$

are linearly independent. The vectors $\mathbf{s}_i$ form a basis in the state space of the process. Thus, if the values of $m(iT)$, $i = 1, 2, \ldots, n$, are not bounded, any initial state $\mathbf{x}(0)$ can be written as a linear combination of the base vectors $\mathbf{s}_i$, and therefore the initial state $\mathbf{x}(0)$ can be brought to the equilibrium state $\mathbf{x}(nT) = \mathbf{0}$ in at most n sampling periods; that is, $t_1 \leq nT$. If the values of $m(iT)$ are bounded, some initial state $\mathbf{x}(0)$ cannot be written as a linear combination of these base vectors without causing $m(iT)$ to exceed the limiting value. Consequently, under such circumstances, it would take a longer time to bring the initial state $\mathbf{x}(0)$ to the equilibrium state $\mathbf{x}(nT) = \mathbf{0}$. This situation is illustrated in Example 4.2-1 and will be discussed in depth in Sec. 4.6.

In like manner, conditions for controllability in the continuous-time case may also be obtained. It can be shown that an nth-order continuous-time process characterized by $\dot{\mathbf{x}} = \mathbf{A}\mathbf{x} + \mathbf{d}m$ is completely controllable if and only if the vectors $\mathbf{d}, \mathbf{A}\mathbf{d}, \ldots, \mathbf{A}^{n-1}\mathbf{d}$ are linearly independent.[87,88]

The concept of controllability may be further clarified from a different point of view.[69] Let a linear multivariable process be characterized by the vector differential equation

$$\dot{\mathbf{x}}(t) = \mathbf{A}\mathbf{x}(t) + \mathbf{D}\mathbf{m}(t) \tag{4.4-12}$$

where $\mathbf{x}$ = an n-vector representing the state variables
$\mathbf{m}$ = an r-vector representing the control variables
$\mathbf{A}$ = the $n \times n$ coefficient matrix
$\mathbf{D}$ = the $n \times r$ driving matrix

It is shown in Sec. 2.3 that the matrix $\mathbf{A}$ may be transformed into a diagonal matrix:

$$\boldsymbol{\Lambda} = \mathbf{T}^{-1}\mathbf{A}\mathbf{T} = \begin{bmatrix} \lambda_1 & 0 & \cdots & \cdots & \cdots & 0 \\ 0 & \lambda_2 & \cdots & \cdots & \cdots & \cdots \\ \cdots & \cdots & \cdots & \cdots & \cdots & \cdots \\ \cdots & \cdots & \cdots & \lambda_i & \cdots & \cdots \\ \cdots & \cdots & \cdots & \cdots & \cdots & \cdots \\ 0 & \cdots & \cdots & \cdots & \cdots & \lambda_n \end{bmatrix} \tag{4.4-13}$$

where the λ_i denote the eigenvalues of matrix $\mathbf{A}$ of the linear process and are assumed to be distinct.

Converting Eq. (4.4-12) into the canonical form by the substitution

$$\mathbf{x} = \mathbf{T}\mathbf{z} \tag{4.4-14}$$

the result is

$$\dot{\mathbf{z}}(t) = \boldsymbol{\Lambda}\mathbf{z}(t) + \boldsymbol{\Delta}\mathbf{m}(t) \tag{4.4-15}$$

In Eq. (4.4-15), the vector $\mathbf{z}$ is referred to as the canonical state vector, and the matrix $\mathbf{\Delta}$ is given by

$$\mathbf{\Delta} = \mathbf{T}^{-1}\mathbf{D} = \begin{bmatrix} \delta_{11} & \delta_{12} & \delta_{13} & \cdots & \delta_{1r} \\ \delta_{21} & \delta_{22} & \delta_{23} & \cdots & \delta_{2r} \\ \cdots & \cdots & \cdots & \cdots & \cdots \\ \delta_{n1} & \delta_{n2} & \delta_{n2} & \cdots & \delta_{nr} \end{bmatrix} \tag{4.4-16}$$

In the preceding transformation, the eigenvalues λ_i are usually arranged in the order of increasing magnitude and the column vectors of $\mathbf{T}$ are chosen to have unit euclidean length. Two complex eigenvalues with equal magnitudes are arranged in the order of increasing angle.

Expanding Eq. (4.4-15) leads to the following set of first-order differential equations:

$$\begin{aligned} \dot{z}_1(t) &= \lambda_j z_1(t) + \sum_{k=1}^{r} \delta_{1k} m_k(t) \\ \dot{z}_2(t) &= \lambda_j z_2(t) + \sum_{k=1}^{r} \delta_{2k} m_k(t) \\ &\cdots\cdots\cdots\cdots\cdots \\ \dot{z}_j(t) &= \lambda_j z_j(t) + \sum_{k=1}^{r} \delta_{jk} m_k(t) \\ &\cdots\cdots\cdots\cdots\cdots \\ \dot{z}_n(t) &= \lambda_j z_n(t) + \sum_{k=1}^{r} \delta_{nk} m_k(t) \end{aligned} \tag{4.4-17}$$

It will be observed that the control signal m_k will have no influence upon the state variable z_j when

$$\sum_{k=1}^{r} \delta_{jk} m_k(t) = 0 \tag{4.4-18}$$

that is, when $\delta_{jk} = 0$ for $k = 1, 2, \ldots, r$. Equation (4.4-18) implies that the jth row of matrix $\mathbf{\Delta}$ is all zero. Thus the canonical state variables corresponding to zero rows of matrix $\mathbf{\Delta}$ are uncontrollable. Since all elements of these rows of $\mathbf{\Delta}$ are zero, the corresponding state variables can in no way be influenced by the control signals. In other words, the uncontrollable state variables are decoupled from the control signals. As a result, the dynamic behavior of an uncontrollable process depends only upon initial conditions and disturbance inputs. The above discussion leads to this definition of controllability: The process described by Eq. (4.4-12) is said to be controllable if the matrix $\mathbf{\Delta}$ has no rows which contain only zero elements. The state variables corresponding to nonzero rows of $\mathbf{\Delta}$ are considered controllable.

On the basis of the above definition of controllability, Gilbert derived the following general results concerning the controllability of composite systems:

1. *Cascade connection of two multivariable processes.* Shown in Fig. 4.4-1 is a composite system in which process P_a is followed by process P_b. Let the

eigenvalues of process P_a be $\lambda_{1a}, \lambda_{2a}, \ldots, \lambda_{pa}$ and the eigenvalues of process P_b be $\lambda_{1b}, \lambda_{2b}, \ldots, \lambda_{qb}$. It can be shown that:

a. The composite system is controllable if both processes P_a and P_b are controllable.

b. If processes P_a and P_b are both controllable, any uncontrollable state variables of the composite system must originate in process P_b, where the state variables are designated according to the eigenvalues of the process.

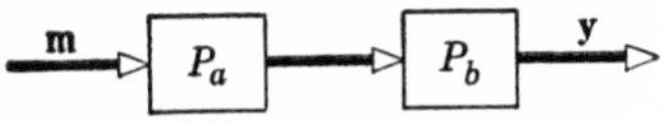

Fig. 4.4-1 Cascade connection.

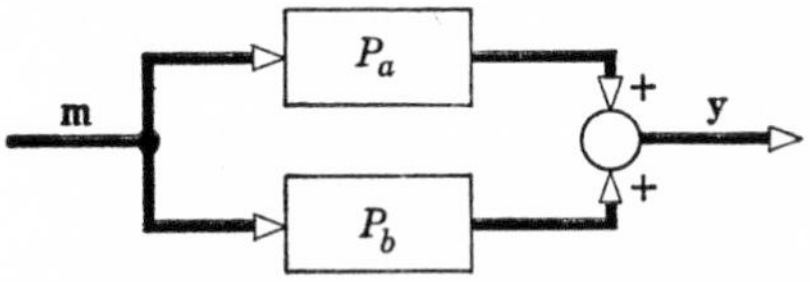

Fig. 4.4-2 Parallel connection.

2. *Parallel connection of two multivariable processes.* Shown in Fig. 4.4-2 is a composite system consisting of processes P_a and P_b connected in parallel. It can be shown that a necessary and sufficient condition for the composite system to be controllable is that both process P_a and process P_b be controllable.

3. *Feedback connection of two multivariable processes.* A feedback connection of two multivariable processes is illustrated in Fig. 4.4-3, in which process P_a is in the forward branch and process P_b is in the feedback branch. Let the cascade connection of process P_a followed by process P_b be designated by P_1 and the cascade connection of process P_b followed by process P_a be denoted by P_2. Then it can be shown that:

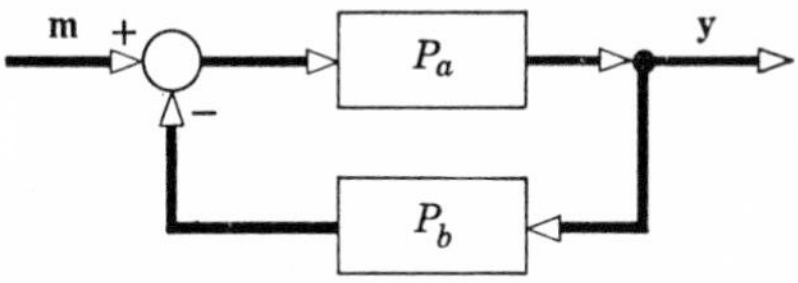

Fig. 4.4-3 Feedback connection.

a. A necessary and sufficient condition for the composite system to be controllable is that the cascaded process P_1 be controllable.

b. The composite system is controllable if both process P_a and process P_b are controllable.

c. If processes P_a and P_b are both controllable, any uncontrollable state variables of the composite system are uncontrollable state variables of process P_1 and originate in process P_b.

Regional Controllability

A process is said to be regionally controllable[146] if it is possible to take the process from some initial state $\mathbf{x}(t_0)$ to within the neighborhood of a desired equilibrium state $\mathbf{x}(t_1)$ in a finite interval of time $t_1 - t_0$. When constraints are applied to control variables $\mathbf{m}$, even though the process is considered controllable, only certain initial states $\mathbf{x}(0)$ can be brought exactly to the equilibrium state $\mathbf{x}(nT) = 0$ in n sampling periods. The concept of regional controllability is used for certain nonlinear systems in the sense that control within a neighborhood of the equilibrium state is considered satisfactory.

Observability

The output vector $\mathbf{y}$ of a linear multivariable process is described by Eq. (3.1-11) and repeated here:

$$\mathbf{y}(t) = \mathcal{B}\mathbf{x}(t) = \mathbf{Gm}(t) \tag{4.4-19}$$

where $\mathbf{y}$ = a p-vector representing the output variables
$\mathcal{B}$ = $p \times n$ output matrix
$\mathbf{G}$ = $p \times r$ transmission matrix

Let the output matrix $\mathcal{B}$ be defined by

$$\mathcal{B} = \begin{bmatrix} b_{11} & b_{12} & \cdots & b_{1n} \\ b_{21} & b_{22} & \cdots & b_{2n} \\ \cdots & \cdots & \cdots & \cdots \\ b_{p1} & b_{p2} & \cdots & b_{pn} \end{bmatrix} \tag{4.4-20}$$

and the transmission matrix $\mathbf{G}$ be defined by

$$\mathbf{G} = \begin{bmatrix} g_{11} & g_{12} & \cdots & g_{1r} \\ g_{21} & g_{22} & \cdots & g_{2r} \\ \cdots & \cdots & \cdots & \cdots \\ g_{p1} & g_{p2} & \cdots & g_{pr} \end{bmatrix} \tag{4.4-21}$$

Thus, expanding Eq. (4.4-19) yields

$$\begin{aligned} y_1(t) &= \sum_{k=1}^{n} b_{1k}x_k(t) + \sum_{j=1}^{r} g_{1j}m_j(t) \\ y_2(t) &= \sum_{k=1}^{n} b_{2k}x_k(t) + \sum_{j=1}^{r} g_{2j}m_j(t) \\ &\cdots\cdots\cdots\cdots\cdots \\ y_i(t) &= \sum_{k=1}^{n} b_{ik}x_k(t) + \sum_{j=1}^{r} g_{ij}m_j(t) \\ &\cdots\cdots\cdots\cdots\cdots \\ y_p(t) &= \sum_{k=1}^{n} b_{pk}x_k(t) + \sum_{j=1}^{r} g_{pj}m_j(t) \end{aligned} \tag{4.4-22}$$

A state variable is said to be observable if it can be determined or estimated from the measurable output variables. Examination of Eqs. (4.4-22) reveals that the state variable x_k can be determined or estimated from output variables $y_1, y_2, \ldots, y_i, \ldots, y_p$ if the coefficients b_{ik} for $i = 1, 2, \ldots, p$ are not all zero. In other words, x_k is observable if the elements of the kth column of the output matrix are not all equal to zero. If this condition is not satisfied, the state variable x_k is said to be unobservable. Thus a linear process is observable if the output matrix $\mathfrak{B}$ contains no zero columns.

4.5 TIME-OPTIMAL CONTROL FOR LINEAR DISCRETE SYSTEMS

The performance requirements of many dynamic systems, such as space vehicles, guided missiles, aircraft, and chemical processes, include optimization of the overall response to commands in order to ensure successful missions. One of the important modes of optimum control is the time-optimal control mode, which is also referred to as the minimum-time control mode. A time-optimal control system strives to reduce error and its derivatives to zero in the shortest possible time. In the operation of a batch process in the chemical industry, the major controllable costs in the application considered are labor, overhead, and apportioned plan investment. All these increase with process time so that the time required for batch is the controlling factor. Thus the optimum path is the minimum-time path. In the control of a space vehicle, the objective is to keep the vehicle on a prescribed path. If errors should occur, it is desirable to return the vehicle to the optimum trajectory in a minimum time. In general terms, the design of time-optimal control involves the determination of a control law or a control sequence so that the control process can be taken from the given initial state $\mathbf{x}(0)$ to a desired state $\mathbf{x}^d$ in minimum time. A *control law*, $m(\mathbf{x}, t)$ or $m[\mathbf{x}(kT), kT]$, is the control signal expressed as a function of the state variables of the system and possibly time. A *control function* $m(t)$ is the control signal expressed as a function of time. A *control sequence* $m(kT)$ is the control signal expressed as a function of discrete-sampling instants.

A dynamic system with lumped parameters may be described by an n-dimensional state vector $\mathbf{x}(t)$, which satisfies the differential equation

$$\dot{\mathbf{x}}(t) = \mathbf{f}[\mathbf{x}(t), \mathbf{m}(t), t] \tag{4.5-1}$$

where $\mathbf{m}(t)$ is the control function, assumed to be an r-dimensional vector, and $\mathbf{m} \in \mathbf{\Omega}$. The solutions of Eq. (4.5-1) depend upon the choice of $\mathbf{m}(t)$. If $\mathbf{x}(t)$ is a solution of Eq. (4.5-1) for a particular control function $\mathbf{m}(t)$, with initial-state vector $\mathbf{x}(0) = \mathbf{x}^0$, and if $\mathbf{x}(t_f) = \mathbf{x}^d$ for $t_f > 0$, the system is said to be taken from the initial state $\mathbf{x}^0$ to the desired state $\mathbf{x}^d$ in t_f sec. The time-optimal-control problem consists in finding an *admissible control* which transfers $\mathbf{x}^0$ to $\mathbf{x}^d$ in minimum time. In the case of linear systems or systems under linear operation, the process dynamics may be characterized by the vector-matrix differential equation

$$\dot{\mathbf{x}}(t) = \mathbf{A}\mathbf{x}(t) + \mathbf{D}\mathbf{m}(t) \tag{4.5-2}$$

where $\mathbf{A}$ denotes the coefficient matrix of the process, and $\mathbf{D}$ stands for the driving matrix. For an nth-order system subject to r control signals, $\mathbf{A}$ is an $n \times n$ matrix and $\mathbf{D}$ is an $n \times r$ matrix. This section is concerned with the determination of the control sequence and the control law for achieving time-optimal control of linear processes.

Design via Transformation of Coordinates

It has been shown in Sec. 4.3 that the transition equation for this process is given by

$$\mathbf{x}(\overline{k+1}\,T) = \boldsymbol{\phi}(T)\mathbf{x}(kT) + \mathbf{h}(T)\mathbf{m}(kT) \tag{4.5-3}$$

The optimum design makes repeated use of the transition equation and utilizes the simple fact that, if the system will reach the equilibrium state in k sampling periods, all the state variables at $t = kT$ are equal to zero.

In the following discussion, the process is assumed to be subject to a single control signal. This assumption is made for the sake of convenience in explaining the design procedure. However, as the extension of the design technique to multiple input is a relatively easy task, the minimum-time control of a second-order process is first considered. The discussion will then be generalized to minimum-time control of nth-order control processes.

1. Second-order Process. A second-order process can be characterized by two state variables, x_1 and x_2. The state vector of this process may be expressed as

$$\mathbf{x}(kT) = x_1(kT)\mathbf{u}_1 + x_2(kT)\mathbf{u}_2 \tag{4.5-4}$$

where $\mathbf{u}_1$ and $\mathbf{u}_2$ are two basis vectors.

If the process can be taken from the initial state $\mathbf{x}(0)$ to the equilibrium state in one sampling period,

$$\mathbf{x}(T) = \mathbf{0}$$

and from Eq. (4.5-3),

$$\boldsymbol{\phi}(T)\mathbf{x}(0) + \mathbf{h}(T)m(0) = \mathbf{0} \tag{4.5-5}$$

Solving for $\mathbf{x}(0)$,

$$\mathbf{x}(0) = -m(0)\boldsymbol{\phi}(-T)\mathbf{h}(T) \tag{4.5-6}$$

By defining

$$\mathbf{s}_1 = \boldsymbol{\phi}(-T)\mathbf{h}(T) \tag{4.5-7}$$

the initial-state vector $\mathbf{x}(0)$ becomes

$$\mathbf{x}(0) = -m(0)\mathbf{s}_1 \tag{4.5-8}$$

which defines a straight line in the state space. It can be observed that the process will reach the equilibrium state in one sampling period, provided $\mathbf{x}(0)$ is a one-dimensional vector. For the sake of convenience in later development, Eq. (4.5-8) is written as

$$\mathbf{x}(0) = z_1(0)\mathbf{s}_1 \tag{4.5-9}$$

where

$$z_1(0) = -m(0) \tag{4.5-10}$$

It is to be noted that the z_i's in this section have nothing to do with the z's used in Sec. 4.4.

If the process can be taken from the initial state $\mathbf{x}(0)$ to the equilibrium state in two sampling periods, it can be taken from the state $\mathbf{x}(T)$ to the equilibrium state in one sampling period. The state vector $\mathbf{x}(0)$ is a two-dimensional vector, and the state vector $\mathbf{x}(T)$ is a one-dimensional vector. Thus, by analogy with Eq. (4.5-9), $\mathbf{x}(T)$ may be expressed as

$$\mathbf{x}(T) = z_1(T)\mathbf{s}_1 \tag{4.5-11}$$

Since

$$\mathbf{x}(T) = \boldsymbol{\phi}(T)\mathbf{x}(0) + \mathbf{h}(T)m(0) \tag{4.5-12}$$

combining Eqs. (4.5-11) and (4.5-12) yields

$$\mathbf{x}(0) = z_1(T)\boldsymbol{\phi}(-2T)\mathbf{h}(T) - m(0)\boldsymbol{\phi}(-T)\mathbf{h}(T) \tag{4.5-13}$$

which may be written as

$$\mathbf{x}(0) = z_1(0)\mathbf{s}_1 + z_2(0)\mathbf{s}_2 \tag{4.5-14}$$

where $\mathbf{s}_1$ and $z_1(0)$ are defined in Eqs. (4.5-7) and (4.5-10), respectively, and

$$\mathbf{s}_2 = \boldsymbol{\phi}(-2T)\mathbf{h}(T) \tag{4.5-15}$$

$$z_2(0) = z_1(T) \tag{4.5-16}$$

Equation (4.5-10) gives the desired control signal at $t = 0$ as

$$m(0) = -z_1(0) \tag{4.5-17}$$

The above analysis transforms the state vectors $\mathbf{x}(0)$ and $\mathbf{x}(T)$ from

$$\mathbf{x}(0) = x_1(0)\mathbf{u}_1 + x_2(0)\mathbf{u}_2 \tag{4.5-18}$$

$$\mathbf{x}(T) = x_1(T)\mathbf{u}_1 + x_2(T)\mathbf{u}_2 \tag{4.5-19}$$

into

$$\mathbf{x}(0) = z_1(0)\mathbf{s}_1 + z_2(0)\mathbf{s}_2 \tag{4.5-20}$$

$$\mathbf{x}(T) = z_1(T)\mathbf{s}_1 \tag{4.5-21}$$

If $\mathbf{x}(T)$ is to be reduced to zero in one step, then

$$\mathbf{x}(2T) = \boldsymbol{\phi}(T)\mathbf{x}(T) + \mathbf{h}(T)m(T) = 0 \tag{4.5-22}$$

In view of Eq. (4.5-21),

$$\mathbf{x}(2T) = z_1(T)\boldsymbol{\phi}(T)\mathbf{s}_1 + m(T)\mathbf{h}(T) \tag{4.5-23}$$

Using Eq. (4.5-7),

$$\mathbf{x}(2T) = [z_1(T) + m(T)]\mathbf{h}(T) \tag{4.5-24}$$

Consequently, the condition for $\mathbf{x}(T)$ to be reduced to zero in one step is

$$m(T) = -z_1(T) \tag{4.5-25}$$

which is the desired control signal at $t = T$. The above analysis reveals that the desired control sequence or strategy can readily be determined if the transformations of the state vectors from Eqs. (4.5-18) and (4.5-19) to Eqs. (4.5-20) and (4.5-21) are carried out.

The determination of the control sequence is developed as follows: From the above analysis one has

$$\mathbf{s}_1 = \boldsymbol{\phi}(-T)\mathbf{h}(T)$$
$$\mathbf{s}_2 = \boldsymbol{\phi}(-2T)\mathbf{h}(T)$$

Let the basis vectors $\mathbf{s}_1$ and $\mathbf{s}_2$ be related to the basis vectors $\mathbf{u}_1$ and $\mathbf{u}_2$ by

$$\mathbf{s}_1 = a_{11}\mathbf{u}_1 + a_{12}\mathbf{u}_2 \tag{4.5-26}$$
$$\mathbf{s}_2 = a_{21}\mathbf{u}_1 + a_{22}\mathbf{u}_2 \tag{4.5-27}$$

In matrix notation, these equations may be written as

$$[\mathbf{s}] = \mathbf{P}[\mathbf{u}] \tag{4.5-28}$$

where

$$[\mathbf{s}] = \begin{bmatrix} \mathbf{s}_1 \\ \mathbf{s}_2 \end{bmatrix} \tag{4.5-29}$$

$$\mathbf{P} = \begin{bmatrix} a_{11} & a_{12} \\ a_{21} & a_{22} \end{bmatrix} \tag{4.5-30}$$

$$[\mathbf{u}] = \begin{bmatrix} \mathbf{u}_1 \\ \mathbf{u}_2 \end{bmatrix} \tag{4.5-31}$$

Equations (4.5-18) and (4.5-19) may also be written as

$$\begin{bmatrix} \mathbf{x}(0) \\ \mathbf{x}(T) \end{bmatrix} = \begin{bmatrix} x_1(0) & x_2(0) \\ x_1(T) & x_2(T) \end{bmatrix} \begin{bmatrix} \mathbf{u}_1 \\ \mathbf{u}_2 \end{bmatrix} \tag{4.5-32}$$

and similarly, Eqs. (4.5-20) and (4.5-21) can be expressed in matrix notation:

$$\begin{bmatrix} \mathbf{x}(0) \\ \mathbf{x}(T) \end{bmatrix} = \begin{bmatrix} z_1(0) & z_2(0) \\ z_1(T) & 0 \end{bmatrix} \begin{bmatrix} \mathbf{s}_1 \\ \mathbf{s}_2 \end{bmatrix} \tag{4.5-33}$$

Equating Eq. (4.5-32) to (4.5-33) and making use of Eq. (4.5-28) yields

$$\begin{bmatrix} z_1(0) & z_2(0) \\ z_1(T) & 0 \end{bmatrix} = \frac{1}{|\mathbf{P}|} \begin{bmatrix} x_1(0) & x_2(0) \\ x_1(T) & x_2(T) \end{bmatrix} \begin{bmatrix} a_{22} & -a_{12} \\ -a_{21} & a_{11} \end{bmatrix} \tag{4.5-34}$$

where the determinant $|\mathbf{P}|$ is given by

$$|\mathbf{P}| = \begin{vmatrix} a_{11} & a_{12} \\ a_{21} & a_{22} \end{vmatrix} \tag{4.5-35}$$

It follows from Eq. (4.5-34) upon expansion that

$$z_1(0) = \frac{a_{22}}{|\mathbf{P}|} x_1(0) - \frac{a_{21}}{|\mathbf{P}|} x_2(0) \tag{4.5-36}$$

$$z_1(T) = \frac{a_{22}}{|\mathbf{P}|} x_1(T) - \frac{a_{21}}{|\mathbf{P}|} x_2(T) \tag{4.5-37}$$

$$z_2(0) = -\frac{a_{12}}{|\mathbf{P}|} x_1(0) + \frac{a_{11}}{|\mathbf{P}|} x_2(0) \tag{4.5-38}$$

Thus the desired control law for minimum-time performance is given by

$$m(0) = \beta_1 x_1(0) + \beta_2 x_2(0) \qquad (4.5\text{-}39)$$

and

$$m(T) = \beta_1 x_1(T) + \beta_2 x_2(T) \qquad (4.5\text{-}40)$$

where

$$\beta_1 = -\frac{a_{22}}{|\mathbf{P}|} \qquad (4.5\text{-}41)$$

and

$$\beta_2 = \frac{a_{21}}{|\mathbf{P}|} \qquad (4.5\text{-}42)$$

The control signal $m(kT)$ expressed as a function of the state variables $x_i(kT)$ is referred to as the control law.

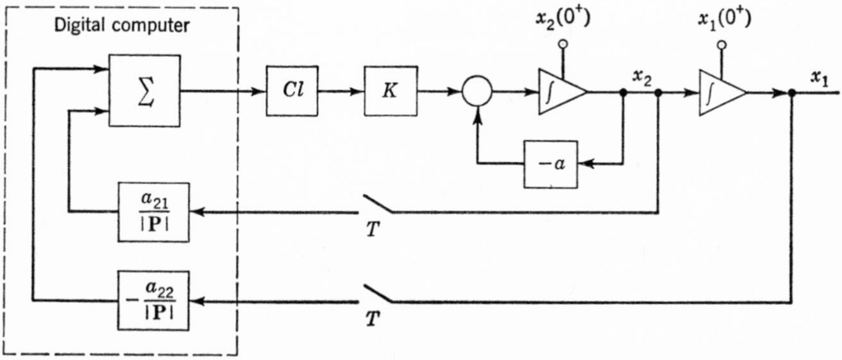

Fig. 4.5-1 Optimum control of a second-order process.

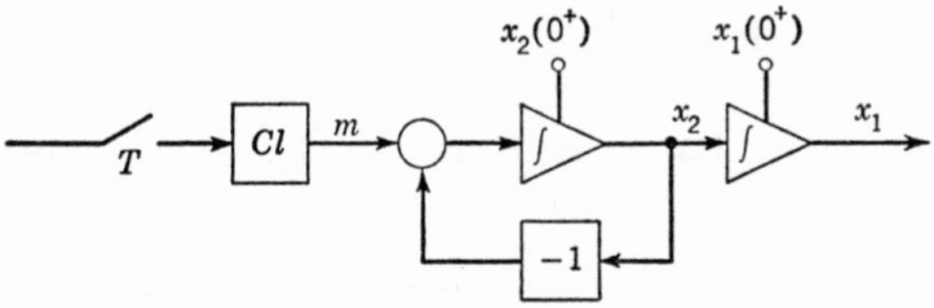

Fig. 4.5-2 State-variable diagram of a second-order process.

The state-variable diagram describing the minimum-time system is illustrated in Fig. 4.5-1. It is noted that both the state variables are fed back through time-invariant elements β_1 and β_2, respectively. This minimum-time system remains as a time-invariant system. To clarify the above development of the design technique, a numerical example is illustrated in the following paragraphs.

Example 4.5-1 A Regulator Problem

Consider the second-order process characterized by the state-variable diagram shown in Fig. 4.5-2, with initial conditions $x_1(0)$ and $x_2(0)$. The reference input is set at zero. Determine the control law required for moving the process from the given initial state $\mathbf{x}(0)$ to the equilibrium state in minimum time.

The transition matrix of the process is found to be

$$\phi(T) = \begin{bmatrix} 1 & 1 - e^{-T} \\ 0 & e^{-T} \end{bmatrix}$$

and the control transition matrix $\mathbf{h}(T)$ is

$$\mathbf{h}(T) = \begin{bmatrix} T - 1 + e^{-T} \\ 1 - e^{-T} \end{bmatrix}$$

The basis vectors $\mathbf{s}_1$ and $\mathbf{s}_2$ are readily determined from Eqs. (4.5-7) and (4.5-15). Thus

$$\mathbf{s}_1 = \begin{bmatrix} T + 1 - e^{T} \\ e^{T} - 1 \end{bmatrix}$$
$$\mathbf{s}_2 = \begin{bmatrix} T - e^{2T} + e^{T} \\ e^{2T} - e^{T} \end{bmatrix}$$

In view of Eqs. (4.5-26) and (4.5-27), the basis vectors $\mathbf{s}_1$ and $\mathbf{s}_2$ may be expressed as

$$\mathbf{s}_1 = (T + 1 - e^{T})\mathbf{u}_1 + (e^{T} - 1)\mathbf{u}_2$$
$$\mathbf{s}_2 = (T - e^{2T} + e^{T})\mathbf{u}_1 + (e^{2T} - e^{T})\mathbf{u}_2$$

Hence the $\mathbf{P}$ matrix is given by

$$\mathbf{P} = \begin{bmatrix} T + 1 - e^{T} & e^{T} - 1 \\ T - e^{2T} + e^{T} & e^{2T} - e^{T} \end{bmatrix}$$

It follows from Eqs. (4.5-39) and (4.5-40), by proper substitution, that the optimum-control law is given by

$$m^{o}(0) = \beta_1 x_1(0) + \beta_2 x_2(0)$$
$$m^{o}(T) = \beta_1 x_1(T) + \beta_2 x_2(T)$$

where the feedback coefficients are, respectively,

$$\beta_1 = \frac{e^{T}}{T(1 - e^{T})} \qquad \text{and} \qquad \beta_2 = \frac{T + e^{T} - e^{2T}}{T(1 - e^{T})^2}$$

The state-variable diagram of this control system is shown in Fig. 4.5-3.

2. nth-order Process. An nth-order process can be characterized by n state variables, $x_1, x_2, \ldots, x_n$, and the state vector $\mathbf{x}$ may be expressed in terms of n basis vectors, $\mathbf{u}_1, \mathbf{u}_2, \ldots, \mathbf{u}_n$, as

$$\mathbf{x}(kT) = x_1(kT)\mathbf{u}_1 + x_2(kT)\mathbf{u}_2 + \cdots + x_n(kT)\mathbf{u}_n \qquad (4.5\text{-}43)$$

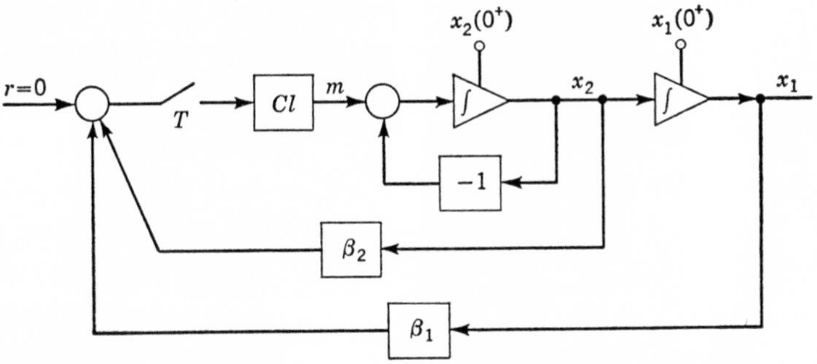

Fig. 4.5-3 Optimum control of the illustrative regulator problem.

where $k = 0, 1, 2, \ldots, n-1$. In matrix notation, one has

$$[\mathbf{x}] = \mathbf{X}[\mathbf{u}] \tag{4.5-44}$$

where
$$[\mathbf{x}] = \begin{bmatrix} \mathbf{x}(0) \\ \mathbf{x}(T) \\ \cdot \\ \cdot \\ \cdot \\ \mathbf{x}(\overline{n-1}\;T) \end{bmatrix} \tag{4.5-45}$$

$$[\mathbf{u}] = \begin{bmatrix} \mathbf{u}_1 \\ \mathbf{u}_2 \\ \cdot \\ \cdot \\ \cdot \\ \mathbf{u}_n \end{bmatrix} \tag{4.5-46}$$

and
$$\mathbf{X} = \begin{bmatrix} x_1(0) & x_2(0) & \cdots & x_n(0) \\ x_1(T) & x_2(T) & \cdots & x_n(T) \\ \cdots & \cdots & \cdots & \cdots \\ x_1(\overline{n-1}\;T) & x_2(\overline{n-1}\;T) & \cdots & x_n(\overline{n-1}\;T) \end{bmatrix} \tag{4.5-47}$$

If the nth-order process can be taken from the initial state $\mathbf{x}(0)$ to the equilibrium state $\mathbf{x}(nT) = \mathbf{0}$ in n sampling periods, the initial-state vector is an n-dimensional vector and may be written as

$$\mathbf{x}(0) = z_1(0)\mathbf{s}_1 + z_2(0)\mathbf{s}_2 + \cdots + z_n(0)\mathbf{s}_n \tag{4.5-48}$$

where $\mathbf{s}_1, \mathbf{s}_2, \ldots, \mathbf{s}_n$ are the new basis vectors. The process can be taken from state $\mathbf{x}(T)$ to the equilibrium state $\mathbf{x}(nT) = \mathbf{0}$ in $n-1$ sampling periods. Thus the state vector $\mathbf{x}(T)$ may be expressed as an $(n-1)$-dimensional vector:

$$\mathbf{x}(\mathbf{T}) = z_1(T)\mathbf{s}_1 + z_2(T)\mathbf{s}_2 + \cdots + z_{n-1}(T)\mathbf{s}_{n-1} \tag{4.5-49}$$

Since the process can be taken from state $\mathbf{x}(2T)$ to the equilibrium state $\mathbf{x}(nT) = \mathbf{0}$ in $n - 2$ sampling periods, the state vector $\mathbf{x}(2T)$ is an $(n - 2)$-dimensional vector and may be written as

$$\mathbf{x}(2T) = z_1(2T)\mathbf{s}_1 + z_2(2T)\mathbf{s}_2 + \cdots + z_{n-2}(2T)\mathbf{s}_{n-2} \tag{4.5-50}$$

In like manner, the process can be taken from state $\mathbf{x}(kT)$ to the equilibrium state $\mathbf{x}(nT) = \mathbf{0}$ in $n - k$ sampling periods, and the state vector $\mathbf{x}(kT)$ is an $(n - k)$-dimensional vector:

$$\mathbf{x}(kT) = z_1(kT)\mathbf{s}_1 + z_2(kT)\mathbf{s}_2 + \cdots + z_{n-k}(kT)\mathbf{s}_{n-k} \tag{4.5-51}$$

Since the process can be taken from the state $\mathbf{x}(\overline{n-1}\,T)$ to the equilibrium state $\mathbf{x}(nT) = \mathbf{0}$ in one sampling period, the state vector $\mathbf{x}(\overline{n-1}\,T)$ is a one-dimensional vector:

$$\mathbf{x}(\overline{n-1}\,T) = z_1(\overline{n-1}\,T)\mathbf{s}_1 \tag{4.5-52}$$

The state vectors given in Eqs. (4.5-48) to (4.5-52) may be expressed in matrix notation as

$$[\mathbf{x}] = \mathbf{Z}[\mathbf{s}] \tag{4.5-53}$$

where $[\mathbf{x}]$ is as defined in Eq. (4.5-45),

$$[\mathbf{s}] = \begin{bmatrix} \mathbf{s}_1 \\ \mathbf{s}_2 \\ \cdot \\ \cdot \\ \cdot \\ \mathbf{s}_n \end{bmatrix} \tag{4.5-54}$$

is the matrix for the new basis vector, and the matrix $\mathbf{Z}$ is a triangular matrix

$$\mathbf{Z} = \begin{bmatrix} z_1(0) & z_2(0) & z_3(0) & \cdots & z_{n-1}(0) & z_n(0) \\ z_1(T) & z_2(T) & z_3(T) & \cdots & z_{n-1}(T) & 0 \\ \cdots & \cdots & \cdots & \cdots & \cdots & \cdots \\ z_1(\overline{n-2}\,T) & z_2(\overline{n-2}\,T) & 0 & \cdots & 0 & 0 \\ z_1(\overline{n-1}\,T) & 0 & 0 & \cdots & 0 & 0 \end{bmatrix} \tag{4.5-55}$$

The elements $z_1(kT)$ of the triangular matrix $\mathbf{Z}$ are related to the control sequence $m(kT)$ for minimum-time performance by

$$m(kT) = -z_1(kT) \tag{4.5-56}$$

Since

$$\mathbf{x}(\overline{k+1}\,T) = \boldsymbol{\phi}(T)\mathbf{x}(kT) + \mathbf{h}(T)m(kT) \tag{4.5-57}$$

and for a $(k + 1)$-step process

$$\mathbf{x}(\overline{k+1}\,T) = \mathbf{0} \tag{4.5-58}$$

and

$$\mathbf{x}(kT) = z_1(kT)\mathbf{s}_1 \tag{4.5-59}$$

then

$$\boldsymbol{\phi}(T)z_1(kT)\mathbf{s}_1 + \mathbf{h}(T)m(kT) = \mathbf{0} \tag{4.5-60}$$

In view of Eq. (4.5-7), Eq. (4.5-60) reduces to

$$[z_1(kT) + m(kT)]\mathbf{h}(T) = \mathbf{0} \tag{4.5-61}$$

from which Eq. (4.5-56) follows. Consequently, when the state vector given in Eq. (4.5-44) is transformed to the expression given by Eq. (4.5-53), the control sequence for minimum-time operation is readily determined.

The validity of Eq. (4.5-51) may be demonstrated as follows: For a one-step process, $\mathbf{x}(T) = \mathbf{0}$, which implies that $m(0) = -z_1(0)$. Then

$$\mathbf{x}(0) = -m(0)\boldsymbol{\phi}(-T)\mathbf{h}(T) = z_1(0)\mathbf{s}_1 \tag{4.5-62}$$

and

$$\mathbf{Z} = z_1(0) \tag{4.5-63}$$

For a two-step process, $\mathbf{x}(2T) = \mathbf{0}$, which implies that $m(T) = -z_1(T)$. Then

$$\mathbf{x}(T) = \boldsymbol{\phi}(T)\mathbf{x}(0) + \mathbf{h}(T)m(0) = z_1(T)\mathbf{s}_1 \tag{4.5-64}$$

$$\begin{aligned}\mathbf{x}(0) &= \boldsymbol{\phi}(-T)[z_1(T)\mathbf{s}_1 - \mathbf{h}(T)m(0)] \\ &= z_1(T)\boldsymbol{\phi}(-2T)\mathbf{h}(T) - m(0)\boldsymbol{\phi}(-T)\mathbf{h}(T) \\ &= z_1(0)\mathbf{s}_1 + z_2(0)\mathbf{s}_2\end{aligned} \tag{4.5-65}$$

and

$$\mathbf{Z} = \begin{bmatrix} z_1(0) & z_2(0) \\ z_1(T) & 0 \end{bmatrix} \tag{4.5-66}$$

For a three-step process, $\mathbf{x}(3T) = \mathbf{0}$, which implies $m(2T) = z_1(2T)$. Then

$$\mathbf{x}(2T) = \boldsymbol{\phi}(T)\mathbf{x}(T) + \mathbf{h}(T)m(T) = z_1(2T)\mathbf{s}_1 \tag{4.5-67}$$

$$\begin{aligned}\mathbf{x}(T) &= \boldsymbol{\phi}(T)\mathbf{x}(0) + \mathbf{h}(T)m(0) \\ &= z_1(T)\mathbf{s}_1 + z_2(T)\mathbf{s}_2\end{aligned} \tag{4.5-68}$$

From Eq. (4.5-68),

$$\mathbf{x}(0) = \boldsymbol{\phi}(-T)[z_1(T)\boldsymbol{\phi}(-T)\mathbf{h}(T) + z_2(T)\boldsymbol{\phi}(-2T)\mathbf{h}(T) - m(0)\mathbf{h}(T)]$$

In deriving the above equation, use is made of Eqs. (4.5-7) and (4.5-15). The initial-state vector can then be written as

$$\mathbf{x}(0) = z_1(0)\mathbf{s}_1 + z_2(0)\mathbf{s}_2 + z_3(0)\mathbf{s}_3 \tag{4.5-69}$$

where

$$z_1(0) = -m(0)$$
$$z_2(0) = z_1(T)$$
$$z_3(0) = z_2(T)$$

and

$$\mathbf{s}_3 = \boldsymbol{\phi}(-3T)\mathbf{h}(T)$$

Then the $\mathbf{Z}$ matrix is given by

$$\mathbf{Z} = \begin{bmatrix} z_1(0) & z_2(0) & z_3(0) \\ z_1(T) & z_2(T) & 0 \\ z_1(2T) & 0 & 0 \end{bmatrix} \tag{4.5-70}$$

For an n-step process, $\mathbf{x}(nT) = \mathbf{0}$ implies that $m(\overline{n-1}\,T) = -z_1(\overline{n-1}\,T)$.

The following equations can easily be derived:

$$
\begin{aligned}
\mathbf{x}(\overline{n-1\ T}) &= z_1(\overline{n-1\ T})\mathbf{s}_1 \\
\mathbf{x}(\overline{n-2\ T}) &= z_1(\overline{n-2\ T})\mathbf{s}_1 + z_2(\overline{n-2\ T})\mathbf{s}_2 \\
&\cdots\cdots\cdots\cdots \\
\mathbf{x}(kT) &= z_1(kT)\mathbf{s}_1 + z_2(kT)\mathbf{s}_2 + \cdots + z_{n-k}(kT)\mathbf{s}_{n-k} \\
&\cdots\cdots\cdots\cdots \\
\mathbf{x}(0) &= z_1(0)\mathbf{s}_1 + z_2(0)\mathbf{s}_2 + \cdots + z_{n-1}(0)\mathbf{s}_{n-1} + z_n(0)\mathbf{s}_n
\end{aligned} \tag{4.5-71}
$$

where

$$\mathbf{s}_i = \boldsymbol{\phi}(-iT)\mathbf{h}(T) \tag{4.5-72}$$

The triangular matrix $\mathbf{Z}$ of Eq. (4.5-55) follows immediately from Eqs. (4.5-71). It can be shown that the elements in the major and the minor diagonals are equal; that is,

$$z_1(kT) = z_2(\overline{k-1\ T}) = z_3(\overline{k-2\ T}) = \cdots = z_{k+1}(0) \tag{4.5-73}$$

The basis vectors $[\mathbf{s}]$ are related to the basis vectors $[\mathbf{u}]$ by

$$[\mathbf{s}] = \mathbf{P}[\mathbf{u}] \tag{4.5-74}$$

where

$$\mathbf{P} = \begin{bmatrix} a_{11} & a_{12} & \cdots & a_{1n} \\ a_{21} & a_{22} & \cdots & a_{2n} \\ \cdots & \cdots & \cdots & \cdots \\ a_{n1} & a_{n2} & \cdots & a_{nn} \end{bmatrix} \tag{4.5-75}$$

Equating Eq. (4.5-44) to Eq. (4.5-53),

$$\mathbf{X}[\mathbf{u}] = \mathbf{Z}[\mathbf{s}] \tag{4.5-76}$$

Using Eq. (4.5-74),

$$\mathbf{Z}[\mathbf{s}] = \mathbf{X}\mathbf{P}^{-1}[\mathbf{s}] \tag{4.5-77}$$

Hence

$$\mathbf{Z} = \mathbf{X}\mathbf{P}^{-1} \tag{4.5-78}$$

which leads to the following n equations:

$$
\begin{aligned}
z_1(0) &= -\sum_{i=1}^{n} \beta_i x_i(0) \\
z_1(T) &= -\sum_{i=1}^{n} \beta_i x_i(T) \\
&\cdots\cdots\cdots\cdots \\
z_1(kT) &= -\sum_{i=1}^{n} \beta_i x_i(kT) \\
&\cdots\cdots\cdots\cdots \\
z_1(\overline{n-1\ T}) &= -\sum_{i=1}^{n} \beta_i x_i(\overline{n-1\ T})
\end{aligned} \tag{4.5-79}
$$

where β_i are functions of the elements of $\mathbf{P}$ matrix. Since the control signals are related to $z_i(kT)$ by Eq. (4.5-56), the control law for minimum-time performance is given by

$$m(kT) = \boldsymbol{\beta}\mathbf{x}(kT) \tag{4.5-80}$$

where $\boldsymbol{\beta}$, often referred to as the feedback matrix, is the row matrix

$$\boldsymbol{\beta} = [\beta_1 \quad \beta_2 \quad \beta_3 \quad \cdots \quad \beta_n]$$

and $\mathbf{x}(kT)$ is the column vector

$$\mathbf{x}(kT) = \begin{bmatrix} x_1(kT) \\ x_2(kT) \\ \cdot \\ \cdot \\ \cdot \\ x_n(kT) \end{bmatrix}$$

The result is a feedback control system with all the advantages which accrue from such operation.

An Iterative Design Procedure

1. Single-input Process. The optimum-control sequence for minimum-time performance may be derived in a simple, straightforward manner as follows: The state-transition equation for the nth-order process is

$$\mathbf{x}(\overline{k+1}\ T) = \boldsymbol{\phi}(T)\mathbf{x}(kT) + \mathbf{h}(T)m(kT) \tag{4.5-81}$$

where $\mathbf{x}$ is an $n \times 1$ vector. For $k = 0$, Eq. (4.5-81) reduces to

$$\mathbf{x}(T) = \boldsymbol{\phi}(T)\mathbf{x}(0) + \mathbf{h}(T)m(0)$$

which is a function of the initial-state vector $\mathbf{x}(0)$ and the initial control signal $m(0)$ and may be expressed as

$$\mathbf{x}(T) = \mathbf{f}_1[\mathbf{x}(0); m(0)] \tag{4.5-82}$$

For $k = 1$,

$$\begin{aligned} \mathbf{x}(2T) &= \boldsymbol{\phi}(T)\mathbf{x}(T) + \mathbf{h}(T)m(T) \\ &= \boldsymbol{\phi}(2T)\mathbf{x}(0) + \boldsymbol{\phi}(T)\mathbf{h}(T)m(0) + \mathbf{h}(T)m(T) \end{aligned}$$

which may be written as

$$\mathbf{x}(2T) = \mathbf{f}_2[\mathbf{x}(0); m(0), m(T)] \tag{4.5-83}$$

and for $k = n - 1$,

$$\mathbf{x}(nT) = \boldsymbol{\phi}(T)\mathbf{x}(\overline{n-1}\ T) + \mathbf{h}(T)m(\overline{n-1}\ T) \tag{4.5-84}$$

By successive elimination, $\mathbf{x}(nT)$ may be expressed as a linear function of the initial-state vector $\mathbf{x}(0)$ and the successive control signals $m(0)$, $m(T)$,

$\ldots, m(\overline{n-1}\,T)$; that is,

$$\mathbf{x}(nT) = \boldsymbol{\phi}(nT)\mathbf{x}(0) + \sum_{i=0}^{n-1} \boldsymbol{\phi}(iT)\mathbf{h}(T)m(\overline{n-1-i}\,T) \qquad (4.5\text{-}85a)$$

$$\mathbf{x}(nT) = \mathbf{f}_n[\mathbf{x}(0); m(0), m(T), \ldots, m(\overline{n-1}\,T)] \qquad (4.5\text{-}85b)$$

Since, for minimum-time control of the nth-order process, $\mathbf{x}(nT)$ is a null vector,

$$\mathbf{f}_n[\mathbf{x}(0); m(0), m(T), \ldots, m(\overline{n-1}\,T)] = \mathbf{0} \qquad (4.5\text{-}86)$$

This condition leads to n simultaneous equations in $m(kT)$, $k = 0, 1, 2, \ldots, n-1$. Solving these n simultaneous equations for $m(kT)$ in terms of $x_k(0)$ yields the control sequence

$$m(kT) = F_k[x_1(0), x_2(0), \ldots, x_n(0)] \qquad (4.5\text{-}87)$$

Clearly, this design procedure is quite simple. It turns out to be particularly well adapted for programming on a digital computer. The design consists mainly of the solution of n linear algebraic equations. This procedure can be extended to the design of saturating discrete systems, as discussed in Sec. 4.6.

The use of the state-transition equation and the optimum-control sequence is sufficient to predict the entire future evolution of the process. However, because of tolerance in manufacture, parameter variations due to aging, inaccurate knowledge of the plant transition matrix, unknown disturbances acting on the process, and other possible random effects of various kinds, the prediction based upon the state-transition equation will become less and less correct as the prediction interval increases. By remeasuring the state variables of the system at successive sampling instants, the prediction errors are corrected and the control variables will assume very nearly optimum values at all times. A small sampling period is chosen so that the one-step prediction based upon the state-transition equation is sufficiently correct. This mode of operation results in a feedback control system.

Expressing $x_i(0)$ in terms of $x_i(kT)$ by proper substitution yields the optimum-control law

$$m^o(kT) = \boldsymbol{\beta}\mathbf{x}(kT) \qquad (4.5\text{-}88)$$

where the feedback matrix $\boldsymbol{\beta}$ and the state vector $\mathbf{x}(kT)$ are as previously defined. The design of minimum-time control by use of the alternative approach is illustrated by the following numerical example.

Example 4.5-2 A Regulator Problem

Consider the same problem as in Example 4.5-1. Determine the desired control sequence by use of the iterative approach discussed above.

The design is initiated with the state-transition equation

$$\mathbf{x}(\overline{k+1}\,T) = \boldsymbol{\phi}(T)\mathbf{x}(kT) + \mathbf{h}(T)m(kT)$$

where the transition matrix of the process is

$$\boldsymbol{\phi}(T) = \begin{bmatrix} 1 & 1 - e^{-T} \\ 0 & e^{-T} \end{bmatrix}$$

and the control transition matrix $\mathbf{h}(T)$ is

$$\mathbf{h}(T) = \begin{bmatrix} T - 1 + e^{-T} \\ 1 - e^{-T} \end{bmatrix}$$

For $k = 0$,

$$\mathbf{x}(T) = \boldsymbol{\phi}(T)\mathbf{x}(0) + \mathbf{h}(T)m(0)$$

which leads to

$$\begin{aligned} x_1(T) &= x_1(0) + (1 - e^{-T})x_2(0) + (T - 1 + e^{-T})m(0) \\ x_2(T) &= e^{-T}x_2(0) + (1 - e^{-T})m(0) \end{aligned}$$

For $k = 1$,

$$\mathbf{x}(2T) = \boldsymbol{\phi}(T)\mathbf{x}(0) + \mathbf{h}(T)m(T)$$

which yields, upon expansion,

$$\begin{aligned} x_1(2T) &= x_1(T) + (1 - e^{-T})x_2(T) + (T - 1 + e^{-T})m(T) \\ x_2(2T) &= e^{-T}x_2(T) + (1 - e^{-T})m(T) \end{aligned}$$

By proper substitution, the above two equations reduce to

$$\begin{aligned} x_1(2T) &= x_1(0) + (1 - e^{-2T})x_2(0) + (T - e^{-T} + e^{-2T})m(0) \\ &\qquad + (T - 1 + e^{-T})m(T) \\ x_2(2T) &= e^{-2T}x_2(0) + (e^{-T} - e^{-2T})m(0) + (1 - e^{-T})m(T) \end{aligned}$$

Since, for minimum-time control, $\mathbf{x}(2T)$ is a null vector,

$$\begin{aligned} x_1(0) + (1 - e^{-2T})x_2(0) + (T - e^{-T} + e^{-2T})m(0) & \\ + (T - 1 + e^{-T})m(T) &= 0 \\ e^{-2T}x_2(0) + (e^{-T} - e^{-2T})m(0) + (1 - e^{-T})m(T) &= 0 \end{aligned}$$

Solving for $m(0)$ and $m(T)$,

$$m(0) = \beta_1 x_1(0) + \beta_2 x_2(0)$$

and

$$m(T) = \beta_1 x_1(T) + \beta_2 x_2(T)$$

or the control law may be expressed as

$$m(k) = \boldsymbol{\beta}\mathbf{x}(kT) \qquad k = 0, 1$$

where $\boldsymbol{\beta}$ is the row matrix with elements given by

$$\beta_1 = \frac{e^T}{T(1 - e^T)} \qquad \text{and} \qquad \beta_2 = \frac{T + e^T - e^{2T}}{T(1 - e^T)^2}$$

This result agrees with the solution obtained in Example 4.5-1.

2. Multi-input Process. The preceding design technique can be extended to multi-input systems. Consider an nth-order process subject to r control inputs, which is characterized by the state-transition equation

$$\mathbf{x}(\overline{k+1}\,T) = \boldsymbol{\phi}(T)\mathbf{x}(kT) + \mathbf{h}(T)\mathbf{m}(kT) \tag{4.5-89}$$

where $\mathbf{m}$ is an r-vector representing the control signals, and matrix $\mathbf{h}$ is an $n \times r$ matrix. Assume that the process can be taken from the initial state $\mathbf{x}(0)$ to the equilibrium state in p sampling periods. Then $\mathbf{x}(pT) = \mathbf{0}$, and from Eq. (4.5-85$a$),

$$\boldsymbol{\phi}(pT)\mathbf{x}(0) + \sum_{i=1}^{p} \boldsymbol{\phi}(\overline{p-i}\,T)\mathbf{h}(T)\mathbf{m}(\overline{i-1}\,T) = \mathbf{0} \tag{4.5-90}$$

Transposing the second term to the right and postmultiplying both members by $\boldsymbol{\phi}^{-1}(pT)$ yields

$$\mathbf{x}(0) = -\sum_{i=1}^{p} \mathbf{s}_i\mathbf{m}(\overline{i-1}\,T) \tag{4.5-91}$$

where

$$\mathbf{s}_i = \boldsymbol{\phi}(-iT)\mathbf{h}(T) \tag{4.5-92}$$

is an $n \times r$ matrix. It is to be noted that $r \times p = n$, and the minimum number of steps for the process to reach equilibrium is equal to the ratio n/r.

Equation (4.5-91) may be expressed as

$$\mathbf{x}(0) = -\mathbf{S}\begin{bmatrix} \mathbf{m}(0) \\ \mathbf{m}(1) \\ \cdot \\ \cdot \\ \cdot \\ \mathbf{m}(p-1) \end{bmatrix} \tag{4.5-93}$$

where the sampling period T is dropped and the matrix

$$\mathbf{S} = [\mathbf{s}_1 \quad \mathbf{s}_2 \quad \cdots \quad \mathbf{s}_p] \tag{4.5-94}$$

is an $n \times n$ matrix since $r \times p = n$. Matrix manipulation reduces Eq. (4.5-93) to

$$\begin{bmatrix} \mathbf{m}(0) \\ \mathbf{m}(1) \\ \cdot \\ \cdot \\ \cdot \\ \mathbf{m}(p-1) \end{bmatrix} = \mathbf{B}\mathbf{x}(0) \tag{4.5-95}$$

where $\mathbf{B}$ is an $n \times n$ matrix given by

$$\mathbf{B} = -\mathbf{S}^{-1} = \begin{bmatrix} \mathbf{B}_1 \\ \mathbf{B}_2 \\ \cdot \\ \cdot \\ \cdot \\ \mathbf{B}_j \\ \cdot \\ \cdot \\ \cdot \\ \mathbf{B}_p \end{bmatrix} \tag{4.5-96}$$

It should be noted that the $\mathbf{B}$ matrix here is different from the $\mathbf{B}$ matrix defined in Chap. 3.

In the above expression, all $\mathbf{B}_j$ are $r \times n$ matrices. Thus the control vectors are given by

$$\begin{aligned} \mathbf{m}(0) &= \mathbf{B}_1\mathbf{x}(0) \\ \mathbf{m}(1) &= \mathbf{B}_2\mathbf{x}(0) \\ &\cdots\cdots\cdots \\ \mathbf{m}(j) &= \mathbf{B}_{j+1}\mathbf{x}(0) \\ &\cdots\cdots\cdots\cdots \\ \mathbf{m}(p-1) &= \mathbf{B}_p\mathbf{x}(0) \end{aligned} \tag{4.5-97}$$

The feedback matrices $\mathbf{B}_j$ are readily determined from the inverse matrix $\mathbf{S}^{-1}$ by partitioning. Matrix $\mathbf{B}_1$ is formed from the first r rows of matrix $\mathbf{S}^{-1}$; matrix $\mathbf{B}_2$ is formed from the second r rows of $\mathbf{S}^{-1}$; and matrix $\mathbf{B}_j$ is comprised of the jth r rows of $\mathbf{S}^{-1}$.

If the process can be taken from the initial state $\mathbf{x}(0)$ to the equilibrium state in p sampling periods, it can be taken from the state $\mathbf{x}(T)$ to the equilibrium state in $p-1$ sampling periods. Then it follows, from Eq. (4.5-90), that

$$\boldsymbol{\phi}(\overline{p-1\ T})\mathbf{x}(T) + \sum_{i=1}^{p-1} \boldsymbol{\phi}(\overline{p-i-1\ T})\mathbf{h}(T)\mathbf{m}(iT) = \mathbf{0} \tag{4.5-98}$$

Transposing the second term to the right and postmultiplying both members by $\boldsymbol{\phi}^{-1}(\overline{p-1\ T})$ yields

$$\mathbf{x}(T) = -\sum_{i=1}^{p-1} \mathbf{s}_i\mathbf{m}(iT) \tag{4.5-99}$$

where $\mathbf{s}_i$ is defined in Eq. (4.5-92). Since $\mathbf{m}(p) = \mathbf{0}$, Eq. (4.5-99) may be written as

$$\mathbf{x}(T) = -\mathbf{S}\begin{bmatrix} \mathbf{m}(T) \\ \mathbf{m}(2T) \\ \cdot \\ \cdot \\ \cdot \\ \mathbf{m}(pT) \end{bmatrix} \tag{4.5-100}$$

Matrix $\mathbf{S}$ is defined in Eq. (4.5-94). Postmultiplying both members of Eq. (4.5-100) by $-\mathbf{S}^{-1}$ yields

$$\begin{bmatrix} \mathbf{m}(T) \\ \mathbf{m}(2T) \\ \cdot \\ \cdot \\ \cdot \\ \mathbf{m}(pT) \end{bmatrix} = \mathbf{B}\mathbf{x}(T) \tag{4.5-101}$$

where $\mathbf{B}$ is as defined in Eq. (4.5-96). Hence

$$\mathbf{m}(T) = \mathbf{B}_1\mathbf{x}(T) \tag{4.5-102}$$

In like manner, it can readily be shown that

$$\mathbf{m}(2T) = \mathbf{B}_1\mathbf{x}(2T) \tag{4.5-103}$$

and

$$\mathbf{m}(kT) = \mathbf{B}_1\mathbf{x}(kT) \tag{4.5-104}$$

which describes the control law for minimum-time control. Matrix $\mathbf{B}_1$ is the feedback matrix for time-optimal control. The application of this design technique is best understood by means of illustrative examples.

Example 4.5-3 A Multi-input, Multioutput Control Process

Consider a multi-input, multioutput process characterized by the transfer matrix

$$\mathbf{G}(s) = \begin{bmatrix} \dfrac{1}{s+2} & \dfrac{1}{s+1} \\ \dfrac{1}{s+1} & \dfrac{1}{s} \end{bmatrix}$$

Design a digital controller so that the process may be taken from the given initial state $\mathbf{x}(0)$ to the equilibrium state in the shortest time.

Shown in Fig. 4.5-4 is the state-variable diagram of the system. The plant transition matrix is found to be

$$\boldsymbol{\phi}(T) = \begin{bmatrix} \alpha^2 & 0 & 0 & 0 \\ 0 & \alpha & 0 & 0 \\ 0 & 0 & \alpha & 0 \\ 0 & 0 & 0 & 1 \end{bmatrix}$$

and the control transition matrix is

$$\mathbf{h}(T) = \begin{bmatrix} 1-\alpha^2 & 0 \\ 1-\alpha & 0 \\ 0 & 1-\alpha \\ 0 & T \end{bmatrix}$$

where $\alpha = e^{-T}$ and T is the sampling period. Since there are four state variables and two control inputs, the system can be made to reach the

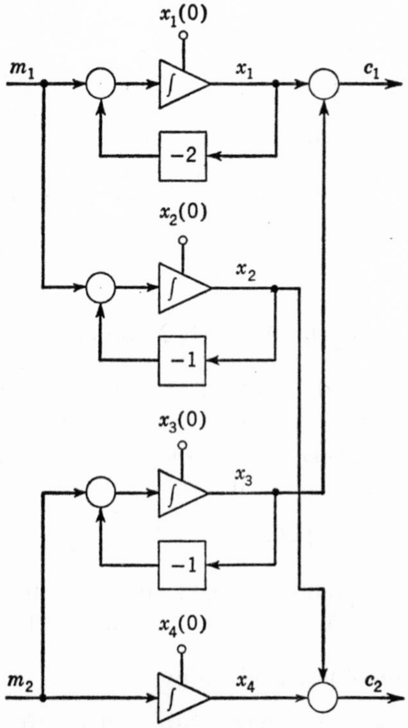

Fig. 4.5-4 State-variable diagram for the system in Example 4.5-3.

equilibrium state in two sampling periods and $\mathbf{x}(2T) = \mathbf{0}$. Thus the $\mathbf{S}$ matrix is given by

$$\mathbf{S} = [\mathbf{s}_1 \quad \mathbf{s}_2]$$

where
$$\mathbf{s}_1 = \boldsymbol{\phi}(-T)\mathbf{h}(T) = \begin{bmatrix} \alpha^{-2}-1 & 0 \\ \alpha^{-1}-1 & 0 \\ 0 & \alpha^{-1}-1 \\ 0 & T \end{bmatrix}$$

and
$$\mathbf{s}_2 = \boldsymbol{\phi}(-2T)\mathbf{h}(T) = \begin{bmatrix} \alpha^{-2}(\alpha^{-2}-1) & 0 \\ \alpha^{-1}(\alpha^{-1}-1) & 0 \\ 0 & \alpha^{-1}(\alpha^{-1}-1) \\ 0 & T \end{bmatrix}$$

When the values of $\mathbf{s}_1$ and $\mathbf{s}_2$ are substituted into matrix $\mathbf{S}$, the result is

$$\mathbf{S} = \begin{bmatrix} \alpha^{-2}-1 & 0 & \alpha^{-2}(\alpha^{-2}-1) & 0 \\ \alpha^{-1}-1 & 0 & \alpha^{-1}(\alpha^{-1}-1) & 0 \\ 0 & \alpha^{-1}-1 & 0 & \alpha^{-1}(\alpha^{-1}-1) \\ 0 & T & 0 & T \end{bmatrix}$$

The $\mathbf{B}$ matrix is then given by

$$\mathbf{B} = -\mathbf{S}^{-1} = \begin{bmatrix} \dfrac{\alpha^3}{(1-\alpha^2)(1-\alpha)} & \dfrac{\alpha}{(1-\alpha)^2} & 0 & 0 \\ 0 & 0 & \dfrac{\alpha^2}{(1-\alpha)^2} & \dfrac{1}{T(1-\alpha)} \\ -\dfrac{\alpha^4}{(1-\alpha)^2(1-\alpha)} & \dfrac{\alpha^3}{(1-\alpha)^2} & 0 & 0 \\ 0 & 0 & -\dfrac{\alpha^2}{(1-\alpha)^2} & \dfrac{\alpha^2}{T(1-\alpha)^2} \end{bmatrix}$$

Assuming that $T = 1$ sec, the $\mathbf{B}$ matrix is found to be

$$\mathbf{B} = \begin{bmatrix} 0.091 & -0.92 & 0 & 0 \\ 0 & 0 & 0.338 & -1.58 \\ -0.0334 & 0.1245 & 0 & 0 \\ 0 & 0 & -0.338 & 0.338 \end{bmatrix}$$

Hence the feedback matrix $\mathbf{B}_1$ is

$$\mathbf{B}_1 = \begin{bmatrix} 0.091 & -0.92 & 0 & 0 \\ 0 & 0 & 0.338 & -1.58 \end{bmatrix}$$

and the optimum-control law is given by

$$\begin{aligned} m_1{}^o(0) &= 0.091x_1(0) - 0.92x_2(0) \\ m_2{}^o(0) &= 0.338x_3(0) - 1.58x_4(0) \\ m_1{}^o(1) &= 0.091x_1(1) - 0.92x_2(1) \\ m_2{}^o(1) &= 0.338x_3(1) - 1.58x_4(1) \end{aligned}$$

This example points out that the optimum-control signal $m_1{}^o$ is a linear function of state variables x_1 and x_2, and the optimum-control signal $m_2{}^o$ is a linear function of state variables x_3 and x_4. The control system will reach the equilibrium state in two sampling periods.

Now, if it is desired that the output variables reach the equilibrium state in the shortest time, it is demonstrable that this can be done in one sampling period. Since the output variables and the state variables are related by

$$c_1 = x_1 + x_3 \qquad \text{and} \qquad c_2 = x_2 + x_4$$

their relationship may be expressed in matrix notation as

$$\mathbf{c} = \mathbf{M}\mathbf{x}$$

where
$$\mathbf{M} = \begin{bmatrix} 1 & 0 & 1 & 0 \\ 0 & 1 & 0 & 1 \end{bmatrix}$$

At $k = 0$, the state-transition equation is

$$\mathbf{x}(T) = \boldsymbol{\phi}(T)\mathbf{x}(0) + \mathbf{h}(T)\mathbf{m}(0)$$

Then the output vector $\mathbf{c}(T)$ is given by

$$\mathbf{c}(T) = \mathbf{M}[\boldsymbol{\phi}(T)\mathbf{x}(0) + \mathbf{h}(T)\mathbf{m}(0)]$$

If the output variables can reach the equilibrium state in one sampling period, $\mathbf{c}(T) = \mathbf{0}$ and

$$\mathbf{M}[\boldsymbol{\phi}(T)\mathbf{x}(0) + \mathbf{h}(T)\mathbf{m}(0)] = \mathbf{0}$$

Thus the control vector is

$$\mathbf{m}(0) = -[\mathbf{M}\mathbf{h}(T)]^{-1}\mathbf{M}\boldsymbol{\phi}(T)\mathbf{x}(0)$$

provided that the matrix $[\mathbf{M}\mathbf{h}(T)]$ is nonsingular.

Assuming $T = 1$ sec and evaluating the matrices yields

$$[\mathbf{M}\mathbf{h}(T)]^{-1} = \begin{bmatrix} 2.15 & -1.36 \\ -1.36 & 1.86 \end{bmatrix}$$

and
$$\mathbf{M}\boldsymbol{\phi}(T) = \begin{bmatrix} 0.135 & 0 & 0.368 & 0 \\ 0 & 0.368 & 0 & 1 \end{bmatrix}$$

Hence the optimum-control law is given by

$$m_1^o(0) = -0.29x_1(0) + 0.501x_2(0) - 0.791x_3(0) + 1.36x_4(0)$$
$$m_2^o(0) = 0.174x_1(0) - 0.684x_2(0) + 0.501x_3(0) - 1.86x_4(0)$$

It should be observed that this system requires the feedback of all the state variables to both input channels. In this way the output variables can be made to reach the equilibrium state from the given initial state in one sampling period.

Example 4.5-4 A Turboprop-engine Control System

Consider the design of digital controls for a turboprop-engine control system. The variables of the operation of such an engine are the speed of rotation, the turbine-inlet temperature, the propeller-blade angle, and the fuel rate. The control system has to be designed for various possible steady-state normal operating conditions. For each steady-state operating condition, the control performance in nonsteady states near that particular operating point is investigated. The assumed transfer characteristic for the plant is shown in Fig. 4.5-5. The control signals are the deviation of the propeller-blade angle and the deviation of fuel rate. The controlled output signals are the engine speed and the turbine-inlet temperature. Determine the optimum-control law for the system to reach the equilibrium state from the given initial state $\mathbf{x}(0)$ in minimum time.

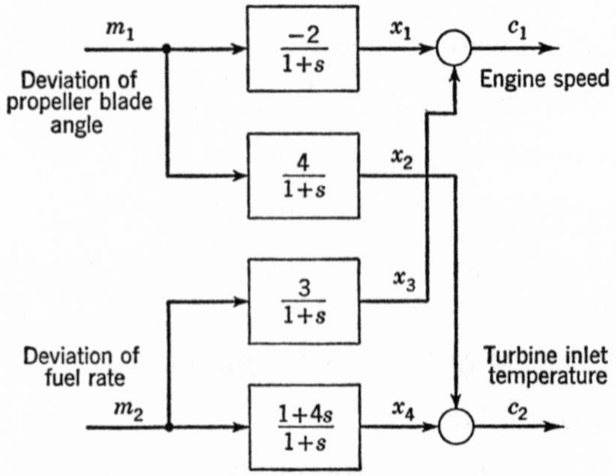

Fig. 4.5-5 Block diagram of a simplified turboprop-engine control system.

From the state-variable diagram of this system are obtained, by inspection, the plane transition matrix

$$\phi(T) = \begin{bmatrix} \alpha & 0 & 0 & 0 \\ 0 & \alpha & 0 & 0 \\ 0 & 0 & \alpha & 0 \\ 0 & 0 & 0 & -\frac{\alpha}{3} \end{bmatrix}$$

and the control transition matrix

$$\mathbf{h}(T) = \begin{bmatrix} -2(1-\alpha) & 0 \\ 4(1-\alpha) & 0 \\ 0 & 3(1-\alpha) \\ 0 & 1+3\alpha \end{bmatrix}$$

where $\alpha = e^{-T}$ and T is the sampling period. The state-transition equation at $k = 0$ is

$$\mathbf{x}(T) = \phi(T)\mathbf{x}(0) + \mathbf{h}(T)\mathbf{m}(0)$$

Since the output vector $\mathbf{c}$ and the state vector $\mathbf{x}$ are related by the matrix equation

$$\mathbf{c} = \mathbf{M}\mathbf{x}$$

where
$$\mathbf{M} = \begin{bmatrix} 1 & 0 & 1 & 0 \\ 0 & 1 & 0 & 1 \end{bmatrix}$$

postmultiplying the state-transition equation by $\mathbf{M}$ gives

$$\mathbf{c}(T) = \mathbf{M}[\boldsymbol{\phi}(T)\mathbf{x}(0) + \mathbf{h}(T)\mathbf{m}(0)]$$

If the output variables can reach the equilibrium state in one sampling period, $\mathbf{c}(T) = \mathbf{0}$, and this leads to the control vector

$$\mathbf{m}(0) = -[\mathbf{Mh}(T)]^{-1}\mathbf{M}\boldsymbol{\phi}(T)\mathbf{x}(0)$$

provided that the matrix $[\mathbf{Mh}(T)]$ is nonsingular. The substitution of proper values yields the inverse matrix

$$[\mathbf{Mh}(T)]^{-1} = \begin{bmatrix} -\dfrac{1+3\alpha}{2(1-\alpha)(7-3\alpha)} & \dfrac{3}{2(7-3\alpha)} \\ \dfrac{2}{7-3\alpha} & \dfrac{1}{7-3\alpha} \end{bmatrix}$$

Hence the optimum-control law is

$$\mathbf{m}^o(0) = -\frac{\alpha}{7-3\alpha}\begin{bmatrix} -\dfrac{1+3\alpha}{2(1-\alpha)} & 1.5 & -\dfrac{1+3\alpha}{2(1-\alpha)} & -4.5 \\ 2 & 1 & 2 & -3 \end{bmatrix}\mathbf{x}(0)$$

Assuming $T = 1$ sec, the optimum-control signals are given by

$$m_1{}^o(0) = 0.104x_1(0) - 0.0938x_2(0) + 0.104x_3(0) + 0.281x_4(0)$$
$$m_2{}^o(0) = -0.125x_1(0) - 0.625x_2(0) - 0.125x_3(0) + 0.187x_4(0)$$

This optimum-control system requires the feedback of all the state variables to both input channels in order to generate the optimum-control law.

4.6 TIME-OPTIMAL CONTROL FOR SATURATING DISCRETE SYSTEMS

In the preceding sections the control strategy for minimum-time control of linear processes is determined. A linear nth-order process can be taken from a specified initial state $\mathbf{x}(0)$ to the equilibrium state in n sampling periods. When the control signals are subject to saturation, the desired forcing effort applied to the process is restricted by the saturation limit. It is conceivable that, in the presence of control-signal saturation, the minimum time required to take an nth-order process from an initial state $\mathbf{x}(0)$ to the equilibrium state would be longer than nT. To obtain minimum-time response generally requires a full amount of energy to be applied to the control process at the successive sampling instants, but the presence of saturation constraint on the control signal would prevent the application of full energy at certain sampling instants. As a result, it would take a longer time for the process with saturation to reach the equilibrium state.

The design technique described in Sec. 4.5 can be extended to the optimum design of discrete systems with saturation after some fundamental geometrical aspects of saturation are investigated.[141]

Assume that the control sequence for time-optimal control of an nth-order process without saturation is represented by the set

$$M = \{m(kT)\} \tag{4.6-1}$$

where $k = 0, 1, 2, \ldots, (n-1)T$. This set of control sequence may be viewed as the mutually orthogonal axes constituting an n-dimensional euclidean space E^n, which may be referred to as the *control space* of the system. The origin of this n-dimensional control space represents the equilibrium state of the control process. For instance, if the time-optimal control will take two sampling periods, the control space is a two-dimensional space with mutually orthogonal axes $m(0)$ and $m(T)$; if the time-optimal control will take three sampling periods, the control space is a

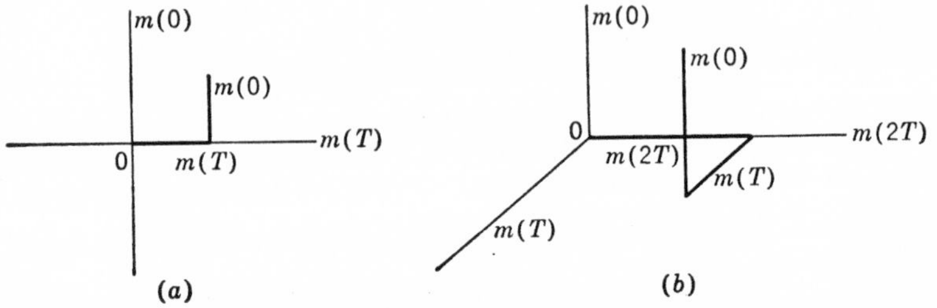

Fig. 4.6-1 (*a*) Two-dimensional control space; (*b*) three-dimensional control space.

three-dimensional space with mutually orthogonal axes $m(0)$, $m(T)$, $m(2T)$. Starting with the initial control signal $m(0)$ determined from the specified initial-state vector $\mathbf{x}(0)$, the process will reach the origin in n steps. Each control step of the optimum strategy will reduce the dimension of the control space by 1. After n consecutive steps, the origin of the control space is reached. Figure 4.6-1 illustrates this operation for a two-dimensional and a three-dimensional control space.

When the control signal is subject to saturation such that

$$|m(kT)| \leq 1 \tag{4.6-2}$$

it may happen that some of the control steps determined under the assumption of no saturation will exceed the saturation limit. These saturated steps may not be able to reduce the dimension of the control space. Consequently, based upon the above geometrical visualization, it would take more steps for the saturated system to reach the equilibrium state. Saturation limitation of the more general form

$$|m_i(kT)| \leq \alpha_i \qquad i = 1, 2, \ldots, r \tag{4.6-3}$$

can be normalized to the form of Eq. (4.6-2) if $m_i(t)$ is replaced by $m_i(t)/\alpha_i$ and the matrix $\mathbf{D}$ is replaced by $\mathbf{D}[\alpha_i]$, where $[\alpha_i]$ is the diagonal matrix

$$[\alpha_i] = \begin{bmatrix} \alpha_1 & 0 & \cdots & 0 \\ 0 & \alpha_2 & \cdots & 0 \\ \cdot & \cdot & \cdots & \cdot \\ 0 & 0 & \cdots & \alpha_r \end{bmatrix} \tag{4.6-4}$$

The control signal constrained by Eq. (4.6-2) may be represented by the set

$$M = \{[m(k)]: |m(k)| \leq 1,\ k = 0, 1, 2, \ldots, n-1\} \tag{4.6-5}$$

which describes the set of points lying inside and on the hypercube with its center located at the origin of the control space.

In Eq. (4.6-5), the sampling period T is dropped for the sake of convenience. For a two-dimensional control space, the saturation-constrained control set is given by

$$M = \{[m(0), m(1)]: |m(0)| \leq 1,\ |m(1)| \leq 1\} \tag{4.6-6}$$

which describes a unit square with center at the origin, as illustrated in Fig. 4.6-2. For a three-dimensional control space, the saturation-constrained control set is given by

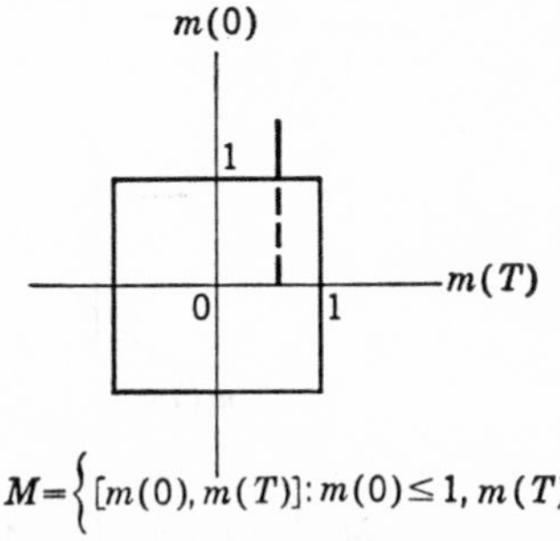

Fig. 4.6-2 Saturation square in a two-dimensional control space.

$$M = \{[m(0), m(1), m(2)]: |m(0)| \leq 1,\ |m(1)| \leq 1,\ |m(2)| \leq 1\} \tag{4.6-7}$$

which describes a unit cube with center at the origin, as shown in Fig. 4.6-3. The set of control sequence given in Eq. (4.6-5) forms the admissible set. If all the desired control signals $m(k)$ lie inside the hypercube, the saturation limit can be ignored and the control process will reach the equilibrium state in n sampling periods. If the control signal exceeds the saturation limit, the corresponding control step should be broken into smaller steps equal to or smaller than the saturation limit. Under such situations, the minimum response time will be prolonged as illustrated in Figs. 4.6-2 and 4.6-3 for the two-dimensional and the three-dimensional cases. Since a large control step can be broken into smaller steps in an infinite number of ways, there exist an infinity of optimal solutions to this control problem.

Now assume that, in the presence of saturation, the nth-order control process will reach the equilibrium state in $n + q$ sampling periods, where $q \geq 0$. It follows from Eq. (4.5-85a) that

$$\boldsymbol{\phi}(\overline{n + q}\ T)\mathbf{x}(0) + \sum_{i=0}^{n+q-1} \boldsymbol{\phi}(iT)\mathbf{h}(T)m(\overline{n + q - i - 1}\ T) = \mathbf{0} \qquad (4.6\text{-}8)$$

which yields, upon premultiplying by $\boldsymbol{\phi}(-\overline{n + q}\ T)$ and transposing,

$$\sum_{i=0}^{p-1} \mathbf{s}_{p-i}m(\overline{p - i - 1}\ T) = -\mathbf{x}(0) \qquad (4.6\text{-}9)$$

where

$$\mathbf{s}_{p-i} = \boldsymbol{\phi}(-\overline{p - i}\ T)\mathbf{h}(T) \qquad (4.6\text{-}10)$$

Equation (4.6-9) describes a hyperplane in the control space. If this hyperplane, which may be referred to as the *solution plane*, does not intersect

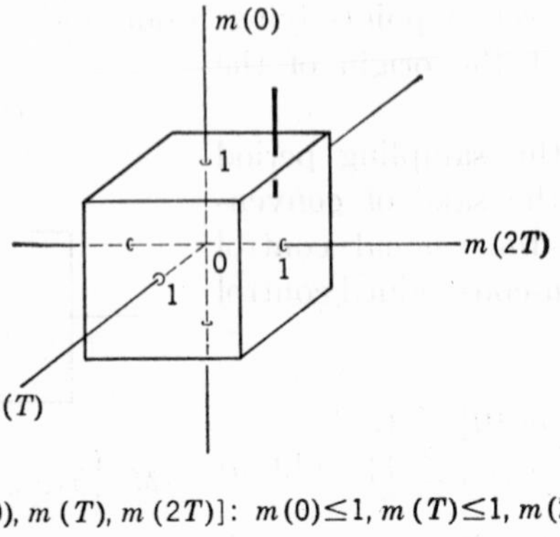

Fig. 4.6-3 Saturation cube in a three-dimensional control space.

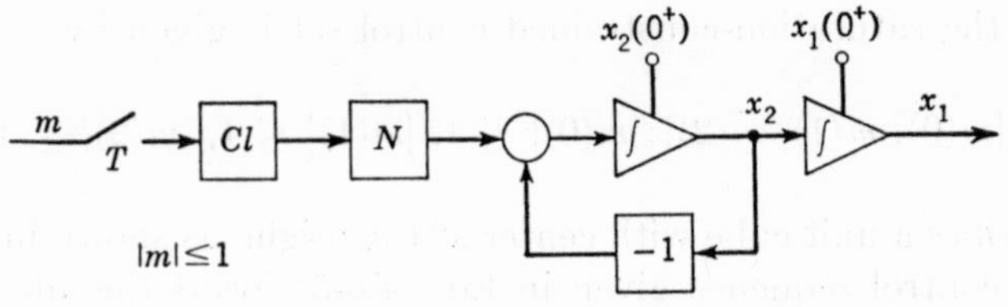

Fig. 4.6-4 A second-order control process subject to saturation.

the hypercube formed by the saturation constraint, the above assumption is not valid and the control process will not be able to reach the equilibrium state in $n + q$ sampling periods, but the process may be made to reach the equilibrium state in $n + q + 1$ or more steps. If the solution plane intersects the hypercube, there is one or an infinite number of solutions to this optimum-design problem.

As an illustration, consider the second-order process characterized by the state-variable diagram shown in Fig. 4.6-4. The plant transition matrix

$\phi(T)$ and the control transition matrix $\mathbf{h}(T)$ are found to be

$$\phi(T) = \begin{bmatrix} 1 & 1 - e^{-T} \\ 0 & e^{-T} \end{bmatrix} \quad \text{and} \quad \mathbf{h}(T) = \begin{bmatrix} T - 1 + e^{-T} \\ 1 - e^{-T} \end{bmatrix}$$

By ignoring the saturation effect, it is found that

$$m(0) = \frac{e^T}{T(1 - e^T)} x_1(0) + \frac{T + e^T - e^{2T}}{T(1 - e^T)^2} x_2(0) \qquad (4.6\text{-}11)$$

$$m(T) = \frac{e^T}{T(1 - e^T)} x_1(T) + \frac{T + e^T - e^{2T}}{T(1 - e^T)^2} x_2(T) \qquad (4.6\text{-}12)$$

If $|m(0)| > 1$, as illustrated in Fig. 4.6-5, the above solution is incorrect, and a three-dimensional control space should be tried. Figure 4.6-5 shows

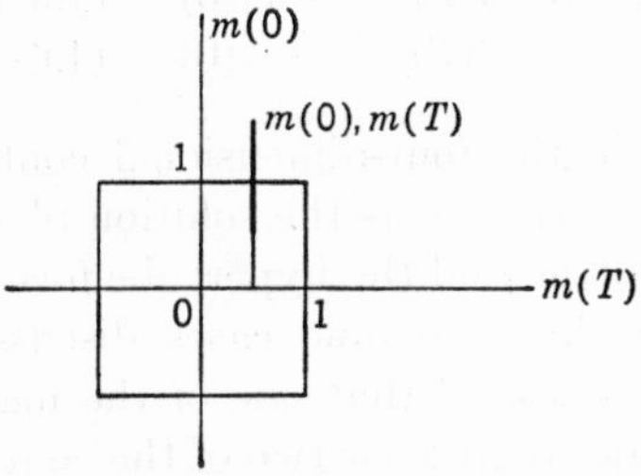

Fig. 4.6-5 Control signal exceeding the saturation limit.

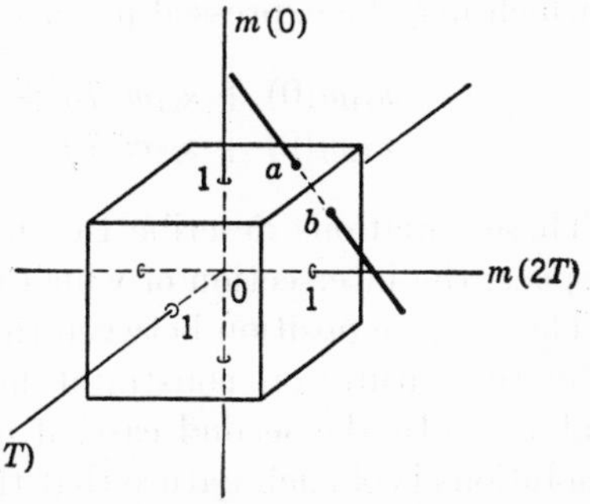

Fig. 4.6-6 Saturation cube and admissible control vectors in a three-dimensional control space for a second-order system.

the saturation square and the control steps determined under the assumption of settling in two sampling periods. Now, assuming that the process can be made to reach the equilibrium state in three control steps, it is obtained from Eq. (4.6-9) that

$$\mathbf{s}_1 m(0) + \mathbf{s}_2 m(T) + \mathbf{s}_3 m(2T) = -\mathbf{x}(0) \qquad (4.6\text{-}13)$$

where

$$\mathbf{s}_i = \phi(-iT)\mathbf{h}(T) \qquad i = 1, 2, 3 \qquad (4.6\text{-}14)$$

By expressing the vectors in terms of their components, Eq. (4.6-13) leads to

$$s_{11} m(0) + s_{21} m(T) + s_{31} m(2T) = -x_1(0) \qquad (4.6\text{-}15)$$

$$s_{12} m(0) + s_{22} m(T) + s_{32} m(2T) = -x_2(0) \qquad (4.6\text{-}16)$$

These two equations represent two planes in the three-dimensional control space, the intersection of which is a straight line, as shown in Fig. 4.6-6. This straight line, referred to as the *solution line*, may touch the saturation cube at the edge, or it may pierce through the saturation cube, or it does not intersect the saturation cube. These three different situations will lead to (1) a unique solution, (2) an infinite number of solutions, and (3) no solution. In the first case, the magnitudes of either two or three of the control signals $m(0)$, $m(T)$, $m(2T)$ are equal to 1. In the second case, the solution is not unique and there are an infinite number of optimum solutions. Any point on the dashed-line segment inside the cube is an optimum solution. One of the many solutions is such that either $|m(0)|$ or $|m(T)|$ or $|m(2T)|$ is equal to 1 and the other two may be equal to or less than 1, as can easily be seen from Fig. 4.6-6. The third possibility will not occur unless the above assumption of three control steps is not valid. If this were the case, a four-step optimum control should be assumed. Under this assumption, one has

$$\mathbf{s}_1 m(0) + \mathbf{s}_2 m(T) + \mathbf{s}_3 m(2T) + \mathbf{s}_4 m(3T) = -\mathbf{x}(0) \qquad (4.6\text{-}17)$$

which may be expressed in terms of the components of the vectors as

$$s_{11} m(0) + s_{21} m(T) + s_{31} m(2T) + s_{41} m(3T) = -x_1(0) \qquad (4.6\text{-}18)$$
$$s_{12} m(0) + s_{22} m(T) + s_{32} m(2T) + s_{42} m(3T) = -x_2(0) \qquad (4.6\text{-}19)$$

These equations describe two hyperplanes in the four-dimensional control space, the intersection of which is a plane, referred to as the solution plane. The relative position between this solution plane and the hypercube formed by the saturation constraint leads to the three possible cases discussed above. In the second case, it can always be found that one of the many solutions is of such nature that the magnitudes of at least two of the control signals $m(0)$, $m(T)$, $m(2T)$, $m(3T)$ are equal to 1 and the other two have values equal to or less than 1.

In general, it is discovered that one of the many possible sets of optimum-control sequence possesses the following property:[142] If an nth-order saturating discrete-data system can be taken from a given initial state to the equilibrium state in the shortest time of $n + q$ sampling periods, $q \geq 0$, then q of the $n + q$ control signals in the sequence $\{m(kT)\}$ are equal to the saturation limit, and the magnitude of the remaining n control signals will stay within the saturation limit. Quite often the first q of the $n + q$ control signals are equal to the saturation limit. This is a very useful property that may be utilized to derive an optimum solution by extending the techniques developed in Sec. 4.5. Clearly, this argument reduces the time-optimal-control problem to the problem of determining the q saturating control signals of the optimum-control sequence. Once the saturating control signals are determined, the optimum-control sequence follows from the solution of the n algebraic equations obtained from Eq. (4.6-8), which may be written as

$$\mathbf{f}_{n+q}[\mathbf{x}(0); m(0), m(T), \ldots, m(\overline{n + q - 1}\, T)] = \mathbf{0} \qquad (4.6\text{-}20)$$

However, when deadbeat performance is desired, there exists an admissible control sequence such that the magnitudes of the first q control signals are equal to the saturation limit and the magnitudes of the remaining n control signals stay within the saturation limit.

Assume that an nth-order control process with saturation can be made to reach the equilibrium state in $n + q$ sampling periods, where $q \geq 0$. Then the $n + q$ control signals are defined by the following set of n linear equations:

$$\begin{aligned} \sum_{i=0}^{n+q-1} a_{1i}m_i &= \alpha_{10} \\ \sum_{i=0}^{n+q-1} a_{2i}m_i &= \alpha_{20} \\ &\cdots\cdots\cdots\cdots \\ \sum_{i=0}^{n+q-1} a_{ki} &= \alpha_{k0} \\ &\cdots\cdots\cdots\cdots \\ \sum_{i=0}^{n+q-1} a_{ni}m_i &= \alpha_{n0} \end{aligned} \tag{4.6-21}$$

where a_{ki} and α_{k0} are known constants. These equations follow immediately from Eq. (4.6-9), upon the substitution of proper values. Each equation describes an $(n + q)$-dimensional hyperplane. The intersection of these hyperplanes forms a $(q + 1)$-dimensional solution plane which intersects the $(n + q)$-dimensional hypercube describing the saturation phenomenon. When the solution plane intersects the hypercube in the m_j direction, the control signal $m(j)$ may be put equal to 1. The possible saturating control signals can be determined from the intersection between the solution plane and the hypercube, which may be characterized by the inequalities

$$-1 \leq m_i \leq 1 \qquad i = 0, 1, 2, \ldots, n + q \tag{4.6-22a}$$

Thus the possible saturating control signals may be determined from Eqs. (4.6-21) subject to the constraints defined in Eq. (4.6-22a). To facilitate calculations, the constraints given above are reduced to

$$0 \leq m'_i \leq 2 \qquad i = 0, 1, 2, \ldots, n + q \tag{4.6-22b}$$

where

$$m_i = m'_i - 1 \tag{4.6-23}$$

An alternative method of determining the saturating control signals is to convert the inequalities in (4.6-22b) into equations. This can be done by introducing slack variables. Thus

$$m'_i + m'_{i0} = 2 \tag{4.6-24}$$

where m'_{i0} are slack variables whose values lie between 0 and 2. The possible saturating control signals can be determined by solving Eqs.

(4.6-21) and (4.6-24). After the control sequence is determined, it may be converted into a control law by proper substitution, as demonstrated in Example 4.6-1.

This iterative method of design of time-optimal control for discrete systems subject to control-signal saturation is simple and easy to apply. Starting with $q = 0$, if one of the control signals determined from Eq. (4.6-21) exceeds the saturation limit, try $q = 1$ and determine the saturating control signal. If one of the control signals calculated from Eqs. (4.6-21) again exceeds the saturation limit, try $q = 2$ and determine the two saturating control signals. If the control signals calculated by solving Eqs. (4.6-21) all stay within the saturation limit, an optimum-control sequence is found. If not, try $q = 3$ and repeat the process. This design procedure imposes no limitations upon the order of the control process, the nature of its poles, and the number of control inputs, as long as the process is controllable. When the control process is relatively simple, the design of the optimum control by manual computation presents no problem. In the case of complex systems, it seems desirable to write a computer program for carrying out the iterative design procedure.

Example 4.6-1 Saturating Discrete System

Consider the saturating-amplitude discrete-data system shown in Fig. 4.6-4. The sampling period is 1 sec, and the control signal is subject to the constraint $|m| \leq 1$. The initial conditions on the control process are set at $x_1(0) = 10$ and $x_2(0) = -12$. Find the minimum number of sampling periods required to take the process from the initial state $\mathbf{x}(0)$ to the equilibrium state, and determine the optimum-control sequence $\{m^o\}$.

The design is initiated with the determination of the transition matrices $\boldsymbol{\phi}(\lambda)$ and $\mathbf{h}(\lambda)$. Examination of the state-variable diagram in Fig. 4.6-4 reveals that

$$\boldsymbol{\phi}(\lambda) = \begin{bmatrix} 1 & 1 - e^{-\lambda} \\ 0 & e^{-\lambda} \end{bmatrix} \qquad \text{and} \qquad \mathbf{h}(\lambda) = \begin{bmatrix} \lambda - 1 + e^{-\lambda} \\ 1 - e^{-\lambda} \end{bmatrix}$$

Since $T = 1$ sec and

$$\mathbf{x}(2T) = \boldsymbol{\phi}(2T)\mathbf{x}(0) + \boldsymbol{\phi}(T)\mathbf{h}(T)m_0 + \mathbf{h}(T)m_1$$

$$\mathbf{x}(0) = \boldsymbol{\phi}^{-1}(2T)\mathbf{x}(2T) + \begin{bmatrix} 0.722m_0 + 3.68m_1 \\ -1.72m_0 - 4.68m_1 \end{bmatrix} = \begin{bmatrix} 10 \\ -12 \end{bmatrix}$$

where $m_0 = m(0)$, and $m_1 = m(T)$. If the saturation effect were ignored, the system could reach equilibrium in two sampling periods. Thus, by letting $\mathbf{x}(2T) = \mathbf{0}$, the control vector may be derived:

$$\begin{bmatrix} m_0 \\ m_1 \end{bmatrix} = \begin{bmatrix} -0.98 \\ 3.00 \end{bmatrix}$$

Since $m_1 > 1$, the system cannot reach equilibrium in two sampling periods.

Now assume that the system would be able to reach equilibrium in three steps. This leads to

$$\boldsymbol{\phi}(3T)\mathbf{x}(0) + \boldsymbol{\phi}(2T)\mathbf{h}(T)m_0 + \boldsymbol{\phi}(T)\mathbf{h}(T)m_1 + \mathbf{h}(T)m_2 = \mathbf{0}$$

Proper substitution and simplification yields

$$\begin{aligned} 0.722m_0 + 3.68m_1 + 11.73m_2 &= 10 \\ 1.72m_0 + 4.68m_1 + 12.7m_2 &= 12 \end{aligned}$$

The substitution of $m_i = m_i' - 1$ converts the above equations into

$$\begin{aligned} 0.722m_0' + 3.68m_1' + 11.73m_2' &= 26.13 \\ 1.72m_0' + 4.68m_1' + 12.7m_2' &= 31.10 \end{aligned}$$

Solving these two equations for m_1' and m_2',

$$\begin{aligned} m_1' &= 4.02 - 1.35m_0' \\ m_2' &= 0.915 + 0.36m_0' \end{aligned}$$

Since $0 \le (m_1', m_2') \le 2$, it is found that

$$1.49 \le m_0' \le 2.98 \qquad \text{and} \qquad -2.98 \le m_0' \le 3.01$$

Since $0 \le m_0' \le 2$, the above inequalities yield

$$1.49 \le m_0' \le 2 \qquad \text{or} \qquad 0.49 \le m_0 \le 1$$

This implies that m_0 can be set equal to 1. The ranges of m_1 and m_2 are found to be

$$0.32 \le m_1 \le 1 \qquad \text{and} \qquad 0.45 \le m_2 \le 0.64$$

Thus m_1 can also be made equal to 1. These inequalities describe the intersection with the unit cube. The system may reach equilibrium in three steps. Choosing $m_0 = 1$ gives the optimum-control sequence

$$\{m^o\} = \{1, 0.305, 0.683\}$$

Letting $m_1 = 1$, the following optimum-control sequence is derived:

$$\{m^o\} = \{0.46, 1, 0.51\}$$

Now let the initial conditions on the given process be set at $x_1(0) = 1$ and $x_2(0) = 1$. Find the minimum number of sampling periods required to take the process from the initial state to the equilibrium state, and determine the optimum-control sequence $\{m^o\}$.

Since $T = 1$ sec, it is found that

$$\mathbf{x}(2T) = \begin{bmatrix} 1.865 + 0.767m_0 + 0.368m_1 \\ 0.335 + 0.233m_0 + 0.632m_1 \end{bmatrix}$$

If the saturation effect were ignored, the system could reach equilibrium in two sampling periods. Thus, by letting $\mathbf{x}(2T) = \mathbf{0}$, the control vector so derived is

$$\begin{bmatrix} m_0 \\ m_1 \end{bmatrix} = \begin{bmatrix} -2.8296 \\ 0.8296 \end{bmatrix}$$

Since $m_0 < -1$, the system will not be able to reach equilibrium in two sampling periods.

Now assume that the system was able to reach equilibrium in three steps. This leads to the following equations:

$$\boldsymbol{\phi}(3T)\mathbf{x}(0) + \boldsymbol{\phi}(2T)\mathbf{h}(T)m_0 + \boldsymbol{\phi}(T)\mathbf{h}(T)m_1 + \mathbf{h}(T)m_2 = \mathbf{0}$$

and

$$\begin{aligned} 0.722m_0 + 3.68m_1 + 11.73m_2 &= 1 \\ -1.72m_0 - 4.68m_1 - 12.70m_2 &= 1 \end{aligned}$$

where $m_2 = m(2T)$. Replacing m_i by $m_i' - 1$ yields

$$\begin{aligned} 0.722m_0' + 3.68m_1' + 11.73m_2' &= 17.13 \\ 1.720m_0' + 4.68m_1' + 12.70m_2' &= 18.10 \end{aligned}$$

Then

$$\begin{aligned} m_1' &= -0.723 - 1.33m_0' \\ m_2' &= 4.580 + 0.36m_0' \end{aligned}$$

These two equations reveal that there is no intersection between the solution plane and the hypercube. Thus the system cannot be made to reach equilibrium in three sampling periods.

Assume that the system was able to reach equilibrium in four sampling periods. This implies that

$$\boldsymbol{\phi}(4T)\mathbf{x}(0) + \boldsymbol{\phi}(3T)\mathbf{h}(T)m_0 + \boldsymbol{\phi}(2T)\mathbf{h}(T)m_1 + \boldsymbol{\phi}(T)\mathbf{h}(T)m_2 + \mathbf{h}(T)m_3 = \mathbf{0}$$

which reduces to

$$\begin{aligned} 0.722m_0 + 3.68m_1 + 11.73m_2 + 33.6m_3 &= 1 \\ -1.720m_0 - 4.68m_1 - 12.70m_2 - 34.8m_3 &= 1 \end{aligned}$$

Following the foregoing procedure, it can be shown that the solution plane intersects with the unit hypercube in the $-m_0$ and $-m_1$ directions. Hence it can be assumed that $m_0 = -1$ and $m_1 = -1$, and the above two equations become

$$\begin{aligned} 11.72m_0 + 33.6m_3 - 5.402 &= 0 \\ 12.70m_2 + 34.8m_3 - 5.400 &= 0 \end{aligned}$$

Solving these two equations for m_2 and m_3 yields

$$m_2 = -0.2439 \qquad \text{and} \qquad m_3 = 0.2459$$

Therefore it will take four sampling periods for the control process to reach equilibrium from the specified initial conditions $x_1(0) = 1$ and $x_2(0) = 1$. The optimum control sequence is

$$\{m^o\} = \{-1, -1, -0.2439, 0.2459\}$$

To mechanize the time-optimal control, it is desirable to express the control signals as functions of the state variables. Let the optimum-control law be

$$m(2T) = \beta_1 x_1(2T) + \beta_2 x_2(2T)$$
$$m(3T) = \beta_1 x_1(3T) + \beta_2 x_2(3T)$$

Substituting the numerical values into these two equations and expressing in matrix notation yields

$$\begin{bmatrix} -0.2439 \\ 0.2459 \end{bmatrix} = \begin{bmatrix} 0.730 & -0.730 \\ 0.176 & -0.422 \end{bmatrix} \begin{bmatrix} \beta_1 \\ \beta_2 \end{bmatrix}$$

Hence $\beta_1 = -1.582$ and $\beta_2 = -1.243$

and the optimum-control law is given by

$$m^o(kT) = \boldsymbol{\beta}\mathbf{x}(kT) \qquad |m| \leq 1$$

where the feedback matrix is

$$\boldsymbol{\beta} = [-1.582 \quad -1.243]$$

The schematic diagram of the optimum system is depicted in Fig. 4.6-7.

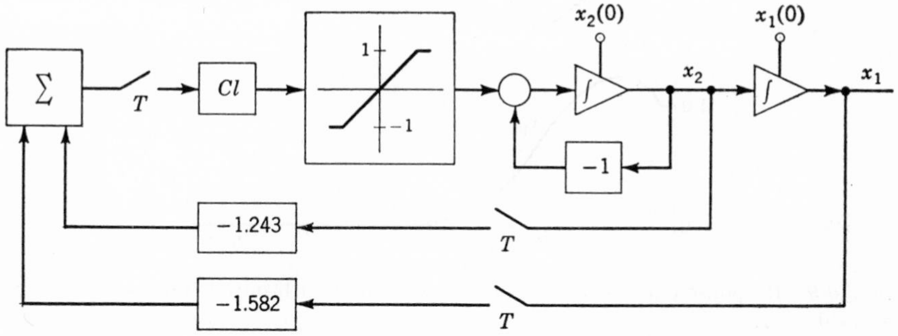

Fig. 4.6-7 Schematic diagram of the time-optimal discrete system.

This minimum-time discrete-data system is simulated on an analog computer with the schematic diagram illustrated in Fig. 4.6-8. The plotted response curves, as shown in Fig. 4.6-9, make it evident that the control process can be taken to the equilibrium state from the specified initial state in four sampling periods when the optimum-control sequence determined above is applied. The hump in Fig. 4.6-9 is caused by imperfection in the sampler hold and in the nonlinear element.

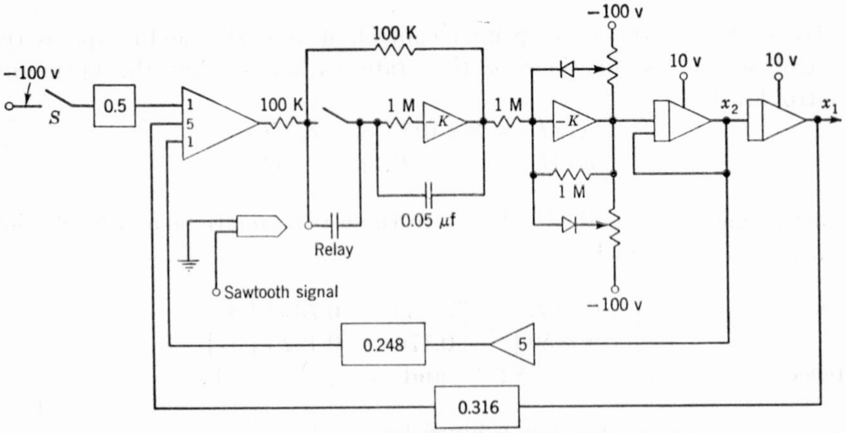

Fig. 4.6-8 Circuit diagram for analog simulation.

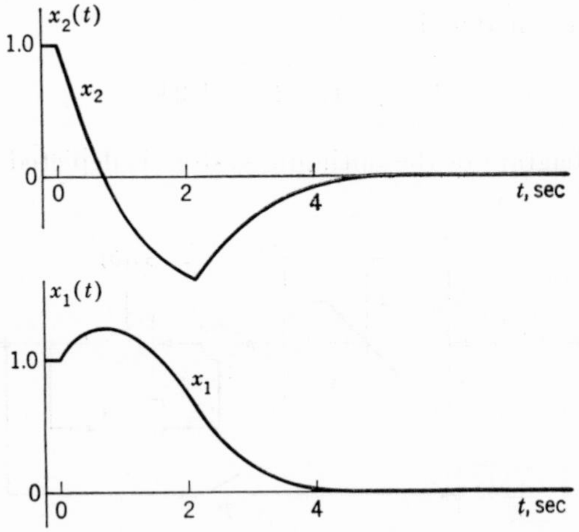

Fig. 4.6-9 Response curves for the saturating system with initial conditions $x_1(0) = 1$ and $x_2(0) = 1$.

Furthermore, following the foregoing procedure, it can be found that the solution plane also intersects with the unit hypercube in the $-m_1$ and $-m_2$ directions. Hence, by letting $m_1 = -1$ and $m_2 = -1$,

$$1.45m_0 - 2.75m_3 + 2.08 = 0$$
$$0.50m_0 - 3.75m_3 + 2.60 = 0$$

Solving these two equations for m_0 and m_3 yields

$$m_0 = -0.161 \qquad \text{and} \qquad m_3 = 0.677$$

Therefore the optimum-control sequence

$$\{m^o\} = \{-0.161, -1, -1, 0.677\}$$

is also a possible solution.

The above results are summarized in the following table for comparison:

Initial state	*Optimum-control sequence*	
(10, −12)	{1, 0.305, 0.683}	{0.46, 1, 0.51}
(1, 1)	{−1, −1, −0.244, 0.246}	{−0.161, −1, −1, 0.677}

4.7 TIME-OPTIMAL CONTROL OF CONTINUOUS SYSTEMS

One important mode of optimum control is time-optimal control. Many industrial processes can realize a substantial gain in performance by following time-optimal programs for startup, shutdown, and changing set points. In the design of the depth control of a submarine, it is desired to go from one depth to another in the shortest time, with limitations on the maximum rate of control deflection, maximum amount of control deflection, and maximum pitch angle of the deck. The problem of time-optimal control for continuous systems has received considerable attention during the past decade. It may be formulated as follows: Given an nth-order system characterized by a state vector $\mathbf{x}(t)$, satisfying the differential equation

$$\dot{\mathbf{x}}(t) = \mathbf{f}[\mathbf{x}(t), \mathbf{m}(t), t] \tag{4.7-1}$$

where the control vector $\mathbf{m}(t)$ is an r-dimensional vector which is restricted to a closed region, $\mathbf{m} \in \mathbf{\Omega}$, determine the admissible control vector $\mathbf{m}(t)$ which will take the control system from an initial state $\mathbf{x}(0)$ to a desired state $\mathbf{x}^d(t)$ in the shortest possible time. An admissible control vector is the control vector which belongs to the region $\mathbf{\Omega}$ and for which Eq. (4.7-1) has a solution.

In this section, the problem under consideration is time-optimal regulation of linear systems with control-signal saturation. The system is described by the vector-matrix differential equation

$$\dot{\mathbf{x}}(t) = \mathbf{A}(t)\mathbf{x}(t) + \mathbf{D}(t)\mathbf{m}(t) \tag{4.7-2}$$

where the symbols are as previously defined. The control vector is subject to the constraint $|m_i| \leq 1$. It is desired to determine a control vector $\mathbf{m}^o(t)$ which will move the system from an initial state $\mathbf{x}(0)$ to the desired final state $\mathbf{x}^d(t_f)$ in the shortest time. This problem has been a subject of considerable interest. It was first studied on an intuitive basis by McDonald in 1950. Later Bushaw gave this problem a mathematical treatment, with emphasis upon autonomous second-order systems. Bellman and others are the first to prove the fundamental theorem of time-optimal control. The theorem states that:

1. For the control system characterized by Eq. (4.7-2), if there exists an optimum controller for minimum-time control

$$\min_{\substack{\mathbf{m}\in\Omega \\ t_f\in(0,\infty)}} \int_0^{t_f} dt \tag{4.7-3}$$

then it is of the bang-bang type.

2. If matrix **A** of Eq. (4.7-2) is a constant matrix and has real and distinct eigenvalues, then each component of the optimum-control vector $\mathbf{m}^o(t)$ will change sign at most $n - 1$ times in the time interval $(0, t_f)$.

The solution to Eq. (4.7-2) is found to be

$$\mathbf{x}(t) = \boldsymbol{\phi}(t)\mathbf{x}(0) + \int_0^t \boldsymbol{\phi}(t, \tau)\mathbf{D}(\tau)\mathbf{m}(\tau)\, d\tau \tag{4.7-4}$$

where $\boldsymbol{\phi}(t, \tau)$ is the transition matrix of the system. At the termination of the control $t = t_f$, the final-state vector is given by

$$\begin{aligned} \mathbf{x}^d(t_f) &= \mathbf{x}(t_f) \\ &= \boldsymbol{\phi}(t_f)\mathbf{x}(0) + \int_0^{t_f} \boldsymbol{\phi}(t_f, \tau)\mathbf{D}(\tau)\mathbf{m}(\tau)\, d\tau \end{aligned} \tag{4.7-5}$$

Premultiplying Eq. (4.7-5) by $\boldsymbol{\phi}^{-1}(t_f)$ and rearranging yields

$$\boldsymbol{\phi}^{-1}(t_f)\mathbf{x}(t_f) - \mathbf{x}(0) = \int_0^{t_f} \boldsymbol{\phi}^{-1}(t_f)\boldsymbol{\phi}(t_f, \tau)\mathbf{D}(\tau)\mathbf{m}(\tau)\, d\tau \tag{4.7-6}$$

which may be expressed as

$$[\boldsymbol{\phi}^{-1}(0) - 1]\mathbf{x}(0) = \int_0^{t_f} \left\{\boldsymbol{\phi}^{-1}(t_f)\boldsymbol{\phi}(t_f, \tau)\mathbf{D}(\tau)\mathbf{m}(\tau) - \frac{d}{d\tau}[\boldsymbol{\phi}^{-1}(\tau)\mathbf{x}(\tau)]\right\} d\tau \tag{4.7-7}$$

since

$$\int_0^{t_f} \frac{d}{d\tau}[\boldsymbol{\phi}^{-1}(\tau)\mathbf{x}(\tau)]\, d\tau = \boldsymbol{\phi}^{-1}(0)\mathbf{x}(0) - \boldsymbol{\phi}^{-1}(t_f)\mathbf{x}(t_f) \tag{4.7-8}$$

Equation (4.7-7) provides a constraint on the initial state $\mathbf{x}(0)$, which may be adjointed with (4.7-3) to perform the minimization process.

Introducing the Lagrange multiplier μ, the minimization problem now becomes

$$\min_{\substack{\mathbf{m}\in\Omega \\ t_f\in(0,\infty)}} \int_0^{t_f} \left(1 - \mu\left\{\boldsymbol{\phi}^{-1}(t_f)\boldsymbol{\phi}(t_f,\tau)\mathbf{D}(\tau)\mathbf{m}(\tau) - \frac{d}{d\tau}[\boldsymbol{\phi}^{-1}(\tau)\mathbf{x}(\tau)]\right\}\right) d\tau \tag{4.7-9}$$

Examination of this expression reveals that a minimum occurs for $\mathbf{m} \in \Omega$ when

$$\mu\boldsymbol{\phi}^{-1}(t_f)\boldsymbol{\phi}(t_f, \tau)\mathbf{D}(\tau)\mathbf{m}(\tau)$$

is positive. This leads to the relationship

$$\mathbf{m}(\tau) = \operatorname{sgn} \mathbf{S}(\tau) \tag{4.7-10}$$

where the switching function $\mathbf{S}(\tau)$ is the $r \times 1$ matrix given by

$$\mathbf{S}(\tau) = [\boldsymbol{\phi}^{-1}(t_f)\boldsymbol{\phi}(t_f, \tau)\mathbf{D}(\tau)]'\mathbf{c} \tag{4.7-11}$$

or

$$\mathbf{S}(\tau) = \mathbf{D}'(\tau)[\boldsymbol{\phi}^{-1}(t_f)\boldsymbol{\phi}(t_f, \tau)]'\mathbf{c} \tag{4.7-12}$$

where $\mathbf{c}$ is an $n \times 1$ column matrix, and sgn designates "taking the sign of." If the kth element of $\mathbf{S}(\tau)$ is greater than zero, $m_k(\tau)$ is positive; if it is zero, $m_k(\tau) = 0$; and if it is less than zero, $m_k(\tau)$ is negative. The control signals change signs in accordance with the switching function $\mathbf{S}(\tau)$.

Since the control vector $\mathbf{m}(t)$ is restricted by the constraint $|m_i| \leq 1$, minimization of the expression given in (4.7-9) requires that $|m_i| = 1$. The above analysis points out that, to achieve time-optimal control, the control signals have their magnitudes equal to the maximum allowable value and their signs determined by the sign of the switching function $\mathbf{S}(t)$. In other words, the time-optimal control system is of the bang-bang type.

If the coefficient matrix $\mathbf{A}$ of the control system is time-invariant, the switching function reduces to

$$\mathbf{S}(\tau) = \mathbf{D}'(\tau)\boldsymbol{\phi}'(-\tau)\mathbf{c} \tag{4.7-13}$$

where

$$\boldsymbol{\phi}'(-\tau) = e^{-\mathbf{A}'\tau} \tag{4.7-14}$$

When the eigenvalues of matrix $\mathbf{A}$ are real and distinct, each component of the transpose of the transition matrix given in Eq. (4.7-14) will be made up of terms of the form $e^{\alpha_i\tau}$. Consequently, the jth component of the switching function may be written as

$$s_j(\tau) = \sum_{i=1}^{n} c_i d_{ij} e^{\alpha_i \tau} \tag{4.7-15}$$

where c_i and d_{ij} are the elements of matrices $\mathbf{c}$ and $\mathbf{D}$, respectively. Since the right-hand member of Eq. (4.7-15) either is identically equal to zero or can have at most $n - 1$ real zeros, the control signal $m_j(\tau)$ will be able to change sign at most $n - 1$ times.

From the above analysis it is noted that minimum-time control is a bang-bang control. The optimum controller switches between the upper and the lower limits. The design of such an optimal control system consists mainly of the determination of the switching boundary and its mechanization. If, for a control system, no component of the switching function $\mathbf{S}(t)$ is identically zero in any time interval of positive length, the system is said to be normal. It can be shown that, for a normal system, optimum control is unique and is of the bang-bang type.

Now consider the design of time-optimal control for a second-order system characterized by Eq. (4.7-2), with the coefficient matrix and the driving matrix given, respectively, by

$$\mathbf{A} = \begin{bmatrix} 0 & a_{12} \\ a_{21} & a_{22} \end{bmatrix} \tag{4.7-16}$$

and

$$\mathbf{D} = \begin{bmatrix} d_{11} & 0 \\ 0 & d_{22} \end{bmatrix} \tag{4.7-17}$$

The eigenvalues of **A** are assumed to be λ_1 and λ_2, which are real and distinct. The control vector is subject to the saturation constraint $|m_i| \leq 1$. Design the optimum control required to move the system from a specified initial state $\mathbf{x}(0)$ to the equilibrium state $\mathbf{x}(t_f) = \mathbf{0}$ in the shortest time.

The optimum design is initiated with the determination of the transition matrix of the system, which is found to be

$$\boldsymbol{\phi}(t) = \begin{bmatrix} \dfrac{-\lambda_2 e^{\lambda_1 t} + \lambda_1 e^{\lambda_2 t}}{\lambda_1 - \lambda_2} & -\dfrac{e^{\lambda_1 t} - e^{\lambda_2 t}}{\lambda_1 - \lambda_2} \\ \dfrac{\lambda_1 \lambda_2 (e^{\lambda_1 t} - e^{\lambda_2 t})}{\lambda_1 - \lambda_2} & \dfrac{\lambda_1 e^{\lambda_1 t} - \lambda_2 e^{\lambda_2 t}}{\lambda_1 - \lambda_2} \end{bmatrix} \tag{4.7-18}$$

The state vector $\mathbf{x}(t)$ is given by the general solution

$$\mathbf{x}(t) = \boldsymbol{\phi}(t)\mathbf{x}(0) + \int_0^t \boldsymbol{\phi}(t - \tau)\mathbf{D}\mathbf{m}(\tau)\, d\tau \tag{4.7-19}$$

Transposing and simplifying yields

$$\mathbf{x}(0) = \boldsymbol{\phi}(-t)\mathbf{x}(t) - \int_0^t \boldsymbol{\phi}(-\tau)\mathbf{D}\mathbf{m}(\tau)\, d\tau \tag{4.7-20}$$

Since, at $t = t_f$, $\mathbf{x}(t_f) = \mathbf{0}$, the initial-state vector $\mathbf{x}(0)$ can be written as

$$\mathbf{x}(0) = -\int_0^{t_f} \boldsymbol{\phi}(-\tau)\mathbf{D}\mathbf{m}(\tau)\, d\tau \tag{4.7-21}$$

Upon proper substitution, the initial-state vector expands into the following equations describing the initial states:

$$x_1(0) = \int_0^{t_f} \left[\frac{\lambda_2 e^{-\lambda_1 \tau} - \lambda_1 e^{-\lambda_2 \tau}}{\lambda_1 - \lambda_2} d_{11} m_1(\tau) + \frac{e^{-\lambda_1 \tau} - e^{-\lambda_2 \tau}}{\lambda_1 - \lambda_2} d_{22} m_2(\tau) \right] d\tau \tag{4.7-22}$$

and

$$x_2(0) = \int_0^{t_f} \left[\frac{-\lambda_1 \lambda_2 (e^{-\lambda_1 \tau} - e^{-\lambda_2 \tau})}{\lambda_1 - \lambda_2} d_{11} m_1(\tau) - \frac{\lambda_1 e^{-\lambda_1 \tau} - \lambda_2 e^{\lambda_2 \tau}}{\lambda_1 - \lambda_2} d_{22} m_2(\tau) \right] d\tau \tag{4.7-23}$$

In the above equations, x_1 and x_2 are the components of the state vector **x**, and m_1 and m_2 are the components of the control vector **m**. The optimum design requires the determination of the switching function so that the time interval t_f is minimized.

To simplify the design computations, the state vector is translated into the canonical form. Let the state vector $\mathbf{x}$ be transposed by the linear transformation

$$\mathbf{x} = \mathbf{T}\mathbf{y} \tag{4.7-24}$$

or

$$\mathbf{y} = \mathbf{T}^{-1}\mathbf{x} \tag{4.7-25}$$

As has been discussed in Sec. 2.3, the transformation matrix $\mathbf{T}$ is formed by using the eigenvectors as columns. It is found that

$$\mathbf{T} = \begin{bmatrix} 1 & 1 \\ -\lambda_1 & -\lambda_2 \end{bmatrix} \tag{4.7-26a}$$

and

$$\mathbf{T}^{1} = \frac{1}{\lambda_1 - \lambda_2}\begin{bmatrix} -\lambda_2 & -1 \\ \lambda_1 & -1 \end{bmatrix} \tag{4.7-26b}$$

The state vector is now transformed to the canonical form

$$\mathbf{y}(t) = e^{\mathbf{\Lambda} t}\mathbf{y}(0) + \int_0^t e^{\mathbf{\Lambda}(t-\tau)}\mathbf{T}^{-1}\mathbf{D}\mathbf{m}(\tau)\,d\tau \tag{4.7-27}$$

where

$$\mathbf{\Lambda} = \mathbf{T}^{-1}\mathbf{A}\mathbf{T} = \begin{bmatrix} \lambda_1 & 0 \\ 0 & \lambda_2 \end{bmatrix} \tag{4.7-28}$$

Thus the new initial-state vector is

$$\mathbf{y}(0) = \frac{1}{\lambda_1 - \lambda_2}\begin{bmatrix} -\lambda_2 & -1 \\ \lambda_1 & 1 \end{bmatrix}\mathbf{x}(0) \tag{4.7-29}$$

which leads to the following equations, upon expansion,

$$y_1(0) = \frac{-[\lambda_2 x_1(0) + x_2(0)]}{\lambda_1 - \lambda_2} \tag{4.7-30}$$

$$y_2(0) = \frac{\lambda_1 x_1(0) + x_2(0)}{\lambda_1 - \lambda_2} \tag{4.7-31}$$

Substitution of Eqs. (4.7-22) and (4.7-23) into Eqs. (4.7-30) and (4.7-31) and simplifying yields

$$y_1(0) = \int_0^{t_f} \frac{e^{-\lambda_1\tau}}{\lambda_1 - \lambda_2}[d_{22}m_2(\tau) + \lambda_2 d_{11}m_1(\tau)]\,d\tau \tag{4.7-32}$$

$$y_2(0) = -\int_0^{t_f} \frac{e^{-\lambda_2\tau}}{\lambda_1 - \lambda_2}[d_{22}m_2(\tau) - \lambda_1 d_{11}m_1(\tau)]\,d\tau \tag{4.7-33}$$

Since, according to the fundamental theorem of time-optimal control, the control signals will change signs once in the time interval $(0, t_f)$, it can be assumed that the control signal m_1 will switch at t_1 and control signal m_2 will switch at t_2. Then Eqs. (4.7-32) and (4.7-33) may be written as

$$y_1(0) = \frac{1}{\lambda_1 - \lambda_2}\left\{\int_0^{t_1} e^{-\lambda_1\tau}\lambda_2 d_{11}m_1(\tau)\,d\tau - \int_{t_1}^{t_f} e^{-\lambda_1\tau}\lambda_2 d_{11}m_1(\tau)\,d\tau \right.$$
$$\left. + \int_0^{t_2} e^{-\lambda_1\tau}d_{22}m_2(\tau)\,d\tau - \int_{t_2}^{t_f} e^{-\lambda_1\tau}d_{22}m_2(\tau)\,d\tau\right\} \tag{4.7-34}$$

and

$$y_2(0) = \frac{-1}{\lambda_1 - \lambda_2}\left\{\int_0^{t_1} e^{-\lambda_2\tau}\lambda_1 d_{11} m_1(\tau)\, d\tau - \int_{t_1}^{t_f} e^{\lambda_2\tau}\lambda_1 d_{11} m_1(\tau)\, d\tau \right.$$
$$\left. + \int_0^{t_2} e^{-\lambda_2\tau} d_{22} m_2(\tau)\, d\tau - \int_{t_2}^{t_f} e^{-\lambda_2\tau} d_{22} m_2(\tau)\, d\tau\right\} \quad (4.7\text{-}35)$$

Assuming an initial sign for m_1 and for m_2 such that $m_1 = 1$ for $0 < t < t_1$ and $m_2 = 1$ for $0 < t < t_2$ and integrating yields

$$y_1(0) = \frac{-1}{\lambda_1(\lambda_1 - \lambda_2)}\{2\lambda_2 d_{11} e^{-\lambda_1 t_1} + 2d_{22} e^{-\lambda_1 t_2} - (\lambda_2 d_{11} + d_{22})(1 + e^{-\lambda_1 t_f})\} \quad (4.7\text{-}36)$$

$$y_2(0) = \frac{1}{\lambda_2(\lambda_1 - \lambda_2)}\{2\lambda_1 d_{11} e^{-\lambda_2 t_1} + 2d_{22} e^{-\lambda_2 t_2} - (\lambda_1 d_{11} + d_{22})(1 + e^{-\lambda_2 t_f})\} \quad (4.7\text{-}37)$$

Solving for t_f gives

$$t_f = P_1(t_1, t_2) = \ln\left[\frac{2\lambda_2 d_{11} e^{-\lambda_1 t_1} + 2d_{22} e^{-\lambda_1 t_2} + \lambda_1(\lambda_1 - \lambda_2) y_1(0)}{d_{22} + \lambda_2 d_{11}} - 1\right]^{-1/\lambda_1} \quad (4.7\text{-}38)$$

where $d_{22} + \lambda_2 d_{11} \neq 0$, and

$$t_f = P_2(t_1, t_2) = \ln\left[\frac{2\lambda_1 d_{11} e^{-\lambda_2 t_1} + 2d_{22} e^{-\lambda_2 t_2} - \lambda_2(\lambda_1 - \lambda_2) y_2(0)}{d_{22} + \lambda_1 d_{11}} - 1\right]^{-1/\lambda_2} \quad (4.7\text{-}39)$$

where $d_{22} + \lambda_1 d_{11} \neq 0$. Since the control signal can switch at most once in the time interval $(0, t_f)$, $m_1 = -1$ for $t_1 < t < t_f$ and $m_2 = -1$ for $t_2 < t < t_f$.

Now the optimization problem is reduced to minimizing $P_1(t_1, t_2)$ or $P_2(t_1, t_2)$ subject to the constraint

$$Q(t_1, t_2) = P_1(t_1, t_2) - P_2(t_1, t_2) = 0 \quad (4.7\text{-}40)$$

Applying the method of the Lagrange multiplier, the design problem requires the minimization of the synthetic function

$$F(t_1, t_2, \mu) = P_1(t_1, t_2) + \mu Q(t_1, t_2) \quad (4.7\text{-}41)$$

Taking the partial derivatives of the synthetic function and equating them to zero yields the following equations:

$$\frac{\partial F}{\partial t_1} = 0 \qquad \frac{\partial F}{\partial t_2} = 0 \qquad \frac{\partial F}{\partial \mu} = 0 \quad (4.7\text{-}42)$$

from which the switching time t_1 and t_2 and the Lagrange multiplier μ can be determined. It is found that the switching time t_1 and t_2 are related by

$$\lambda_2 e^{-(\lambda_1-\lambda_2)t_1} = \lambda_1 e^{-(\lambda_1-\lambda_2)t_2} \quad (4.7\text{-}43)$$

Equations (4.7-40) and (4.7-43) determine the values of t_1 and t_2 which can be used to evaluate the time of control t_f from Eq. (4.7-38) or (4.7-39). Hence the control signal m_1 is equal to $+1$ during the interval $(0, t_1)$ and is equal to -1 during the interval (t_1, t_f); the control signal m_2 is equal to $+1$ during the interval $(0, t_2)$ and is equal to -1 during the interval (t_2, t_f).

The above design procedure may be extended to the nth-order control systems. In this case, the control signal $m_i(t)$ will switch $n - 1$ times during the interval $(0, t_f)$, and t_f can be expressed as functions of the switching instants. Thus

$$t_f = P_1(t_1, t_2, \ldots, t_N) = P_2(t_1, t_2, \ldots, t_N) = \cdots = P_r(t_1, t_2, \ldots, t_N) \qquad (4.7\text{-}44)$$

Here it is assumed that the control vector $\mathbf{m}$ is an r-dimensional vector. It is easy to see that $N = r(n - 1)$. The constraining functions $Q_j(t_1, t_2, \ldots, t_N)$ are formed by taking the difference of two P functions. Hence the synthetic function is

$$F(t_1, t_2, \ldots, t_N; \mu_1, \mu_2, \ldots, \mu_{r-1}) = \sum_k P_k + \sum_j \mu_j Q_j \qquad (4.7\text{-}45)$$

Carrying out the minimization procedure by elementary calculus leads to a set of equations from which the switching instants may be determined.

The above design procedure attempts to convert the time-optimal-control problem into a minimization problem in elementary calculus by the use of the Lagrange multipliers. When the control system is of higher order, this design procedure requires the solution of a number of complicated transcendental equations. When the system is subject to many control signals, the choice of their initial signs may present some problem. With the operating conditions and physical limitations of the system specified, plus some physical insight, this problem may be partially circumvented. It should be noted that the design techniques developed in the preceding section for discrete systems are applicable to continuous systems, provided that they are approximated by discrete models. In this case, the choice of the sampling period will be made to ensure that the discrete approximation is satisfactory. The time-optimal-control problems can be solved by the calculus of variations, the maximum principle, and the dynamic-programming techniques, as discussed in the chapters to follow.

Example 4.7-1 Minimum-time Control for a Second-order System

Consider the second-order system characterized by

$$\dot{\mathbf{x}}(t) = \mathbf{A}\mathbf{x}(t) + \mathbf{D}\mathbf{m}(t)$$

where
$$\mathbf{A} = \begin{bmatrix} 0 & -1 \\ 2 & -3 \end{bmatrix} \quad \text{and} \quad \mathbf{D} = \begin{bmatrix} 1 & 0 \\ 0 & 1 \end{bmatrix}$$

The control vector is subject to the saturation constraint $|m_i| \leq |$. Determine the optimum-control function which will move the system from a specified initial state $\mathbf{x}(0)$ to the equilibrium state $\mathbf{x}(t_f) = \mathbf{0}$ in minimum time. The initial state is assumed to be $\mathbf{x}(0) = [1 \quad 1]'$.

The eigenvalues of the given system are $\lambda_1 = -1$ and $\lambda_2 = -2$. Substituting the proper values into Eqs. (4.7-22) and (4.7-23) yields the initial states as

$$x_1(0) = -\int_0^{t_f} \{(2e^\tau - e^{2\tau})m_1(\tau) - (e^\tau - e^{2\tau})m_2(\tau)\}\, d\tau$$
$$x_2(0) = -\int_0^{t_f} \{2(e^\tau - e^{2\tau})m_1(\tau) - (e^\tau - 2e^{2\tau})m_2(\tau)\}\, d\tau$$

It follows from Eqs. (4.7-32) and (4.7-33) that

$$y_1(0) = -\int_0^{t_f} e^\tau[2m_1(\tau) - m_2(\tau)]\, d\tau$$
$$y_2(0) = \int_0^{t_f} e^{2\tau}[m_1(\tau) - m_2(\tau)]\, d\tau$$

Choosing $m_1 = 1$ for $0 < t < t_1$ and $m_2 = -1$ for $0 < t < t_2$, the initial states $y_1(0)$ and $y_2(0)$ reduce to

$$y_1(0) = -4e^{t_1} - 2e^{t_2} + 3e^{t_f} + 3$$
$$y_2(0) = e^{2t_1} + e^{2t_2} - e^{2t_f} - 1$$

Solving for t_f yields

$$t_f = P_1(t_1, t_2) = \ln \tfrac{1}{3}[y_1(0) + 4e^{t_1} + 2e^{t_2} - 3]$$

and

$$t_f = P_2(t_1, t_2) = \ln\,[-y_2(0) + e^{2t_1} + e^{2t_2} - 1]^{\frac{1}{2}}$$

Thus the synthetic function is

$$F(t_1, t_2, \mu) = (1 + \mu) \ln \frac{y_1(0) + 4e^{t_1} + 2e^{t_2} - 3}{3} - \frac{\mu}{2} \ln\,[-y_2(0) + 2e^{2t_1} + e^{2t_2} - 1]$$

Combining $\partial F/\partial t_1 = 0$ and $\partial F/\partial t_2 = 0$ leads to the relationship

$$e^{t_1} = 2e^{t_2}$$

Solving for the switching times t_1 and t_2 from the above equation and the relationship

$$P_1(t_1, t_2) = P_2(t_1, t_2)$$

with $x_1(0) = 1$, $x_2(0) = 1$ or $y_1(0) = 1$, $y_2(0) = 0$, yields

$$t_1 = 4.31 \qquad \text{and} \qquad t_2 = 3.61$$

Substituting these two values into either expression for t_f gives

$$t_f = 4.81$$

In this illustrative example it should be noted that, for $0 < t < t_2$, m_2 cannot be made equal to 1. If so, the denominator $d_{22} + \lambda_1 d_{11}$ would vanish. Therefore the optimum-control function is

$$m_1(t) = \begin{cases} 1 & \text{for } 0 < t < 4.31 \\ -1 & \text{for } 4.31 < t < 4.81 \end{cases}$$

$$m_2(t) = \begin{cases} -1 & \text{for } 0 < t < 3.61 \\ 1 & \text{for } 3.61 < t < 4.81 \end{cases}$$

4.8 CONCLUSION

This chapter presents in some detail a discussion of the design of control systems by the state-transition method. The variable-gain concept is developed in the design of digital control for linear and nonlinear control systems, to exhibit deadbeat performance in response to step-function inputs. By this approach the design problem is reduced to the determination of the various gain constants of the variable-gain element. Evaluation of these gain constants is carried out by solving a set of algebraic equations. This design procedure is well adapted for obtaining a solution by a digital computer.

Some useful properties of the transition matrix are summarized. The concept of controllability and observability is likewise discussed. A process is said to be completely controllable if it can be moved from some initial state to a desired equilibrium state in a finite time interval. It has been shown that a necessary and sufficient condition for complete controllability in the discrete-time case is that the n vectors

$$\mathbf{s}_i = \phi(-iT)\mathbf{h}(T) \qquad i = 1, 2, \ldots, n$$

for a linear nth-order system are linearly independent. Conditions for controllability in the continuous-time case can be obtained in like manner. An nth-order continuous-time process characterized by $\dot{\mathbf{x}} = \mathbf{A}\mathbf{x} + \mathbf{d}m$ is completely controllable if and only if the vectors $\mathbf{d}, \mathbf{A}\mathbf{d}, \ldots, \mathbf{A}^{n-1}\mathbf{d}$ are linearly independent. From another point of view, the conditions for controllability of a process can be interpreted in terms of the driving matrix $\boldsymbol{\Delta}$ expressed in canonical form. A linear process is said to be controllable if the driving matrix $\boldsymbol{\Delta}$ contains no zero rows. Furthermore, it has been demonstrated that a linear process is observable if the output matrix $\mathcal{B}$ contains no zero columns.

The design for time-optimal control of linear discrete systems by the state-transition method is discussed at length. Two design procedures are introduced. The first one makes use of the transformation of coordinates; the second design procedure is based upon successive elimination of the state vectors $\mathbf{x}(jT)$ from the transition equations. The latter iterative procedure provides a simple, straightforward technique for the determination of the optimum-control sequence. The design procedure for single-input processes is extended to multi-input systems. Designing a time-optimum control for a multi-input system is no more difficult than for a single-input system. It has been demonstrated that the state-space approach facilitates the optimum design of multivariable control systems. This iterative design procedure can readily be programmed on a digital computer, and appears to be a better approach.

The iterative procedure is also extended to the optimal design of saturating discrete systems. The concept of control space is introduced as the basis for the design. The control space of a system is the n-dimensional euclidean space with the control sequence forming the mutually orthogonal axes. If in the presence of saturation an nth-order control process can be made to reach the equilibrium state from a given initial state $\mathbf{x}(0)$ in $p = n + q$ sampling periods, the hyperplane formed by

$$\sum_{i=0}^{p-1} \mathbf{s}_{p-i} m(\overline{p - i - 1}\, T) = -\mathbf{x}(0)$$

intersects the hypercube formed by the saturation constraints in the control space. It is found that, if an nth-order saturating discrete-data system can be taken from a given initial state to the equilibrium state in the shortest time of p sampling periods, then q of the p control signals in the sequence $\{m(kT)\}$ are equal to the saturation limit, and the magnitudes of the remaining n control signals will stay within the saturation limit. Methods for the determination of these q saturating control signals are developed. Once the saturating control signals are determined, the optimum-control sequence follows from the solution of n algebraic equations as in the case of no saturation. When the control process is relatively simple, the design of the optimum control by manual computation presents no problem. In complex systems, it seems desirable to write a computer program for carrying out the design procedure.

This chapter concludes with a discussion of the design of time-optimal control for continuous systems by the state-transition techniques. It has been shown that, for an nth-order linear system subject to control-signal saturation, the time-optimal controller is of the bang-bang type, and that, if the coefficient matrix $\mathbf{A}$ is a constant $n \times n$ matrix and has real and distinct eigenvalues, then each component of the optimum-control vector will change sign at most $n - 1$ times in the control interval. A method of determining the switching function is developed. This method, which makes use of the Lagrange multipliers, reduces the design problem to the minimization problem in elementary calculus. The time-optimal control for continuous systems may also be designed by use of the techniques developed for discrete systems, if the continuous systems are approximated by discrete versions. In this case, the sampling period will be so chosen that the discrete approximation is satisfactory.

References

References for this chapter are Bellman, Glicksberg, and Gross,[24] Coddington and Levinson,[45] Desoer and Wing,[49–51] Fuller,[62] Gamkrelidze,[63–65] Gilbert,[69] Ho,[78] Kalman,[88,89] Kalman and Bertram,[90] Krasovskii,[97–99] Kurzweil,[101] LaSalle,[103,104] Lee,[107,108] Letov,[114] Pontryagin,[129] Pontryagin et al.,[130] Proceedings on State Space Techniques,[132] Tou,[136–138,140–142] Tou and Lewis,[146] Tou and Vadhanaphuti,[147] Wing and Desoer,[149] and Zadeh and Desoer.[152]

5

VARIATIONAL CALCULUS IN OPTIMUM CONTROL

The preceding chapter is devoted to the optimum design of control systems by direct application of the state-transition method in a fairly straightforward manner. Attention is focused upon the minimum-time-control problem, and various techniques for time-optimal control of discrete and continuous systems are developed. In this chapter and the remaining chapters of this book, the study of optimum-control problems will be carried out on a broad basis. The more general optimum-control problems will be investigated by other techniques. These include the method of variational calculus, the maximum principle of Pontryagin, and the dynamic programming of Bellman. This chapter is concerned with the study of the optimum-control problems by the classical calculus of variations.

5.1 PROBLEM FORMULATION IN CALCULUS OF VARIATIONS

The variational calculus is that branch of calculus which is concerned with optimization problems under more general conditions than those considered in the ordinary theory of maxima and minima. It deals with the maximization and minimization of functional expressions where entire functions must be determined.[29,35,94,112] The calculus of variations was founded as an independent mathematical discipline by Euler, a noted Russian mathematician, about 150 years ago. Applications of the variational calculus are found in many fields of science and engineering, among them, classical mechanics, electromagnetic theory, fluid mechanics, optics, aerodynamics, and control theory. This chapter is devoted to variational calculus in optimum control. The three fundamental problems in the calculus of variations are the Lagrange problem, the Mayer problem, and the Bolza problem. These three general problems are first briefly reviewed, before the applications to optimum-control problems are discussed in the sections to follow.

The *Lagrange problem* in one independent variable is concerned with the determination of a function $\mathbf{m}(t)$ which minimizes the integral of a given function. This problem may be stated as follows:

Given (1) a set of differential equations

$$\dot{x}_i = f_i(\mathbf{x}, \mathbf{m}, t) \qquad i = 1, 2, \ldots, n \tag{5.1-1a}$$

or more generally,

$$\varphi_i(\mathbf{x}, \dot{\mathbf{x}}, \mathbf{m}, t) = 0 \tag{5.1-1b}$$

where $\mathbf{x}$ is an $n \times 1$ vector and $\mathbf{m}$ is an $r \times 1$ vector; (2) a set of initial conditions

$$x_i(t_0) = a_i \qquad i = 1, 2, \ldots, n \tag{5.1-2}$$

(3) a criterion function

$$I = \int_{t_0}^{t_f} F(\mathbf{x}, \mathbf{m}, t)\, dt \tag{5.1-3}$$

where $F(\mathbf{x}, \mathbf{m}, t)$ is a continuous function of the arguments, determine the function $\mathbf{m}(t)$ which minimizes I over all functions of $\mathbf{m}(t)$, subject to the conditions given in Eqs. (5.1-1) and (5.1-2).

The *Mayer problem* is concerned with the determination of a function $\mathbf{m}(t)$ which minimizes a given function evaluated at the end point, containing some variables whose final values are unspecified in advance. This problem may be stated as follows:

Given (1) a set of differential equations as described in Eqs. (5.1-1), (2) a set of initial conditions as described in Eq. (5.1-2), (3) a set of final conditions

$$x_j(t_f) = b_j \tag{5.1-4}$$

where j belongs to some subset of the integers 1, 2, . . . , n, and t_f is unspecified, (4) a criterion function

$$I = G(\mathbf{x}, \mathbf{m}, t) \Big|_{t_0}^{t_f} \tag{5.1-5}$$

determine the function $\mathbf{m}(t)$ which minimizes I over all functions of $\mathbf{m}(t)$ subject to the conditions given in Eqs. (5.1-1), (5.1-2), and (5.1-4).

A Special Case

When the criterion function is

$$I = G(t) \Big|_{t_0}^{t_f} = t_f - t_0 \tag{5.1-6}$$

the problem reduces to transforming certain initial states into the desired final states in minimum time. This is the time-optimal-control problem discussed in the preceding chapter.

The *Bolza problem* is concerned with the determination of a function $\mathbf{m}(t)$ which minimizes the integral of a function plus a function evaluating at the end point, containing some variables whose final values are unspecified in advance. This problem may be stated as follows:

Given (1) a set of differential equations as described in Eqs. (5.1-1), (2) a set of initial conditions as described in Eq. (5.1-2), (3) a set of final conditions as described in Eq. (5.1-4), (4) a criterion function

$$I = G(\mathbf{x}, \mathbf{m}, t) \Big|_{t_0}^{t_f} + \int_{t_0}^{t_f} F(\mathbf{x}, \mathbf{m}, t)\, dt \tag{5.1-7}$$

determine the function $\mathbf{m}(t)$ which minimizes I over all functions of $\mathbf{m}(t)$ subject to the conditions given in Eqs. (5.1-1), (5.1-2), and (5.1-4).

When $\mathbf{x}$ is identified as the state vector of a process and $\mathbf{m}$ stands for the control vector, the minimum-integral control may be formulated as the Lagrange problem. Similarly, the terminal control and the minimum-time control may be formulated as the Mayer problem. The Bolza problem may be used to describe a minimum-integral control subject to terminal constraint, or a terminal N minimum-time control subject to an integral constraint. The process of obtaining $\mathbf{m}$ is often referred to as the variational method.

The foregoing discussions point out that the formulation of the Bolza problem is the most general case. However, some auxiliary variables can always be introduced which transform a Lagrange problem into a Bolza problem or a Mayer problem, and vice versa. Although there are many optimum-control problems which do not seem to belong to any of these three formulations, there is always some mathematical artifice which may be resorted to that will reduce the initial scheme to one of those considered above. The following examples are given to illustrate the transformation.

Example 5.1-1 Problem Involving Higher Derivatives

Consider the problem of minimizing the criterion function

$$I = \int_{t_0}^{t_f} F(x, \dot{x}, \ddot{x}, t)\, dt \tag{5.1-8}$$

The end values for x and $\dot{x}$ are specified.

Since this problem involves the second derivative of the unknown function, apparently it does not belong to the three basic formulations considered above. However, it can be transformed to a problem of the Lagrange type by introducing an auxiliary variable y such that

$$y = \dot{x} \tag{5.1-9}$$

Then Eq. (5.1-8) may be rewritten as

$$I = \int_{t_0}^{t_f} F(x, y, \dot{y}, t)\, dt \tag{5.1-10}$$

Clearly, this becomes a Lagrange problem.

Example 5.1-2 Reducing a Lagrange Problem to a Mayer Problem

Consider the problem of minimizing the criterion function

$$I = \int_{t_0}^{t_f} F(\mathbf{x}, \dot{\mathbf{x}}, t) \tag{5.1-11}$$

under the assumption that the end values for $\mathbf{x}$ are specified. Equation (5.1-11) reduces to Eq. (5.1-3) by letting $\dot{\mathbf{x}} = \mathbf{m}$. This Lagrange problem may be transformed to a Mayer problem by introducing an auxiliary variable x_{n+1} such that

$$\dot{x}_{n+1}(t) = F(\mathbf{x}, \dot{\mathbf{x}}, t) \tag{5.1-12}$$

where $\mathbf{x}$ is assumed to be an $n \times 1$ vector. The problem now becomes one of minimizing

$$I = \int_{t_0}^{t_f} \dot{x}_{n+1}(t)\, dt = x_{n+1}(t) \Big|_{t_0}^{t_f} \tag{5.1-13}$$

which is a problem of the Mayer type.

Example 5.1-3 Problem Containing Inequalities

Consider the problem of minimizing the criterion function

$$I = \int_{t_0}^{t_f} F(\mathbf{x}, \dot{\mathbf{x}}, t)\, dt \tag{5.1-14}$$

assuming that the end values of x are specified and that $\dot{x}$ is subject to the inequality constraint

$$a \leq \dot{x} \leq b \tag{5.1-15}$$

This minimization problem can be transformed into a Lagrange problem by replacing the above inequality constraint with the equality constraint

$$\varphi(\dot{x}, y) = (\dot{x} - a)(b - \dot{x}) - y^2 = 0 \tag{5.1-16}$$

where the auxiliary variable y is a real variable.

Example 5.1-4 Isoperimetric Problem

Consider the problem of minimizing the criterion function

$$I(\mathbf{m}) = \int_{t_0}^{t_f} F(\mathbf{x}, \mathbf{m}, t) \tag{5.1-17}$$

subject to the constraint

$$\dot{\mathbf{x}} = \mathbf{f}(\mathbf{x}, \mathbf{m}, t) \tag{5.1-18}$$

with the initial conditions

$$\mathbf{x}(t_0) = \mathbf{a} \tag{5.1-19}$$

and the final conditions

$$x_i(t_f) = b_i(t_f) \qquad i = 1, 2, \ldots, k \leq n \tag{5.1-20}$$

where

$$\mathbf{x} = \begin{bmatrix} x_1 \\ x_2 \\ x_3 \\ \cdot \\ \cdot \\ \cdot \\ x_n \end{bmatrix} \quad \text{and} \quad \mathbf{m} = \begin{bmatrix} m_1 \\ m_2 \\ m_3 \\ \cdot \\ \cdot \\ \cdot \\ m_r \end{bmatrix}$$

The boundary conditions at $t = t_f$ may be replaced by the set of integral constraints

$$b_i(t_f) - a_i = \int_{t_0}^{t_f} f_i(\mathbf{x}, \mathbf{m}, t)\, dt \qquad i = 1, 2, \ldots, k \leq n \tag{5.1-21}$$

where the function f_i is the ith component of the function $\mathbf{f}$. Under these conditions, application of the method of the Lagrange multiplier leads to the problem of minimizing the new criterion function

$$I(\mathbf{m}) = \int_{t_0}^{t_f} \left[F(\mathbf{x}, \mathbf{m}, t) + \sum_{i=1}^{k} \mu_i f_i(\mathbf{x}, \mathbf{m}, t) \right] dt \tag{5.1-22}$$

where the μ_i's are constant Lagrangian multipliers. This is the standard form of a classical isoperimetric problem in the calculus of variations. The problem has either a fixed or variable end point, depending upon whether t_f is specified or free.

Example 5.1-5 A Chemical-process Control Problem

One of the common control problems encountered in chemical processes is the optimum control of a stirred-tank reactor. A simplified schematic diagram of the reactor is shown in Fig. 3.2-13. This problem may be formulated as an optimization problem in the calculus of variations.[94] The state differential equations are derived in Example 3.2-2 and repeated here:

$$\dot{x}_1 = f_1 - (f_1 + f_2 - e^{\alpha_1 - \beta_1/x_3})x_1 \tag{5.1-23a}$$
$$\dot{x}_2 = (1 - x_1 - x_2)e^{\alpha_2 - \beta_2/x_3} - (f_1 + f_2)x_2 \tag{5.1-23b}$$
$$\dot{x}_3 = H_1 x_1 e^{\alpha_1 - \beta_1/x_3} + H_2(1 - x_1 - x_2)e^{\alpha_2 - \beta_2/x_3} + f_1(T_1 - x_3) + f_2(T_2 - x_3) + m \tag{5.1-23c}$$

where the symbols are as defined in Sec. 3.2.

The performance criterion which measures the actual return from the stirred-tank reactor of a chemical plant is of the form

$$I = \int_{t_0}^{t_f} \{[p_{o2}(1 - x_1 - x_2) + p_{o3}x_2](f_1 + f_2) - p_{i1}f_1 - p_{i2}f_2 - g(m)\}\, dt \tag{5.1-24}$$

when p_{o2} and p_{o3} denote the prices of components C_2 and C_3 at the reactor outlet; p_{i1} and p_{i2} are the prices of components C_1 and C_2 at the reactor inlet; and the function $g(m)$ represents the cost of control, which includes the heating or refrigerating cost and the constraint on the control signal m. The optimization problem is to determine the rate of heat transfer from the reactor, m, so as to maximize the performance index specified in Eq. (5.1-24), subject to the relationships defined in Eqs. (5.1-23) and given initial conditions $x_1(t_0)$, $x_2(t_0)$, and $x_3(t_0)$. Clearly, this is a problem of the Lagrange type in the calculus of variations.

5.2 A BASIC MINIMIZATION PROBLEM

a. Fixed-end-point System

Consider the problem of minimizing the integral

$$I = \int_{t_0}^{t_f} F(x, \dot{x}, t)\, dt \tag{5.2-1}$$

where $x = x(t)$ is a twice-differentiable function and satisfies the conditions $x(t_0) = x_0$ and $x(t_f) = x_f$, and F is a continuous function of the arguments x, $\dot{x}$, t. Determine the function $x(t)$, which minimizes the integral of Eq. (5.2-1). To interpret geometrically, the problem is to determine the curve $x(t)$ connecting the points (x_0, t_0) and (x_f, t_f) such that the integral along the curve of some given function $F(x, \dot{x}, t)$ is a minimum.[29,35]

In control terminology, if x is the output of a controlled system, then the integral given in Eq. (5.2-1) describes a measure of the overall performance of the system. The criterion of the performance is that this integral is to be minimized. The index of performance may represent the integral of speed error squared in a turboprop-engine control system if x is the engine speed. The optimal-control problem is to minimize the speed error. The performance index may describe the propellant consumption of a missile, with x denoting the displacement and $\dot{x}$ the velocity. The optimal-control problem is to find the optimum-flight trajectory which leads to minimum propellant consumption. The time interval for which the integral is to be a minimum must be chosen. A reasonable time interval is any duration during which the system to be controlled moves from one essential level of operation to another. An essential level of operation is any specific condition of only those variables that must be continuous. In the case of a turboprop engine, the transient behavior of which can be described by a first-order differential equation, the engine speed determines the level of operation.

Let $x(t)$ be the minimizing function and $\bar{x}(t)$ be a neighboring function of $x(t)$. Then $x(t)$ and $\bar{x}(t)$ are related by

$$\bar{x}(t) = x(t) + \epsilon\eta(t) \tag{5.2-2}$$
$$\dot{\bar{x}}(t) = \dot{x}(t) + \epsilon\dot{\eta}(t) \tag{5.2-3}$$

where ϵ is a small parameter, and $\eta(t)$ is an arbitrary differentiable function for which

$$\eta(t_0) = \eta(t_f) = 0 \tag{5.2-4}$$

since the end point is assumed to be fixed, as shown in Fig. 5.2-1. The condition given in Eq. (5.2-4) ensures that $\bar{x}(t_0) = x(t_0) = x_0$ and

$$\bar{x}(t_f) = x(t_f) = x_f$$

that is, all the neighboring functions possess the required end-point values of the functions with respect to which the minimization is carried out. By suitable choice of $\eta(t)$ and ϵ, it is possible to represent any differentiable function having the required end-point values, by an expression of the form given in Eq. (5.2-2). The vertical deviation of any curve $\bar{x}(t)$ from the actual minimizing curve is given by $\epsilon\eta(t)$, as illustrated in Fig. 5.2-1. No matter which $\eta(t)$ is chosen, the minimizing function $x(t)$ is a member of that family for the choice of parameter value $\epsilon = 0$.

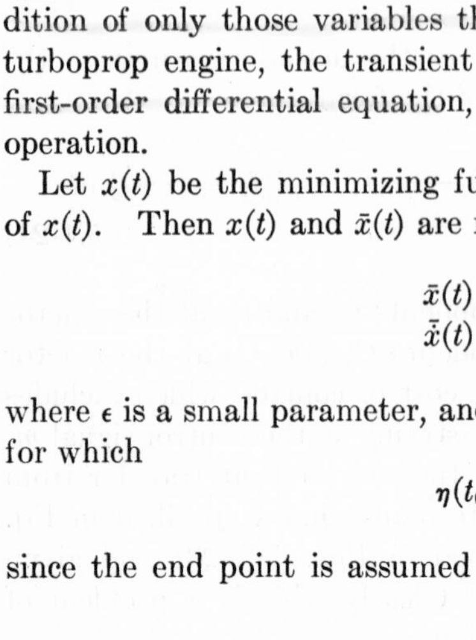

Fig. 5.2-1 Optimum trajectory with fixed end points.

Replacing x and $\dot{x}$ in Eq. (5.2-1), respectively, by $\bar{x}$ and $\dot{\bar{x}}$ yields

$$I(\epsilon) = \int_{t_0}^{t_f} F(x + \epsilon\eta,\ \dot{x} + \epsilon\dot{\eta},\ t)\, dt \tag{5.2-5}$$

By Taylor's series expansion, the integrand of Eq. (5.2-5) becomes

$$F(x + \epsilon\eta, \dot{x} + \epsilon\dot{\eta}, t) = F(x, \dot{x}, t) + \epsilon\eta \frac{\partial F}{\partial x} + \epsilon\dot{\eta} \frac{\partial F}{\partial \dot{x}} + \text{terms in } \epsilon^2, \epsilon^3, \ldots \tag{5.2-6}$$

Then the criterion function may be written as

$$I(\epsilon) = \int_{t_0}^{t_f} \left[F(x, \dot{x}, t) + \epsilon\eta \frac{\partial F}{\partial x} + \epsilon\dot{\eta} \frac{\partial F}{\partial \dot{x}} + \text{terms in } \epsilon^2, \epsilon^3, \ldots \right] dt \tag{5.2-7}$$

The necessary condition for I to be a maximum or a minimum is that

$$\left. \frac{\partial I(\epsilon)}{\partial \epsilon} \right|_{\epsilon=0} = 0 \tag{5.2-8}$$

This leads to the condition that

$$\int_{t_0}^{t_f} \left(\eta \frac{\partial F}{\partial x} + \dot{\eta} \frac{\partial F}{\partial \dot{x}} \right) dt = 0 \tag{5.2-9}$$

Integrating by parts the second term of this integral yields

$$\int_{t_0}^{t_f} \dot{\eta} \frac{\partial F}{\partial \dot{x}}\, dt = \eta \frac{\partial F}{\partial \dot{x}} \Bigg|_{t_0}^{t_f} - \int_{t_0}^{t_f} \eta \frac{d}{dt}\left(\frac{\partial F}{\partial \dot{x}}\right) dt \tag{5.2-10}$$

In view of Eq. (5.2-4),

$$\int_{t_0}^{t_f} \dot{\eta} \frac{\partial F}{\partial \dot{x}}\, dt = - \int_{t_0}^{t_f} \eta \frac{d}{dt}\left(\frac{\partial F}{\partial \dot{x}}\right) dt \tag{5.2-11}$$

Then Eq. (5.2-9) reduces to

$$\int_{t_0}^{t_f} \eta \left[\frac{\partial F}{\partial x} - \frac{d}{dt}\left(\frac{\partial F}{\partial \dot{x}}\right) \right] dt = 0 \tag{5.2-12}$$

Since Eq. (5.2-12) must hold for all η, the necessary condition for I to be an extremum is

$$\frac{\partial F}{\partial x} - \frac{d}{dt}\frac{\partial F}{\partial \dot{x}} = 0 \tag{5.2-13}$$

This second-order equation is known as the *Euler-Lagrange differential equation*, the solution of which gives the minimizing function of the integral of the problem provided the minimum exists.

The Euler-Lagrange differential equation given in Eq. (5.2-13) is integrable when:

1. The function F does not depend on $\dot{x}$; that is,

$$F = F(x, t)$$

2. The function F depends only on x and $\dot{x}$; that is,

$$F = F(x, \dot{x})$$

3. The function F is independent of x; that is,

$$F = F(\dot{x}) \qquad \text{or} \qquad F = F(\dot{x}, t)$$

4. The function F is linear in $\dot{x}$, such as

$$F = \alpha(x, t) + \beta(x, t)\dot{x}$$

In the case of multidimensional functions, the criterion integral of Eq. (5.2-1) becomes

$$I = \int_{t_0}^{t_f} F(\mathbf{x}, \dot{\mathbf{x}}, t) \tag{5.2-14}$$

where $\mathbf{x} = \mathbf{x}(t)$ is an $n \times 1$ vector function of t,

$$\mathbf{x}(t) = \begin{bmatrix} x_1(t) \\ x_2(t) \\ x_3(t) \\ \cdot \\ \cdot \\ \cdot \\ x_n(t) \end{bmatrix} \tag{5.2-15}$$

the components of which are twice-differentiable functions and satisfy the end conditions. Following the derivations similar to the one-dimensional case results in the Euler-Lagrange differential equation for the multidimensional case,

$$\nabla_{\mathbf{x}} F - \frac{d}{dt}(\nabla_{\dot{\mathbf{x}}} F) = 0 \tag{5.2-16}$$

where

$$\nabla_{\mathbf{x}} F = \begin{bmatrix} \dfrac{\partial F}{\partial x_1} \\ \dfrac{\partial F}{\partial x_2} \\ \cdot \\ \cdot \\ \cdot \\ \dfrac{\partial F}{\partial x_n} \end{bmatrix} \tag{5.2-17}$$

and

$$\nabla_{\dot{x}} F = \begin{bmatrix} \dfrac{\partial F}{\partial \dot{x}_1} \\ \dfrac{\partial F}{\partial \dot{x}_2} \\ \cdot \\ \cdot \\ \cdot \\ \dfrac{\partial F}{\partial \dot{x}_n} \end{bmatrix} \tag{5.2-18}$$

b. Movable-end-point Systems

In the preceding minimization problem, the end point of the integral criterion is assumed fixed. Now the minimization problem with the end

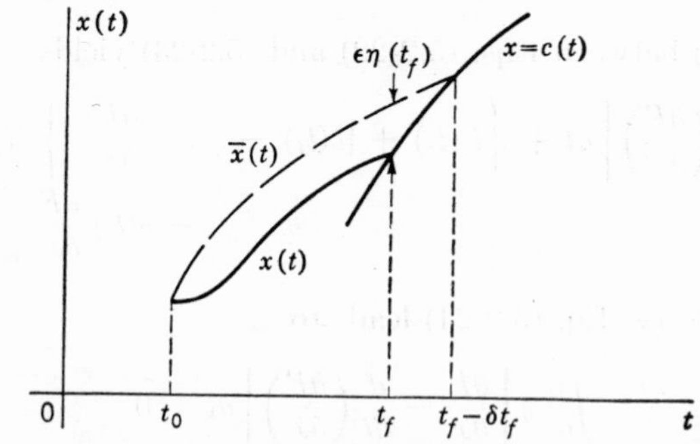

Fig. 5.2-2 Optimum trajectory with movable end point.

point of the trajectory lying on a curve is to be studied. During the time interval of control, the external disturbances are assumed to be constant. At the end of the transient, the control process reaches the end level of x.

Let $x(t)$ be the function which minimizes the integral criterion given in Eq. (5.2-1). The end point of the trajectory is assumed to lie on the curve $x = c(t)$, as shown in Fig. 5.2-2. Assume that $\bar{x}(t)$ is a neighboring function of $x(t)$. The relationship between $x(t)$ and $\bar{x}(t)$ is given by Eqs. (5.2-2) and (5.2-3). The arbitrary function $\eta(t)$ satisfies the initial condition

$$\eta(t_0) = 0 \tag{5.2-19}$$

but the final condition is yet undefined. This allows the proper boundary conditions for movement from one essential level of operation to another.

By replacing x and $\dot{x}$ in Eq. (5.2-1), respectively, by $\bar{x}$ and $\dot{\bar{x}}$, and the upper limit of integration by $t_f + \epsilon\, \delta t_f$, it becomes possible to form the integral

$$I(\epsilon) = \int_{t_0}^{t_f + \epsilon\, \delta t_f} F(x + \epsilon\eta,\ \dot{x} + \epsilon\dot{\eta},\ t)\, dt \tag{5.2-20}$$

The variation δt_f occurs because the end point of the trajectory is not fixed, but lies on the curve $x = c(t)$. Following the same argument as in the fixed-end-point case, it can be shown that the necessary condition for I to be an extremum is that

$$\int_{t_0}^{t_f} \left(\eta \frac{\partial F}{\partial x} + \dot{\eta} \frac{\partial F}{\partial \dot{x}} \right) dt + F(t_f)\, \delta t_f = 0 \tag{5.2-21}$$

Integrating by parts the second term of the integrand and rearranging,

$$\int_{t_0}^{t_f} \eta \left[\frac{\partial F}{\partial x} - \frac{d}{dt}\left(\frac{\partial F}{\partial \dot{x}} \right) \right] dt + \eta(t_f) \left. \frac{\partial F}{\partial \dot{x}} \right|_{t_f} - \eta(t_0) \left. \frac{\partial F}{\partial \dot{x}} \right|_{t_0} + F(t_f)\, \delta t_f = 0 \tag{5.2-22}$$

Examination of the end conditions shown in Fig. 5.2-2 reveals that $\eta(t_f)$ and δt_f are related by

$$\dot{x}\, \delta t_f + \eta(t_f) = \dot{c}(t_f)\, \delta t_f \tag{5.2-23}$$

Eliminating $\eta(t_f)$ between Eqs. (5.2-22) and (5.2-23) yields

$$\int_{t_0}^{t_f} \eta \left[\frac{\partial F}{\partial x} - \frac{d}{dt}\left(\frac{\partial F}{\partial \dot{x}} \right) \right] dt + \left\{ F(t_f) + [\dot{c}(t_f) - \dot{x}(t_f)] \left. \frac{\partial F}{\partial \dot{x}} \right|_{t_f} \right\} \delta t_f - \eta(t_0) \left. \frac{\partial F}{\partial \dot{x}} \right|_{t_0} = 0 \tag{5.2-24}$$

Since δt_f is arbitrary, Eq. (5.2-24) leads to

$$\int_{t_0}^{t_f} \eta \left[\frac{\partial F}{\partial x} - \frac{d}{dt}\left(\frac{\partial F}{\partial \dot{x}} \right) \right] dt = 0 \tag{5.2-25}$$

and

$$\left\{ F(t_f) + [\dot{c}(t_f) - \dot{x}(t_f)] \left. \frac{\partial F}{\partial \dot{x}} \right|_{t_f} \right\} \delta t_f - \eta(t_0) \left. \frac{\partial F}{\partial \dot{x}} \right|_{t_0} = 0 \tag{5.2-26}$$

In view of the fact that Eq. (5.2-25) must hold for all η, the Euler-Lagrange differential equation for this variational problem becomes

$$\frac{\partial F}{\partial x} - \frac{d}{dt}\left(\frac{\partial F}{\partial \dot{x}} \right) = 0 \tag{5.2-27}$$

which is identical with Eq. (5.2-13). However, in the case of the free end point, the solution of the Euler-Lagrange equation must satisfy Eq. (5.2-26). If $\partial F/\partial \dot{x}$ is finite at $t = t_0$, Eq. (5.2-26) reduces to

$$F(t_f) = [\dot{x}(t_f) - \dot{c}(t_f)] \left. \frac{\partial F}{\partial \dot{x}} \right|_{t_f} \tag{5.2-28}$$

which is referred to as the *transversality condition*. Note that Eq. (5.2-27) need not hold at $t = t_0$, because $\eta(t_0) = 0$. The only conditions that need hold at $t = t_0$ are that x is continuous and $\partial F/\partial \dot{x}$ is finite at $t = t_0$.

In regulator problems, during the operating interval the process moves from one essential operating level to another, that is, from one definite value of x to another definite value of x. Thus the end curve $x = c(t)$ is a horizontal straight line and

$$\dot{c}(t_f) = 0 \tag{5.2-29}$$

The transversality condition given in Eq. (5.2-28) now becomes

$$F(t_f) = \dot{x}(t_f) \left. \frac{\partial F}{\partial \dot{x}} \right|_{t_f} \tag{5.2-30}$$

The first integral of Eq. (5.2-27) is found to be

$$\frac{d}{dt}\left(-F + \dot{x}\frac{\partial F}{\partial \dot{x}}\right) + \frac{\partial F}{\partial t} = 0 \tag{5.2-31}$$

When the integrand F does not explicitly depend upon t, the first integral of Eq. (5.2-27) which satisfies the boundary condition of Eq. (5.2-30) is

$$F(x, \dot{x}) = \dot{x}\frac{\partial F}{\partial \dot{x}} \tag{5.2-32}$$

Differentiating both sides of Eq. (5.2-32) with respect to t and simplifying yields

$$\dot{x}\left[\frac{\partial F}{\partial x} - \frac{d}{dt}\left(\frac{\partial F}{\partial \dot{x}}\right)\right] = 0 \tag{5.2-33}$$

Since $\dot{x}$ does not generally vanish during the transient, Eq. (5.2-27) is satisfied. Hence the two conditions on $x(t)$ as specified by Eqs. (5.2-27) and (5.2-30) are now replaced by the single condition of Eq. (5.2-32), which provides the description of the optimum system that moves from one operating level to another operating level during the time interval (t_0, t_f).

Example 5.2-1 An Interception Problem

A typical optimization problem in which the end point of the trajectory is variable is the interception problem in the launching of a rocket, as shown in Fig. 5.2-3. It is required that the rocket be launched to meet with and match the speed of an orbiting vehicle moving on a known path $c(t)$ with minimum fuel consumption in the process. The control variable in this system is the rocket thrust $m(t)$, which is related to the fuel flow $q(t)$ by

$$q(t) = F[m(t)]$$

Since the fuel flow is always positive, the function $F[m(t)]$ is an even function of $m(t)$.

Assume that $x(t)$ denotes the rocket position. A simplified differential equation characterizing the rocket motion in one dimension is given by

$$M(t)\ddot{x}(t) + \dot{M}(t)\dot{x}(t) = m(t) - G[x(t)] - P[x(t), \dot{x}(t)]$$

where $M(t)$ is the rocket mass, $G[x(t)]$ is the gravitational force, and $P[x(t), \dot{x}(t)]$ denotes the aerodynamic drag. The mass of the rocket is assumed to be an independent function of time, to account, in part, for its decrease as fuel is consumed.

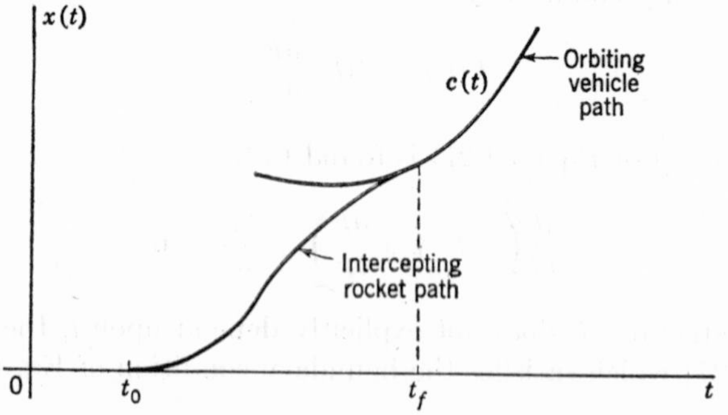

Fig. 5.2-3 Optimum trajectory of the system in Example 5.2-1.

Let the state variables of the system be x_1 and x_2. Then the state differential equations are

$$\dot{x}_1(t) = -\frac{\dot{M}(t)}{M(t)}x_1(t) - \frac{G[x_1(t)] + P[x_1(t), x_2(t)]}{M(t)} + \frac{1}{M(t)}m(t)$$
$$\dot{x}_2(t) = x_1(t)$$

The problem is to determine the optimum-control signal $m(t)$ so that the performance index

$$I = \int_{t_0}^{t_f} F[m(t)]\, dt$$

is minimized. The terminating time t_f is the time at which the intercepting rocket path meets the orbiting vehicle path; that is, at $t = t_f$, some functional

$$\varphi\{[x_1(t_f) - c(t_f)], [x_2(t_f) - \dot{c}(t_f)]\} = 0$$

is satisfied. The above performance index gives a measure of the fuel consumption during the interval (t_0, t_f).

5.3 MINIMUM-INTEGRAL CONTROL

This section is concerned with the application of the variational calculus to the optimum design of control processes with respect to integral performance criteria.[27,29,35,47,94,108,112] Consider a control process characterized by

$$\dot{x}(t) = g(x, m) \tag{5.3-1}$$

where x and m are scalar functions of t, and at $t = t_0$,

$$x(t_0) = x_0 \tag{5.3-2}$$

Determine the optimum-control signal $m(t)$ which minimizes the integral-criterion function

$$I = \int_{t_0}^{t_f} F(x, m)\, dt \tag{5.3-3}$$

where the function $F(x, m)$ may describe the deviation from the desired state, the fuel consumption, and the control cost of the system. In the interception problem considered in Example 5.2-1, the function $F[m(t)]$ represents the fuel flow in the rocket, which is a function of the control signal $m(t)$. The optimum-control problem is to determine the rocket thrust so that the total fuel consumption during the flight interval (t_0, t_f) is minimized.

Let x and m be a pair of functions which yield the minimum of Eq. (5.3-3). Then the neighboring functions $\bar{x}$ and $\bar{m}$ may be expressed as

$$\bar{x} = x + \epsilon\eta \tag{5.3-4}$$
$$\bar{m} = m + \epsilon\xi \tag{5.3-5}$$

where η and ξ are arbitrary functions of t, defined for $t_0 \le t \le t_f$, and ϵ is a small parameter. Replacing x and m in Eq. (5.3-3), respectively, by $\bar{x}$ and $\bar{m}$ gives the value of the integral for the neighboring functions as

$$I(\epsilon) = \int_{t_0}^{t_f} F(x + \epsilon\eta, m + \epsilon\xi)\, dt \tag{5.3-6}$$

By use of the Taylor series expansion, Eq. (5.3-6) may be written in the form

$$I(\epsilon) = \int_{t_0}^{t_f} F(x, m)\, dt + \epsilon \int_{t_0}^{t_f} \left(\eta \frac{\partial F}{\partial x} + \xi \frac{\partial F}{\partial m} \right) dt + O(\epsilon^2) \tag{5.3-7}$$

where $O(\epsilon^2)$ represents the high-order infinitesimal terms. Since the minimum of the integral occurs when

$$\left. \frac{\partial I}{\partial \epsilon} \right|_{\epsilon=0} = 0 \tag{5.3-8}$$

the necessary condition for I to be an extremum is

$$\int_{t_0}^{t_f} \left(\eta \frac{\partial F}{\partial x} + \xi \frac{\partial F}{\partial m} \right) dt = 0 \tag{5.3-9}$$

Replacing x and m in Eq. (5.3-1), respectively, by $\bar{x}$ and $\bar{m}$ gives

$$\dot{x} + \epsilon\dot{\eta} = g(x + \epsilon\eta, m + \epsilon\xi) \tag{5.3-10}$$

Application of the Taylor series expansion reduces Eq. (5.3-10) to

$$\dot{x} + \epsilon\dot{\eta} = g(x, m) + \epsilon\left(\eta \frac{\partial g}{\partial x} + \xi \frac{\partial g}{\partial m}\right) + O(\epsilon^2) \tag{5.3-11}$$

As ϵ approaches zero, $O(\epsilon^2)$ becomes zero, and

$$\dot{x} = g(x, m) \tag{5.3-12}$$

$$\dot{\eta} = \eta \frac{\partial g}{\partial x} + \xi \frac{\partial g}{\partial m} \tag{5.3-13}$$

Equation (5.3-13) is subject to the initial condition that

$$\eta(t_0) = 0 \tag{5.3-14}$$

Solving for ξ from Eq. (5.3-13) yields

$$\xi = \frac{\dot{\eta} - \eta(\partial g/\partial x)}{\partial g/\partial m} \tag{5.3-15}$$

Substituting the value of ξ into Eq. (5.3-9) gives

$$\int_{t_0}^{t_f} \left[\eta \frac{\partial F}{\partial x} + \left(\dot{\eta} - \eta \frac{\partial g}{\partial x}\right) \frac{\partial F/\partial m}{\partial g/\partial m}\right] dt = 0 \tag{5.3-16}$$

Integrating by parts,

$$\begin{aligned}\int_{t_0}^{t_f} \frac{\partial F/\partial m}{\partial g/\partial m} \dot{\eta}\, dt &= \eta \frac{\partial F/\partial m}{\partial g/\partial m}\bigg|_{t_0}^{t_f} - \int_{t_0}^{t_f} \eta \frac{d}{dt}\left(\frac{\partial F/\partial m}{\partial g/\partial m}\right) dt \\ &= -\int_{t_0}^{t_f} \eta \frac{d}{dt}\left(\frac{\partial F/\partial m}{\partial g/\partial m}\right) dt\end{aligned} \tag{5.3-17}$$

since $x(t_0) = x_0$, a fixed value, $\eta(t_0) = 0$, and

$$\frac{\partial F/\partial m}{\partial g/\partial m}\bigg|_{t_f} = 0 \tag{5.3-18}$$

Combining Eqs. (5.3-16) and (5.3-17) leads to

$$\int_{t_0}^{t_f} \left[\frac{\dfrac{\partial F}{\partial x}\dfrac{\partial g}{\partial m} - \dfrac{\partial F}{\partial m}\dfrac{\partial g}{\partial x}}{\partial g/\partial m} - \frac{d}{dt}\left(\frac{\partial F/\partial m}{\partial g/\partial m}\right)\right] \eta\, dt = 0 \tag{5.3-19}$$

Since Eq. (5.3-19) must hold for all η, the Euler-Lagrange differential equation for this optimum-control problem evolves as

$$\frac{\dfrac{\partial F}{\partial x}\dfrac{\partial g}{\partial m} - \dfrac{\partial F}{\partial m}\dfrac{\partial g}{\partial x}}{\partial g/\partial m} - \frac{d}{dt}\left(\frac{\partial F/\partial m}{\partial g/\partial m}\right) = 0 \tag{5.3-20}$$

The solution of this differential equation, subject to the boundary conditions specified in Eqs. (5.3-2) and (5.3-18), gives the optimum control $m(t)$ for the process. This is a two-point boundary-value problem of the classical variational calculus, since the two boundary conditions are given by both ends of the trajectory.

A Special Case

When

$$\dot{x} = g(x, m) = m \tag{5.3-21}$$

the integral criterion function becomes

$$I = \int_{t_0}^{t_f} F(x, \dot{x})\, dt \tag{5.3-22}$$

Since $$\frac{\partial g}{\partial m} = 1 \qquad \text{and} \qquad \frac{\partial g}{\partial x} = 0$$

the Euler-Lagrange equation for this special case reduces to

$$\frac{\partial F}{\partial x} - \frac{d}{dt}\left(\frac{\partial F}{\partial m}\right) = 0 \tag{5.3-23}$$

or

$$\frac{\partial F}{\partial x} - \frac{d}{dt}\left(\frac{\partial F}{\partial \dot{x}}\right) = 0 \tag{5.3-24}$$

with the boundary conditions

$$x(t_0) = x_0 \qquad \text{and} \qquad \left.\frac{\partial F}{\partial \dot{x}}\right|_{t_f} = 0 \tag{5.3-25}$$

which are prescribed in part at the initial point and in part at the final point.

Generally speaking, analytical solutions for two-point boundary-value problems are possible only in special cases. Consequently, where closed-form solutions cannot be obtained, trial-and-error techniques must be resorted to. These techniques consist in guessing a value for the missing initial condition, as, for instance, a value of $x(t_0) = x_0$, and integrating numerically the Euler-Lagrange equation and the constraining equation. The given value of $x(t_0) = x_0$ and the guessed value of $x(t_0)$ are used in performing the integration. The difference between the resulting final condition and the specified condition is determined. Since this difference is generally not zero, the trial-and-error process must be repeated several times until the value of the final condition obtained in this way agrees sufficiently closely with the specified value of the final condition.

Multidimensional Control Process

The above discussions are now extended to the optimum design of multi-dimensional control processes with respect to integral performance criteria. Consider a multidimensional control process characterized by

$$\dot{\mathbf{x}} = \mathbf{g}(\mathbf{x}, \mathbf{m}) \tag{5.3-26}$$

subject to the initial conditions $\mathbf{x}(t_0) = \mathbf{x}_0$, where $\mathbf{x}$ denotes the state vector of the process and $\mathbf{m}$ is the control vector. It is assumed that $\mathbf{x}$ is a column vector of dimension n and that $\mathbf{m}$ is a column vector of dimension r. Determine the optimum-control vector $\mathbf{m}(t)$ which minimizes the integral criterion function

$$I = \int_{t_0}^{t_f} F(\mathbf{x}, \mathbf{m})\, dt \tag{5.3-27}$$

Let $\mathbf{x}(t)$ and $\mathbf{m}(t)$ be a pair of vector functions which yield the minimum of Eq. (5.3-27). Then the neighboring functions $\bar{\mathbf{x}}(t)$ and $\bar{\mathbf{m}}(t)$ may be expressed as

$$\bar{\mathbf{x}}(t) = \mathbf{x}(t) + \epsilon \boldsymbol{\eta}(t) \tag{5.3-28}$$
$$\bar{\mathbf{m}}(t) = \mathbf{m}(t) + \epsilon \boldsymbol{\xi}(t) \tag{5.3-29}$$

where $\boldsymbol{\eta}$ and $\boldsymbol{\xi}$ are arbitrary vector functions of t, defined for the interval (t_0, t_f), and ϵ is a small parameter. $\boldsymbol{\eta}(t)$ is an $n \times 1$ vector, and $\boldsymbol{\xi}(t)$ is an $r \times 1$ vector. In terms of the components, the neighboring functions are

$$\bar{x}_i = x_i + \epsilon\eta_i \qquad i = 1, 2, \ldots, n \tag{5.3-30}$$
$$\bar{m}_k = m_k + \epsilon\xi_k \qquad k = 1, 2, \ldots, r \tag{5.3-31}$$

Replacing $\mathbf{x}$ and $\mathbf{m}$ in Eq. (5.3-27), respectively, by $\bar{\mathbf{x}}$ and $\bar{\mathbf{m}}$ gives the value of the integral for the neighboring functions as

$$I(\epsilon) = \int_{t_0}^{t_f} F(\mathbf{x} + \epsilon\boldsymbol{\eta}, \mathbf{m} + \epsilon\boldsymbol{\xi})\, dt \tag{5.3-32}$$

Taylor series expansion of the integrand leads to

$$I(\epsilon) = \int_{t_0}^{t_f} \left[F(\mathbf{x}, \mathbf{m}) + \epsilon \left(\sum_{i=1}^{n} \eta_i \frac{\partial F}{\partial x_i} + \sum_{k=1}^{r} \xi_k \frac{\partial F}{\partial m_k} \right) \right] dt + O(\epsilon^2) \tag{5.3-33}$$

where $O(\epsilon^2)$ denotes the high-order infinitesimal terms.

For $I(\epsilon)$ to be a minimum,

$$\left. \frac{dI(\epsilon)}{d\epsilon} \right|_{\epsilon=0} = 0 \tag{5.3-34}$$

Carrying out the minimization procedure and simplifying yields

$$\int_{t_0}^{t_f} \left(\sum_{i=1}^{n} \eta_i \frac{\partial F}{\partial x_i} + \sum_{k=1}^{r} \xi_k \frac{\partial F}{\partial m_k} \right) dt = 0 \tag{5.3-35}$$

This integral equation may be written in vector notation as

$$\int_{t_0}^{t_f} [(\nabla_{\mathbf{x}} F)'\boldsymbol{\eta} + (\nabla_{\mathbf{m}} F)'\boldsymbol{\xi}]\, dt = 0 \tag{5.3-36}$$

where the prime denotes the transpose of the matrix, and the vector differentiation operators ∇_x and ∇_m are defined by

$$\nabla_x = \begin{bmatrix} \dfrac{\partial}{\partial x_1} \\ \dfrac{\partial}{\partial x_2} \\ \cdot \\ \cdot \\ \cdot \\ \dfrac{\partial}{\partial x_n} \end{bmatrix} \tag{5.3-37}$$

and

$$\nabla_m = \begin{bmatrix} \dfrac{\partial}{\partial m_1} \\ \dfrac{\partial}{\partial m_2} \\ \cdot \\ \cdot \\ \cdot \\ \dfrac{\partial}{\partial m_r} \end{bmatrix} \tag{5.3-38}$$

Replacing $\dot{\mathbf{x}}$, $\mathbf{x}$, and $\mathbf{m}$ in Eq. (5.3-26), respectively, by $\dot{\bar{\mathbf{x}}}$, $\bar{\mathbf{x}}$, and $\bar{\mathbf{m}}$ yields the differential equation in neighboring functions,

$$\dot{\mathbf{x}} + \epsilon\dot{\mathbf{n}} = \mathbf{g}(\mathbf{x} + \epsilon\mathbf{n}, \mathbf{m} + \epsilon\boldsymbol{\xi}) \tag{5.3-39}$$

Expanding the right-hand term in a Taylor's series and equating the coefficients of like terms gives

$$\dot{\mathbf{n}} = \sum_{i=1}^{n} \eta_i \frac{\partial \mathbf{g}}{\partial x_i} + \sum_{k=1}^{r} \xi_k \frac{\partial \mathbf{g}}{\partial m_k} \tag{5.3-40}$$

Define

$$\mathbf{g} = \begin{bmatrix} g_1 \\ g_2 \\ \cdot \\ \cdot \\ \cdot \\ g_n \end{bmatrix} \tag{5.3-41}$$

Equation (5.3-40) may be written as

$$\dot{\mathbf{n}} = [\nabla_x \mathbf{g}']'\mathbf{n} + [\nabla_m \mathbf{g}']'\boldsymbol{\xi} \tag{5.3-42}$$

where

$$[\nabla_x \mathbf{g}']'\mathbf{n} = \sum_{i=1}^{n} \eta_i \frac{\partial \mathbf{g}}{\partial x_i} \tag{5.3-43}$$

and

$$[\nabla_m \mathbf{g}']'\boldsymbol{\xi} = \sum_{k=1}^{r} \xi_k \frac{\partial \mathbf{g}}{\partial m_k} \tag{5.3-44}$$

$[\nabla_x \mathbf{g}']'$ is an $n \times n$ matrix, and $[\nabla_m \mathbf{g}']'$ is an $n \times r$ matrix.

By letting $\mathbf{g}^{(r)}$ be the $1 \times r$ row vector given by

$$\mathbf{g}^{(r)} = [g_1 \quad g_2 \quad g_3 \quad \cdots \quad g_r] \tag{5.3-45}$$

and letting $\boldsymbol{\eta}^{(r)}$ be the $n \times 1$ column vector given by

$$\boldsymbol{\eta}^{(r)} = \begin{bmatrix} \eta_1 \\ \eta_2 \\ \cdot \\ \cdot \\ \cdot \\ \eta_r \\ 0 \\ \cdot \\ \cdot \\ \cdot \\ 0 \end{bmatrix} \tag{5.3-46}$$

where the last $n - r$ elements are zeros, the following derivative may be obtained from Eq. (5.3-42):

$$\dot{\boldsymbol{\eta}}^{(r)} = [\nabla_x \mathbf{g}^{(r)}]'\boldsymbol{\eta} + [\nabla_m \mathbf{g}^{(r)}]'\boldsymbol{\xi} \tag{5.3-47}$$

where matrix $[\nabla_m \mathbf{g}^{(r)}]'$ is nonsingular. Solving Eq. (5.3-47) for $\boldsymbol{\xi}$ gives

$$\boldsymbol{\xi} = [(\nabla_m \mathbf{g}^{(r)})']^{-1}\dot{\boldsymbol{\eta}}^{(r)} - [(\nabla_m \mathbf{g}^{(r)})']^{-1}(\nabla_x \mathbf{g}^{(r)})'\boldsymbol{\eta} \tag{5.3-48}$$

Substitution for $\boldsymbol{\xi}$ into Eq. (5.3-36) yields

$$\int_{t_0}^{t_f} \{(\nabla_x F)' - (\nabla_m F)'[(\nabla_x \mathbf{g}^{(r)})(\nabla_m \mathbf{g}^{(r)})^{-1}]'\}\boldsymbol{\eta}\, dt + \int_{t_0}^{t_f} (\nabla_m F)'[(\nabla_m \mathbf{g}^{(r)})']^{-1}\dot{\boldsymbol{\eta}}^{(r)}\, dt = 0 \tag{5.3-49}$$

Performing integration by parts of the second integral and making use of the boundary conditions $\boldsymbol{\eta}(t_0) = \mathbf{0}$ and

$$(\nabla_m F)'[(\nabla_m \mathbf{g}^{(r)})']^{-1}\Big|_{t_f} = 0 \tag{5.3-50}$$

reduces Eq. (5.3-49) to

$$\int_{t_0}^{t_f} \{(\nabla_x F)' - (\nabla_m F)'[(\nabla_x \mathbf{g}^{(r)})(\nabla_m \mathbf{g}^{(r)})^{-1}]'\}\boldsymbol{\eta}\, dt - \int_{t_0}^{t_f} \frac{d}{dt}\{(\nabla_m F)'[(\nabla_m \mathbf{g}^{(r)})']^{-1}\}\boldsymbol{\eta}^{(r)}\, dt = 0 \tag{5.3-51}$$

Equation (5.3-51) may be written as

$$\int_{t_0}^{t_f} \boldsymbol{\eta}'[(\nabla_x F) - (\nabla_x \mathbf{g}^{(r)})(\nabla_m \mathbf{g}^{(r)})^{-1}(\nabla_m F)]\, dt - \int_{t_0}^{t_f} [\boldsymbol{\eta}^{(r)}]' \frac{d}{dt}[(\nabla_m \mathbf{g}^{(r)})^{-1}(\nabla_m F)]\, dt = 0 \tag{5.3-52}$$

To eliminate $\mathbf{n}^{(r)}$ the following $n \times r$ matrix is introduced:

$$\mathbf{R} = \begin{bmatrix} (\nabla_{\mathbf{m}}\mathbf{g}^{(r)})^{-1} \\ 0 \\ \cdot \\ \cdot \\ \cdot \\ 0 \end{bmatrix} \tag{5.3-53}$$

where the last $n - r$ rows are zeros. Then

$$[\mathbf{n}^{(r)}]'(\nabla_{\mathbf{m}}\mathbf{g}^{(r)})^{-1} = \mathbf{n}'\mathbf{R} \tag{5.3-54}$$

Substituting from Eq. (5.3-54) into Eq. (5.3-52) gives

$$\int_{t_0}^{t_f} \mathbf{n}'\{(\nabla_{\mathbf{x}}F) - (\nabla_{\mathbf{x}}\mathbf{g}^{(r)})(\nabla_{\mathbf{m}}\mathbf{g}^{(r)})^{-1}(\nabla_{\mathbf{m}}F) - \frac{d}{dt}[\mathbf{R}(\nabla_{\mathbf{m}}F)]\}\, dt = 0 \tag{5.3-55}$$

Since Eq. (5.3-55) must hold for all η, the quantity in the braces must equal zero. The Euler-Lagrange differential equation for the given multidimensional control process is

$$(\nabla_{\mathbf{x}}F) - (\nabla_{\mathbf{x}}\mathbf{g}^{(r)})(\nabla_{\mathbf{m}}\mathbf{g}^{(r)})^{-1}(\nabla_{\mathbf{m}}F) - \frac{d}{dt}[\mathbf{R}(\nabla_{\mathbf{m}}F)] = 0 \tag{5.3-56}$$

The solution of this differential equation subject to the boundary conditions given in Eq. (5.3-50) and $\mathbf{x}(t_0) = \mathbf{x}_0$ yields the optimum-control vector $\mathbf{m}(t)$ for the system.

For the special case that

$$\mathbf{m} = \dot{\mathbf{x}} \tag{5.3-57}$$

there results $\nabla_{\mathbf{m}}\mathbf{g} = \nabla_{\dot{\mathbf{x}}}\dot{\mathbf{x}} = \mathbf{1}'$ and $\nabla_{\mathbf{x}}\mathbf{g} = \nabla_{\mathbf{x}}\dot{\mathbf{x}} = \mathbf{0}$. Thus the Euler-Lagrange equation reduces to

$$\nabla_{\mathbf{x}}F - \frac{d}{dt}(\nabla_{\dot{\mathbf{x}}}F) = 0 \tag{5.3-58}$$

which checks with Eq. (5.2-16).

5.4 LAGRANGE MULTIPLIERS AND CONSTRAINTS

The preceding section discussed the design of optimum control to minimize an integral performance criterion under the assumption that both the control signals and the state variables are subject to no constraints. However, in a great many practical control processes, certain physical constraints are imposed upon the control signals or the state variables. In order to derive realistic optimum controls for physical processes, the constraints on the control signals or the state variables must be taken into consideration.

This section is concerned with the treatment of physical constraints in optimum-control design by the method of the Lagrange multiplier. As discussed in textbooks on applied mathematics, the technique of the Lagrange multiplier offers a refined approach to the problem of maximizing or minimizing a function subject to one or more constraints, when the constraint relations are so complex that they cannot be readily used to eliminate free parameters. By use of the method of the Lagrange multiplier, solution of the constraint equations to eliminate free parameters is made unnecessary.

Let $P(\mathbf{m}) = P(m_1, m_2, \ldots, m_r)$ be the function that is to be maximized or minimized subject to the constraint

$$\mathbf{Q}(\mathbf{m}) = \mathbf{Q}(m_1, m_2, \ldots, m_r) \leq \mathbf{c} \tag{5.4-1}$$

where $\mathbf{Q}$ is an $r \times 1$ matrix and $\mathbf{c}$, given by

$$\mathbf{c} = \begin{bmatrix} c_1 \\ c_2 \\ \cdot \\ \cdot \\ \cdot \\ c_r \end{bmatrix} \tag{5.4-2}$$

is a constant $r \times 1$ column matrix. For instance, the constraint given in Eq. (5.4-1) may describe the condition that $m_i^2 \leq c_i$; that is, the squares of the control signals are bounded. Or Eq. (5.4-1) may describe the condition that $q_i(m_i) \leq c_i$, which implies that some functions of the control signals are bounded. Then, according to Lagrange, the desired vector $\mathbf{m}$ which maximizes or minimizes the given function $P(\mathbf{m})$ may be obtained by maximizing or minimizing the synthetic function

$$G(\mathbf{m}) = P(\mathbf{m}) + \boldsymbol{\lambda}'\mathbf{Q}(\mathbf{m}) \tag{5.4-3}$$

where $\boldsymbol{\lambda}$ is a constant $r \times 1$ column matrix referred to as the *vector Lagrange multiplier*. Maximizing or minimizing this synthetic function gives the desired vector $\mathbf{m}$ as a function of the vector Lagrange multiplier $\boldsymbol{\lambda}$. Substitution of the vector $\mathbf{m}(\boldsymbol{\lambda}) = \mathbf{m}(\lambda_1, \lambda_2, \ldots, \lambda_r)$ into the constraint relationship given in Eq. (5.4-1) leads to r equations from which the elements λ_i of the vector Lagrange multiplier can be determined.[27,29,35,52,94,99,112,135]

Linear Control Process with Quadratic Criterion

Consider a linear, multivariable control process characterized by

$$\dot{\mathbf{x}}(t) = \mathbf{A}\mathbf{x}(t) + \mathbf{D}\mathbf{m}(t) \tag{5.4-4}$$

where the state vector $\mathbf{x}$ is of dimension n, the control vector $\mathbf{m}$ is of dimension r, and the coefficient matrix $\mathbf{A}$ and the driving matrix $\mathbf{D}$ are $n \times n$

and $n \times r$ matrices, respectively. Determine the optimum-control vector $\mathbf{m}(t)$ which minimizes the integral criterion function

$$I(\mathbf{m}) = \int_0^T \mathbf{m}'\mathbf{H}\mathbf{m}\,dt \tag{5.4-5a}$$

subject to the constraint on the state variables given by

$$\mathbf{x}(T) = \mathbf{0} \tag{5.4-5b}$$

In the criterion function of Eq. (5.4-5*a*), the integrand

$$F(\mathbf{m}) = \mathbf{m}'\mathbf{H}\mathbf{m} \tag{5.4-6}$$

is a quadratic function. The matrix $\mathbf{H}$ is symmetrical and positive-definite. The initial-state vector of the given control process is assumed to be

$$\mathbf{x}(0) = \mathbf{x}_0 \quad \text{(yet unknown)} \tag{5.4-7}$$

To facilitate the application of the method of the Lagrange multiplier, the constraint given in Eq. (5.4-5*b*) is first converted into an integral constraint since the specified criterion function is expressed in the form of an integral. The solution to Eq. (5.4-4) has been found to be

$$\mathbf{x}(t) = \boldsymbol{\phi}(t)\mathbf{x}_0 + \int_0^t \boldsymbol{\phi}(t-\tau)\mathbf{D}\mathbf{m}(\tau)\,d\tau \tag{5.4-8}$$

by the state transition method

where $\boldsymbol{\phi}(t)$ is the transition matrix of the process. At the end of the trajectory, $t = T$, the state vector is

$$\mathbf{x}(T) = \boldsymbol{\phi}(T)\mathbf{x}_0 + \int_0^T \boldsymbol{\phi}(T-\tau)\mathbf{D}\mathbf{m}(\tau)\,d\tau \tag{5.4-9}$$

In view of Eq. (5.4-5*b*),

$$\boldsymbol{\phi}(T)\mathbf{x}_0 + \int_0^T \boldsymbol{\phi}(T-\tau)\mathbf{D}\mathbf{m}(\tau)\,d\tau = \mathbf{0} \tag{5.4-10}$$

Solving for $\mathbf{x}_0$ and replacing τ by t yields

$$\mathbf{x}_0 = -\int_0^T \boldsymbol{\phi}(-t)\mathbf{D}\mathbf{m}(t)\,dt \tag{5.4-11}$$

see comments.

The optimum-design problem may now be reformulated as the minimization of $I(\mathbf{m})$, which is given in Eq. (5.4-5*a*), with respect to the control vector $\mathbf{m}$, subject to the constraint of Eq. (5.4-11). In other words, the specified [on x(T)] constraint relationship is converted into an integral constraint. [on x_0]

Introducing the vector Lagrange multiplier $\boldsymbol{\lambda}$, the optimization problem becomes the minimization of the criterion function

$$I_1(\mathbf{m}) = \int_0^T [\mathbf{m}'(t)\mathbf{H}\mathbf{m}(t) + \boldsymbol{\lambda}'\boldsymbol{\phi}(-t)\mathbf{D}\mathbf{m}(t)]\, dt \tag{5.4-12}$$

Applying the Euler-Lagrange equation,

$$\nabla_{\mathbf{m}}[\mathbf{m}'(t)\mathbf{H}\mathbf{m}(t) + \boldsymbol{\lambda}'\boldsymbol{\phi}(-t)\mathbf{D}\mathbf{m}(t)] = (\mathbf{H} + \mathbf{H}')\mathbf{m}(t) + \mathbf{D}'[\boldsymbol{\phi}(-t)]'\boldsymbol{\lambda} \tag{5.4-13}$$

and

$$\nabla_{\dot{\mathbf{m}}}[\mathbf{m}'(t)\mathbf{H}\mathbf{m}(t) + \boldsymbol{\lambda}'\boldsymbol{\phi}(-t)\mathbf{D}\mathbf{m}(t)] = \mathbf{0} \tag{5.4-14}$$

Hence the necessary condition for $I_1(\mathbf{m})$ to be an extremum is

$$(\mathbf{H} + \mathbf{H}')\mathbf{m}(t) + \mathbf{D}'[\boldsymbol{\phi}(-t)]'\boldsymbol{\lambda} = \mathbf{0} \tag{5.4-15}$$

Since the matrix $\mathbf{H}$ is symmetrical, $\mathbf{H} = \mathbf{H}'$. Equation (5.4-15) reduces to

$$2\mathbf{H}\mathbf{m}(t) + \mathbf{D}'[\boldsymbol{\phi}(-t)]'\boldsymbol{\lambda} = \mathbf{0} \tag{5.4-16}$$

and the optimum-control vector over the time interval $(0, T)$ is given by

$$\mathbf{m}^o(t) = -\tfrac{1}{2}\mathbf{H}^{-1}\mathbf{D}'[\boldsymbol{\phi}(-t)]'\boldsymbol{\lambda} \tag{5.4-17}$$

The vector Lagrange multiplier $\boldsymbol{\lambda}$ can be determined by making use of the constraint given in Eq. (5.4-11). Substituting the optimum-control vector $\mathbf{m}^o(t)$ into Eq. (5.4-11) yields

$$\mathbf{x}_0 = \mathbf{V}(T)\boldsymbol{\lambda} \tag{5.4-18}$$

where

$$\mathbf{V}(T) = \tfrac{1}{2}\int_0^T \boldsymbol{\phi}(-t)\mathbf{D}\mathbf{H}^{-1}\mathbf{D}'[\boldsymbol{\phi}(-t)]'\, dt \tag{5.4-19}$$

If the matrix $\mathbf{V}(T)$ is nonsingular, the vector Lagrange multiplier is then given by

$$\boldsymbol{\lambda} = \mathbf{V}^{-1}(T)\mathbf{x}_0 \tag{5.4-20}$$

Therefore the optimum-control vector is

$$\mathbf{m}^o(t) = -\tfrac{1}{2}\mathbf{H}^{-1}\mathbf{D}'[\boldsymbol{\phi}(-t)]'\mathbf{V}^{-1}(T)\mathbf{x}_0 \tag{5.4-21}$$

The foregoing discussion illustrates the application of the method of the Lagrange multiplier to the minimization of an integral criterion function, subject to a nonintegral constraint relationship. In the following paragraphs, the problem of minimizing a nonintegral criterion function subject to an integral constraint is to be studied.

A Terminal-control Problem Subject to an Integral Constraint

Consider a multivariable control process characterized by

$$\dot{\mathbf{x}}(t) = \mathbf{f}(\mathbf{x}, \mathbf{m}) = \mathbf{X}(\mathbf{x}, t) + \mathbf{D}(t)\mathbf{m}(t) \tag{5.4-22}$$

where the state vector $\mathbf{x}$ is of dimension n, the control vector is of dimension r, the driving matrix $\mathbf{D}(t)$ is a function of time, and the function $\mathbf{X}(\mathbf{x}, t)$ is differentiable. Determine the optimum-control vector $\mathbf{m}$ which minimizes the criterion function

$$\varphi(\mathbf{x}) = x_1(T) + x_2(T) \tag{5.4-23}$$

subject to the constraint

$$\int_0^T g(\mathbf{m})\, dt = K \tag{5.4-24}$$

In Eq. (5.4-23), $x_1(T)$ and $x_2(T)$ denote the state $x_1(t)$ and $x_2(t)$ of the control process at the terminal of the trajectory. The initial state vector is $\mathbf{x}(0) = \mathbf{0}$.

The above problem formulation describes the design of terminal control for an aircraft landing system, when x_1 represents the altitude error and x_2 denotes the altitude-rate error. The altitude and altitude rate at a particular time, corresponding to the termination of flare, are controlled to desired values by minimizing the errors subject to specified constraints on the control signals.

To make direct application of the method of the Lagrange multiplier, the criterion function given in Eq. (5.4-23) is converted into the integral form. Define the functional

$$I = \int_0^T F(\mathbf{x}, \mathbf{m}, t)\, dt \tag{5.4-25}$$

where

$$F(\mathbf{x}, \mathbf{m}, t) = \dot{x}_1(t) + \dot{x}_2(t) \tag{5.4-26}$$

The optimum-control problem is reduced to the minimization of the integral given in Eq. (5.4-25) subject to the constraint relation specified in Eq. (5.4-24). By defining an $n \times 1$ column vector with (5.4-22)

$$\mathbf{b} = \begin{bmatrix} 1 \\ 1 \\ 0 \\ \cdot \\ \cdot \\ \cdot \\ 0 \end{bmatrix} \tag{5.4-27}$$

the integrand $F(\mathbf{x}, \mathbf{m}, t)$ may be expressed as

$$F(\mathbf{x}, \mathbf{m}, t) = \dot{\mathbf{x}}'(t)\mathbf{b} = \mathbf{X}'(\mathbf{x}, t)\mathbf{b} + \mathbf{m}'(t)\mathbf{D}'(t)\mathbf{b} \tag{5.4-28}$$

Introduction of a Lagrange multiplier λ gives the synthetic function

$$I_1 = \int_0^T [F(\mathbf{x}, \mathbf{m}, t) + \lambda g(\mathbf{m})]\, dt \tag{5.4-29}$$

The control problem now becomes the determination of the optimum-control vector $\mathbf{m}$ which minimizes the integral defined in Eq. (5.4-29).

It has been shown in Sec. 5.3 that the necessary condition for I_1 to be a minimum is the Euler-Lagrange equation

$$(\nabla_{\mathbf{x}}G) - [\nabla_{\mathbf{x}}\mathbf{f}^{(r)}][\nabla_{\mathbf{m}}\mathbf{f}^{(r)}]^{-1}(\nabla_{\mathbf{m}}G) - \frac{d}{dt}[\mathbf{R}(\nabla_{\mathbf{m}}G)] = 0 \tag{5.4-30}$$

where $\nabla_{\mathbf{x}}$ and $\nabla_{\mathbf{m}}$ are as defined in Sec. 5.3, $G(\mathbf{x}, \mathbf{m})$ is the integrand of I_1,

$$G(\mathbf{x}, \mathbf{m}) = F(\mathbf{x}, \mathbf{m}, t) + \lambda g(\mathbf{m}) \tag{5.4-31}$$

$\mathbf{f}^{(r)}$ is a $1 \times r$ row vector given by

$$\mathbf{f}^{(r)} = [f_1 \quad f_2 \quad \cdots \quad f_r] \tag{5.4-32}$$

and $\mathbf{R}$ is an $n \times r$ matrix with the last $n - r$ rows equal to zero:

$$\mathbf{R} = \begin{bmatrix} (\nabla_{\mathbf{m}}\mathbf{f}^{(r)})^{-1} \\ 0 \\ \cdot \\ \cdot \\ \cdot \\ 0 \end{bmatrix} \tag{5.4-33}$$

Performing partial differentiation of Eq. (5.4-31) with respect to x_i gives

$$\nabla_{\mathbf{x}}G = \begin{bmatrix} \dfrac{\partial F}{\partial x_1} \\ \dfrac{\partial F}{\partial x_2} \\ \cdot \\ \cdot \\ \cdot \\ \dfrac{\partial F}{\partial x_n} \end{bmatrix} = \mathbf{J}'(\mathbf{x})\mathbf{b} \tag{5.4-34}$$

where $\mathbf{J}(\mathbf{x})$ is the Jacobian matrix given by

$$\mathbf{J}(\mathbf{x}) = \begin{bmatrix} \dfrac{\partial X_1}{\partial x_1} & \dfrac{\partial X_1}{\partial x_2} & \cdots & \dfrac{\partial X_1}{\partial x_n} \\ \dfrac{\partial X_2}{\partial x_1} & \dfrac{\partial X_2}{\partial x_2} & \cdots & \dfrac{\partial X_2}{\partial x_n} \\ \cdots & \cdots & \cdots & \cdots \\ \dfrac{\partial X_n}{\partial x_1} & \dfrac{\partial X_n}{\partial x_2} & \cdots & \dfrac{\partial X_n}{\partial x_n} \end{bmatrix} \tag{5.4-35}$$

Taking the partial derivative of Eq. (5.4-31) with respect to $\mathbf{m}$ yields

$$\nabla_{\mathbf{m}}G = \mathbf{D}'(t)\mathbf{b} + \lambda\nabla_{\mathbf{m}}g(\mathbf{m}) \tag{5.4-36}$$

The partial derivatives of Eq. (5.4-32) with respect to $\mathbf{x}$ and $\mathbf{m}$ are given, respectively, by

$$\nabla_{\mathbf{x}}\mathbf{f}^{(r)} = \begin{bmatrix} \frac{\partial X_1}{\partial x_1} & \frac{\partial X_2}{\partial x_1} & \cdots & \frac{\partial X_r}{\partial x_1} \\ \frac{\partial X_1}{\partial x_2} & \frac{\partial X_2}{\partial x_2} & \cdots & \frac{\partial X_r}{\partial x_2} \\ \cdots & \cdots & \cdots & \cdots \\ \frac{\partial X_1}{\partial x_n} & \frac{\partial X_2}{\partial x_n} & \cdots & \frac{\partial X_r}{\partial x_n} \end{bmatrix} \tag{5.4-37}$$

and

$$\nabla_{\mathbf{m}}\mathbf{f}^{(r)} = \begin{bmatrix} d_{11}(t) & d_{21}(t) & \cdots & d_{r1}(t) \\ d_{12}(t) & d_{22}(t) & \cdots & d_{r2}(t) \\ \cdots & \cdots & \cdots & \cdots \\ d_{1r}(t) & d_{2r}(t) & \cdots & d_{rr}(t) \end{bmatrix} \tag{5.4-38}$$

It can readily be shown that the following relationships hold:

$$[\nabla_{\mathbf{m}}\mathbf{f}^{(r)}]^{-1}(\nabla_{\mathbf{m}}G) = \mathbf{b} + \lambda[\nabla_{\mathbf{m}}\mathbf{f}^{(r)}]^{-1}[\nabla_{\mathbf{m}}g] \tag{5.4-39}$$

$$\mathbf{R}(\nabla_{\mathbf{m}}G) = \mathbf{b} + \lambda\mathbf{R}[\nabla_{\mathbf{m}}g] \tag{5.4-40}$$

$$\mathbf{J}'(\mathbf{x})\mathbf{b} = [\nabla_{\mathbf{x}}\mathbf{f}^{(r)}]\mathbf{b} \tag{5.4-41}$$

In view of Eqs. (5.4-39) to (5.4-41), the Euler-Lagrange equation given in Eq. (5.4-30) can be reduced to

$$[\nabla_{\mathbf{x}}\mathbf{f}^{(r)}][\nabla_{\mathbf{m}}\mathbf{f}^{(r)}]^{-1}[\nabla_{\mathbf{m}}g] + \frac{d}{dt}[\mathbf{R}(\nabla_{\mathbf{m}}g)] = 0 \tag{5.4-42}$$

The solution of this differential equation subject to the boundary conditions

$$\mathbf{x}(0) = \mathbf{0} \tag{5.4-43}$$

and

$$(\nabla_{\mathbf{m}}G)'[(\nabla_{\mathbf{m}}\mathbf{f}^{(r)})']^{-1}\Big|_T = 0 \tag{5.4-44}$$

results in the optimum-control vector $\mathbf{m}(t)$ for the given control process.

The optimum design of control systems by the calculus of variations generally leads to a two-point boundary-value problem. Since the resulting Euler-Lagrange differential equations are usually nonlinear, recourse to numerical trial-and-error solutions is necessary. One possible method of solution makes use of the familiar hill-climbing techniques.

5.5 CONCLUSION

This chapter considers some of the fundamental principles of the variational calculus which are applicable to optimum-control problems. The calculus of variations is that branch of the calculus which is concerned with optimization problems under more general conditions than those considered in the ordinary theory of maxima and minima. The three fundamental problems in the calculus of variations are the Lagrange, Mayer, and Bolza problems. Some auxiliary variables can always be introduced to transform a problem of one type into either of the other two, and many optimum-control problems can be formulated as one of these three fundamental problems. The minimum-integral-control problem belongs to the Lagrange type. Time-optimal-control and terminal-control problems may be classified as the Mayer problem. Optimum-control systems subject to certain constraints can be studied as a problem of the Bolza type.

The optimum design of control systems by the calculus of variations generally leads to a two-point boundary-value problem. Analytical solutions for such problems are possible only in special cases. In view of the fact that the resulting Euler-Lagrange differential equations are usually nonlinear, numerical trial-and-error techniques must be resorted to. These techniques consist in guessing a value for the missing initial condition and integrating numerically the set of Euler-Lagrange equations and constraining equations. The reader is referred to modern textbooks on applied mathematics and numerical analysis for a complete discussion of these retrogressive trial-and-error techniques.

The difficulty in solving the two-point boundary-value problem makes the classical calculus of variations less attractive in the design of optimum-control systems. Furthermore, the variational-calculus approach is generally limited to systems subject to control signals with unrestricted bounds.

References

Suggested references are Bliss,[29] Bolza,[35] Gould and Kipiniak,[71] Kipiniak,[94] and Leitmann.[112] Also:

Cicala, P.: "An Engineering Approach to the Calculus of Variations," Levrotto & Bella, Torino, Italy, 1957.

Kulakowski, L. J., and R. T. Stancil: Rocket Boost Trajectories for Maximum Burnout Velocity, *ARS J.*, vol. 30, no. 7, 1960.

6

INTRODUCTION TO THE PRINCIPLE OF MAXIMUM

Optimization has been recognized as the number-one problem in automation. Automation may be defined as the branch of science and technology concerned with the development of devices, plants, and systems that operate without direct human intervention and assume responsibility for performing certain types of human mental work. Among many techniques for solving problems in optimization, two methods are generally regarded as most promising for the solution of complex problems. They are the *maximum principle* of Pontryagin and the method of *dynamic programming* developed by Bellman. The principle of dynamic programming forms the subject matter of Chap. 7; the principle of maximum is introduced in this chapter. As will be seen in later sections of this book, Pontryagin's principle of maximum bears a close correspondence to the classical problem of

Mayer. According to Pontryagin, the maximum principle was originally derived from the classical variational calculus. It differs, however, from the classical problem of Mayer in one respect. In the Mayer problem, every control signal has unrestricted bounds. In Pontryagin's work, on the other hand, the control signal is permitted to be a member of a closed set, or in other words, the values of the control signal may be restricted to certain limits. Furthermore, by applying the maximum principle, the nature of control and the general structure of the optimum-control system can readily be determined. This chapter is devoted to the study of the maximum principle in optimum control.

6.1 OPTIMUM–CONTROL PROBLEMS

Modern control engineering has placed considerable emphasis upon problems of system optimization and of optimum control, which are of vital importance in automation. A scientist who wishes to carry out experiments using satellite-borne apparatus may desire an optimum-ascent trajectory which results in maximum payload in orbit. A chemical engineer who designs chemical reactors may desire a maximum yield from a chemical process. Among the many types of optimum-control problems, three basic modes of optimum control are of fundamental importance and thus have received considerable attention. They are the minimum-time-control problem, the terminal-control problem, and the minimum-integral-control problem.[140]

The design of minimum-time control systems by the state-transition method is studied in some detail in Chap. 4. In the study of the calculus of variations, the minimum-time-control problem is formulated as a problem of the Mayer type. In this chapter, the minimum-time design problem is to be solved by use of the maximum principle of Pontryagin. Consider an nth-order control process characterized by

$$\dot{\mathbf{x}} = \mathbf{f}(\mathbf{x}, \mathbf{m}, t) \tag{6.1-1}$$

where $\mathbf{x}$ and $\mathbf{m}$ are the plant state vector and the control vector, respectively, and are defined by

$$\mathbf{x} = \begin{bmatrix} x_1 \\ x_2 \\ \cdot \\ \cdot \\ \cdot \\ x_n \end{bmatrix} \quad \text{and} \quad \mathbf{m} = \begin{bmatrix} m_1 \\ m_2 \\ \cdot \\ \cdot \\ \cdot \\ m_r \end{bmatrix} \tag{6.1-2}$$

The control process is subject to r control signals. At each moment, the control signals m_i must satisfy the inequality constraint

$$\mathbf{g}(\mathbf{m}) \leq \mathbf{0} \tag{6.1-3}$$

which reflects the restrictions imposed upon the control system. For instance, when the control signals are bounded by saturation, Eq. (6.1-3) becomes

$$a_i > m_i > -b_i \qquad i = 1, 2, \ldots, r \tag{6.1-4}$$

The control vector which satisfies the constraint conditions is referred to as an *admissible control vector*. The minimum-time-control problem may be stated as the determination of an admissible control vector $\mathbf{m}$ so that the process is taken from a specified initial state $\mathbf{x}_0$ to a desired final state $\mathbf{x}_f$ in the shortest possible time.

A terminal control system is one which controls the state variables of the system to specified values at some fixed, terminal time in the future. The concept of terminal control is based on the fact that, if the initial conditions of a system characterized by a set of differential equations are given, the future response of the system can be predicted in the absence of disturbances to the system. The desired terminal state is attained by continuous control and prediction of the terminal conditions. Thus the system is controlled to the desired final value of the output variables even though disturbances occur. The principle of terminal control has been applied to the design of aircraft landing systems and missile-guidance systems, among others. In an aircraft landing system, the values of sinking rate and altitude at a particular time corresponding to the termination of flare are predicted and controlled to desired values. The terminal-control scheme offers the advantage of effecting some control of range by virtue of direct control of total flare time, without the attendant disadvantage of extending the control effort necessary to follow a present trajectory throughout the flare.

The terminal-control problem may be stated as the determination of an admissible control vector $\mathbf{m}$ such that, in a given time interval T, the system is taken from an initial state $\mathbf{x}_0$ into a state in which one or a combination of the state variables (for example, x_1) becomes as large as possible or as small as possible, and the remaining state variables have fixed values within physical limits. In other words, the admissible control vector maximizes or minimizes, for example, the functional

$$x_1(T) = F_1(\mathbf{x}_0, \mathbf{x}, \mathbf{m}, t)\Big|_T \tag{6.1-5}$$

or

$$\sum_{i=1}^{k} c_i x_i(T) = F_2(\mathbf{x}_0, \mathbf{x}, \mathbf{m}, t)\Big|_T \tag{6.1-6}$$

or, more generally, a functional of state variables at the termination of the trajectory. In Eq. (6.1-6), $k \leq n$, and $x_i(T)$ denotes the ith state variable evaluated at the end of the trajectory. In a number of cases, it is not necessary to fix the final values of all the remaining state variables x_{k+1}, $x_{k+2}, \ldots, x_n$ at the end of the trajectory. A terminal controller is thus designed to achieve a desired response at one time only, the response at earlier times being arbitrary within physical limits.

The minimum-integral-control problem involves the optimization of a system with respect to an integral. In a great many control processes encountered in practice, the control engineer is faced with a situation in which deviations of the output product from some desired value are undesirable. At times this deviation can be weighted to mean values in terms of dollars gained or lost; at other times the effect will be weighted to provide an indication of loss in product quality. In many instances the average deviation over some period of time is of particular interest. In such cases the control engineer is interested in what course of action to take to minimize the integral of this variation over a given period of time. This optimum-control problem may be stated as the determination of an admissible control vector **m** in such a manner that the integral

$$I = \int_{t_0}^{t_f} F(\mathbf{x}, \mathbf{m}, t)\, dt \tag{6.1-7}$$

reduces to a minimum during the time of movement $t_f - t_0$.

The three modes of optimum control can be transformed to an optimization with respect to coordinates or state variables, which is referred to as the *generalized mode of optimum control.* The problems of minimum-time control, terminal control, and minimum-integral control are special cases of the problem of minimization with respect to one coordinate. The transformation is carried out using the *invariant-embedding* procedure of increasing the dimensionality of the state vector by adding a new coordinate. The reduction of the three modes of optimum control to the generalized mode is discussed as follows.

a. Reducing a Minimum-time-control Problem to the Generalized Mode of Optimum Control

Consider the nth-order control process characterized by Eq. (6.1-1). In terms of the components of the state vector, Eq. (6.1-1) may be written as

$$\dot{x}_i = f_i(\mathbf{x}, \mathbf{m}, t) \qquad i = 1, 2, \ldots, n \tag{6.1-8}$$

The problem implies the minimization of the time required to move the process from an initial state to a desired final state, i.e.,

$$\min_{\mathbf{m}} \int_{t_0}^{t} dt \tag{6.1-9}$$

By introducing a new state variable $x_{n+1}(t)$ such that

$$\dot{x}_{n+1}(t) = 1 \tag{6.1-10}$$

and

$$x_{n+1}(t) = \int_{t_0}^{t} dt \tag{6.1-11}$$

the optimum-control problem reduces to the determination of an admissible control vector **m** so that the new state variable x_{n+1} is minimized. The optimum-control vector is subject to the constraint given in Eq. (6.1-3). Since $x_{n+1}(t) = t - t_0$, minimization of time means optimization with respect to the new coordinate x_{n+1}.

b. Reducing a Terminal-control Problem to the Generalized Mode of Optimum Control

Consider the nth-order control process characterized by Eq. (6.1-8). The more general description of the terminal-control problem may be stated as the determination of an admissible control vector **m** such that, in a given time interval T, a functional of the final state vector $\mathbf{x}(T)$ is minimized or maximized. In other words, this optimum-control problem requires the determination of an admissible **m** in order to make the functional $F[\mathbf{x}(T)]$ a minimum or maximum. Now introduce a new state variable

$$x_{n+1}(t) = F[x_1(t), x_2(t), \ldots, x_n(t)] \tag{6.1-12}$$

with the initial value given by

$$x_{n+1}(0) = F[x_1(0), x_2(0), \ldots, x_n(0)] \tag{6.1-13}$$

In vector notation, the new state variable is

$$x_{n+1}(t) = F[\mathbf{x}(t)] \tag{6.1-14}$$

and

$$x_{n+1}(0) = F[\mathbf{x}(0)] \tag{6.1-15}$$

Taking the derivative of $x_{n+1}(t)$ with respect to t yields

$$\dot{x}_{n+1}(t) = \frac{\partial F(\mathbf{x})}{\partial x_1}\dot{x}_1 + \frac{\partial F(\mathbf{x})}{\partial x_2}\dot{x}_2 + \cdots + \frac{\partial F(\mathbf{x})}{\partial x_n}\dot{x}_n \tag{6.1-16}$$

In view of Eq. (6.1-8), $x_{n+1}(t)$ becomes

$$\dot{x}_{n+1}(t) = \sum_{k=1}^{n} \frac{\partial F(\mathbf{x})}{\partial x_k} f_k(\mathbf{x}, \mathbf{m}, t) \tag{6.1-17}$$

The derivatives of the other state variables are given by Eq. (6.1-8). The terminal-control problem is now reduced to the problem of optimization with respect to the new coordinate x_{n+1}, at the final moment of time.

c. Reducing a Minimum-integral-control Problem to the Generalized Mode of Optimum Control

Consider the nth-order control process characterized by Eq. (6.1-8). The optimum-design problem requires the minimization of the integral-criterion function given in Eq. (6.1-7) with respect to the control vector **m**.

By introducing a new state variable $x_{n+1}(t)$ defined by

$$x_{n+1}(t) = \int_{t_0}^{t} F(\mathbf{x}, \mathbf{m}, t)\, dt \tag{6.1-18}$$

$$x_{n+1}(t_0) = 0 \tag{6.1-19}$$

and

$$\dot{x}_{n+1}(t) = F(\mathbf{x}, \mathbf{m}, t) \tag{6.1-20}$$

the problem of minimizing the integral given by Eq. (6.1-7) becomes the problem of minimizing the $(n + 1)$st coordinate, $x_{n+1}(t_f)$, at the terminal of the trajectory $t = t_f$. The derivatives of the other coordinates are given in Eq. (6.1-8).

The optimum-control problems discussed above may be considered as special cases of the more general problem of maximizing or minimizing the functional

$$\mathcal{P} = \sum_{i=1}^{n} b_i x_i(t_f) \tag{6.1-21}$$

Consequently, in more general form, the generalized mode of optimum control may be described as the problem of finding a control vector $\mathbf{m}$ from a group of admissible vectors satisfying Eq. (6.1-3), which moves the control process characterized by Eq. (6.1-8) from the initial state $\mathbf{x}(t_0)$ to some defined closed set of the phase space in such a way that the functional given by Eq. (6.1-21) is reduced to a maximum or a minimum. Pontryagin's maximum principle provides an elegant method for the design of such optimum control systems.

Other types of optimum-control problems include several variations of the control problems discussed above: for instance, systems with fixed initial and final states; systems with fixed initial state and variable final state; systems with variable time of movement; the rendezvous control problem. In addition, optimum-control problems involving constraints on the state variables and optimization for functionals of other types than the final value of the state variables, such as minimizing the maximum deviation of some state variable from a prescribed value, are of considerable interest.

6.2 THE MAXIMUM PRINCIPLE

The maximum principle of Pontryagin provides an elegant method of obtaining an optimal solution for very general dynamical processes.[127–129,134] It treats the optimization problem of minimizing or maximizing a functional subject to certain constraints. As discussed in the preceding section, optimum-control problems can be transformed into problems of optimization with respect to one or a combination of the coordinates. In the minimum-time control mode, the terminal control mode, and the minimum-integral control mode, the introduction of a new state variable x_{n+1} converts the optimum-control problem to the optimization of this new coordinate. In general, an optimum-control problem can be transformed into the problem of minimizing or maximizing a Pontryagin function such as

$$\mathcal{P} = (\mathbf{b}, \mathbf{x}(t_f)) = \mathbf{b}'\mathbf{x}(t_f) \tag{6.2-1}$$

subject to certain constraining functionals. The control strategy which minimizes or maximizes the Pontryagin function is referred to as the optimum-control strategy. In Eq. (6.2-1), $\mathbf{x}$ is a state vector of the nth-order control process under consideration, and $\mathbf{b}$ is a column vector which depends upon the coordinates to be minimized or maximized. It is interesting to note that this class of problems is contained within the framework of the Mayer problem in the calculus of variations which is discussed in the preceding chapter. In terms of the components of the state vector $\mathbf{x}$, the Pontryagin function $\mathcal{P}$ may be expressed as

$$\mathcal{P} = \sum_{i=1}^{n} b_i x_i(t_f) \tag{6.2-2}$$

A simple geometrical interpretation of the maximum principle is that the control vector $\mathbf{m}$ is chosen in such a way that the state vector $\mathbf{x}(t_f)$ moves "farthest" in the direction of $-\mathbf{b}$, and thus the Pontryagin function $\mathcal{P}$ takes on a minimum value. In optimum-control problems, the final state of the optimum trajectory may be either free or constrained. In this section the free-final-state optimization problems are discussed first, and the discussions are then extended to the study of the optimum-control problems with constrained final state.

Suppose that the control process under consideration is as characterized by Eq. (6.1-1):

$$\dot{\mathbf{x}} = \mathbf{f}(\mathbf{x}, \mathbf{m}, t) \tag{6.2-3}$$

It is required to determine the control strategy $\mathbf{m}$ so that the Pontryagin function given in Eq. (6.2-1) is minimized or maximized. Frequently, the extremization of the Pontryagin function $\mathcal{P}$ is not easy to accomplish. If some simpler function can be found which is closely related to the Pontryagin function and the process dynamics, and if it is easier to perform the optimization with respect to this simpler function, the solution to the optimum-control problem may then be obtained in a simpler manner. Intuitively, the Pontryagin function may be minimized by maximizing the energy or power in the system. This physical intuition leads to the speculation that there may exist an energy function such that its maximization implies the minimization of the Pontryagin function. In Chap. 2, the concept of the hamiltonian is introduced. This is defined as the sum of the kinetic energy and the potential energy and is expressed as the inner product of the momentum vector and the coordinate vector of the system. The simplicity of the hamiltonian function and its very nature make it tempting to think that maximization of the hamiltonian function may imply minimization of the Pontryagin function, and that the use of the hamiltonian may lead to a simple, elegant method for solving optimization problems. Pontryagin first discovered this nature's secret weapon and formulated his discovery as the celebrated principle of maximum. It has helped scientists to analyze and synthesize various types of physical systems, so that their operation might be optimized to the highest degree of satisfaction.

The maximum (or minimum) principle states that, if the control vector $\mathbf{m}$ is optimum, i.e., if it minimizes (or maximizes) the Pontryagin function $\mathcal{P}$, then the hamiltonian $H(\mathbf{x}, \mathbf{p}, \mathbf{m}, t)$ is maximized (or minimized) with respect to $\mathbf{m}$ over the control interval. The hamiltonian is defined as

$$H(\mathbf{x}, \mathbf{p}, \mathbf{m}, t) = (\mathbf{p}, \mathbf{f}) = \sum_{j=1}^{n} p_j f_j \tag{6.2-4}$$

where $\mathbf{x}$ is the state vector, $\mathbf{p}$ is the momentum vector to be defined later, and the vector function is as given in Eq. (6.2-3). The above statement points out that maximum H implies minimum $\mathcal{P}$ and minimum H implies maximum $\mathcal{P}$. Thus a necessary condition for the control vector $\mathbf{m}(t)$ to minimize the Pontryagin function is the fulfillment of the maximum condition for $\mathbf{m}(t)$. To apply the maximum principle in the solution of optimum-control problems, the design procedure is initiated with the maximization of hamiltonian H with respect to the control vector $\mathbf{m}$. This results in an optimum-control vector as a function of the momentum vector $\mathbf{p}$. The optimum-control vector is then substituted into the Hamilton canonical equations, and the resulting boundary-value problem is solved for the optimum trajectory.

The design of optimum control aims at the determination of an optimum-control law $\mathbf{m}^o(\mathbf{x})$ or an optimum-control sequence $\mathbf{m}^o(t)$. However, direct application of the maximum principle yields the optimum-control vector $\mathbf{m}^o$ as a function of the momentum vector $\mathbf{p}$. In order to find $\mathbf{m}^0$ as a function of $\mathbf{x}$ or t, some equations providing the relationships between $\mathbf{m}$ and $\mathbf{p}$ must be established. The momentum vector $\mathbf{p}$ is defined as the solution to the differential equation

$$\dot{p}_i = -\sum_{j=1}^{n} p_j \frac{\partial f_j}{\partial x_i} \qquad i = 1, 2, \ldots, n \tag{6.2-5}$$

where

$$p_i(t_f) = -b_i \tag{6.2-6}$$

b_i being some known constant specified in the Pontryagin function $\mathcal{P}$, and

$$\dot{x}_i = f_i(\mathbf{x}, \mathbf{m}, t) \tag{6.2-7}$$

Differentiating Eq. (6.2-4) with respect to p_i yields

$$\frac{\partial H}{\partial p_i} = f_i(\mathbf{x}, \mathbf{m}, t) \tag{6.2-8}$$

Differentiating Eq. (6.2-4) with respect to x_i gives

$$\frac{\partial H}{\partial x_i} = \sum_{j=1}^{n} p_j \frac{\partial f_j}{\partial x_i} \qquad i = 1, 2, \ldots, n \tag{6.2-9}$$

Making use of these two equations reduces Eqs. (6.2-7) and (6.2-5) to the Hamilton canonical form

$$\dot{x}_i = \frac{\partial H}{\partial p_i} \tag{6.2-10}$$

$$\dot{p}_i = -\frac{\partial H}{\partial x_i} \tag{6.2-11}$$

These canonical equations are subject to the boundary conditions on $x_i(t_0)$ and $p_i(t_f)$; that is,

$$x_i(t_0) = x_i^0 \tag{6.2-12}$$

and

$$p_i(t_f) = -b_i \qquad i = 1, 2, \ldots, n \tag{6.2-13}$$

The physical interpretation of the maximum principle may be stated as follows: The hamiltonian H is the inner product of $\mathbf{p}$ and $\mathbf{f}$, or that of $\mathbf{p}$ and $\dot{\mathbf{x}}$, which represents the power when $\mathbf{p}$ is identified as the momentum. Thus, to minimize $\mathcal{P}$, the power is maximized, and when $\mathcal{P}$ is a minimum, H is a maximum. The design procedure is to maximize H with respect to $\mathbf{m}$, substitute the optimum-control vector $\mathbf{m}^o(\mathbf{p})$ into the Hamilton canonical equations given in Eqs. (6.2-10) and (6.2-11), and solve the resulting boundary-value problem for the optimum trajectory $\mathbf{x}(t)$ and the momentum vector $\mathbf{p}(t)$ subject to the boundary condition given in Eqs. (6.2-12) and (6.2-13). With the optimum trajectory $\mathbf{x}(t)$ and the momentum vector $\mathbf{p}(t)$ known, the optimum-control strategy $\mathbf{m}^o$ can be determined.

The Pontryagin function $\mathcal{P}$ given in Eq. (6.2-1) and the boundary condition given by Eq. (6.2-13) are valid for control processes with free final state. When the final state of the process is constrained by

$$R_k[\mathbf{x}(t_f)] = 0 \qquad k = 1, 2, \ldots, \nu \tag{6.2-14}$$

the Pontryagin function takes the form

$$\mathcal{P} = \mathbf{b}'\mathbf{x}(t_f) + \boldsymbol{\mu}'\mathbf{R}[\mathbf{x}(t_f)] \tag{6.2-15}$$

where $\boldsymbol{\mu}$ is a vector Lagrange multiplier. The canonical equations (6.2-10) and (6.2-11) are now subject to the boundary conditions

$$x_i(t_0) = x_i^0 \tag{6.2-16}$$

and

$$p_i(t_f) = -\left[b_i + \sum_{k=1}^{\nu} \mu_k \frac{\partial R_k}{\partial x_i(t_f)}\right] \tag{6.2-17}$$

with the final state $\mathbf{x}(t_f)$ constrained by Eq. (6.2-14).

The main difficulty with effecting optimum design by the maximum principle lies in finding a solution to the two-point boundary-value problem, as will be shown. This problem is inherent in classical variational calculus, and one cannot get around it by using the maximum principle. To date, most methods for solving the two-point boundary-value problem have employed the trial-and-error approach in choosing the initial condition $p_i(t_0)$ such that the canonical equations and the boundary condition given in Eq. (6.2-13) or (6.2-17) are satisfied.

In general, the maximum principle provides a necessary condition for system optimization. However, if the control process is linear and subject to an additive control function, i.e., when the process dynamics is characterized by

$$\dot{x}_i(t) = \sum_{k=1}^{n} a_{ik}(t)x_k(t) + u_i(m_1, m_2, \ldots, m_r) \qquad i = 1, 2, \ldots, n \tag{6.2-18}$$

or in vector notation

$$\dot{\mathbf{x}}(t) = \mathbf{A}(t)\mathbf{x}(t) + \mathbf{u}(\mathbf{m}) \tag{6.2-19}$$

the maximum principle provides the necessary and sufficient condition for optimum control.

Before a proof of the maximum principle is presented, the following simple example is given to illustrate the application of this principle to the design of optimum systems.

Example 6.2-1 Optimum Control of a Linear Process

Consider a simple linear process characterized by

$$\dot{x} = -ax + \gamma m$$

where a and γ are positive constants.

The initial state of the process is $x(t_0) = x_0$, and the control signal is constrained by $|m| \leq M$. Determine the control signal m which minimizes the performance index

$$I(m) = \int_{t_0}^{t_f} x^2(m, t)\, dt$$

Let $x_1 = x$, and let the new coordinate be

$$x_2 = \int_{t_0}^{t_f} x_1^2\, dt$$

Then the differential equations for the augmented system are

$$\dot{x}_1 = -ax_1 + \gamma m$$
$$\dot{x}_2 = x_1^2$$

The Pontryagin function $\mathcal{P}$ is given by

$$\mathcal{P} = b_1x_1 + b_2x_2 = x_2$$

where $b_1 = 0$ and $b_2 = 1$. The optimum-design problem is now reduced to the determination of control signal m so that the Pontryagin function is minimized. The hamiltonian for this system is

$$\begin{aligned} H &= p_1f_1 + p_2f_2 \\ &= p_1(-ax_1 + \gamma m) + p_2x_1^2 \end{aligned}$$

To apply the maximum principle, the hamiltonian of the system is to be maximized with respect to m. It follows that the hamiltonian is a maximum if the sign of the control signal m is the same as that of p_1 and its magnitude is the maximum allowable value M; that is,

$$m = M \operatorname{sgn} p_1$$

where sgn is defined by

$$\operatorname{sgn} \alpha = \begin{cases} +1 & \text{if } \alpha > 0 \\ 0 & \text{if } \alpha = 0 \\ -1 & \text{if } \alpha < 0 \end{cases}$$

The canonical equations are

$$\dot{x}_i = \frac{\partial H}{\partial p_i} \qquad \begin{cases} \dot{x}_1 = -ax_1 + \gamma m \\ \dot{x}_2 = x_1^2 \end{cases}$$
$$\dot{p}_i = -\frac{\partial H}{\partial x_i} \qquad \begin{cases} \dot{p}_1 = ap_1 - 2x_1p_2 \\ \dot{p}_2 = 0 \end{cases}$$

The initial conditions for $\mathbf{x}$ are

$$x_1(t_0) = x_0 \qquad \text{and} \qquad x_2(t_0) = 0$$

and the boundary conditions on $\mathbf{p}$ are

$$p_1(t_f) = 0 \qquad \text{and} \qquad p_2(t_f) = -b_2 = -1$$

Since $\dot{p}_2(t) = 0$ and $p_2(t_f) = -1$, $p_2(t) = \text{const} = -1$. Substituting the condition for maximum hamiltonian into the canonical equations yields

$$\dot{x}_1 = -ax_1 + \gamma M \operatorname{sgn} p_1$$
$$\dot{p}_1 = ap_1 - 2x_1p_2 = ap_1 + 2x_1$$

The known boundary conditions for these two differential equations are

$$x_1(t_0) = x_0 \qquad \text{and} \qquad p_1(t_f) = 0$$

This is a two-point boundary-value problem, since the two boundary conditions are given at both ends of the trajectory. Now it is required to solve for x_1 and p_1 from the above two differential equations subject to these two given boundary conditions. A trial-and-error procedure is to guess values of $p_1(t_0) = p_1$ and to find values for x_1 and p_1 for which the other boundary condition $p_1(t_f) = 0$ is satisfied. After $p_1(t)$ is determined, the control strategy $m = M \operatorname{sgn} p_1$ is found which switches according to the sign of $p_1(t)$. Hence $p_1(t)$ is the required switching function. Once the optimum-control strategy is known in the form $m = M \operatorname{sgn} p_1$, the optimum control system can be readily mechanized, as demonstrated in Fig. 6.2-1. Sometimes it is easier to determine $p_1(t)$ through analog simulation. Inspection of Fig. 6.2-1 reveals that the control signal m is generated by feeding the state variable to a device enclosed in the dashed box, known as the adjoint system, which will be discussed in later sections. The optimum-control signal is a nonlinear function of the state variable. It is to

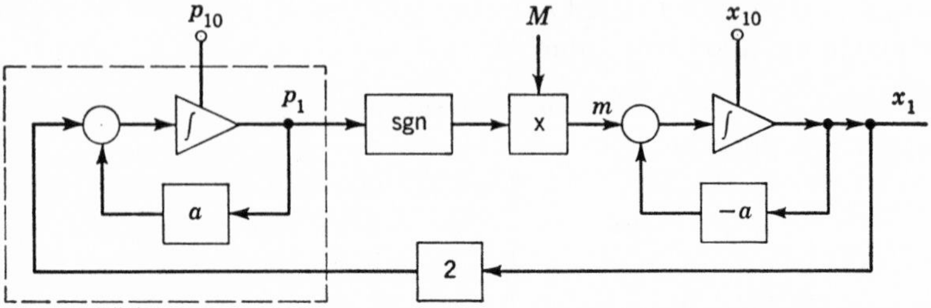

Fig. 6.2-1 Mechanization of the optimum control system.

be noted that the control law cannot be expressed analytically as a function of the state variable. Such an optimum-control scheme is sometimes referred to as the switched mode of optimum control.

Discrete Version of the Maximum Principle[134]

The maximum principle can be applied to the optimum design of linear discrete systems which are characterized by

$$x_i(k+1) - x_i(k) = T\left\{\sum_{j=1}^{n} a_{ij}(k)x_j(k) + u_i[m_1(k), m_2(k), \ldots, m_r(k)]\right\}$$

$$i = 1, 2, \ldots, n \qquad (6.2\text{-}20)$$

where T is the sampling period and

$$\begin{aligned} x_i(k) &= x_i(kT) \\ a_{ij}(k) &= a_{ij}(kT) \\ m_r(k) &= m_r(kT) \end{aligned}$$

It is to be noted that Eq. (6.2-20) is a discrete version of Eq. (6.2-18).

The difference equations defining the momentum vector $\mathbf{p}$ are

$$p_i(k) - p_i(k-1) = -T \sum_{j=1}^{n} p_j(k) \frac{\partial f_j[\mathbf{x}(k), \mathbf{m}(k), k]}{\partial x_i} \qquad i = 1, 2, \ldots, n \tag{6.2-21}$$

Since

$$f_i(\mathbf{x}, \mathbf{m}, t) = \sum_{j=1}^{n} a_{ij}(t)x_j(t) + u_i(\mathbf{m}) \tag{6.2-22}$$

taking the partial derivative of $f_i(\mathbf{x}, \mathbf{m}, t)$ with respect to x_j yields

$$\frac{\partial f_i}{\partial x_j} = a_{ij}(t) \tag{6.2-23}$$

Thus Eq. (6.2-21) can be reduced to

$$p_i(k) - p_i(k-1) = -T \sum_{j=1}^{n} p_j(k)a_{ji}(k) \tag{6.2-24}$$

In the discrete case, the Pontryagin function and the hamiltonian are given by

$$\mathcal{P} = \sum_{i=1}^{n} b_i x_i(N) \tag{6.2-25}$$

and

$$H(k) = \sum_{i=1}^{n} p_j(k)f_j(k) \tag{6.2-26}$$

In Eq. (6.2-25) $NT = t_f$, at which $\mathcal{P}$ assumes a minimum (or maximum) value. Hence the canonical equations are

$$\Delta x_i(k) = \frac{\partial H(k)}{\partial p_i(k)} \tag{6.2-27}$$

$$\Delta p_i(k-1) = -\frac{\partial H(k)}{\partial x_i(k)} \qquad i = 1, 2, \ldots, n \tag{6.2-28}$$

These equations are subject to the boundary conditions given in Eqs. (6.2-12) and (6.2-13).

6.3 A PROOF OF THE MAXIMUM PRINCIPLE

The maximum principle can be proved in various ways. In this section a relatively simple proof of this principle of Pontryagin is presented.[134] The proof is initiated with the determination of a variation of the Pontryagin function, $\delta\mathcal{P}$, due to a variation of the state variables, δx_i, and a change in the control signal, $\delta\mathbf{m}$. Assume that the nth-order control process is characterized by

$$\dot{\mathbf{x}} = \mathbf{f}(\mathbf{x}, \mathbf{m}, t) \tag{6.3-1}$$

where $\mathbf{x}$ is the $n \times 1$ state vector, and $\mathbf{m}$ is the $r \times 1$ control vector. As usual, the Pontryagin function is written as

$$\mathcal{P} = (\mathbf{b}, \mathbf{x}(t_j)) = \sum_{i=1}^{n} b_i x_i(t_f) \tag{6.3-2}$$

and the hamiltonian for the system is given by

$$H = (\mathbf{p}, \mathbf{f}) = \sum_{i=1}^{n} p_i(t) f_i(\mathbf{x}, \mathbf{m}, t) \tag{6.3-3}$$

The variation $\delta\mathcal{P}$ as a function of $\delta\mathbf{m}$ and δx_i is first derived. To begin with, the following summation is formed:

$$\sum_{i=1}^{n} p_i \, \delta x_i \tag{6.3-4}$$

Taking the derivative of this summation with respect to t yields

$$\frac{d}{dt} \sum_{i=1}^{n} p_i \, \delta x_i = \sum_{i=1}^{n} p_i \, \delta \dot{x}_i + \sum_{i=1}^{n} \dot{p}_i \, \delta x_i \tag{6.3-5}$$

Integrating both sides of Eq. (6.3-5) from t_0 to t_j and simplifying gives

$$\sum_{i=1}^{n} p_i \, \delta x_i \Big|_{t_0}^{t_f} = \int_{t_0}^{t_f} \sum_i p_i [f_i(\mathbf{x} + \delta\mathbf{x}, \mathbf{m} + \delta\mathbf{m}, t) - f_i(\mathbf{x}, \mathbf{m}, t)] \, dt + \int_{t_0}^{t_f} \sum_i \dot{p}_i \, \delta x_i \, dt \tag{6.3-6}$$

Since $p_i(t_1) = -b_i$ and $x_i(t_0) = 0$,

$$\sum_i p_i \, \delta x_i \Big|_{t_0}^{t_f} = -\sum_i b_i \, \delta x_i(t_f) = -\delta\mathcal{P} \tag{6.3-7}$$

Thus the variation of the Pontryagin function $\mathcal{P}$ due to changes in x_i and $\mathbf{m}$ is

$$\delta\mathcal{P} = -\int_{t_0}^{t_f} \sum_i p_i [f_i(\mathbf{x} + \delta\mathbf{x}, \mathbf{m} + \delta\mathbf{m}, t) - f_i(\mathbf{x}, \mathbf{m}, t)] \, dt - \int_{t_0}^{t_f} \sum_i \dot{p}_i \, \delta x_i \, dt \tag{6.3-8}$$

Taylor's series expansion with respect to $\mathbf{x}$ gives

$$f_i(\mathbf{x} + \delta\mathbf{x}, \mathbf{m} + \delta\mathbf{m}, t) = f_i(\mathbf{x}, \mathbf{m} + \delta\mathbf{m}, t) + \sum_{j=1}^{n} \frac{\partial f_i(\mathbf{x}, \mathbf{m} + \delta\mathbf{m}, t)}{\partial x_j} \delta x_j + \frac{1}{2} \sum_{j=1}^{n} \sum_{k=1}^{n} \frac{\partial^2 f_i(\mathbf{x} + \theta \, \delta x, \mathbf{m} + \delta\mathbf{m}, t)}{\partial x_j \, \partial x_k} \delta x_j \, \delta x_k \tag{6.3-9}$$

Using the relationship

$$\dot{p}_i = -\frac{\partial H}{\partial x_i} = -\sum_j p_j \frac{\partial f_j}{\partial x_i} \qquad i = 1, 2, \ldots, n \tag{6.3-10}$$

and Eq. (6.3-9) converts $\delta\mathcal{P}$ to

$$\begin{aligned}\delta\mathcal{P} = &\int_{t_0}^{t_f} \sum_i \sum_j p_i \frac{\partial f_i(\mathbf{x}, \mathbf{m}, t)}{\partial x_j} \delta x_j \, dt \\ &- \int_{t_0}^{t_f} \sum_i p_i \Bigg\{ f_i(\mathbf{x}, \mathbf{m} + \delta\mathbf{m}, t) - f_i(\mathbf{x}, \mathbf{m}, t) + \sum_j \frac{\partial f_i(\mathbf{x}, \mathbf{m} + \delta\mathbf{m}, t)}{\partial x_j} \delta x_j \\ &\qquad + \tfrac{1}{2} \sum_j \sum_k \frac{\partial^2 f_i(\mathbf{x} + \theta\, \delta\mathbf{x}, \mathbf{m} + \delta\mathbf{m}, t)}{\partial x_j \, \partial x_k} \partial x_j \, \partial \mathbf{x}_k \Bigg\} dt \end{aligned} \tag{6.3-11}$$

Rearranging,

$$\begin{aligned}\delta\mathcal{P} = &- \int_{t_0}^{t_f} \sum_i p_i \{ f_i(\mathbf{x}, \mathbf{m} + \delta\mathbf{m}, t) - f_i(\mathbf{x}, \mathbf{m}, t) \} \, dt \\ &- \int_{t_0}^{t_f} \sum_i \sum_j p_i \left\{ \frac{\partial[f_i(\mathbf{x}, \mathbf{m} + \delta\mathbf{m}, t) - f_i(\mathbf{x}, \mathbf{m}, t)]}{\partial x_j} \right\} \delta x_j \, dt \\ &- \tfrac{1}{2} \int_{t_0}^{t_f} \sum_i \sum_j \sum_k p_i \frac{\partial^2 f_i(\mathbf{x} + \theta\, \delta\mathbf{x}, \mathbf{m} + \delta\mathbf{m}, t)}{\partial x_j \, \partial x_k} \delta x_j \, \delta x_k \, dt \end{aligned} \tag{6.3-12}$$

In view of Eq. (6.3-3) and defining q as

$$\begin{aligned} q = &\int_{t_0}^{t_f} \sum_i \sum_j p_i \left\{ \frac{\partial[f_j(\mathbf{x}, \mathbf{m} + \delta\mathbf{m}, t) - f_i(\mathbf{x}, \mathbf{m}, t)]}{\partial x_j} \right\} \delta x_j \, dt \\ &+ \tfrac{1}{2} \int_{t_0}^{t_f} \sum_i \sum_j \sum_k p_i \frac{\partial^2 f_i(\mathbf{x} + \theta\, \delta\mathbf{x}, \mathbf{m} + \delta\mathbf{m}, t)}{\partial x_j \, \partial x_k} \delta x_j \, \delta x_k \, dt \end{aligned} \tag{6.3-13}$$

$\delta\mathcal{P}$ may be expressed as

$$\delta\mathcal{P} = -\int_{t_0}^{t_f} [H(\mathbf{x}, \mathbf{p}, \mathbf{m} + \delta\mathbf{m}, t) - H(\mathbf{x}, \mathbf{p}, \mathbf{m}, t)] \, dt - q \tag{6.3-14}$$

To prove that the maximum principle provides a necessary condition for the control vector $\mathbf{m}$ to minimize the Pontryagin function $\mathcal{P}$, it is required to show that at least one control vector $\mathbf{m}$ can be found such that, if the hamiltonian H is not a maximum, the minimum condition for $\mathcal{P}$ is violated. It is to be noted that the condition for the Pontryagin function $\mathcal{P}$ to be the minimum for any small change $\delta\mathbf{m}$ of the control vector $\mathbf{m}$ is

$$\delta\mathcal{P} \geq 0 \tag{6.3-15}$$

Now assume that the maximum condition for H is not satisfied during a small interval (t_a, t_b) which lies within the interval (t_0, t_f). Then, for any small variation $\delta\mathbf{m}$ of the control vector $\mathbf{m}$,

$$H(\mathbf{x}, \mathbf{p}, \mathbf{m} + \delta\mathbf{m}, t) - H(\mathbf{x}, \mathbf{p}, \mathbf{m}, t) > \alpha \tag{6.3-16}$$

where t lies within the interval (t_a, t_b), and α is a positive constant. A control vector $\mathbf{m}$ having the following properties is chosen. During the interval (t_a, t_b), $\mathbf{m}$ may be varied by a very small amount $\delta\mathbf{m}$, and outside this interval, $\mathbf{m}$ remains unchanged. With this control vector, the variation $\delta\mathcal{P}$ of the Pontryagin function given in Eq. (6.3-14) becomes

$$\begin{aligned}\delta\mathcal{P} &= -\int_{t_a}^{t_b} [H(\mathbf{x}, \mathbf{p}, \mathbf{m} + \delta\mathbf{m}, t) - H(\mathbf{x}, \mathbf{p}, \mathbf{m}, t)]\, dt - q \\ &= -\int_{t_a}^{t_b} \sum_s \frac{\partial H}{\partial m_s} \delta m_s \, dt - q \end{aligned}\tag{6.3-17}$$

Since both $\delta\mathbf{m}$ and $\delta\mathbf{x}$ are very small, the second term at the right-hand side of Eq. (6.3-13) is an infinitesimal of higher order, which may be neglected, and q can be approximated by

$$q \doteq \int_{t_0}^{t_f} \sum_i \sum_j p_i \left\{ \frac{\partial[f_i(\mathbf{x}, \mathbf{m} + \delta\mathbf{m}, t) - f_i(\mathbf{x}, \mathbf{m}, t)]}{\partial x_j} \right\} \delta x_j \, dt \tag{6.3-18}$$

Taylor's series expansion of $f_i(\mathbf{x}, \mathbf{m} + \delta\mathbf{m}, t)$ with respect to $\mathbf{m}$ gives

$$f_i(\mathbf{x}, \mathbf{m} + \delta\mathbf{m}, t) = f_i(\mathbf{x}, \mathbf{m}, t) + \sum_s \frac{\partial f_i(\mathbf{x}, \mathbf{m}, t)}{\partial m_s} \delta m_s + \cdots \tag{6.3-19}$$

Since $\delta\mathbf{m}$ is very small, upon transposing $f_i(\mathbf{x}, \mathbf{m}, t)$, Eq. (6.3-19) reduces to

$$f_i(\mathbf{x}, \mathbf{m} + \delta\mathbf{m}, t) - f_i(\mathbf{x}, \mathbf{m}, t) = \sum_s \frac{\partial f_i(\mathbf{x}, \mathbf{m}, t)}{\partial m_s} \delta m_s \tag{6.3-20}$$

Hence q is given by

$$q = \int_{t_0}^{t_f} \sum_i \sum_j p_i \sum_s \frac{\partial^2 f_i(\mathbf{x}, \mathbf{m}, t)}{\partial x_j \, \partial m_s} \delta x_j \, \delta m_s \, dt \tag{6.3-21}$$

In view of Eq. (6.3-3) and the property of this control vector,

$$q = \int_{t_a}^{t_b} \sum_j \sum_s \frac{\partial^2 H}{\partial x_j \, \partial m_s} \delta x_j \, \delta m_s \, dt \tag{6.3-22}$$

Combining Eqs. (6.3-17) and (6.3-22) yields

$$\delta\mathcal{P} = -\int_{t_a}^{t_b} \sum_s \left(\frac{\partial H}{\partial m_s} \delta m_s + \sum_j \frac{\partial^2 H}{\delta x_j \, \partial m_s} \delta x_j \, \delta m_s \right) dt \tag{6.3-23}$$

which is less than zero, since the first term of the integrand is positive and the value of the second term is smaller than the first term. This implies that, for this particular control vector, the Pontryagin function $\mathcal{P}$ is not minimum for any small variation $\delta\mathbf{m}$ of the control vector $\mathbf{m}$. Clearly, the above result points out that, if the maximum condition for H is not satisfied, the minimum condition for $\mathcal{P}$ may be violated. This proves the *necessity condition*.

It is stated in Sec. 6.2 that when the control process is linear and subject to an additive control function, the maximum principle provides a necessary and sufficient condition for optimum control. This can be shown as follows: Let the process dynamics be characterized by

$$\dot{x}_i(t) = \sum_{k=1}^{n} a_{ik}(t)x_k(t) + u_i(\mathbf{m}) \tag{6.3-24}$$

Then the hamiltonian of the system may be expressed in the form

$$H = \sum_i \sum_k a_{ik}(t)p_i(t)x_k(t) + \sum_i p_i(t)u_i(\mathbf{m}) \tag{6.3-25}$$

Since the first term of this hamiltonian is linear in x_k and is independent of $\mathbf{m}$ and the second term is independent of $\mathbf{x}$,

$$\frac{\partial^2 H}{\partial x_j\,\partial m_s} = 0 \tag{6.3-26}$$

and Eq. (6.3-14) becomes

$$\delta\mathcal{P} = -\int_{t_0}^{t_f} [H(\mathbf{x}, \mathbf{p}, \mathbf{m} + \delta\mathbf{m}, t) - H(\mathbf{x}, \mathbf{p}, \mathbf{m}, t)]\,dt \tag{6.3-27}$$

Hence, if the maximum condition holds for the hamiltonian H, the integrand of Eq. (6.3-27) is nonpositive and $\delta\mathcal{P}$ is nonnegative; that is, the minimum condition for the Pontryagin function $\mathcal{P}$ is fulfilled. This proves the *sufficiency condition*.

6.4 DESIGN FOR MINIMUM-TIME CONTROL

The minimum-time-control problem is studied in Sec. 4.5 by use of the state-transition method. It has been shown that the time-optimal control for a linear process subject to saturation is of the bang-bang type. In this section, the maximum principle is applied to the investigation of minimum-time-control problems.[10,112,130,134,140]

Consider the nth-order control process characterized by

$$\dot{\mathbf{x}}(t) = \mathbf{F}(\mathbf{x}, t) + \mathbf{D}(t)\mathbf{m}(t) \tag{6.4-1}$$

where $\mathbf{x}$ is the $n \times 1$ state vector, and $\mathbf{m}$ is the $r \times 1$ control vector. The control signals are subject to the constraints

$$|m_k| \leq M_k \tag{6.4-2}$$

Determine the control strategy which will move the process from a given initial state $\mathbf{x}(t_0)$ to the equilibrium state

$$\mathbf{x}(t_f) = \mathbf{0} \tag{6.4-3}$$

in the shortest time.

By introducing a new coordinate

$$x_{n+1}(t) = \int_{t_0}^{t} dt \tag{6.4-4}$$

the optimum-control problem becomes the minimization of the new coordinate with respect to the control vector $\mathbf{m}$ subject to the constraints given in Eqs. (6.4-1) and (6.4-2). Then the differential equations characterizing the augmented system are

$$\dot{x}_i = F_i(\mathbf{x}, t) + \sum_{j=1}^{r} d_{ij}m_j \qquad i = 1, 2, \ldots, n \tag{6.4-5}$$

$$\dot{x}_{n+1} = 1 \tag{6.4-6}$$

which are subject to the initial conditions

$$\mathbf{x}(t_0) = \mathbf{x}_0 \tag{6.4-7}$$

In Eq. (6.4-5), the functions $d_{ij}(t)$ are the components of matrix $\mathbf{D}(t)$. Since the final state of the optimum trajectory is constrained by Eq. (6.4-3), the Pontryagin function $\mathcal{P}$ is given by

$$\mathcal{P} = (\mathbf{b}, \mathbf{x}(t_f)) + (\boldsymbol{\mu}, \mathbf{x}(t_f)) \tag{6.4-8}$$

where $\boldsymbol{\mu}$ is a vector Lagrangian multiplier,

$$\boldsymbol{\mu} = \begin{bmatrix} \mu_1 \\ \mu_2 \\ \cdot \\ \cdot \\ \cdot \\ \mu_n \end{bmatrix} \tag{6.4-9}$$

In view of Eq. (6.4-4),

$$\mathcal{P} = x_{n+1}(t_f) + (\boldsymbol{\mu}, \mathbf{x}(t_f)) \tag{6.4-10}$$

and

$$b_i = 0 \qquad i = 1, 2, \ldots, n \tag{6.4-11}$$

$$b_{n+1} = 1 \tag{6.4-12}$$

The hamiltonian for this system is

$$H = (\mathbf{p}, \mathbf{f}) = \sum_{i=1}^{n} p_i \left[F_i(\mathbf{x}, t) + \sum_{k=1}^{r} d_{ik}m_k\right] + p_{n+1} \tag{6.4-13}$$

Examination of Eq. (6.4-13) reveals that the conditions for maximizing the hamiltonian H with respect to $\mathbf{m}$ are

$$\sum_{i=1}^{n} p_i \sum_{k=1}^{r} d_{ik}m_k > 0 \tag{6.4-14}$$

and

$$|m_k| = M_k \tag{6.4-15}$$

Interchanging the summation operations in Eq. (6.4-14) leads to

$$\sum_{k=1}^{r} m_k \sum_{i=1}^{n} p_i d_{ik} > 0 \tag{6.4-16}$$

Hence the optimum-control signals which minimize the time required for moving the process from a specified initial state to the equilibrium state are given by

$$m_k = M_k \operatorname{sgn} \sum_{i=1}^{n} p_i d_{ik} \tag{6.4-17}$$

The optimum-control strategy given in Eq. (6.4-17) points out that the optimum-control signals m_k have their magnitudes equal to the maximum allowable values M_k and their signs determined by the sign of the function

$$S(t) = \sum_{i=1}^{n} p_i(t)d_{ik}(t) \tag{6.4-18}$$

In other words, the time-optimal control system with the control signals subject to ideal saturation is of the bang-bang type. This result is in agreement with the result derived in Sec. 4.5. The optimum controller switches between the upper and the lower limits according to the switching function given in Eq. (6.4-18).

The next step in the optimum design is to determine the auxiliary variables $p_i(t)$ from the canonical equations

$$\dot{p}_i = -\frac{\partial H}{\partial x_i} = -\sum_{k=1}^{n} p_k \frac{\partial F_k}{\partial x_i} \tag{6.4-19}$$

$$\dot{x}_i = \frac{\partial H}{\partial p_i} = F_i(\mathbf{x}, t) + \sum_{j=1}^{r} d_{ij}m_j \tag{6.4-20}$$

subject to the boundary conditions

$$\mathbf{x}(t_0) = \mathbf{x}_0 \qquad \mathbf{x}(t_f) = \mathbf{0} \qquad \mathbf{p}(t_f) = -\boldsymbol{\mu} \tag{6.4-21}$$

Since $\dot{p}_{n+1} = 0$ and $p_{n+1}(t_f) = -1$, $p_{n+1}(t) = -1$.

Example 6.4-1 Minimum-time Control for a Second-order System

Given a second-order control process characterized by

$$\dot{x}_1 = x_2$$
$$\dot{x}_2 = -ax_2 - bx_1 + m$$

with initial and final conditions

$$x_1(t_0) = x_{10} \qquad x_2(t_0) = x_{20}$$
$$x_1(t_f) = 0 \qquad x_2(t_f) = 0$$

determine the control signal m such that the system is taken from the initial state $\mathbf{x}(t_0)$ to the equilibrium state $\mathbf{x}(t_f) = \mathbf{0}$ in the shortest possible time, subject to the constraint on the control variable

$$|m| \leq M$$

By introducing a new coordinate x_3 such that

$$x_3(t) = \int_{t_0}^{t} dt$$

the differential equations for the augmented system are

$$\dot{x}_1 = x_2$$
$$\dot{x}_2 = -ax_2 - bx_1 + m$$
$$\dot{x}_3 = 1$$

Clearly, at $t = t_0$, $x_3(t_0) = 0$. The Pontryagin function $\mathcal{P}$ is given by

$$\mathcal{P} = x_3(t_f) + \mu_1 x_1(t_f) + \mu_2 x_2(t_f)$$

The optimum-design problem now reduces to the determination of control signal m so that the Pontryagin function is minimized. The hamiltonian for this system is

$$H = p_1 x_2 + p_2(-ax_2 - bx_1 + m) + p_3$$

where the auxiliary variables p_1 and p_2 are related by the canonical equations

$$\dot{p}_1 = -\frac{\partial H}{\partial x_1} = bp_2$$
$$\dot{p}_2 = -\frac{\partial H}{\partial x_2} = ap_2 - p_1$$

which describe the *adjoint system*, subject to the boundary conditions $p_1(t_f) = -\mu_1$ and $p_2(t_f) = -\mu_2$. These two differential equations are referred to as adjoint equations. Since $p_3(t) = 0$ and $p_3(t_f) = -1$, $p_3(t) = -1$.

Examination of the hamiltonian H reveals that it is a maximum if

$$m = M \operatorname{sgn} p_2(t)$$

where the auxiliary variable p_2 is determined from the above canonical equations. Eliminating p_1 among these equations yields

$$\ddot{p}_2 - a\dot{p}_2 + bp_2 = 0$$

from which one obtains p_2 as

$$p_2(t) = Ke^{at/2} \sin \left(\tfrac{1}{2} \sqrt{4b - a^2}\, t + \theta\right)$$

provided that $a^2 - 4b < 0$, where K and θ are functions of the boundary conditions. Hence the optimum-control signal is

$$m^o = M \operatorname{sgn} \left[Ke^{at/2} \sin \left(\tfrac{1}{2} \sqrt{4b - a^2}\, t + \theta\right)\right]$$

To evaluate the constants of integration K and θ, the initial values $p_1(t_0)$ and $p_2(t_0)$ need to be known, but this is not easy to determine. When the numerical values are specified, the trial-and-error technique can be used to find the initial conditions. The optimum-control system may be mechanized, as shown in Fig. 6.4-1. The adjoint system is constructed

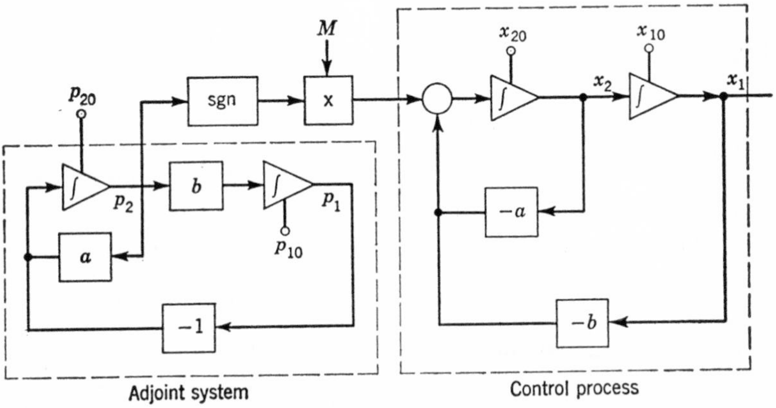

Fig. 6.4-1 Mechanization of the minimum-time control system.

to yield the auxiliary variable $p_2(t)$, which determines the switching of the control signal from $+M$ to $-M$ and vice versa.

Linear Multivariable Process

Now consider the minimum-time control for a linear, multivariable process described by the matrix differential equation

$$\dot{\mathbf{x}}(t) = \mathbf{A}(t)\mathbf{x}(t) + \mathbf{D}(t)\mathbf{m}(t) \tag{6.4-22}$$

where the state vector $\mathbf{x}$ is of dimension n, the control vector $\mathbf{m}$ is of dimension r, and the coefficient matrix $\mathbf{A}(t)$ and the driving matrix $\mathbf{D}(t)$ are $n \times n$ and $n \times r$ matrices, respectively. The control signals are subject to the constraints

$$|m_k| \leq 1 \tag{6.4-23}$$

Application of the maximum principle yields the optimum-control signals which minimize the time required for taking the process from a specified initial state to the equilibrium state. The optimum-control signals are given by

$$m_k(t) = \text{sgn} \sum_{i=1}^{n} d_{ik}(t)p_i(t) \tag{6.4-24}$$

where $d_{ik}(t)$ are the elements of the matrix $\mathbf{D}(t)$. In vector-matrix notations, the optimum-control vector is

$$\mathbf{m}^o(t) = \text{sgn}\,\{\mathbf{D}'(t)\mathbf{p}(t)\} \tag{6.4-25}$$

The auxiliary variables $p_i(t)$ can be determined from the canonical equations

$$\dot{p}_i(t) = -\frac{\partial H}{\partial x_i} = -\sum_{k=1}^{n} a_{ki}(t)p_k(t) \tag{6.4-26}$$

which describe the adjoint system to the given control process. In vector-

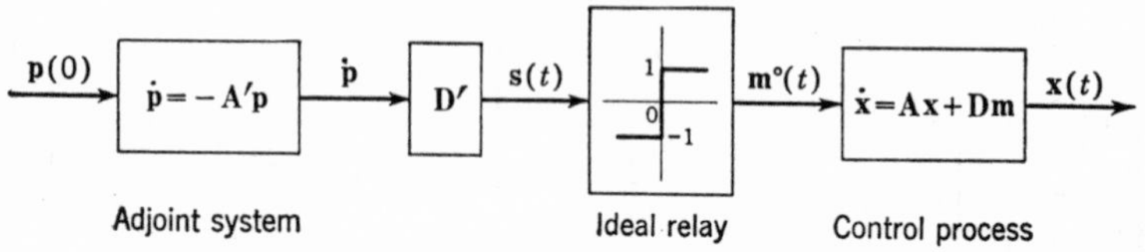

Fig. 6.4-2 General block diagram describing a minimum-time control system.

matrix notations, the adjoint equation is given by

$$\dot{\mathbf{p}}(t) = -\mathbf{A}'(t)\mathbf{p}(t) \tag{6.4-27}$$

which has the solution

$$\mathbf{p}(t) = \boldsymbol{\phi}_a(-t, t_0)\mathbf{p}(t_0) \tag{6.4-28}$$

where $\boldsymbol{\phi}_a(-t, t_0)$ is the transition matrix of the time-varying adjoint system. Hence the optimum-control vector is given by

$$\mathbf{m}^o(t) = \text{sgn}\,\mathbf{s}(t) \tag{6.4-29}$$

where the switching function $\mathbf{s}(t)$ is

$$\mathbf{s}(t) = \mathbf{D}'(t)\boldsymbol{\phi}_a(-t, t_0)\mathbf{p}(t_0) \tag{6.4-30}$$

These two equations point out that, if the initial-condition vector $\mathbf{p}(t_0)$ for the adjoint system is known, the optimum-control vector is determined. However, the values for $\mathbf{p}(t_0)$ are generally not known and are dependent upon the initial and the final state of the given control process. The above analysis by the maximum principle reveals that the minimum-time system may be described conceptually by the block diagram depicted in Fig. 6.4-2. This block diagram illustrates the essential steps underlying the design of minimum-time control. With the initial state vector $\mathbf{p}(t_0)$ for the adjoint system appropriately determined, the adjoint system yields the auxiliary state vector $\mathbf{p}(t)$, which is in turn transformed into the switching function for the optimum-control signal. It can be seen that the optimum-control signal is obtained as the output of an ideal relay-type element.

In the case of time-invariant control processes, the coefficient matrices **A** and **D** are constant matrices and the transition matrix may be expressed as a simple exponential function of time. The solution to the adjoint system to a time-invariant process is

$$\mathbf{p}(t) = e^{-\mathbf{A}'t}\mathbf{p}(t_0) \tag{6.4-31}$$

Thus the switching function $\mathbf{s}(t)$ for the time-invariant control process is

$$\mathbf{s}(t) = \mathbf{D}'e^{-\mathbf{A}'t}\mathbf{p}(t_0) \tag{6.4-32}$$

and the optimum-control vector is given by

$$\mathbf{m}^o(t) = \operatorname{sgn}\,[\mathbf{D}'e^{-\mathbf{A}'t}\mathbf{p}(t_0)] \tag{6.4-33}$$

This result checks with the solution obtained in Sec. 4.7.

6.5 DESIGN FOR TERMINAL CONTROL

In the preceding chapter, the terminal-control problem is studied as a Mayer problem in the classical calculus of variations. The design of the optimum control is carried out under the assumption that no constraint is imposed upon the control signals. This section is concerned with the optimum design of terminal-control problems by use of the maximum principle of Pontryagin.[130] Physical constraints of the control signals are taken into consideration in the design of the system.

Consider the nth-order control process characterized by

$$\dot{\mathbf{x}}(t) = \mathbf{f}(\mathbf{x}, \mathbf{m}, t) = \mathbf{F}(\mathbf{x}, t) + \mathbf{D}(t)\mathbf{m}(t) \tag{6.5-1}$$

with the initial conditions given by $\mathbf{x}(t_0) = \mathbf{x}_0$. In Eq. (6.5-1), $\mathbf{x}$ is the $n \times 1$ state vector and $\mathbf{m}$ is the $r \times 1$ control vector. The control signals are subject to the constraints

$$|m_k| \le M_k \tag{6.5-2}$$

It is now necessary to determine the optimum-control vector $\mathbf{m}(t)$ which minimizes the criterion function

$$I = G[\mathbf{x}(T)] = G[x_1(T), x_2(T), \ldots, x_n(T)] \tag{6.5-3}$$

The functional $G[\mathbf{x}(T)]$, which is differentiable, describes the state variables of the control process at the end of the trajectory.

The design is initiated with the introduction of a new coordinate

$$x_{n+1}(t) = G[x_1(t), x_2(t), \ . \ . \ . \ , x_n(t)] \tag{6.5-4}$$

Then the terminal-control problem becomes the minimization of the new coordinate evaluated at $t = T$ with respect to the control vector $\mathbf{m}$, subject to the constraints given in Eqs. (6.5-1) and (6.5-2). The differential equations describing the augmented system are

$$\dot{x}_i(t) = f_i(\mathbf{x}, \mathbf{m}, t) = F_i(\mathbf{x}, t) + \sum_{j=1}^{r} d_{ij}m_j \qquad i = 1, 2, \ . \ . \ . \ , n \tag{6.5-5}$$

$$\dot{x}_{n+1}(t) = \sum_{i=1}^{n} \frac{\partial G}{\partial x_i} f_i(\mathbf{x}, \mathbf{m}, t) \tag{6.5-6}$$

which are subject to the initial conditions

$$\mathbf{x}(t_0) = \mathbf{x}_0 \tag{6.5-7}$$

$$x_{n+1}(t_0) = G_0 \tag{6.5-8}$$

In Eq. (6.5-5), $d_{ij}(t)$ are the elements of matrix $\mathbf{D}(t)$. Since the Pontryagin function $\mathcal{P}$ is given by

$$\mathcal{P} = x_{n+1}(T) \tag{6.5-9}$$

the coefficients b_i are

$$b_i = 0 \qquad i = 1, 2, \ . \ . \ . \ , n \tag{6.5-10}$$

$$b_{n+1} = 1 \tag{6.5-11}$$

The hamiltonian for this system is

$$H = (\mathbf{p}, \mathbf{f}) = \sum_{i=1}^{n} p_i f_i + p_{n+1} \sum_{i=1}^{n} \frac{\partial G}{\partial x_i} f_i(\mathbf{x}, \mathbf{m}, t) \tag{6.5-12}$$

Using Eq. (6.5-5) and rearranging,

$$H = \sum_{i=1}^{n} \left(p_i + p_{n+1} \frac{\partial G}{\partial x_i}\right) F_i(\mathbf{x}, t) + \sum_{i=1}^{n} \left(p_i + p_{n+1} \frac{\partial G}{\partial x_i}\right) \sum_{j=1}^{r} d_{ij}m_j \tag{6.5-13}$$

This equation makes evident that the conditions for maximizing the hamiltonian H with respect to $\mathbf{m}$ are

$$\sum_{i=1}^{n} \left(p_i + p_{n+1} \frac{\partial G}{\partial x_i}\right) \sum_{j=1}^{r} d_{ij}m_j > 0 \tag{6.5-14}$$

and

$$|m_j| = M_j \tag{6.5-15}$$

Interchanging the summation signs in Eq. (6.5-14) yields

$$\sum_{j=1}^{r} m_j \sum_{i=1}^{n} \left(p_i + p_{n+1} \frac{\partial G}{\partial x_i}\right) d_{ij} > 0 \tag{6.5-16}$$

Since $\dot{p}_{n+1}(t) = 0$ and $p_{n+1}(T) = -1$, then

$$p_{n+1}(t) = -1 \tag{6.5-17}$$

Therefore the optimum-control signals for the given terminal control system are given by

$$m_j(t) = M_j \operatorname{sgn} \{s_j(t)\} \tag{6.5-18}$$

where $s_j(t)$ is the optimum switching function

$$s_j(t) = \sum_{i=1}^{n} \left[p_i(t) - \frac{\partial G}{\partial x_i} \right] d_{ij}(t) \tag{6.5-19}$$

The next step in the optimum design of the terminal control is the determination of the auxiliary variables p_i, which may be evaluated from the canonical equations

$$\dot{p}_i = -\frac{\partial H}{\partial x_i} = -\sum_{k=1}^{n} \left[\left(p_k - \frac{\partial G}{\partial x_k} \right) \frac{\partial f_k}{\partial x_i} - f_k \frac{\partial^2 G}{\partial x_i\, \partial x_k} \right] \tag{6.5-20}$$

$$\dot{x}_i = \frac{\partial H}{\partial p_i} = F_i(\mathbf{x}, t) + \sum_{j=1}^{r} d_{ij} m_j \tag{6.5-21}$$

subject to the initial conditions for $\mathbf{x}$ given in Eqs. (6.5-7) and (6.5-8) and the boundary conditions on $\mathbf{p}$,

$$p_i(T) = 0 \tag{6.5-22}$$

A Linear System

Consider the nth-order linear control process characterized by

$$\dot{\mathbf{x}}(t) = \mathbf{A}(t)\mathbf{x}(t) + \mathbf{D}(t)\mathbf{m}(t) \tag{6.5-23}$$

under the assumption that the initial conditions are $\mathbf{x}(t_0) = \mathbf{x}_0$. The control signals are subject to the constraints given in Eq. (6.5-2). Determine the control vector $\mathbf{m}$ which minimizes the system error at the terminal of the trajectory,

$$e(T) = x_d - x_1(T) \tag{6.5-24}$$

where x_d is the desired system response, and $x_1(T)$ is the actual response at the terminal time T.

Introduce a new coordinate

$$x_{n+1}(t) = x_d - x_1(t) \tag{6.5-25}$$

The terminal-control problem now becomes the minimization of $x_{n+1}(T)$ with respect to the control vector $\mathbf{m}$, subject to the constraints given in Eqs. (6.5-23) and (6.5-2). The differential equations describing the augmented system are

$$\dot{x}_i = \sum_{k=1}^{n} a_{ik}x_k + \sum_{j=1}^{r} d_{ij}m_j \qquad i = 1, 2, \ldots, n \tag{6.5-26}$$

$$\dot{x}_{n+1} = -\dot{x}_1 = -\left[\sum_{k=1}^{n} a_{1k}x_k + \sum_{j=1}^{r} d_{1j}m_j\right] \tag{6.5-27}$$

which are subject to the initial conditions

$$\mathbf{x}(t_0) = \mathbf{x}_0 \tag{6.5-28}$$

$$x_{n+1}(t_0) = e_0 \tag{6.5-29}$$

In Eq. (6.5-26), the functions $a_{ik}(t)$ and $d_{ij}(t)$ are the components of matrices $\mathbf{A}(t)$ and $\mathbf{D}(t)$, respectively.

The hamiltonian for this system is

$$H = \sum_{i=1}^{n} p_i \left[\sum_{k=1}^{n} a_{ik}x_k + \sum_{j=1}^{r} d_{ij}m_j\right] - p_{n+1}\left[\sum_{k=1}^{n} a_{1k}x_k + \sum_{j=1}^{r} d_{1j}m_j\right] \tag{6.5-30}$$

Rearranging,

$$H = \sum_{i=1}^{n} \sum_{k=1}^{n} (p_i a_{ik} - p_{n+1}a_{1k})x_k + \sum_{i=1}^{n} \sum_{j=1}^{r} (p_i d_{ij} - p_{n+1}d_{1j})m_j \tag{6.5-31}$$

Clearly, the hamiltonian H is maximized with respect to $\mathbf{m}$ if

$$\sum_{i=1}^{n} \sum_{j=1}^{r} (p_i d_{ij} - p_{n+1}d_{1j})m_j > 0 \tag{6.5-32}$$

and

$$|m_j| = M_j \tag{6.5-33}$$

Equation (6.5-32) may be written as

$$\sum_{j=1}^{r} m_j \sum_{i=1}^{n} (p_i d_{ij} - p_{n+1}d_{1j}) > 0 \tag{6.5-34}$$

Hence the terminal controller for the given linear process is described by

$$m_j(t) = M_j \operatorname{sgn} \{s_j(t)\} \tag{6.5-35}$$

where $s_j(t)$ is the optimum switching function

$$s_j(t) = \sum_{i=1}^{n} [p_i(t)d_{ij}(t) + d_{1j}(t)] \tag{6.5-36}$$

In the above equation, use is made of the relationship $p_{n+1}(t) = -1$. The auxiliary variables p_i can be determined from the canonical equations

$$\dot{p}_i = -\frac{\partial H}{\partial x_i} = -\left(\sum_{k=1}^{n} a_{ki}p_k + a_{1i}\right) \tag{6.5-37}$$

$$\dot{x}_i = \frac{\partial H}{\partial p_i} = \sum_{k=1}^{n} a_{ik}x_k + \sum_{j=1}^{r} d_{ij}m_j \tag{6.5-38}$$

subject to the initial condition for the state variables as given in Eq. (6.5-28) and the boundary conditions on the auxiliary variables p_i,

$$p_i(T) = 0 \tag{6.5-39}$$

Substituting the functions $p_i(t)$ determined from the above differential equations into Eq. (6.5-35) yields the optimum-control signals as functions of time, $m_j(t)$. By solving for $\mathbf{x}(t)$, the optimum-control signals as functions of the state variables, $m_j(\mathbf{x})$, are obtained.

6.6 MINIMUM-INTEGRAL CONTROL

This section is concerned with the application of the maximum principle to the optimum design of control processes with respect to integral-performance criteria.[40,130,140] Consider the nth-order control process which is characterized by

$$\dot{\mathbf{x}}(t) = \mathbf{F}(\mathbf{x}, t) + \mathbf{D}(t)\mathbf{m}(t) \tag{6.6-1}$$

where $\mathbf{x}$ is the $n \times 1$ state vector, and $\mathbf{m}$ is the $r \times 1$ control vector. The initial conditions are given by

$$\mathbf{x}(t_0) = \mathbf{x}_0 \tag{6.6-2}$$

and the control signals are subject to the constraint

$$\int_{t_0}^{t_f} g(\mathbf{m})\, dt = c \tag{6.6-3}$$

where c is a constant. Determine the control vector $\mathbf{m}$ which minimizes the criterion function

$$I = \int_{t_0}^{t_f} G(\mathbf{x}, \mathbf{m}, t)\, dt \tag{6.6-4}$$

where the function $G(\mathbf{x}, \mathbf{m}, t)$ is differentiable.

Application of the Lagrange multiplier converts this optimization problem into the minimization of the synthetic function

$$I_1 = \int_{t_0}^{t_f} G_1(\mathbf{x}, \mathbf{m}, t)\, dt \tag{6.6-5}$$

where the integrand is given by

$$G_1(\mathbf{x}, \mathbf{m}, t) = G(\mathbf{x}, \mathbf{m}, t) + \lambda g(\mathbf{m}) \tag{6.6-6}$$

Now let the new coordinate $x_{n+1}(t)$ be

$$x_{n+1}(t) = \int_{t_0}^{t_0} G_1(\mathbf{x}, \mathbf{m}, t)\, dt \tag{6.6-7}$$

Then this minimum-integral-control problem becomes the problem of minimizing the new coordinate evaluated at the end of the trajectory, with respect to the control vector $\mathbf{m}$, subject to the constraint given in Eq. (6.6-1). The differential equations describing the augmented system are

$$\dot{x}_i(t) = F_i(\mathbf{x}, t) + \sum_{j=1}^{r} d_{ij}m_j \qquad i = 1, 2, \ldots, n \tag{6.6-8}$$

$$\dot{x}_{n+1}(t) = G_1(\mathbf{x}, \mathbf{m}, t) \tag{6.6-9}$$

which are subject to the initial conditions given in Eq. (6.6-2) and

$$x_{n+1}(t_0) = 0 \tag{6.6-10}$$

The Pontryagin function $\mathcal{P}$ is

$$\mathcal{P} = x_{n+1}(t_f) \tag{6.6-11}$$

with the coefficients b_i given by

$$b_i = 0 \qquad i = 1, 2, \ldots, n \tag{6.6-12}$$

$$b_{n+1} = 1 \tag{6.6-13}$$

The hamiltonian for this system is

$$H = \sum_{i=1}^{n} p_i \left[F_i(\mathbf{x}, t) + \sum_{k=1}^{r} d_{ik}m_k\right] + p_{n+1}G_1(\mathbf{x}, \mathbf{m}, t) \tag{6.6-14}$$

The maximization of the hamiltonian H with respect to $\mathbf{m}$ leads to the equations

$$\sum_{i=1}^{n} p_i d_{ik} - \frac{\partial G_1}{\partial m_k} = 0 \qquad k = 1, 2, \ldots, r \tag{6.6-15}$$

In Eq. (6.6-15), use is made of the condition

$$p_{n+1}(t) = -1 \tag{6.6-16}$$

which follows immediately upon integrating

$$\dot{p}_{n+1}(t) = 0 \tag{6.6-17}$$

subject to the boundary condition $p_{n+1}(t_f) = -1$.

Solving for m_k from these r simultaneous equations included in Eq. (6.6-15) gives the optimum-control signals which minimize the specified criterion function. Since the control signals derived from Eq. (6.6-15) are expressed as functions of the auxiliary variables p_j, the control problem is not completely solved until these auxiliary variables are determined. The auxiliary variables can be determined from the canonical equations

$$\dot{p}_i = -\frac{\partial H}{\partial x_i} = -\sum_{j=1}^{n} p_j \frac{\partial F_j}{\partial x_i} - \frac{\partial G_1}{\partial x_i} \tag{6.6-18}$$

$$\dot{x}_i = \frac{\partial H}{\partial p_i} = F_i(\mathbf{x}, t) + \sum_{j=1}^{r} d_{ij} m_j \tag{6.6-19}$$

subject to the initial conditions for the state variables as given in Eqs. (6.6-2) and (6.6-10) and the boundary conditions on auxiliary variables p_i,

$$p_i(t_f) = 0 \tag{6.6-20}$$

The Lagrange multiplier λ may be evaluated by substituting the optimum-control vector $\mathbf{m}^o$ into Eq. (6.6-3).

Example 6.6-1 A Simple Control Process Subject to an Integral Constraint

Consider a first-order control process characterized by

$$\dot{x} = ax + \gamma m$$

The control signal is subject to the constraint

$$\int_0^{t_1} m^2\,dt = c$$

Determine the optimum-control signal which minimizes the criterion function

$$I = \int_0^{t_1} x^2\,dt$$

Applying the Lagrange multiplier results in the synthetic criterion function

$$I_1 = \int_0^{t_1} (x^2 + Km^2)\,dt$$

Let

$$x_1 = x$$
$$\dot{x}_1 = ax_1 + \gamma m$$
$$\dot{x}_2 = x_1^2 + Km^2$$

where x_2 is the new coordinate and is given by

$$x_2(t) = \int_0^{t} (x_1^2 + Km^2)\,dt$$

The Pontryagin function $\mathcal{P}$ is

$$\mathcal{P} = x_2(t_1)$$

with $\qquad b_1 = 0 \qquad$ and $\qquad b_2 = 1$

The hamiltonian for this system is

$$H = p_1(ax_1 + \gamma m) + p_2(x_1^2 + Km^2)$$

Taking the partial derivative of H with respect to m and equating the derivative to zero yields

$$p_1\gamma + 2p_2Km = 0$$

Hence the optimum-control signal is

$$m = \frac{\gamma}{2K} p_1$$

since $p_2 = -1$. This result follows immediately from Eq. (6.6-15).

The auxiliary variable p_1 is determined from the canonical equations

$$\dot{p}_1 = -ap_1 + 2x_1$$
$$\dot{x}_1 = ax_1 + \frac{\gamma^2}{2K} p_1$$

subject to the boundary conditions

$$x_1(0) = x_0 \qquad \text{and} \qquad p_1(t_1) = 0$$

Solving for $p_1(t)$ results in

$$p_1(t) = \frac{2x_0(e^{-\lambda_1 t} - e^{\lambda_1(t-2t_1)})}{\lambda_2(1 + e^{-2\lambda_1 t_1}) + a(1 - e^{-2\lambda_1 t_1})}$$

where $\quad \lambda_1 = \sqrt{\dfrac{a^2K + \gamma^2}{K}} \quad$ and $\quad \lambda_2 = -\sqrt{\dfrac{a^2K + \gamma^2}{K}}$

Therefore the optimum-control signal is

$$m^o(t) = \frac{\gamma x_0}{K} \frac{e^{-\lambda_1 t} - e^{-\lambda_1(2t_1 - t)}}{\lambda_2(1 + e^{-2\lambda_1 t_1}) + a(1 - e^{-2\lambda_1 t_1})}$$

The Lagrange multiplier K is determined by substituting the above expression for the optimum-control signal into the constraint relationship. It should be observed that the optimum-control signal follows an exponential pattern. At $t = 0$, the control signal is

$$m^o(0) = \frac{\gamma x_0}{2K} \frac{1 - e^{-\lambda_1 t_1}}{\lambda_2 \cosh \lambda_1 t_1 + a \sinh \lambda_1 t_1}$$

At the end of the trajectory, $t = t_1$, and $m^o(t_1) = 0$. The determination of the optimum-control law as a function of the state variable requires the computation of $x_1(t)$ and the elimination of t from the expressions for $x_1(t)$ and $m^o(t)$. This is usually quite difficult to achieve. However, the mechanization of such a feedback control system can be carried out by use of the canonical equations derived above. The state variable x_1 is fed into the adjoint system, which generates the optimum-control signal.

The Minimum-energy-control Problem

Among the many control problems of practical importance, the problem of minimizing the control energy is of special interest and deserves extensive investigation. Since the square of the control signal is proportional to the power required for control, and the time integral of the square of the control signal provides a measure of the energy consumed in achieving optimum control, the minimum-energy-control problem may be formulated as a problem of minimum-integral control.[10,108] Consider an nth-order time-varying control process described by the matrix differential equation

$$\dot{\mathbf{x}}(t) = \mathbf{A}(t)\mathbf{x}(t) + \mathbf{D}(t)\mathbf{m}(t) \tag{6.6-21}$$

with the initial conditions given by $\mathbf{x}(t_0) = \mathbf{x}_0$, where the state vector $\mathbf{x}$ is of dimension n, the control vector $\mathbf{m}$ is of dimension r, and the coefficient matrix $\mathbf{A}(t)$ and the driving matrix $\mathbf{D}(t)$ are $n \times n$ and $n \times r$ matrices, respectively. The optimum-control vector is sought as a means of minimizing the energy function

$$I = \int_{t_0}^{t_f} \sum_{k=1}^{r} m_k^2(t)\,dt \tag{6.6-22}$$

subject to the constraint

$$|m_k| \leq M_k \tag{6.6-23}$$

where M_k is a constant.

By introducing a new coordinate

$$x_{n+1}(t) = \int_{t_0}^{t_f} \sum_{k=1}^{r} m_k^2(t)\,dt \tag{6.6-24}$$

the minimum-energy-control problem becomes the problem of minimizing the new coordinate, evaluated at the terminal of the trajectory, with respect to the control vector $\mathbf{m}$, subject to the constraint relationships given in Eqs. (6.6-21) and (6.6-23). The augmented system is characterized by the differential equations

$$\dot{x}_i(t) = f_i(\mathbf{x}, \mathbf{m}, t) = \sum_{j=1}^{n} a_{ij}(t)x_j(t) + \sum_{k=1}^{r} d_{ik}(t)m_k(t) \qquad i = 1, 2, \ldots, n \tag{6.6-25}$$

$$\dot{x}_{n+1}(t) = \sum_{k=1}^{r} m_k^2(t) \tag{6.6-26}$$

which are subject to the initial conditions

$$\mathbf{x}(t_0) = \mathbf{x}_0 \tag{6.6-27}$$

$$x_{n+1}(t_0) = 0 \tag{6.6-28}$$

In Eq. (6.6-25), $a_{ij}(t)$ are the elements of matrix $\mathbf{A}(t)$, and $d_{ik}(t)$ are the elements of matrix $\mathbf{D}(t)$.

The Pontryagin function $\mathcal{P}$ is given by

$$\mathcal{P} = x_{n+1}(t_f) \tag{6.6-29}$$

and the hamiltonian H for this system is

$$H = (\mathbf{p}, \mathbf{f}) = \mathbf{x}'(t)\mathbf{A}'(t)\mathbf{p}(t) + \mathbf{m}'(t)\mathbf{D}'(t)\mathbf{p}(t) + p_{n+1}(t) \sum_{k=1}^{r} m_k^2(t) \tag{6.6-30}$$

Since it has been shown that $p_{n+1}(t) = -1$, the hamiltonian H reduces to

$$H = \mathbf{x}'(t)\mathbf{A}'(t)\mathbf{p}(t) + \mathbf{m}'(t)\mathbf{D}'(t)\mathbf{p}(t) - \sum_{k=1}^{r} m_k^2(t) \tag{6.6-31}$$

where the auxiliary state vector $\mathbf{p}(t)$ is the solution of the canonical equation

$$\dot{\mathbf{p}}(t) = -\frac{\partial H}{\partial \mathbf{x}} = -\mathbf{A}'(t)\mathbf{p}(t) \tag{6.6-32}$$

describing the adjoint system to the specified control process, and is given by

$$\mathbf{p}(t) = \phi_a(-t, t_0)\mathbf{p}(t_0) \tag{6.6-33}$$

By defining

$$\mathbf{s}(t) = \mathbf{D}'(t)\phi_a(-t, t_0)\mathbf{p}(t_0) \tag{6.6-34}$$

the hamiltonian H may be written as

$$H = \mathbf{x}'(t)\mathbf{A}'(t)\mathbf{p}(t) + \mathbf{m}'(t)\mathbf{s}(t) - \sum_{k=1}^{r} m_k^2(t) \tag{6.6-35}$$

The vector function $\mathbf{s}(t)$ is a column vector of dimension r,

$$\mathbf{s}(t) = \begin{bmatrix} s_1(t) \\ s_2(t) \\ \cdot \\ \cdot \\ \cdot \\ s_r(t) \end{bmatrix} \tag{6.6-36}$$

which, as will be seen later, describes the optimum switching function. Examination of the hamiltonian H given in Eq. (6.6-35) reveals that H is maximum with respect to $\mathbf{m}(t)$ if the function

$$\mathbf{m}'(t)\mathbf{s}(t) - \sum_{k=1}^{r} m_k^2(t) = \sum_{k=1}^{r} [m_k(t)s_k(t) - m_k^2(t)] \tag{6.6-37}$$

is maximum, subject to the constraint of Eq. (6.6-23). It is observed from the right-hand term of Eq. (6.6-37) that, if $|s_k(t)| \leq 2M_k$, the condition for H to be maximum is

$$\frac{\partial[m_k(t)s_k(t) - m_k^2(t)]}{\partial m_k(t)} = 0 \tag{6.6-38}$$

which yields the optimum-control signals as

$$m_k{}^o(t) = \tfrac{1}{2}s_k(t) \qquad k = 1, 2, \ldots, r \tag{6.6-39}$$

and the optimum-control vector is

$$\mathbf{m}^o(t) = \tfrac{1}{2}\mathbf{s}(t) \tag{6.6-40}$$

In this situation the constraint relation given in Eq. (6.6-23) is fulfilled, since $|s_k(t)|$ is less than or equal to $2M_k$. On the other hand, if $|s_k(t)| \geq 2M_k$, the optimum-control signal which maximizes the hamiltonian H is

$$m_k(t) = M_k \operatorname{sgn} \{s_k(t)\} \tag{6.6-41}$$

since the maximum allowable value for $m_k(t)$ is M_k. To summarize, the

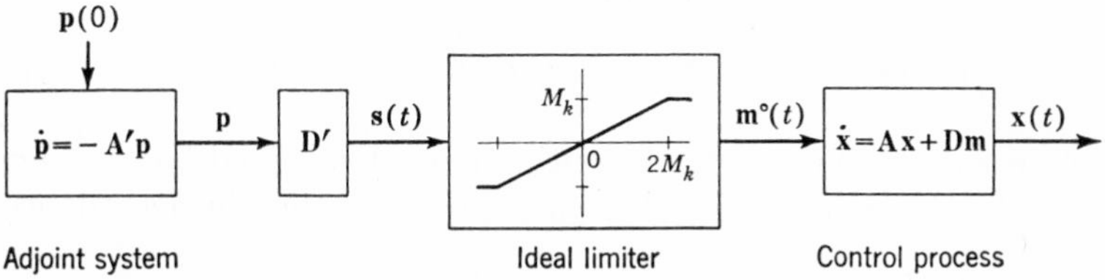

Fig. 6.6-1 General block diagram describing a minimum-energy control system.

optimum-control strategy for accomplishing minimum-energy control of a linear process subject to control-signal saturation is

$$m_k(t) = \tfrac{1}{2}s_k(t) \qquad \text{if } |s_k(t)| \leq 2M_k \tag{6.6-42a}$$
$$m_k(t) = M_k \operatorname{sgn} \{s_k(t)\} \qquad \text{if } |s_k(t)| \geq 2M_k \tag{6.6-42b}$$

where $k = 1, 2, \ldots, r$. In the case of time-invariant control processes, the optimum switching function $\mathbf{s}(t)$ is given by

$$\mathbf{s}(t) = \mathbf{D}'e^{-\mathbf{A}'t}\mathbf{p}(t_0) \tag{6.6-43}$$

The above discussions point out that the minimum-energy control system may be described conceptually by the block diagram depicted in Fig. 6.6-1. This block diagram illustrates the essential steps underlying the design of minimum-energy control systems. With the initial state $\mathbf{p}(t_0)$ for the adjoint system appropriately determined, the adjoint system yields the auxiliary state vector $\mathbf{p}(t)$, which is in turn transformed into the optimum-control signal and the optimum switching function. It is noted from Eqs. (6.6-42) that the control process is driven by a signal which is the output of a limiter-type nonlinear element.

During the linear control region, i.e., when $|s_k(t)| \leq 2M_k$, the optimum-control vector $\mathbf{m}^o$ may be expressed as a function of the state variables of the control process. The solution to Eq. (6.6-21) has been found to be

$$\mathbf{x}(t) = \boldsymbol{\phi}(t, t_0)\mathbf{x}_0 + \int_{t_0}^{t} \boldsymbol{\phi}(t, \tau)\mathbf{D}(\tau)\mathbf{m}(\tau)\, d\tau \tag{6.6-44}$$

Substitution of Eqs. (6.6-34) and (6.6-40) into Eq. (6.6-44) yields

$$\mathbf{x}(t) = \boldsymbol{\phi}(t, t_0)\mathbf{x}_0 + \mathbf{Q}(t)\mathbf{p}(t_0) \tag{6.6-45}$$

where

$$\mathbf{Q}(t) = \tfrac{1}{2} \int_{t_0}^{t} \boldsymbol{\phi}(t, \tau)\mathbf{D}(\tau)\mathbf{D}'(\tau)\boldsymbol{\phi}_a(-\tau, t_0)\, d\tau \tag{6.6-46}$$

which is an $n \times n$ matrix. The initial-state vector $\mathbf{p}(t_0)$ for the adjoint system follows immediately from Eq. (6.6-45),

$$\mathbf{p}(t_0) = \mathbf{Q}^{-1}(t)[\mathbf{x}(t) - \boldsymbol{\phi}(T, t_0)\mathbf{x}_0] \tag{6.6-47}$$

as long as matrix $\mathbf{Q}(t)$ is nonsingular. Therefore the optimum-control law during this control range is given by

$$\mathbf{m}^o(\mathbf{x}, t) = \tfrac{1}{2}\mathbf{D}'(t)\boldsymbol{\phi}_a(-t, t_0)\mathbf{Q}^{-1}(t)[\mathbf{x}(t) - \boldsymbol{\phi}(t, t_0)\mathbf{x}_0] \tag{6.6-48}$$

Within the saturation region, the optimum-control signal has a magnitude equal to the maximum allowable value and switches in accordance with Eq. (6.6-42*b*).

6.7 CONCLUSION

This chapter presents a concise discussion of the design of optimum control systems through the use of the maximum principle. It is demonstrated that various modes of optimum control may be transformed to the generalized mode in which the optimization is carried out with respect to state variables. The transformation makes use of the invariant-embedding procedure of increasing the dimensionality of the state vector. The maximum principle provides an elegant method of obtaining a solution for the generalized mode of optimum control. In general, the maximum principle provides a necessary condition for system optimization. However, if the control process is linear and subject to an additive control function, it provides the necessary and sufficient condition for optimum control. Although the application of the maximum principle is not restricted to systems with unbounded control signals, it is subject to the same difficult two-point boundary-value problem in the variational calculus.

The minimum-time-control problem is studied through use of the maximum principle. It is illustrated that the time-optimal control system which is subject to additive control signals with ideal saturation is of the bang-bang type. For linear systems, the essential steps underlying the design of minimum-time control are illustrated in Fig. 6.4-2. This involves the construction of the adjoint system. When the initial-state vector $\mathbf{p}(t_0)$ of the adjoint system is determined, the adjoint system yields the auxiliary state vector $\mathbf{p}(t)$, which is then transformed into the switching function $\mathbf{s}(t)$. The optimum-control signals may be obtained as the output of an ideal relay-type element. Determination of the initial-state vector $\mathbf{p}(t_0)$ is by no means trivial.

The maximum principle is applied to the design of terminal and minimum-integral control systems. For the nth-order control process characterized by

$$\dot{\mathbf{x}}(t) = \mathbf{F}(\mathbf{x}, t) + \mathbf{D}(t)\mathbf{m}(t)$$

with the control signals subject to the constraints

$$|m_k| \leq M_k$$

the optimum-control signals which minimize the performance index

$$I = G[x_1(T), x_2(T), \ldots, x_n(T)]$$

switch between $+M_k$ and $-M_k$, where $k = 1, 2, \ldots, r$. The switching function may be determined from the canonical equations. The method of the Lagrange multiplier is employed to handle constraints on control signals.

The practical problem of minimum-energy control is analyzed in some detail. For a linear process with control signals subject to ideal saturation, the optimum-control signals for minimum-energy performance are proportional to the switching functions $s_k(t)$ when their values are less than or equal to twice the saturation limits; and the optimum-control signals switch between the limits when the values of the switching functions exceed twice the saturation limits. The essential steps underlying the design of minimum-energy control are illustrated in Fig. 6.6-1. The control process is driven by a signal which is the output of a limiter-type nonlinear element. Although this chapter emphasizes the design of three basic modes of optimal control, the maximum principle is also applicable to other modes of optimal control.

References

Suggested references are Athans,[9,10] Athans, Falb, and Lacoss,[12] Boltyanskii,[30] Boltyanskii et al.,[31,34] Butkovskii,[38] J. W. Chang,[40] S. S. L. Chang,[41] Desoer,[48] Gavrilovic, Petronic, and Siljak,[67] Leitmann,[112] Pontryagin,[127–129] Pontryagin et al.,[130] Roxin,[133] Rozonoer,[134] and Tou.[140]

7
INTRODUCTION TO DYNAMIC PROGRAMMING

Of the various branches of modern mathematics which are being applied to the optimum design of control systems, perhaps the most promising is dynamic-programming theory. Dynamic programming as developed by Richard Bellman is a rather simple but very powerful concept which finds useful applications in the solution of multistage decision problems. The basic idea underlying the method of dynamic programming is the principle of invariant embedding, according to which a very difficult or unsolvable problem is embedded into a class of simpler, solvable problems, so that a solution can be obtained. In the preceding chapter, by expanding the dimension in the augmented system, the technique of invariant embedding is used to convert optimum-control problems of maximizing or minimizing with respect to a new coordinate. In this procedure the optimization problem is solved by direct application of the maximum principle. The principle of invariant embedding also plays an important role in dynamic programming, which provides a powerful tool for the solution of multistage decision problems. Since the optimum-control problems discussed in previous chapters may be viewed as multistage decision processes, the design of optimum control systems from the point of view of dynamic programming is a natural consequence. This chapter is concerned with the application of dynamic-programming techniques to optimum-control design.

7.1 MULTISTAGE DECISION PROCESS AND FUNCTIONAL-EQUATION APPROACH

One of the most important and powerful approaches to the design of optimum control systems is the concept of systematic search for an optimum-control strategy over a multidimensional control space. Thinking along this line, the problem of optimum-system design is essentially visualized as a multistage decision problem.[16,18] Examples of multistage decision processes occur in abundance in practical situations. Perhaps the most common ones are those present in card games, such as the bidding system in contract bridge. In the economic world, investment problems and insurance policies provide other examples of multistage decision processes.

As a simple illustration, the investment problem in the car-rental business may be considered. Suppose there is available an initial amount of money x to be invested in the car-rental business. This money will be used to buy passenger cars and trucks. Assume that y dollars is spent on the purchase of passenger cars and the remaining capital on trucks. The yearly yield on passenger cars is a function of the amount of money invested, y, and is equal to $g(y)$ for the first year. The yearly yield on trucks is a function of the remaining capital $x - y$ and is equal to $h(x - y)$ for the first year. It is the company policy that, after each year, all the used cars and trucks are traded in for new cars and trucks in order to cut the maintenance and repairing expenses to a minimum. The trade-in value of all the cars is a fraction of the total amount of money invested in cars and is equal to ay for the first year, where a is a fraction such that $0 < a < 1$. The trade-in value of all the trucks is a fraction of the total amount of money invested in trucks and is equal to $b(x - y)$ for the first year, where b is a fraction such that $0 < b < 1$. The business executives have to make a sequence of optimum decisions to so allocate the money that the total yield in a period of N years will reach a maximum. To simplify the mathematical analysis in this illustrative example, it is assumed the profit made each year is not reinvested to buy new cars and new trucks.

The multistage decision problems are best solved by means of the functional-equation approach. The original maximization problem is converted into the problem of determining the solution of a functional equation, which is derived as follows: Let

$$\begin{aligned} x &= \text{initial amount of money} \\ y &= \text{amount of money spent on passenger cars} \\ x - y &= \text{amount of money spent on trucks} \\ g(y) &= \text{yield from investment on passenger cars during first year} \\ h(x - y) &= \text{yield from investment on trucks during first year} \\ ay &= \text{trade-in value of passenger cars by end of first year, } 0 < a < 1 \\ b(x - y) &= \text{trade-in value of trucks by end of first year, } 0 < b < 1 \end{aligned}$$

Now it is necessary to allocate the money so as to maximize the total yield in a period of N years. The yield, or return, during the first year is

$$Y_1(x, y) = g(y) + h(x - y) \tag{7.1-1}$$

For a 1-year period, the maximum yield is then given by

$$\begin{aligned} f_1(x) &= \max_{0 \le y \le x} \{Y_1(x, y)\} \\ &= \max_{0 \le y \le x} \{g(y) + h(x - y)\} \end{aligned} \tag{7.1-2}$$

It should be noted that the maximum yield is a function of the initial amount of money invested. When the yield functions g and h are specified or predetermined, the maximum yield can readily be evaluated by differentiating the functions in the braces with respect to y and substituting the maximizing y into the equation describing the total yield. The variable y is subject to the constraint $0 \le y \le x$. The optimum decision, or allocation, $y(x)$, maximizes the functions in the braces of Eq. (7.1-2). Clearly, in the case of a 1-year operation, the investment problem is rather trivial.

The remaining amount of money after 1 year of operation is equal to the total trade-in value of passenger cars and trucks since, according to the simplifying assumption stated above, the profit made during the first year is not reinvested in this operation. Thus the amount of capital during the second year of operation is

$$x_1 = ay + b(x - y) \tag{7.1-3}$$

which may be written as

$$x_1 = y_1 + (x_1 - y_1) \tag{7.1-4}$$

where y_1 is the amount of money spent on the purchase of passenger cars, and $x_1 - y_1$ is the amount of money spent on trucks. Then, during the second year of operation,

$$\begin{aligned} \text{Yield from investment on passenger cars} &= g(y_1) \\ \text{Yield from investment on trucks} &= h(x_1 - y_1) \end{aligned}$$

By the end of the second year,

$$\begin{aligned} \text{Trade-in value of passenger cars} &= ay_1 \\ \text{Trade-in value of trucks} &= b(x_1 - y_1) \end{aligned}$$

The total yield from 2 years of operation is

$$Y_2(x, y, y_1) = g(y) + h(x - y) + g(y_1) + h(x_1 - y_1) \qquad (7.1\text{-}5)$$

and the maximum yield for a 2-year period is

$$\begin{aligned} f_2(x) &= \max_{\substack{0 \le y \le x \\ 0 \le y_1 \le x_1}} \{Y_2(x, y, y_1)\} \\ &= \max_{\substack{0 \le y \le x \\ 0 \le y_1 \le x_1}} \{g(y) + h(x - y) + g(y_1) + h(x_1 - y_1)\} \end{aligned} \qquad (7.1\text{-}6)$$

In view of Eq. (7.1-2), the maximum yield for the 2-year period may be written as

$$f_2(x) = \max_{\substack{0 \le y \le x \\ 0 \le y_1 \le x_1}} \{g(y) + h(x - y) + f_1(x_1)\} \qquad (7.1\text{-}7)$$

By substitution of Eq. (7.1-3), the maximum yield becomes

$$f_2(x) = \max_{0 \le y \le x} \{g(y) + h(x - y) + f_1[ay + b(x - y)]\} \qquad (7.1\text{-}8)$$

This equation implies that the maximum yield for the 2-year period may be determined by differentiating the functions in the braces of Eq. (7.1-8) with respect to y and substituting the maximizing y into the total yield function. The variable y is subject to the constraint relation $0 \le y \le x$. The value of $y(x)$ which maximizes the functions in the braces of Eq. (7.1-8) is the optimum decision to be made at the beginning of a 2-year operation, starting with an amount x.

The remaining amount of money after 2 years is equal to the total trade-in value of passenger cars and trucks and is given by

$$x_2 = ay_1 + b(x_1 - y_1) \qquad (7.1\text{-}9)$$

which may be expressed as

$$x_2 = y_2 + (x_2 - y_2) \qquad (7.1\text{-}10)$$

where y_2 is the amount of money spent on the purchase of passenger cars, and $x_2 - y_2$ is the amount of money spent on trucks. During the third year of operation,

$$\begin{aligned} \text{Yield from investment on passenger cars} &= g(y_2) \\ \text{Yield from investment on trucks} &= h(x_2 - y_2) \end{aligned}$$

By the end of the third year,

$$\begin{aligned} \text{Trade-in value of passenger cars} &= ay_2 \\ \text{Trade-in value of trucks} &= b(x_2 - y_2) \end{aligned}$$

Then the total yield after 3 years of operation is

$$Y_3(x, y, y_1, y_2) = g(y) + h(x - y) + g(y_1) + h(x_1 - y_1) + g(y_2) + h(x_2 - y_2) \quad (7.1\text{-}11)$$

and the maximum yield is

$$\begin{aligned} f_3(x) &= \max_{\substack{0 \le y \le x \\ 0 \le y_1 \le x_1 \\ 0 \le y_2 \le x_2}} \{Y_3(x, y, y_1, y_2)\} \\ &= \max_{\substack{0 \le y \le x \\ 0 \le y_1 \le x_1 \\ 0 \le y_2 \le x_2}} \{g(y) + h(x - y) + g(y_1) + h(x_1 - y_1) + g(y_2) \\ &\qquad + h(x_2 - y_2)\} \end{aligned} \quad (7.1\text{-}12)$$

Making use of Eq. (7.1-6), $f_3(x)$ reduces to

$$f_3(x) = \max_{0 \le y \le x} \{g(y) + h(x - y) + f_2(x_1)\} \quad (7.1\text{-}13)$$

In view of Eq. (7.1-3), the maximum yield is given by

$$f_3(x) = \max_{0 \le y \le x} \{g(y) + h(x - y) + f_2[ay + b(x - y)]\} \quad (7.1\text{-}14)$$

This equation provides a recurrence relationship for the determination of the optimum decisions for the three-stage process.

In like manner, the maximum yield for a 4-year period of operation is found to be

$$f_4(x) = \max_{0 \le y \le x} \{g(y) + h(x - y) + f_3[ay + b(x - y)]\} \quad (7.1\text{-}15)$$

Hence, for an N-year period, the maximum yield is

$$f_N(x) = \max_{0 \le y \le x} \{g(y) + h(x - y) + f_{N-1}[ay + b(x - y)]\} \quad (7.1\text{-}16)$$

This is the basic functional equation for the N-stage decision process. Starting with $f_1(x)$, as determined by Eq. (7.1-2), this functional equation is used to compute $f_2(x)$, which in turn gives $f_3(x)$. By repeating the process, the other maximum yields are determined. At each step of the computation, the optimum decision $y_j(x)$ to be made at the beginning of a j-stage process is also obtained. The value of $y(x)$ which maximizes the functions in the braces of Eq. (7.1-16) is the optimum decision to be made at the beginning of the N-year operation, starting with an initial amount of money x.

Example 7.1-1 A Maximization Problem

Consider the problem of maximizing

$$F(x_1, x_2, \ldots, x_N; y_1, y_2, \ldots, y_N) = \sum_{k=1}^{N} g(x_k, y_k)$$

subject to

$$x_k \geq 0 \qquad \sum_{k=1}^{N} x_k = c_1$$

$$y_k \geq 0 \qquad \sum_{k=1}^{N} y_k = c_2$$

where $g(x, y)$ is a strictly concave function, monotone-increasing in x and y. Determine the functional equation for this multistage decision problem.

Let $f_N(c_1, c_2)$ be the maximum of $F(\mathbf{x}, \mathbf{y})$ with respect to the arguments x_k and y_k. Then, for $N = 1$,

$$f_1(c_1, c_2) = f_1(x_1, y_1) = \max_{\substack{0 \leq x_1 \leq c_1 \\ 0 \leq y_1 \leq c_2}} \{g(x_1, y_1)\}$$

For $N = 2$,

$$\begin{aligned} f_2(c_1, c_2) &= \max_{x,y} \{g(x_2, y_2) + g(x_1, y_1)\} \\ &= \max_{\substack{0 \leq x_2 \leq c_1 \\ 0 \leq y_2 \leq c_2}} \{g(x_2, y_2) + g(c_1 - x_2, c_2 - y_2)\} \\ &= \max_{\substack{0 \leq x_2 \leq c_1 \\ 0 \leq y_2 \leq c_2}} \{g(x_2, y_2) + f_1(c_1 - x_2, c_2 - y_2)\} \end{aligned}$$

For $N = 3$,

$$f_3(c_1, c_2) = \max_{x,y} \{g(x_3, y_3) + g(x_2, y_2) + g(x_1, y_1)\}$$

Since

$$f_2(c_1 - x_3, c_2 - y_3) = \max_{x,y} \{g(x_2, y_2) + f_1(c_1 - x_2 - x_3, c_2 - y_2 - y_3)\}$$

$f_3(c_1, c_2)$ may be written as

$$f_3(c_1, c_2) = \max_{\substack{0 \leq x_3 \leq c_1 \\ 0 \leq y_3 \leq c_2}} \{g(x_3, y_3) + f_2(c_1 - x_3, c_2 - y_3)\}$$

In like manner, for $N = 4$, the result is

$$f_4(c_1, c_2) = \max_{\substack{0 \leq x_4 \leq c_1 \\ 0 \leq y_4 \leq c_2}} \{g(x_4, y_4) + f_3(c_1 - x_4, c_2 - y_4)\}$$

Hence, by induction, it can be shown that

$$f_N(c_1, c_2) = \max_{\substack{0 \leq x_N \leq c_1 \\ 0 \leq y_N \leq c_2}} \{g(x_N, y_N) + f_{N-1}(c_1 - x_N, c_2 - y_N)\}$$

which is the desired functional equation for this multistage decision problem.

7.2 PRINCIPLE OF OPTIMALITY

In the preceding section the functional-equation approach is employed in the study of multistage decision processes. By repeated application of the functional equation, the sequence of optimum decisions for the N-stage process can be determined. Although the investment problem in a car-rental business is chosen as an illustration, the functional-equation approach provides a very useful tool for solving multistage decision problems in general. This section introduces the principle of optimality.[16] As will be seen in later development, the functional equation describing a multistage decision process can readily be derived by invoking the principle of optimality.

To begin with, a single-stage decision process is first considered. Let $\mathbf{x}$ be the state vector characterizing a physical system at any time. The state vector $\mathbf{x}$ is assumed to be a column vector of k dimensions. If the state of the physical system is transformed from $\mathbf{x}^1$ into $\mathbf{x}^2$ by the transformation

$$\mathbf{x}^2 = g(\mathbf{x}^1, m_1) \tag{7.2-1}$$

this operation yields an output, or return,

$$R_1 = r(\mathbf{x}^1, m_1) \tag{7.2-2}$$

The problem is to choose a decision m_1 so as to maximize the return. The decision m_1 is also referred to as a one-stage policy. It is quite clear that the solution to this single-stage decision problem presents no difficulty. The maximum return is given by

$$f_1(\mathbf{x}^1) = \max_{m_1} r(\mathbf{x}^1, m_1) \tag{7.2-3}$$

The decision which yields the maximum value of the return, or criterion function, is referred to as an optimal decision, or optimal-control strategy.

In a two-stage decision process, if the state of the physical system is first transformed from $\mathbf{x}^1$ into $\mathbf{x}^2$ by the transformation

$$\mathbf{x}^2 = g(\mathbf{x}^1, m_1) \tag{7.2-4}$$

and is then transformed from $\mathbf{x}^2$ into $\mathbf{x}^3$ by the transformation

$$\mathbf{x}^3 = g(\mathbf{x}^2, m_2) \tag{7.2-5}$$

this sequence of operations results in a total return

$$R_2 = r(\mathbf{x}^1, m_1) + r(\mathbf{x}^2, m_2) \tag{7.2-6}$$

Then the optimum-design problem is to choose a sequence of allowable decisions m_1 and m_2 so as to maximize the total return. This is a two-stage decision process, where $r(\mathbf{x}^1, m_1)$ is the return from the first choice of a decision and $r(\mathbf{x}^2, m_2)$ is the return from the second choice of a decision.

This sequence of decisions m_1, m_2 is referred to as a two-stage policy. The maximum return is given by

$$f_2(\mathbf{x}^1) = \max_{m_1, m_2} \{r(\mathbf{x}^1, m_1) + r(\mathbf{x}^2, m_2)\} \tag{7.2-7}$$

The total-return function is maximized over the policy $\{m_1, m_2\}$. The policy which maximizes R_2 is referred to as an optimal policy. As can be seen, the two-stage decision problem is more difficult to handle than the single-stage decision problem discussed above. The difficulty and complexity increase with the number of stages of the decision process.

In general, for an N-stage decision process, the problem is to choose an N-stage policy

$$\{m_1, m_2, m_3, \ldots, m_N\}$$

so as to maximize the total return

$$R_N = \sum_{j=1}^{N} r(\mathbf{x}^j, m_j) \tag{7.2-8}$$

The state of the system is transformed from $\mathbf{x}^1$ into $\mathbf{x}^2$ by the transformation $\mathbf{x}^2 = g(\mathbf{x}^1, m_1)$, then from $\mathbf{x}^2$ into $\mathbf{x}^3$ by the transformation $\mathbf{x}^3 = g(\mathbf{x}^2, m_2)$, . . . , and finally from $\mathbf{x}^{N-1}$ into $\mathbf{x}^N$ by the transformation $\mathbf{x}^N = g(\mathbf{x}^{N-1}, m_{N-1})$. The maximum return of the N-stage process is given by

$$f_N(\mathbf{x}^1) = \max_{\{m_j\}} \left\{ \sum_{j=1}^{N} r(\mathbf{x}^j, m_j) \right\} \tag{7.2-9}$$

The policy $\{m_j\}$ which determines $f_N(\mathbf{x}^1)$ is the optimal policy, or optimal-control strategy. In this case, $\{m_j\}$ forms an N-stage control policy.

To carry out the maximization procedure by elementary, brute-force techniques requires the solution of N simultaneous equations obtained by equating to zero the partial derivatives of the quantity in the braces with respect to m_j, $j = 1, 2, \ldots, n$. It is evident that, to solve optimum-decision problems involving a large number of stages, a systematic procedure for obtaining a solution is definitely required to keep the problem from getting out of hand. A systematic solution procedure may be derived by making use of a fundamental principle of dynamic programming—the *principle of optimality*,[16] which states: An optimal policy, or optimal-control strategy, has the property that, whatever the initial state and the initial decision, the remaining decision must form an optimal-control strategy with respect to the state resulting from the first decision.

The principle of optimality, which describes the basic properties of optimal-control strategies, is based upon the fundamental concept of invariant embedding. This concept implies that, to solve a specific optimum-decision problem, the original problem is embedded within a family of similar problems which are easier to solve. For multistage decision processes, this will allow the replacement of the original multistage optimization problem by the problem of solving a sequence of single-stage decision processes, which are undoubtedly simpler to handle.

Invoking the principle of optimality, the total return of an N-stage decision process may be written as

$$R_N = r(\mathbf{x}^1, m_1) + f_{N-1}[g(\mathbf{x}^1, m_1)] \tag{7.2-10}$$

The first term on the right-hand side of Eq. (7.2-10) is the initial return, and the second term represents the maximum return from the final $N - 1$ stages. Then the maximum return is given by

$$f_N(\mathbf{x}^1) = \max_{m_1} \{r(\mathbf{x}^1, m_1) + f_{N-1}[g(\mathbf{x}^1, m_1)]\} \tag{7.2-11}$$

This equation is valid for $N \geq 2$. But, for $N = 1$, the maximum return is

$$f_1(\mathbf{x}^1) = \max_{m_1} \{r(\mathbf{x}^1, m_1)\} \tag{7.2-12}$$

Clearly, by applying this fundamental principle, the N-stage decision process is reduced to a sequence of N single-stage decision processes, thus enabling this optimization problem to be solved in a systematic, iterative manner. It is worth noting here that invariant embedding is the key to dynamic programming.

As an illustration of the application of the optimality principle, the following simple optimum subdivision problem is considered.

Example 7.2-1 An Optimum Subdivision Problem

A positive quantity c is to be divided into n parts in such a way that the product of the n parts is to be a maximum. Determine the optimum subdivision by applying the dynamic-programming technique.

Let $f_n(c)$ be the maximum attainable product, x be the value of the first subdivision, and $(c - x)$ be the value of the remaining $(n - 1)$ parts. Then, invoking the principle of optimality, the functional equation describing this optimum subdivision problem evolves as

$$f_n(c) = \max_{0 \leq x \leq c} \{x f_{n-1}(c - x)\}$$

This equation is valid for $n \geq 2$. It is quite obvious that, when $n = 1$,

$$f_1(c) = c \qquad \text{and} \qquad f_1(c - x) = c - x$$

Thus, for $n = 2$,

$$f_2(c) = \max_{0 \leq x \leq c} \{x f_1(c - x)\} = \max_{0 \leq x \leq c} \{x(c - x)\}$$

By simple calculus, it is found that the value of x which maximizes the product is

$$x = \frac{c}{2}$$

Hence the optimum policy, i.e., optimum subdivision for the two-stage decision process, is

$$\{m_j\} = \left\{\frac{c}{2}, \frac{c}{2}\right\}$$

and the maximum value of the product is

$$f_2(c) = \left(\frac{c}{2}\right)^2$$

Next consider the case $n = 3$. The maximum obtainable product is

$$f_3(c) = \max_{0 \leq x \leq c} \{x f_2(c - x)\} = \max_{0 \leq x \leq c} \left\{\frac{x(c - x)^2}{4}\right\}$$

Application of simple calculus yields the maximizing value of x as

$$x = \frac{c}{3}$$

The subdivision of the remaining part, $2c/3$, constitutes a two-stage decision process. According to the above analysis, this is divided into $c/3$ and $c/3$. Hence the optimum subdivision for the three-stage process is

$$\{m_j\} = \left\{\frac{c}{3}, \frac{c}{3}, \frac{c}{3}\right\}$$

and the maximum value of the product is

$$f_3(c) = \left(\frac{c}{3}\right)^3$$

When the given quantity c is divided into four parts, the maximum attainable product is

$$f_4(c) = \max_{0 \leq x \leq c} \{x f_3(c - x)\} = \max_{0 \leq x \leq c} \left\{\frac{x(c - x)^3}{27}\right\}$$

Simple differentiation leads to the maximizing value of x:

$$x = \frac{c}{4}$$

The subdivision of the remaining part, $3c/4$, constitutes a three-stage process, with the optimum subdivision $c/4$, $c/4$, and $c/4$. Hence the optimum subdivision for the four-stage process is

$$\{m_j\} = \left\{\frac{c}{4}, \frac{c}{4}, \frac{c}{4}, \frac{c}{4}\right\}$$

and the maximum value of the product is

$$f_4(c) = \left(\frac{c}{4}\right)^4$$

The above analysis leads to the conjecture that the solution for this problem, when $n = k$, is that the optimum subdivision would be

$$\{m_j\} = \left\{\frac{c}{k}, \frac{c}{k}, \ldots, \frac{c}{k}\right\}$$

and the maximum value of the product would be

$$f_k(c) = \left(\frac{c}{k}\right)^k$$

It can readily be shown by mathematical induction that the above relationships hold for any k. Invoking the principle of optimality, it follows that

$$f_{k+1}(c) = \max_{0 \le x \le c} \{x f_k(c - x)\} = \max_{0 \le x \le c} \left\{\frac{x(c - x)^k}{k^k}\right\}$$

This yields, by simple calculus, the maximizing x as

$$x = \frac{c}{k + 1}$$

and the maximum value of the product is

$$f_{k+1}(c) = \left(\frac{c}{k + 1}\right)^{k+1}$$

Hence, by mathematical induction, the optimum subdivision for the n-stage process can be obtained as

$$\{m_j\} = \left\{\frac{c}{n}, \frac{c}{n}, \ldots, \frac{c}{n}\right\}$$

with the maximum of the product equal to

$$f_n(c) = \left(\frac{c}{n}\right)^n$$

Clearly, this problem is quite simple and can readily be solved by conventional methods. However, it should be emphasized that this illustrates the idea of rephrasing the given problem as a multistage decision process. The formulation of a problem in this way is indeed the key to much of the usefulness of the dynamic-programming approach.

Time-dependent Multistage Process

In the preceding section, the investment problem in a car-rental business is studied by the functional-equation approach under the simplifying assumption that the multistage decision process is time-invariant. The yield from the investment and the trade-in value of cars and trucks are assumed to be independent of time. However, in more realistic situations, both the yield from the investment and the trade-in value of cars and trucks vary from year to year. Such a multistage decision process is referred to as a time-dependent process.

As an illustration, consider a time-dependent multistage process with periodic sampling. Referring back to the car-rental problem, let the initial amount of money x be divided into y and $x - y$ at the beginning of an N-year operation of the car-rental business. The amount of money y is spent on passenger cars and $x - y$ is spent on trucks. The yield and the trade-in value are dependent upon time. It is assumed that, by the end of the first year of operation, the yield is

$$Y_1(x, y) = g_1(y) + h_1(x - y) \tag{7.2-13}$$

and the trade-in value is

$$x_1 = c_1(x, y) = a_1 y + b_1(x - y) \tag{7.2-14}$$

From the second year of operation, the yield is

$$Y_2(x, y) = g_2(y_1) + h_2(x_1 - y_1) \tag{7.2-15}$$

and the trade-in value is

$$x_2 = c_2(x, y) = a_2 y_1 + b_2(x_1 - y_1) \tag{7.2-16}$$

From the third year of operation, the yield is

$$Y_3(x, y) = g_3(y_2) + h_3(x_2 - y_2) \tag{7.2-17}$$

and the trade-in value is

$$x_3 = c_3(x, y) + a_3 y_2 + b_3(x_2 - y_2) \tag{7.2-18}$$

From the kth year of operation, the yield is

$$Y_k(x, y) = g_k(y_{k-1}) + h_k(x_{k-1} - y_{k-1}) \tag{7.2-19}$$

and the trade-in value is

$$x_k = c_k(x, y) = a_k y_{k-1} + b_k(x_{k-1} - y_{k-1}) \tag{7.2-20}$$

where $Y_k(x, y)$ is continuous in x and y for $x \geq 0$ and $0 \leq y \leq x$, and

$c_k(x, y)$ is continuous in this region and

$$0 \leq c_k(x, y) < \alpha x \qquad \alpha < 1;\, k = 1, 2, \ldots, N \tag{7.2-21}$$

Let $f_{N-k}[c_k(x, y)]$ be the maximum total yield obtained during the remaining $N - k$ years of an N-year operation, starting with an amount of money $x_k = c_k(x, y)$ at the beginning of the $(k + 1)$st year, employing an optimal policy. The yield from the $(k + 1)$st year of operation is $Y_{k+1}(x, y)$. By invoking the principle of optimality, the functional equation for this time-dependent multistage decision process is obtained as

$$f_{N-k}[c_k(x, y)] = \max_{0 \leq y \leq x} \{Y_{k+1}(x, y) + f_{N-\overline{k+1}}[c_{k+1}(x, y)]\}$$
$$k = 0, 1, 2, \ldots, N - 1 \tag{7.2-22}$$

where $c_o(x, y) = x$.

Stochastic Multistage Decision Process

In the above discussions, the multistage decision process is studied under the assumption that the process is deterministic in nature. The yield and the trade-in value for the N-year period are assumed to be known in advance. However, in practice this information is usually not attainable at the beginning of the N-year period of operation. The only available information at that time is the probability of achieving a certain level of yield and trade-in value. In other words, the investment problem discussed above should be regarded as a stochastic multistage decision process. First consider the time-invariant multistage process. As before for the car-rental business, the initial amount of money x is divided into y and $x - y$. The probability that there are a yield

$$Y_a(x, y) = g_a(y) + h_a(x - y) \tag{7.2-23}$$

and a trade-in value

$$x_a = \alpha_a(y) + \beta_a(x - y) \tag{7.2-24}$$

is assumed to be p_a. The probability that there are a yield

$$Y_b(x, y) = g_b(y) + h_b(x, y) \tag{7.2-25}$$

and a trade-in value

$$x_b = \alpha_b(y) + \beta_b(x - y) \tag{7.2-26}$$

is assumed to be p_b. Let $f_N(x)$ be the maximum expected total yield from the N-year operation of the business, obtained by using an optimal policy, starting with an initial capital of x. Then, for a 1-year operation, the maximum expected yield is given by

$$f_1(x) = \max_{0 \leq y \leq x} \{p_a Y_a(x, y) + p_b Y_b(x, y)\} \tag{7.2-27}$$

For $N \geq 2$, by invoking the principle of optimality, the following functional equation is obtained:

$$f_N(x) = \max_{0 \le y \le x} (p_a\{Y_a(x, y) + f_{N-1}[\alpha_a(y) + \beta_a(x - y)]\} + p_b\{Y_b(x, y) + f_{N-1}[\alpha_b(y) + \beta_b(x - y)]\}) \quad (7.2\text{-}28)$$

This is the basic functional equation for the N-stage, stochastic decision process. Repeated application of this equation results in the maximum expected total yield of the operation. The value of $y(x)$ which maximizes the functions in the braces of Eq. (7.2-28) is the optimum decision to be made at the beginning of the N-year operation, starting with an initial amount of money x.

Next consider the time-dependent multistage process. With reference to the car-rental business, let p_{a1} be the probability that, by the end of the first year of operation, the yield is

$$Y_{a1}(x, y) = g_{a1}(y) + h_{a1}(x - y) \quad (7.2\text{-}29)$$

and the trade-in value is

$$x_1 = c_1(x, y) = \alpha_1(y) + \beta_1(x - y) \quad (7.2\text{-}30)$$

and p_{b1} be the probability that, by the end of the first year of operation, the yield is

$$Y_{b1}(x, y) = g_{b1}(y) + h_{b1}(x - y) \quad (7.2\text{-}31)$$

and the trade-in value is as given in Eq. (7.2-30). Similarly, let p_{a2} be the probability that the yield from the second year of operation is

$$Y_{a2}(x, y) = g_{a2}(y_1) + h_{a2}(x_1 - y_1) \quad (7.2\text{-}32)$$

and the trade-in value is

$$x_2 = c_2(x, y) = \alpha_2(y_1) + \beta_2(x_1 - y_1) \quad (7.2\text{-}33)$$

and p_{b2} be the probability that the yield from the second year of operation is

$$Y_{b2}(x, y) = g_{b2}(y_1) + h_{b2}(x_1 - y_1) \quad (7.2\text{-}34)$$

and the trade-in value is as given in Eq. (7.2-33). More generally, let p_{ak} be the probability that the yield from the kth year of operation is

$$Y_{ak}(x, y) = g_{ak}(y_{k-1}) + h_{ak}(x_{k-1} - y_{k-1}) \quad (7.2\text{-}35)$$

and the trade-in value is

$$x_k = c_k(x, y) = \alpha_k(y_{k-1}) + \beta_k(x_{k-1} - y_{k-1}) \quad (7.2\text{-}36)$$

and p_{bk} be the probability that the yield from the kth year of operation is

$$Y_{bk}(x, y) = g_{bk}(y_{k-1}) + h_{bk}(x_{k-1} - y_{k-1}) \quad (7.2\text{-}37)$$

and the trade-in value is as given in Eq. (7.2-36). In the above equations, $Y_{ak}(x, y)$ and $Y_{bk}(x, y)$ are continuous in x and y for $x \ge 0$ and $0 \le y \le x$, and $c_k(x, y)$ is continuous in this region and $0 \leq c_k(x, y) \leq \lambda x$, $\lambda < 1$, $k = 1, 2, \ldots, N$. Invoking the principle of optimality leads to the functional equation for this multistage decision process,

$$f_{N-\overline{k-1}}[c_{k-1}(x, y)] = \max_{0 \leq y \leq x} \{p_{ak}Y_{ak}(x, y) + p_{bk}Y_{bk}(x, y) + (p_{ak} + p_{bk})f_{N-k}[c_k(x, y)]\} \quad (7.2\text{-}38)$$

where $c_0(x, y) = x$. By repeated application of this recursive relationship is derived the optimum decision $y(x)$, to be made at the beginning of the N-year operation, which maximizes the expected total yield.

Example 7.2-2 Production-control Problem

A certain manufacturing firm with a capitalization of x dollars is equipped to make N different products in varying quantities. The cost of producing a quantity q_j of the jth item is

$$g_j(q_j) = \begin{cases} (a_j + b_j + c_j)q_j + K_j & \text{for } q_j > 0 \\ 0 & \text{for } q_j = 0 \end{cases}$$

where a_j = unit cost of raw materials required for jth item
b_j = unit cost of machine production of jth item
c_j = unit cost of labor required for jth item
K_j = a fixed cost, independent of amount produced of jth item, if $q_j > 0$

The total production cost satisfies the relationship

$$\sum_{j=1}^{N} g_j(q_j) \leq x$$

where $q_j \geq 0$, and x is the initial capital. The profit made per unit of the jth item is p_j. The problem is to choose q_j so as to maximize the total profit derived from the N products

$$P_N = \sum_{j=1}^{N} p_j q_j$$

For the sake of simplicity, it is assumed that there is an unlimited supply of labor and machines for the production of any items in any quantities.

Let $f_N(x)$ be the maximum total profit. Then

$$f_N(x) = \max_{\{q_j\}} P_N$$

If the company manufactures only one product, the maximum profit will be

$$f_1(x) = \max_{q_1} (p_1 q_1)$$

Since
$$x = (a_1 + b_1 + c_1)q_1 + K_1$$

then
$$q_1 = \frac{x - K_1}{a_1 + b_1 + c_1}$$

Thus, when the initial capital is greater than the fixed cost, the maximum profit is

$$f_1(x) = \frac{p_1(x - K_1)}{a_1 + b_1 + c_1}$$

When the initial capital is less than or equal to the fixed cost, the maximum profit is

$$f_1(x) = 0$$

If the company manufactures two products, the maximum profit will be

$$\begin{aligned} f_2(x) &= \max_{q_1, q_2} \{p_2 q_2 + p_1 q_1\} \\ &= \max_{\substack{q_2 \geq 0 \\ g_2(q_2) \leq x}} \left\{p_2 q_2 + p_1 \left[\frac{x - g_2(q_2) - K_1}{a_1 + b_1 + c_1}\right]\right\} \\ &= \max_{\substack{q_2 \geq 0 \\ g_2(q_2) \leq x}} \{p_2 q_2 + f_1[x - g_2(q_2)]\} \end{aligned}$$

since

$$f_1[x - g_2(q_2)] = p_1 \left[\frac{x - g_2(q_2) - K_1}{a_1 + b_1 + c_1}\right]$$

For $N = 3$, the maximum profit is

$$f_3(x) = \max_{\{q_j\}} \{p_3 q_3 + p_2 q_2 + p_1 q_1\} \qquad j = 1, 2, 3$$

From the given conditions,

$$(a_1 + b_1 + c_1)q_1 + K_1 + g_2(q_2) + g_3(q_3) = x$$

and

$$q_1 = \frac{x - g_2(q_2) - g_3(q_3) - K_1}{a_1 + b_1 + c_1}$$

Hence

$$\begin{aligned} f_3(x) &= \max_{q_2, q_3} \left\{p_3 q_3 + p_2 q_2 + \frac{p_1[x - g_2(q_2) - g_3(q_3) - K_1]}{a_1 + b_1 + c_1}\right\} \\ &= \max_{q_2, q_3} \{p_3 q_3 + p_2 q_2 + f_1[x - g_2(q_2) - g_3(q_3)]\} \end{aligned}$$

Making use of the recursion relationship for $N = 2$, $f_3(x)$ reduces to

$$f_3(x) = \max_{\substack{q_3 \geq 0 \\ g_3(q_3) \leq x}} \{p_3 q_3 + f_2[x - g_3(q_3)]\}$$

Therefore, by induction, the functional equation for the production-control problem is derived as

$$f_N(x) = \max_{\substack{q_N \geq 0 \\ g_N(q_N) \leq x}} \{p_N q_N + f_{N-1}[x - g_N(q_N)]\}$$

which may be employed to determine the optimum-production policy $\{q_j\}$. It is interesting to note that the above functional equation is followed immediately by the application of the principle of optimality. This example provides another justification of the optimality principle.

Computational Solution

The foregoing discussions lead to the conclusion that an application of the principle of optimality reduces an N-stage decision process to a sequence of N single-stage decision processes. Then the multistage decision problem can be solved by repeated application of the functional equation describing the decision process.[22] The solution of the functional equation can readily be obtained by use of a digital computer. As an illustration, the computational solution of a one-dimensional multistage decision process is discussed below. The computational scheme is readily extended to the multidimensional case. Consider the functional equation

$$f_N(x_1) = \max_{m_1} \{r(x_1, m_1) + f_{N-1}[g(x_1, m_1)]\} \tag{7.2-39}$$

where $N \geq 2$. For $N = 1$,

$$f_1(x_1) = \max_{m_1} \{r(x_1, m_1)\} \tag{7.2-40}$$

The numerical design is initiated with these recurrence relationships. Starting with $N = 1$, the values of $r(x_1, m_1)$ and the corresponding m_1 are computed for various values of x_1. For each x_1, the maximum value of $r(x_1, m_1)$ is selected which is equal to $f_1(x_1)$. For $N = 1$, the maximizing m_1 will be referred to as $m_1{}^1$, and a table for x_1, $m_1{}^1$, and $f_1(x_1)$ is formed.

TABLE I

x_1	$m_1{}^1$	$f_1(x_1)$
...	...	...
...	...	...
...	...	...

For $N = 2$, try various values of x_1 as above. For each x_1, tabulate m_1 and $r(x_1, m_1) + f_1[g(x_1, m_1)]$, and select the maximum value of $r(x_1, m_1) + f_1[g(x, m_1)]$ from the tabulation which is equal to $f_2(x_1)$. The values of $f_1[g(x_1, m_1)]$ are obtained from Table I either directly or by interpolation or extrapolation. The maximizing m_1 is denoted by $m_1{}^2$, and a table for x_1, $m_1{}^2$, and $f_2(x_1)$ is formed.

TABLE II

x_1	$m_1{}^2$	$f_2(x_1)$
...	...	...
...	...	...
...	...	...

For $N = 3$, try the same set of values of x_1, and repeat the procedure as above. For each x_1, tabulate m_1 and $r(x_1, m_1) + f_2[g(x_1, m_1)]$ and select the maximum value of $r(x_1, m_1) + f_2[g(x_1, m_1)]$ from the tabulation which is equal to $f_3(x_1)$. The values of $f_2[g(x_1, m_1)]$ are obtained from Table II either directly or by interpolation or extrapolation. The maximizing m_1 is denoted by $m_1{}^3$, and a table for x_1, $m_1{}^3$, and $f_3(x_1)$ is formed.

TABLE III

x_1	$m_1{}^3$	$f_3(x_1)$
...	...	...
...	...	...
...	...	...

Continue the above procedure for $N = 4, 5, \ldots,$ and try the same set of values of x_1. Finally, for the N-stage process, tabulate m_1 and $r(x_1, m_1) + f_{N-1}[g(x_1, m_1)]$ for each x_1 and select the maximum value of $r(x_1, m_1) + f_{N-1}[g(x_1, m_1)]$ from the tabulation. The values of $f_{N-1}[g(x_1, m_1)]$ are obtained from Table $N - 1$. A table for x_1, $m_1{}^N$, and $f_N(x_1)$ is formed, with $m_1{}^N$ defined as the maximizing m_1.

TABLE N

x_1	$m_1{}^N$	$f_N(x_1)$
...	...	...
...	...	...
...	...	...

The optimum-control policy for the N-stage decision process is then determined from the above tabulations.

It should be noted that the dynamic-programming approach does not remove computational difficulties, although this approach provides a systematic computational procedure. Multistage decision processes of high dimension cannot be solved in a routine manner because of the storage requirements involved in the computation.

7.3 A BASIC OPTIMIZATION PROBLEM

The optimization problem discussed in Sec. 5.2 is studied in this section by use of the theory of dynamic programming.[16] The problem is to choose $x(t)$ such that the value of the integral

$$I = \int_{t_0}^{t_f} F(x, \dot{x}, t)\, dt \tag{7.3-1}$$

is a minimum. In the preceding equation, $x = x(t)$ is a twice-differentiable function and satisfies the condition $x(t_0) = x_0$ and $x(t_f) = x_f$, and F is a continuous function of the arguments x, $\dot{x}$, t. Geometrically, the problem is to determine the curve or trajectory $x(t)$ connecting the points (x_0, t_0) and (x_f, t_f) such that the integral along the curve of some given function $F(x, \dot{x}, t)$ is minimized.

Let $f(x, t)$ be the minimum of I with respect to x, with the lower limit of integration replaced by the independent variable t. Then

$$f(x, t) = \min_{x} \int_{t}^{t_f} F(x, \dot{x}, t)\, dt \tag{7.3-2}$$

where the minimum is taken over all x, and at $t = t_f$,

$$f(x, t_f) = 0 \tag{7.3-3}$$

Equation (7.3-2) results from the application of the invariant-embedding theory. It is assumed that the function $f(x, t)$ possesses continuous first and second partial derivatives. The minimization may be carried out with respect to $\dot{x}$, since, if the integral is minimum with respect to $\dot{x}$, it is minimum with respect to x. Thus the minimum function $f(x, t)$ can be determined from

$$f(x, t) = \min_{\dot{x}} \int_{t}^{t_f} F(x, \dot{x}, t)\, dt \tag{7.3-4}$$

where the minimum is taken over all $\dot{x}$, and at $t = t_0$, $f(x, t_0) = f(x_0)$. The optimization process may be carried out in two steps: (1) from t to $t + \Delta$ and (2) from $t + \Delta$ to t_f. The time interval Δ is very small. Whatever the initial choice of x over the interval $(t, t + \Delta)$, there will be, over the remaining interval, a problem of the same form as the original, except that the initial condition is now changed to $x(t + \Delta)$. For the first step, the initial condition is $x(t)$, with the initial choice of the minimizing function $x(t)$. During the second step, the initial condition is $x(t + \Delta)$, with the initial choice of the minimizing function $x(t + \Delta)$. Thus the function $f(x, t)$ is given by

$$f(x, t) = \min_{\dot{x}} \left\{ \int_{t}^{t+\Delta} F(x, \dot{x}, t)\, dt + \int_{t+\Delta}^{t_f} F(x, \dot{x}, t)\, dt \right\} \tag{7.3-5}$$

Invoking the principle of optimality leads to the functional equation

$$f(x, t) = \min_{\dot{x}} \left\{ \int_{t}^{t+\Delta} F(x, \dot{x}, t)\, dt + f(x + \dot{x}\Delta, t + \Delta) \right\} \tag{7.3-6}$$

where
$$f(x + \dot{x}\Delta, t + \Delta) = \min_{\dot{x}} \int_{t+\Delta}^{t_f} F(x, \dot{x}, t)\, dt \tag{7.3-7}$$

On the right-hand side of Eq. (7.3-6), the first term represents the value of the integral during the interval Δ, and the second term denotes the minimum value of the integral during the remaining interval $(t + \Delta, t_f)$.

Since Δ is very small, Eq. (7.3-6) reduces to

$$f(x, t) = \min_{\dot{x}} \{F(x, \dot{x}, t)\Delta + f(x + \dot{x}\Delta, t + \Delta)\} + \epsilon(\Delta) \tag{7.3-8}$$

which states that the value of the integral from any point (x, t) to the end point (x_f, t_f) is equal to the integral from t to $t + \Delta$ plus the minimum value of the integral from the new starting point $(x + \dot{x}\Delta, t + \Delta)$ to the end point (x_f, t_f), as demonstrated in Fig. 7.3-1. The function $f(x, t)$ is the minimum of this sum with respect to the initial direction $\dot{x}$. In the reduction from Eq. (7.3-6) to Eq. (7.3-8), the integral from t to $t + \Delta$ is

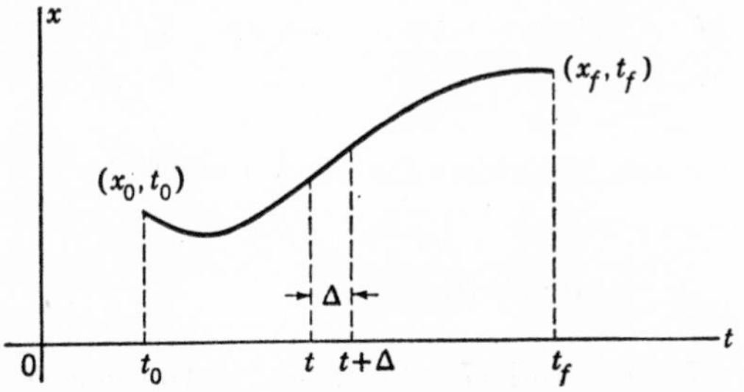

Fig. 7.3-1 Optimum trajectory.

replaced by $F(x, \dot{x}, t)\Delta$, with an error of the order of $\epsilon(\Delta)$. Taylor's series expansion will evolve

$$f(x, \dot{x}\Delta, t + \Delta) = f(x, t) + \frac{\partial f}{\partial t}\Delta + \frac{\partial f}{\partial x}\dot{x}\Delta + \cdots \tag{7.3-9}$$

Then the minimum of I is given by

$$f(x, t) = \min_{\dot{x}} \left\{ F(x, \dot{x}, t)\Delta + f(x, t) + \frac{\partial f}{\partial t}\Delta + \dot{x}\frac{\partial f}{\partial x}\Delta \right\} + \epsilon_1(\Delta) \tag{7.3-10}$$

which reduces to

$$\min_{\dot{x}} \left\{ F(x, \dot{x}, t) + \frac{\partial f}{\partial t} + \dot{x}\frac{\partial f}{\partial x} \right\} + \epsilon_2(\Delta) = 0 \tag{7.3-11}$$

In the limit as Δ approaches zero, Eq. (7.3-11) yields

$$\min_{\dot{x}} \left\{ F(x, \dot{x}, t) + \frac{\partial f}{\partial t} + \dot{x}\frac{\partial f}{\partial x} \right\} = 0 \tag{7.3-12}$$

Now this minimization problem may be determined by applying elementary calculus. Taking the partial derivatives of the functions in the braces of Eq. (7.3-12) with respect to $\dot{x}$ gives the necessary condition for a minimum as

$$\frac{\partial F}{\partial \dot{x}} + \frac{\partial f}{\partial x} = 0 \tag{7.3-13}$$

Substitution of the minimizing $\dot{x}$ into Eq. (7.3-12) leads to

$$F + \frac{\partial f}{\partial t} + \dot{x}\frac{\partial f}{\partial x} = 0 \tag{7.3-14}$$

Differentiating Eq. (7.3-13) with respect to t,

$$\frac{d}{dt}\frac{\partial F}{\partial \dot{x}} + \frac{\partial^2 f}{\partial x\,\partial t} + \frac{\partial^2 f}{\partial x^2}\frac{dx}{dt} = 0 \tag{7.3-15}$$

Partial differentiation of Eq. (7.3-14) with respect to x yields

$$\frac{\partial F}{\partial x} + \frac{\partial F}{\partial \dot{x}}\frac{\partial \dot{x}}{\partial x} + \frac{\partial^2 f}{\partial x\,\partial t} + \frac{\partial^2 f}{\partial x^2}\frac{dx}{dt} + \frac{\partial f}{\partial \dot{x}}\frac{\partial \dot{x}}{\partial x} = 0 \tag{7.3-16}$$

In view of Eq. (7.3-13), the above equation reduces to

$$\frac{\partial F}{\partial x} + \frac{\partial^2 f}{\partial x\,\partial t} + \frac{\partial^2 f}{\partial x^2}\frac{dx}{dt} = 0 \tag{7.3-17}$$

Combining Eqs. (7.3-15) and (7.3-17) leads to the necessary condition for the integral I to be a minimum,

$$\frac{\partial F}{\partial x} - \frac{d}{dt}\frac{\partial F}{\partial \dot{x}} = 0 \tag{7.3-18}$$

This is the Euler-Lagrange differential equation, which is derived in Sec. 5.2 by the classical calculus of variations. The solution of this differential equation gives the minimizing function of the integral I, provided that the minimum exists.

According to elementary calculus, in order to ensure a minimum, the second partial derivative of the functions in the braces in Eq. (7.3-12) with respect to $\dot{x}$ must be positive. This leads to the classical *Legendre condition*

$$\frac{\partial^2 F}{\partial \dot{x}^2} > 0 \tag{7.3-19}$$

which provides the sufficient condition for the integral I to be a minimum.

In control processes of moderate complexity, there may exist several minimum points of the integral I; but the Legendre condition given in Eq. (7.3-19) does not eliminate the possibility of a relative minimum. Assume that the integral I will have an absolute minimum at $\dot{x}$, and it will have a relative minimum for all other minimizing variables, $\dot{x}^m$. Then there exists the following inequality:

$$F(x, \dot{x}, t) + \frac{\partial f}{\partial t} + \dot{x}\frac{\partial f}{\partial x} \le F(x, \dot{x}^m, t) + \frac{\partial f}{\partial t} + \dot{x}^m\frac{\partial f}{\partial x} \tag{7.3-20}$$

for all functions $\dot{x}^m = \dot{x}^m(x, t)$. Transposing and simplifying gives

$$F(x, \dot{x}^m, t) - F(x, \dot{x}, t) + (\dot{x}^m - \dot{x})\frac{\partial f}{\partial x} \ge 0 \tag{7.3-21}$$

In view of Eq. (7.3-13), the above inequality may be written as

$$F(x, \dot{x}^m, t) - F(x, \dot{x}, t) - (\dot{x}^m - \dot{x}) \frac{\partial F}{\partial \dot{x}} \geq 0 \tag{7.3-22}$$

which is referred to as the *Weierstrass necessary condition* for an absolute minimum.

In the preceding discussions, the optimization problem is solved under the assumption that the optimum trajectory $x(t)$ connects two fixed points (x_0, t_0) and (x_f, t_f). When the initial value $x(t_0)$ at $t = t_0$ is partially specified or unspecified, the optimum trajectory $x(t)$ has the property that the change in the minimum value of the integral I, caused by a change in the initial point $x(t_0)$, is zero. This leads to the condition

$$\left. \frac{\partial f}{\partial x} \right|_{t_0} = 0 \tag{7.3-23}$$

which is referred to as the *natural boundary condition* associated with the unspecified boundary value. For the case of unspecified initial value, the minimum value $f(x, t)$ must satisfy the natural boundary condition. Combining Eqs. (7.3-13) and (7.3-23) yields the condition

$$\left. \frac{\partial F}{\partial \dot{x}} \right|_{t_0} = 0 \tag{7.3-24}$$

which is necessary to determine the solution of the Euler-Lagrange differential equation. It can readily be shown that, when the final value $x(t_f)$ is partially specified or unspecified, the natural boundary condition is

$$\left. \frac{\partial f}{\partial x} \right|_{t_f} = 0 \tag{7.3-25}$$

which leads, when Eq. (7.3-13) is used, to the boundary condition

$$\left. \frac{\partial F}{\partial \dot{x}} \right|_{t_f} = 0 \tag{7.3-26}$$

This condition is necessary in the solution of the Euler-Lagrange equation for problems with an undetermined end point.

The foregoing discussion points out that the function $x(t)$ which minimizes the integral I is the solution to the Euler-Lagrange differential equation (7.3-18), with one boundary condition specified at $t = t_0$ and the other at $t = t_f$. Since the Euler-Lagrange equation is a second-order equation of the form

$$\ddot{x} = \varphi(x, \dot{x}, t) \tag{7.3-27}$$

to integrate it in convenient fashion, the values of x and $\dot{x}$ at $t = t_0$ or at

$t = t_f$ are required. However, in this situation the two boundary conditions are prescribed at both ends of the trajectory, resulting in a two-point boundary-value problem.

Now consider that the optimum trajectory must initiate somewhere from a given curve $x = c(t)$. Then neither is the initial point specified nor is it constrained to the vertical line $t = t_0$. In these circumstances, on the optimum trajectory the change in $f(x, t)$, as the initial point varies along the specified curve $x = c(t)$, must be zero. Thus

$$\frac{\partial f}{\partial t} + \dot{c}\,\frac{\partial f}{\partial x}\bigg|_{x=c(t)} = 0 \tag{7.3-28}$$

Combining Eqs. (7.3-14) and (7.3-28) yields

$$F + \dot{x}\,\frac{\partial f}{\partial x} - \dot{c}\,\frac{\partial f}{\partial x}\bigg|_{x=c(t)} = 0 \tag{7.3-29}$$

Hence, by using Eq. (7.3-13), the condition is that

$$F + (\dot{c} - \dot{x})\,\frac{\partial F}{\partial \dot{x}} = 0 \tag{7.3-30}$$

which is valid along the specified curve $x = c(t)$. This condition on the initial derivative $\dot{x}$ in terms of the initial point (x, t) and the slope of the initial locus $c(t)$ is referred to as a *classical transversality condition.* In like manner, it can be shown that Eq. (7.3-30) is also valid along the final locus, provided that the initial point $x(t_0)$ is specified and the optimum trajectory terminates somewhere on a given curve $x = c(t)$.

Multidimensional System

The foregoing analysis may be extended to the study of multivariable optimization problems. Consider the problem of determining $\mathbf{x}(t)$ which minimizes the integral

$$I = \int_{t_0}^{t_f} F(\mathbf{x}, \dot{\mathbf{x}}, t)\, dt \tag{7.3-31}$$

where $\mathbf{x}$ is an $n \times 1$ vector. The vector function $\mathbf{x} = \mathbf{x}(t)$ is a twice-differentiable function and satisfies the conditions $\mathbf{x}(t_0) = \mathbf{x}_0$ and $\mathbf{x}(t_f) = \mathbf{x}_f$, and F is a continuous function of the arguments $\mathbf{x}, \dot{\mathbf{x}}, t$. Thus the optimization problem here becomes one of determining the trajectory $\mathbf{x}(t)$ connecting the points $(\mathbf{x}_0, t_0)$ and $(\mathbf{x}_f, t_f)$ in a multidimensional space such that the integral given in Eq. (7.3-31) is a minimum.

Let $f(\mathbf{x}, t)$ be the minimum of I with the lower limit of integration replaced by the independent variable t. Then

$$f(\mathbf{x}, t) = \min_{\mathbf{x}} \int_{t}^{t_f} F(\mathbf{x}, \dot{\mathbf{x}}, t)\, dt \tag{7.3-32}$$

where the minimum is taken over $\mathbf{x}$, and at $t = t_f$,

$$f(\mathbf{x}_f, t_f) = 0 \tag{7.3-33}$$

Equation (7.3-32) follows from the principle of invariant embedding. The function $f(\mathbf{x}, t)$ is assumed to possess continuous first and second partial derivatives. It will be observed that, since the minimization may be carried out with respect to $\dot{\mathbf{x}}$ to yield the same minimum, the function $f(x, t)$ can be determined from

$$f(\mathbf{x}, t) = \min_{\dot{\mathbf{x}}} \int_t^{t_f} F(\mathbf{x}, \dot{\mathbf{x}}, t)\, dt \tag{7.3-34}$$

where the minimum is taken over all $\dot{\mathbf{x}}$.

Invoking the principle of optimality yields the functional equation

$$f(\mathbf{x}, t) = \min_{\dot{\mathbf{x}}} \left\{ \int_t^{t+\Delta} F(\mathbf{x}, \dot{\mathbf{x}}, t)\, dt + f(\mathbf{x} + \dot{\mathbf{x}}\Delta, t + \Delta) \right\} \tag{7.3-35}$$

where

$$f(\mathbf{x} + \dot{\mathbf{x}}\Delta, t + \Delta) = \min_{\dot{\mathbf{x}}} \int_{t+\Delta}^{t_f} F(\mathbf{x}, \dot{\mathbf{x}}, t)\, dt \tag{7.3-36}$$

For Δ to be a very small interval of time, Eq. (7.3-35) reduces to

$$f(\mathbf{x}, t) = \min_{\dot{\mathbf{x}}} \{F(\mathbf{x}, \dot{\mathbf{x}}, t)\Delta + f(\mathbf{x} + \dot{\mathbf{x}}\Delta, t + \Delta)\} + \epsilon(\Delta) \tag{7.3-37}$$

where the integral from t to $t + \Delta$ is replaced by $F(\mathbf{x}, \dot{\mathbf{x}}, t)$ with an error of the order of $\epsilon(\Delta)$. By expanding the function $f(\mathbf{x} + \dot{\mathbf{x}}\Delta, t + \Delta)$ into a Taylor series, Eq. (7.3-37) may be written as

$$f(\mathbf{x}, t) = \min_{\dot{\mathbf{x}}} \left\{ F(\mathbf{x}, \dot{\mathbf{x}}, t)\Delta + f(\mathbf{x}, t) + \frac{\partial f}{\partial t} + \frac{\partial f}{\partial \mathbf{x}} \dot{x}\Delta \right\} + \epsilon_1(\Delta) \tag{7.3-38}$$

which reduces to

$$\min_{\dot{\mathbf{x}}} \left\{ F(\mathbf{x}, \dot{\mathbf{x}}, t) + \frac{\partial f}{\partial t} + \frac{\partial f}{\partial \mathbf{x}} \dot{\mathbf{x}} \right\} + \epsilon_2(\Delta) = 0 \tag{7.3-39}$$

As Δ approaches zero, $\epsilon_2(\Delta) = 0$ and

$$\min_{\dot{\mathbf{x}}} \left\{ F(\mathbf{x}, \dot{\mathbf{x}}, t) + \frac{\partial f}{\partial t} + \frac{\partial f}{\partial \mathbf{x}} \dot{\mathbf{x}} \right\} = 0 \tag{7.3-40}$$

To facilitate differentiation, Eq. (7.3-40) is expressed in terms of the components of the vectors as

$$\min_{\dot{x}_j} \left\{ F(\mathbf{x}, \dot{\mathbf{x}}, t) + \frac{\partial f}{\partial t} + \sum_{j=1}^{n} \dot{x}_j \frac{\partial f}{\partial x_j} \right\} = 0 \tag{7.3-41}$$

Taking the partial derivatives of the functions in the braces of Eq. (7.3-41) with respect to $\dot{x}_i$ gives the necessary condition for a minimum:

$$\frac{\partial F}{\partial \dot{x}_i} + \frac{\partial f}{\partial x_i} = 0 \tag{7.3-42}$$

If $\dot{\mathbf{x}}(t)$ is the minimizing vector, then

$$F + \frac{\partial f}{\partial t} + \sum_{j=1}^{n} \dot{x}_j \frac{\partial f}{\partial x_j} = 0 \tag{7.3-43}$$

Differentiating Eq. (7.3-42) with respect to t results in

$$\frac{d}{dt}\frac{\partial F}{\partial \dot{x}_i} + \frac{\partial^2 f}{\partial x_i\,\partial t} + \sum_{j=1}^{n} \dot{x}_j \frac{\partial^2 f}{\partial x_i\,\partial x_j} = 0 \qquad i = 1, 2, \ldots, n \tag{7.3-44}$$

Partial differentiation of Eq. (7.3-43) with respect to x_i yields

$$\frac{\partial F}{\partial x_i} + \sum_{j=1}^{n} \frac{\partial F}{\partial \dot{x}_j}\frac{\partial \dot{x}_j}{\partial x_i} + \frac{\partial^2 f}{\partial x_i\,\partial t} + \sum_{j=1}^{n} \dot{x}_j \frac{\partial^2 f}{\partial x_i\,\partial x_j} + \sum_{j=1}^{n} \frac{\partial f}{\partial x_j}\frac{\partial \dot{x}_j}{\partial x_i} = 0$$
$$i = 1, 2, \ldots, n \tag{7.3-45}$$

and making use of Eq. (7.3-42) reduces Eq. (7.3-45) to

$$\frac{\partial F}{\partial x_i} + \frac{\partial^2 f}{\partial x_i\,\partial t} + \sum_{j=1}^{n} \dot{x}_j \frac{\partial^2 f}{\partial x_i\,\partial x_j} = 0 \tag{7.3-46}$$

Then the necessary condition for the integral I to be a minimum follows upon combining Eqs. (7.3-44) and (7.3-46):

$$\frac{\partial F}{\partial x_i} - \frac{d}{dt}\frac{\partial F}{\partial \dot{x}_i} = 0 \tag{7.3-47}$$

In vector notation, the necessary condition is

$$\nabla_{\mathbf{x}} F - \frac{d}{dt}(\nabla_{\dot{\mathbf{x}}} F) = 0 \tag{7.3-48}$$

which is the Euler-Lagrange differential equation for multidimensional systems.

The previous study deals with cost functions F which contain only the variables x_i and their first derivatives $\dot{x}_i$, but no higher derivatives. However, when the F function involves higher derivatives, the optimization problem may be reduced to a multidimensional case of higher dimension by considering the higher derivatives as additional state variables, thus removing the higher derivatives in the F function. In this way the Euler-Lagrange equation given in Eq. (7.3-48) may be used to determine the optimum trajectory.

Hamilton-Jacobi Equation

By applying the principle of optimality, the optimum-control problem may be reduced to the solution of the Hamilton-Jacobi differential equation.[22,52] In classical mechanics, $L(\mathbf{q}, \dot{\mathbf{q}}, t)$ is used to denote the Lagrangian of a system characterized by the state vector $\mathbf{q}$, as discussed in Sec. 2.5. According to the Hamilton principle, the system moves from the initial state $\mathbf{q}_0$ at $t = t_0$ to any state $\mathbf{q}$ at time t in such a way as to minimize the Lagrangian integral

$$I = \int_{t_0}^{t} L(\mathbf{q}, \dot{\mathbf{q}}, t)\, dt \tag{7.3-49}$$

Let the minimum value of the above integral be denoted by $S(\mathbf{q}_0, t_0; \mathbf{q}, t)$. Then

$$S(\mathbf{q}_0, t_0; \mathbf{q}, t) = \min_{\dot{\mathbf{q}}} \left\{ \int_{t_0}^{t} L(\mathbf{q}, \dot{\mathbf{q}}, \tau)\, d\tau \right\} \tag{7.3-50}$$

Applying the principle of optimality at the initial point $(\mathbf{q}_0, t_0)$ yields

$$\begin{aligned} S(\mathbf{q}_0, t_0; \mathbf{q}, t) &= \min_{\dot{\mathbf{q}}_0} \left\{ \int_{t_0}^{t_0+\Delta} L(\mathbf{q}, \dot{\mathbf{q}}, \tau)\, d\tau + \int_{t_0+\Delta}^{t} L(\mathbf{q}, \dot{\mathbf{q}}, \tau)\, d\tau \right\} \\ &= \min_{\dot{\mathbf{q}}_0} \{ L(\mathbf{q}_0, \dot{\mathbf{q}}_0, t_0)\Delta + S(\mathbf{q}_0, \dot{\mathbf{q}}_0\Delta, t_0 + \Delta; \mathbf{q}, t) \} + \epsilon(\Delta) \end{aligned} \tag{7.3-51}$$

where Δ is a very small time interval, and the minimization process is carried out in two steps. Taylor's series expansion reduces Eq. (7.3-51) to

$$\min_{\dot{\mathbf{q}}_0} \left\{ L(\mathbf{q}_0, \dot{\mathbf{q}}_0, t_0) + \frac{\partial S}{\partial t_0} + \frac{\partial S}{\partial \mathbf{q}_0} \dot{\mathbf{q}}_0 \right\} + \epsilon_1(\Delta) = 0 \tag{7.3-52}$$

In the limit as Δ approaches zero,

$$\min_{\dot{\mathbf{q}}_0} \left\{ L + \frac{\partial S}{\partial t_0} + \frac{\partial S}{\partial \mathbf{q}_0} \dot{\mathbf{q}}_0 \right\} = 0 \tag{7.3-53}$$

Then a necessary condition for the integral to be a minimum is

$$\frac{\partial L}{\partial \dot{\mathbf{q}}_0} + \frac{\partial S}{\partial \mathbf{q}_0} = 0 \tag{7.3-54}$$

or

$$\frac{\partial L}{\partial \dot{\mathbf{q}}_0} = -\frac{\partial S}{\partial \mathbf{q}_0} \triangleq \mathbf{p}_0 \tag{7.3-55}$$

where $\mathbf{p}_0$ is defined as the momentum vector at $t = t_0$.

Next, applying the principle of optimality at any point $(\mathbf{q}, t)$ on the trajectory derives

$$S(\mathbf{q}_0, t_0; \mathbf{q}, t) = \min_{\dot{\mathbf{q}}} \left\{ \int_{t_0}^{t-\Delta} L(\mathbf{q}, \dot{\mathbf{q}}, \tau)\, d\tau + \int_{t-\Delta}^{t} L(\mathbf{q}, \dot{\mathbf{q}}, \tau)\, d\tau \right\}$$
$$= \min_{\dot{\mathbf{q}}} \{L(\mathbf{q}, \dot{\mathbf{q}}, t)\Delta + S(\mathbf{q}_0, t_0; \mathbf{q} - \dot{\mathbf{q}}\Delta, t - \Delta)\} + \epsilon(\Delta) \tag{7.3-56}$$

where Δ is a very small interval of time, and the minimization process is also carried out in two steps. Following the normal procedure, Eq. (7.3-56) may be simplified to

$$\min_{\dot{\mathbf{q}}} \left\{ L(\mathbf{q}, \dot{\mathbf{q}}, t) - \frac{\partial S}{\partial t} - \frac{\partial S}{\partial \mathbf{q}} \dot{\mathbf{q}} \right\} + \epsilon_1(\Delta) = 0 \tag{7.3-57}$$

and upon passing through the limit $\Delta \to 0$,

$$\min_{\dot{\mathbf{q}}} \left\{ L - \frac{\partial S}{\partial t} - \frac{\partial S}{\partial \mathbf{q}} \dot{\mathbf{q}} \right\} = 0 \tag{7.3-58}$$

which leads to the two equations

$$\frac{\partial L}{\partial \dot{\mathbf{q}}} - \frac{\partial S}{\partial \mathbf{q}} = 0 \tag{7.3-59}$$

and

$$\frac{\partial S}{\partial \mathbf{q}} \dot{\mathbf{q}} - L + \frac{\partial S}{\partial t} = 0 \tag{7.3-60}$$

These equations result from the application of elementary calculus. By defining the momentum vector

$$\mathbf{p} \triangleq \frac{\partial L}{\partial \dot{\mathbf{q}}} \tag{7.3-61}$$

and the hamiltonian function

$$H(\mathbf{p}, \mathbf{q}, t) \triangleq \mathbf{p}\dot{\mathbf{q}} - L \tag{7.3-62}$$

Eq. (7.3-60) may be written as

$$H\left(\mathbf{q}, \frac{\partial S}{\partial \mathbf{q}}, t\right) + \frac{\partial S}{\partial t} = 0 \tag{7.3-63}$$

which is the Hamilton-Jacobi differential equation in classical mechanics, as discussed in Sec. 2.5.

Methods for solving the Hamilton-Jacobi equation are available in standard texts on classical mechanics and applied mathematics. Basically, when the initial conditions $\mathbf{q}(t_0) = \mathbf{q}_0$ are specified, the solution function $S(\mathbf{q}_0, t_0; \mathbf{q}, t)$ is determined from Eq. (7.3-63). Then the state vector, or optimum trajectory,

$$\mathbf{q} = \mathbf{q}(\mathbf{p}_0, \mathbf{q}_0, t_0; t) \tag{7.3-64}$$

as a function of the initial conditions and time, follows from Eq. (7.3-55), and the momentum vector

$$\mathbf{p} = \mathbf{p}(\mathbf{p}_0, \mathbf{q}_0, t_0; t) \tag{7.3-65}$$

as a function of the initial conditions and time may be derived from Eqs. (7.3-59) and (7.3-61). The foregoing analysis points out that the optimum-control problem can be reduced to the determination of the solution of the Hamilton-Jacobi equation, when an integral-criterion function of the form as given in Eq. (7.3-49) is specified.

Numerical Solution

The foregoing study of the optimization problem leads to elegant partial differential equations, which can also be derived by classical approaches. Solutions to these partial differential equations determine the minimizing functions. However, with the advent of high-speed digital computers, mathematical thinking has been greatly affected. Analytical techniques are now evaluated, not only with respect to their mathematical elegance, but also with relation to their computational feasibility. The Euler-Lagrange equation rates very high so far as its analytical aspects are concerned, but solution of the partial differential equation often presents some difficulties. On the other hand, the functional-equation approach of dynamic programming provides a way of obtaining the computational solution of the original variational problem which does not depend upon the solution of the partial differential equation.

Consider the problem of minimizing the integral

$$I = \int_{t_0}^{t_f} F(x, \dot{x}, t)\, dt \tag{7.3-66}$$

which is described at the beginning of this section. Let

$$f(x, t) = \min_{\dot{x}} \int_t^{t_f} F(x, \dot{x}, t)\, dt \tag{7.3-67}$$

An application of the principle of optimality yields the functional equation

$$f(x, t) = \min_{\dot{x}} \left\{ \int_t^{t+\Delta} F(x, \dot{x}, t)\, dt + f(x + \dot{x}\Delta, t + \Delta) \right\} \tag{7.3-68}$$

For computational purposes, Eq. (7.3-68) is expressed as

$$f(x, t) = \min_{\dot{x}} \{F(x, \dot{x}, t)\Delta + f(x + \dot{x}\Delta, t + \Delta)\} \tag{7.3-69}$$

where Δ is a predetermined small time interval. By letting $t = t_0 + j\Delta$, with $j = 0, 1, 2, \ldots, N$, and $t_f = t_0 + N\Delta$, Eq. (7.3-69) may be approximated by an N-stage process characterized by

$$f_{N-j}(x, t) = \min_{\dot{x}} \{F(x, \dot{x}, t)\Delta + f_{N-\overline{j+1}}(x + \dot{x}\Delta, t + \Delta)\} \qquad (7.3\text{-}70)$$

with

$$f_0(x, t_f) = 0 \qquad (7.3\text{-}71)$$

The computations follow the procedure outlined in Sec. 7.2. Starting with Eq. (7.3-71), for $j = N - 1$,

$$f_1(x, t_f - \Delta) = \min_{\dot{x}} \{F(x, \dot{x}, t_f - \Delta)\Delta\} \qquad (7.3\text{-}72)$$

from which one tabulates the values of $\dot{x}$ and $f_1(x, t_f - \Delta)$ for successive values of x. For $j = N - 2$,

$$f_2(x, t_f - 2\Delta) = \min_{\dot{x}} \{F(x, \dot{x}, t_f - 2\Delta)\Delta + f_1(x, t_f - \Delta)\} \qquad (7.3\text{-}73)$$

which is used to tabulate the values of $\dot{x}$ and $f_2(x, t_f - 2\Delta)$ for the same set of values of x. The values of $f_1(x, t_f - \Delta)$ may be obtained from the foregoing tabulation either directly or by interpolation or extrapolation. Continuing in this fashion, one can tabulate the values of $\dot{x}$ and $f_N(x, t_0)$ for the same set of values of x. The minimizing function is then determined from these tabulated values.

7.4 MINIMUM-INTEGRAL-CONTROL PROCESSES

This section discusses the application of dynamic-programming techniques to the optimum design of control processes with respect to integral-performance criteria.[15,16,18] Consider a control process characterized by the differential equation

$$\dot{x}(t) = g(x, m) \qquad (7.4\text{-}1)$$

where the state variable x and the control signal m are scalar functions of t, and at $t = t_0$,

$$x(t_0) = x_0 \qquad (7.4\text{-}2)$$

Determine the optimum-control signal m which minimizes the integral-criterion function

$$I(m) = \int_{t_0}^{t_f} F(x, m)\, dt \qquad (7.4\text{-}3)$$

The function $F(x, m)$ is differentiable with respect to the arguments.

In order to apply the functional-equation technique of dynamic programming, this optimization problem is embedded within the wider problem of minimizing

$$\int_{t}^{t_f} F(x, m)\, dt \qquad (7.4\text{-}4)$$

subject to the relationships given in Eqs. (7.4-1) and (7.4-2), with t ranging over the interval (t_0, t_f). Let the minimum be given by

$$f(x, t) = \min_m \int_t^{t_f} F(x, m)\, dt \tag{7.4-5}$$

where $f(x, t_0) = f(x_0)$ at $t = t_0$. The minimum is taken over all m. As discussed in the preceding section, the optimization process may be carried out in two steps: (1) from t to $t + \Delta$ and (2) from $t + \Delta$ to t_f. For the first step, the initial condition is $x(t)$, with the initial choice of the control signal $m(t)$. During the second step, the initial condition is $x(t + \Delta)$, with the initial choice of the control signal $m(t + \Delta)$. Thus the minimum function $f(x, t)$ is

$$f(x, t) = \min_m \left\{ \int_t^{t+\Delta} F(x, m)\, dt + \int_{t+\Delta}^{t_f} F(x, m)\, dt \right\} \tag{7.4-6}$$

An application of the principle of optimality yields the functional equation

$$f(x, t) = \min_m \left\{ \int_t^{t+\Delta} F(x, m)\, dt + f(x + \dot{x}\Delta, t + \Delta) \right\} \tag{7.4-7}$$

which is reduced to the following expression by integration and Taylor series expansion:

$$f(x, t) = \min_m \left\{ F(x, m)\Delta + f(x, t) + \dot{x} \frac{\partial f}{\partial x} \Delta + \frac{\partial f}{\partial t} \Delta \right\} + \epsilon(\Delta) \tag{7.4-8}$$

Simplifying,

$$-\frac{\partial f}{\partial t} = \min_m \left\{ F(x, m) + g(x, m) \frac{\partial f}{\partial x} \right\} + \epsilon_1(\Delta) \tag{7.4-9}$$

In the preceding equation, use is made of Eq. (7.4-1). As Δ approaches zero, $\epsilon_1(\Delta) = 0$ and

$$-\frac{\partial f}{\partial t} = \min_m \left\{ F(x, m) + g(x, m) \frac{\partial f}{\partial x} \right\} \tag{7.4-10}$$

By elementary calculus, the following two equations may be obtained from Eq. (7.4-10):

$$\frac{\partial F}{\partial m} + \frac{\partial g}{\partial m} \frac{\partial f}{\partial x} = 0 \tag{7.4-11}$$

$$F(x, m) + g(x, m) \frac{\partial f}{\partial x} + \frac{\partial f}{\partial t} = 0 \tag{7.4-12}$$

Solving for $\partial f/\partial x$ and $\partial f/\partial t$ from Eqs. (7.4-11) and (7.4-12),

$$\frac{\partial f}{\partial x} = -\frac{\partial F/\partial m}{\partial g/\partial m} \triangleq P(x, m) \tag{7.4-13}$$

and

$$\frac{\partial f}{\partial t} = -F(x, m) + g(x, m) \frac{\partial F/\partial m}{\partial g/\partial m} \triangleq Q(x, m) \tag{7.4-14}$$

Taking the partial derivatives of Eq. (7.4-13) with respect to t results in

$$\frac{\partial^2 f}{\partial x\, \partial t} = \frac{\partial P}{\partial m}\frac{\partial m}{\partial t} + \frac{\partial P}{\partial x}\frac{\partial x}{\partial t} \tag{7.4-15}$$

Partial differentiation of Eq. (7.4-14) with respect to x yields

$$\frac{\partial^2 f}{\partial x\, \partial t} = \frac{\partial Q}{\partial x} + \frac{\partial Q}{\partial m}\frac{\partial m}{\partial x} \tag{7.4-16}$$

Equating Eq. (7.4-15) to Eq. (7.4-16) leads to the first-order partial differential equation for m:

$$g(x, m)\frac{\partial P(x, m)}{\partial x} + \frac{\partial P(x, m)}{\partial m}\frac{\partial m}{\partial t} = \frac{\partial Q(x, m)}{\partial x} + \frac{\partial Q(x, m)}{\partial m}\frac{\partial m}{\partial x} \tag{7.4-17}$$

where the functions P and Q are defined in Eqs. (7.4-13) and (7.4-14), respectively. The solution of Eq. (7.4-17) determines the optimum-control signal m.

Infinite Process

The foregoing discussions are concerned with the study of optimum control of a finite process. Now the problem of minimizing the integral-criterion function

$$I(m) = \int_0^\infty F(x, m)\, dt \tag{7.4-18}$$

is considered. It can be observed that the minimum value of $I(m)$ will be a function only of the initial value of x; that is, $x(0) = x_0$. Thus the minimum value of $I(m)$ may be expressed as

$$f(x_0) = \min_m I(m) \tag{7.4-19}$$

The minimum is taken over all m. Let

$$f(x) = \min_m \int_t^\infty F(x, m)\, dt \tag{7.4-20}$$

where $f(x) = f(x_0)$ at $t = 0$. Equation (7.4-20) results from the application of the invariant-embedding theory.

Invoking the principle of optimality, Eq. (7.4-20) may be reduced to the functional equation

$$f(x) = \min_m \left\{\int_t^{t+\Delta} F(x, m)\, dt + f(x + \dot{x}\Delta)\right\} \tag{7.4-21}$$

where

$$f(x + \dot{x}\Delta) = \min_m \int_{t+\Delta}^\infty F(x, m)\, dt \tag{7.4-22}$$

representing the minimum value of the integral from $t + \Delta$ to infinity.

In view of Eq. (7.4-1), the functional equation becomes

$$f(x) = \min_m \left\{ \int_t^{t+\Delta} F(x, m)\, dt + f[x + g(x, m)\Delta] \right\} \tag{7.4-23}$$

For Δ very small, Eq. (7.4-23) reduces to

$$f(x) = \min_m \left\{ F(x, m)\Delta + f(x) + g(x, m) \frac{\partial f}{\partial x} \Delta \right\} + \epsilon(\Delta) \tag{7.4-24}$$

or

$$\min_m \left\{ F(x, m) + g(x, m) \frac{\partial f}{\partial x} \right\} + \epsilon_1(\Delta) = 0 \tag{7.4-25}$$

As Δ approaches zero, $\epsilon_1(\Delta) = 0$ and

$$\min_m \left\{ F(x, m) + g(x, m) \frac{\partial f}{\partial x} \right\} = 0 \tag{7.4-26}$$

Application of elementary calculus to determine the minimum yields the following equations:

$$\frac{\partial F}{\partial m} + \frac{\partial g}{\partial m} \frac{\partial f}{\partial x} = 0 \tag{7.4-27}$$

$$F(x, m) + g(x, m) \frac{\partial f}{\partial x} = 0 \tag{7.4-28}$$

Eliminating $\partial f/\partial x$ between Eqs. (7.4-27) and (7.4-28) leads to the partial differential equation

$$g(x, m) \frac{\partial F(x, m)}{\partial m} - F(x, m) \frac{\partial g(x, m)}{\partial m} = 0 \tag{7.4-29}$$

which determines the optimum-control signal m as a function of the state variable x.

Time-dependent Control Process

The preceding paragraphs deal with the time-independent processes for which the functions g and F are not explicit functions of time. Now the more general time-dependent processes are studied. Consider a control process characterized by

$$\dot{x}(t) = g(x, m, t) \tag{7.4-30}$$

The variables x and m are scalar functions of t, and at $t = t_0$,

$$x(t_0) = x_0 \tag{7.4-31}$$

Determine the optimum-control signal m such that the integral-criterion function

$$I(m) = \int_{t_0}^{t_f} F(x, m, t)\, dt \tag{7.4-32}$$

is minimized.

Application of the principle of invariant embedding transforms the given problem into the wider problem of minimizing

$$\int_t^{t_f} F(x, m, t)\, dt \tag{7.4-33}$$

subject to the relationships given in Eqs. (7.4-30) and (7.4-31), where t ranges over the interval (t_0, t_f). Let the minimum be given by

$$f(x, t) = \min_m \int_t^{t_f} F(x, m, t)\, dt \tag{7.4-34}$$

Invoking the principle of optimality results in the functional equation

$$f(x, t) = \min_m \left\{ \int_t^{t+\Delta} F(x, m, t)\, dt + f(x + \dot{x}\Delta, t + \Delta) \right\} \tag{7.4-35}$$

where Δ is a very small interval of time. Carrying out the formal procedure and simplifying yields

$$-\frac{\partial f}{\partial t} = \min_m \left\{ F(x, m, t) + g(x, m, t) \frac{\partial f}{\partial x} \right\} + \epsilon_1(\Delta) \tag{7.4-36}$$

In the limit as Δ approaches zero, Eq. (7.4-36) reduces to

$$-\frac{\partial f}{\partial t} = \min_m \left\{ F(x, m, t) + g(x, m, t) \frac{\partial f}{\partial t} \right\} \tag{7.4-37}$$

Performing the minimization procedure by elementary calculus leads to

$$\frac{\partial F}{\partial m} + \frac{\partial g}{\partial m} \frac{\partial f}{\partial x} = 0 \tag{7.4-38}$$

$$F(x, m, t) + g(x, m, t) \frac{\partial f}{\partial x} + \frac{\partial f}{\partial t} = 0 \tag{7.4-39}$$

Solving for $\partial f/\partial x$ and $\partial f/\partial t$ from Eqs. (7.4-38) and (7.4-39), respectively, yields

$$\frac{\partial F}{\partial x} = -\frac{\partial F/\partial m}{\partial g/\partial m} \triangleq P(x, m, t) \tag{7.4-40}$$

and

$$\frac{\partial f}{\partial t} = -F(x, m, t) + g(x, m, t) \frac{\partial F/\partial m}{\partial g/\partial m} \triangleq Q(x, m, t) \tag{7.4-41}$$

Then it follows by partial differentiation that

$$\frac{\partial^2 f}{\partial x\, \partial t} = \frac{\partial P}{\partial t} + \frac{\partial P}{\partial m} \frac{\partial m}{\partial t} + \frac{\partial P}{\partial x} \frac{\partial x}{\partial t} \tag{7.4-42}$$

$$\frac{\partial^2 f}{\partial x\, \partial t} = \frac{\partial Q}{\partial x} + \frac{\partial Q}{\partial m} \frac{\partial m}{\partial x} \tag{7.4-43}$$

Combining Eqs. (7.4-42) and (7.4-43),

$$\frac{\partial P}{\partial t} + g\frac{\partial P}{\partial x} + \frac{\partial P}{\partial m}\frac{\partial m}{\partial t} = \frac{\partial Q}{\partial x} + \frac{\partial Q}{\partial m}\frac{\partial m}{\partial x} \tag{7.4-44}$$

which gives the optimum-control signal m upon solving.

Multidimensional Systems

The foregoing analysis may be extended to multivariable problems. Consider an nth-order control process characterized by the vector differential equation

$$\dot{\mathbf{x}}(t) = \mathbf{g}(\mathbf{x}, \mathbf{m}) \tag{7.4-45}$$

where $\mathbf{x}$ = an n-vector representing state of the process
$\mathbf{m}$ = an r-vector denoting control signals
$\mathbf{g}$ = a differentiable vector function of the arguments

The initial conditions of the control process are given by the initial-state vector

$$\mathbf{x}(t_0) = \mathbf{x}_0 \tag{7.4-46}$$

Determine the optimum-control vector $\mathbf{m}$ which minimizes the integral-criterion function

$$I(\mathbf{m}) = \int_{t_0}^{t_f} F(\mathbf{x}, \mathbf{m})\, dt \tag{7.4-47}$$

The integrand $F(\mathbf{x}, \mathbf{m})$ is a differentiable scalar function of the state vector and the control vector.

Following the previous arguments, let

$$f(\mathbf{x}, t) = \min_{\mathbf{m}} \int_{t}^{t_f} F(\mathbf{x}, \mathbf{m})\, dt \tag{7.4-48}$$

where t ranges over the interval (t_0, t_f), the minimum is taken over all $\mathbf{m}$, and $f(\mathbf{x}, t_0) = f(\mathbf{x}_0)$ at $t = t_0$. Application of the principle of optimality reduces Eq. (7.4-48) to the functional equation

$$f(\mathbf{x}, t) = \min_{\mathbf{m}} \left\{ \int_{t}^{t+\Delta} F(\mathbf{x}, \mathbf{m})\, dt + f(\mathbf{x} + \dot{\mathbf{x}}\Delta, t + \Delta) \right\} \tag{7.4-49}$$

In the limit as Δ approaches zero, the functional equation becomes

$$-\frac{\partial f}{\partial t} = \min_{m} \left\{ F(\mathbf{x}, \mathbf{m}) + \frac{\partial f}{\partial \mathbf{x}} \mathbf{g}(\mathbf{x}, \mathbf{m}) \right\} \tag{7.4-50}$$

which yields the following two differential equations:

$$\frac{\partial F}{\partial \mathbf{m}} + \frac{\partial f}{\partial \mathbf{x}}\frac{\partial \mathbf{g}}{\partial \mathbf{m}} = 0 \tag{7.4-51}$$

$$F + \frac{\partial f}{\partial \mathbf{x}} \mathbf{g}(\mathbf{x}, \mathbf{m}) + \frac{\partial f}{\partial t} = 0 \tag{7.4-52}$$

From Eqs. (7.4-51) and (7.4-52) the optimum control $\mathbf{m}$ may be determined.

It may be seen that any explicit dependence of a function upon t can always be removed by considering t as an additional state variable, x_{n+1}, defined by

$$\dot{x}_{n+1}(t) = 1 \qquad \text{and} \qquad x_{n+1}(t) = t \tag{7.4-53}$$

with $x_{n+1}(0) = 0$. Consequently, the time-dependent control process may be treated as a multidimensional time-independent process, and the preceding results can be used to advantage.

In conventional control theory, minimum-integral control refers to the special case of minimizing an infinite-time integral of the square of the system error. Because the criterion function is in simple quadratic form and the integration is carried to infinity, a general solution for the optimum control of linear stationary systems can be obtained. Parseval's theorem is applied to formulate the integral square error in the frequency domain. The concept of the translation function is used in the process of expressing the integral square error in the time domain. However, the conventional optimization techniques are not applicable when the criterion function is not a simple quadratic form or when a finite-time integral of the criterion function is chosen as a measure of the system performance. On the other hand, the modern approach may be applied to solve a large class of the more general optimum-control problems. The optimum-design procedure leads to the solution of a partial differential equation. In relatively simple systems, it may be solved for the optimum-control signal. However, for systems of moderate complexity, a solution to the partial differential equation is rather difficult to derive, and resort is often had to numerical analysis. Frequently most control problems encountered in engineering practice must be reduced to the discrete-time case for solution. The functional-equation approach can readily be extended, however, to take into account physical constraints on control signals, as demonstrated in the following paragraphs.

Constraints on Control Signals

In the foregoing study, the design of an optimum-control process to satisfy an integral-performance criterion is carried out under the assumption that no constraint is imposed upon the control signals and the state variables. This, however, is an idealized situation. In common practice, because of the physical limitations of controlling devices and saturation effects in the system, physical constraints on control signals or state variables must be taken into account in the design of optimum controls. If the constraints are not considered, the design may lead to a system demanding excessively large control signals, which is unrealistic and impracticable. Commonly encountered constraints on control signals may be described as (1) amplitude saturation,

$$a_i \leq m_i(t) \leq b_i \qquad t_0 \leq t \leq t_f \tag{7.4-54}$$

and (2) integral constraint,

$$\int_{t_0}^{t_f} \mathbf{H}(\mathbf{m})\,dt \leq \mathbf{c} \tag{7.4-55}$$

where a_i,b_i = constants

$\mathbf{c}$ = a constant vector

$\mathbf{H}(\mathbf{m})$ = a vector function of the control signals

The first type of constraint generally arises when the magnitudes of the control signals are limited by the maximum displacement, maximum velocity, or maximum acceleration of the controlling devices or because of the saturation effect of the system components. The second type of constraint is often introduced to account for power limitation or the cost of control. Furthermore, this type of constraint provides a mathematically convenient way to ensure the avoidance of saturating the control signals. For analytical simplicity and convenience, the integral constraint is sometimes employed in the design of optimum control, instead of the actual amplitude saturation being imposed on the control signals.

As discussed in Sec. 5.4, constraints of the second type can readily be handled by the method of the Lagrange multiplier.[14] The optimization problem is transformed into the problem of minimizing the synthetic function

$$I_1(\mathbf{m}) = I(\mathbf{m}) + \boldsymbol{\lambda}' \int_{t_0}^{t_f} \mathbf{H}(\mathbf{m})\,dt \tag{7.4-56}$$

where $I(\mathbf{m})$ is the specified performance index to be minimized, and $\boldsymbol{\lambda}$ is the vector Lagrange multiplier. After the minimization of the synthetic function is achieved, the desired control vector results as a function of the vector Lagrange multiplier $\boldsymbol{\lambda}$. Substitution of the vector $\mathbf{m}(\boldsymbol{\lambda})$ into Eq. (7.4-55) leads to r equations, which can be solved for the elements λ_i of the vector Lagrange multiplier. This does not seem to present any problem in principle, if the analytical solution to the two-point boundary-value problem is obtainable.

However, when constraints of the first type are taken into consideration, the analytical solutions of the partial differential equations derived in the preceding paragraphs and the Euler-Lagrange equation derived in Sec. 7.3 are extremely difficult to obtain. The two-point boundary-value problem is itself hard to determine. The presence of saturation constraints makes the situation even more involved. To circumvent the difficulties, use can be made of the functional equations derived in the foregoing paragraphs. Consider, for instance, the finite, time-independent control process discussed previously. The functional equation is as given in Eq. (7.4-7):

$$f(x, t) = \min_m \left\{ \int_t^{t+\Delta} F(x, m)\,dt + f(x + \dot{x}\Delta, t + \Delta) \right\} \tag{7.4-57}$$

which can be reduced to

$$f(x, t) = \min_m \{F(x, m)\Delta + f(x + g\Delta; t + \Delta)\} \tag{7.4-58}$$

where the control signal satisfies the constraint $|m| \leq M$, and Δ is a predetermined small interval of time. To carry out the computational procedure, as outlined in Sec. 7.2, Eq. (7.4-58) may be described by the N-stage process

$$f_{N-j}(x, t) = \min_m \{F(x, m)\Delta + f_{N-\overline{j+1}}(x + g\Delta, t + \Delta)\} \tag{7.4-59}$$

with $t = t_0 + j\Delta$, $j = 0, 1, 2, \ldots, N$, and $t_f = t_0 + N\Delta$. For $j = 0$,

$$f_N(x, t_0) = \min_m \{F(x, m)\Delta + f_{N-1}(x + g\Delta, t_0 + \Delta)\} \tag{7.4-60}$$

and for $j = N$,

$$f_0(x, t_f) = 0 \tag{7.4-61}$$

For $j = N - 1$,

$$\begin{aligned} f_1(x, t_f - \Delta) &= \min_m \{F(x, m)\Delta + f_0(x, t_f)\} \\ &= \min_m \{F(x, m)\Delta\} \end{aligned} \tag{7.4-62}$$

from which the values of $f_1(x, t_f - \Delta)$ and the corresponding m_1 are determined for successive values of x.

Similarly, from the recurrence relation

$$f_2(x, t_f - 2\Delta) = \min_m \{F(x, m)\Delta + f_1(x, t_f - \Delta)\} \tag{7.4-63}$$

the values of $f_2(x, t_f - 2\Delta)$ and the corresponding m_2 are determined for successive values of x. The values of $f_1(x, t_f - \Delta)$ may be obtained from the previous calculations either directly or by interpolation or extrapolation. By this method can be ascertained the optimum-control signal m which minimizes the specified integral-criterion function. In the foregoing calculations, the constraint on the control signal provides a finite range of possible values for m. This makes the computational procedure easier. The dynamic-programming approach affords a way to circumvent the difficulties inherent in solving partial differential equations subject to two-point boundary conditions. Furthermore, computational solution through dynamic programming is aided by the presence of constraints. The use of a numerical procedure for solving variational problems in control system was first suggested by Bellman, and is discussed in some detail in Ref. 22, chap. 5. This usage avoids much of the difficulty of establishing certain analytical properties of the criterion function, such as continuity, differentiability, and convexity.

Example 7.4-1 A Simple Optimum-control Problem

Consider a first-order control process characterized by

$$\dot{x} = -ax + \gamma m$$

where a and γ are positive constants, and the control signal m is subject to the constraint

$$|m| \leq M$$

Determine the optimum-control signal m which minimizes the integral-criterion function

$$I(m) = \int_0^{t_1} x^2\,dt$$

Let the minimum of the integral from t to t_1 be

$$f(x, t) = \min_m \int_t^{t_1} x^2\,dt$$

Then, from Eq. (7.4-10),

$$-\frac{\partial f}{\partial t} = \min_m \left\{x^2 + (-ax + \gamma m)\frac{\partial f}{\partial x}\right\}$$

It is found from this equation that the functions in the braces are minimum if

$$m = -M \operatorname{sgn} \frac{\partial f}{\partial x}$$

Thus the optimum-control signal switches between $+M$ and $-M$ according to the sign of the partial derivative $\partial f/\partial x$, which satisfies the partial differential equation

$$-\frac{\partial f}{\partial t} = x^2 - ax\frac{\partial f}{\partial x} - \gamma M\left|\frac{\partial f}{\partial x}\right|$$

Although the general nature of the optimum-control signal is readily determined, the evaluation of the switching function is by no means simple. Analytical solution is generally difficult to obtain, and numerical approaches are often used.

Linear Process Subject to a Quadratic Criterion

The foregoing discussions are concerned with optimum design of control processes with respect to a general integral-criterion function. The functional-equation approach of dynamic programming is employed in the study of such optimum-control problems. Investigation leads to partial differential equations, solution of which yields the optimum-control signals. Analytical solutions of these partial differential equations are generally quite difficult to obtain, and thus resort is often had to numerical methods.

However, when the control process under consideration is linear and is optimized with respect to a quadratic-criterion function, the analytical expressions of the optimum-control signals can be determined. Use of a quadratic performance criterion generally leads to a workable analysis.

Consider a linear nth-order control process characterized by the differential equation

$$\dot{\mathbf{x}}(t) = \mathbf{A}(t)\mathbf{x}(t) + \mathbf{D}(t)m(t) \tag{7.4-64}$$

where $\mathbf{x}$ = an n-vector representing state of the process
m = control signal
$\mathbf{A}$ = coefficient matrix
$\mathbf{D}$ = driving matrix

At the beginning of the trajectory $t = 0$, $\mathbf{x}(0) = \mathbf{x}_0$. Here a single control signal is assumed for the sake of simplicity. The control problem of interest here is to determine the optimum-control signal $m(t)$ which minimizes an integral-criterion function of the form

$$I(m) = \int_0^T F(\mathbf{x}, m, t)\, dt \tag{7.4-65}$$

over the interval of time $(0, T)$, throughout which the system performance is of interest. In Eq. (7.4-65), F is a quadratic function given by

$$F(\mathbf{x}, m, t) = \mathbf{x}'\mathbf{Q}(t)\mathbf{x} + \lambda m^2 \tag{7.4-66}$$

where $\mathbf{Q}(t)$ is an $n \times n$ symmetrical matrix associated with the quadratic form $\mathbf{x}\mathbf{Q}(t)\mathbf{x}$, and λ is a constant. The term λm^2 is introduced to ensure the avoidance of saturating the control signals.

Following the previous argument, define the minimum of the integral over the interval (t, T) by

$$f(\mathbf{x}, t) = \min_m \int_t^T F(\mathbf{x}, m, t)\, dt \tag{7.4-67}$$

The first consideration in the minimization of the performance index is the derivation of the condition under which the minimum exists. Application of the principle of optimality to Eq. (7.4-67) leads to the functional equation

$$-\frac{\partial f}{\partial t} = \min_m \left\{ \mathbf{x}'\mathbf{Q}(t)\mathbf{x} + \lambda m^2 + \sum_{j=1}^{n} \dot{x}_j \frac{\partial f}{\partial x_j} \right\} \tag{7.4-68}$$

where x_j is the jth component of the state vector $\mathbf{x}$ and

$$\dot{x}_j(t) = \sum_{k=1}^{n} a_{jk}(t)x_k(t) + d_j(t)m(t) \tag{7.4-69}$$

In Eq. (7.4-69), $a_{jk}(t)$ and $d_j(t)$ are the elements of the coefficient matrix $\mathbf{A}(t)$ and the driving matrix $\mathbf{D}(t)$, respectively. Equation (7.4-68) gives the condition under which the performance index of Eq. (7.4-65) is a minimum.

The minimizing control signal m^o can be determined from Eq. (7.4-68) by elementary calculus through differentiation. Setting the derivative with respect to m of the expression in the braces of Eq. (7.4-68) equal to zero yields the minimizing control signal m^o as

$$m^o = -\frac{1}{2\lambda} \sum_{j=1}^{n} d_j(t) \frac{\partial f}{\partial x_j} \tag{7.4-70}$$

Substitution of Eqs. (7.4-69) and (7.4-70) into the right-hand side of Eq. (7.4-68) gives the condition for a minimum:

$$-\frac{\partial f}{\partial t} = \mathbf{x}'\mathbf{Q}(t)\mathbf{x} + \frac{1}{4\lambda}\left[\sum_{j=1}^{n} d_j(t)\frac{\partial f}{\partial x_j}\right]^2 + \sum_{j=1}^{n}\left[\sum_{k=1}^{n} a_{jk}(t)x_k - \frac{1}{2\lambda} d_j(t) \sum_{k=1}^{n} d_k(t)\frac{\partial f}{\partial x_k}\right]\frac{\partial f}{\partial x_j} \tag{7.4-71}$$

The problem now becomes one of solving this equation for the function $f(\mathbf{x}, t)$. Since $F(\mathbf{x}, m, t)$ is a quadratic function in x and m, it can be shown that $f(\mathbf{x}, t)$ is also expressible in a quadratic function in x and can be written in the form

$$f(\mathbf{x}, t) = \mathbf{x}'\mathbf{P}(t)\mathbf{x} \tag{7.4-72}$$

where $\mathbf{P}(t)$ is an $n \times n$ symmetrical matrix associated with the n-dimensional quadratic form $\mathbf{x}'\mathbf{P}(t)\mathbf{x}$. It follows from Eq. (7.4-72) that the partial derivative of $f(\mathbf{x}, t)$ with respect to $\mathbf{x}$ is

$$\frac{\partial f}{\partial \mathbf{x}} = 2\mathbf{P}(t)\mathbf{x} \tag{7.4-73}$$

The matrix $\mathbf{P}(t)$ may be determined as follows: Combining Eqs. (7.4-71) and (7.4-73) and expressing the resulting equation in vector-matrix notations yields

$$-\frac{\partial f}{\partial t} = \mathbf{x}'\left[\mathbf{Q}(t) + 2\mathbf{P}(t)\mathbf{A}(t) - \frac{1}{\lambda}\mathbf{P}(t)\mathbf{D}(t)\mathbf{D}'(t)\mathbf{P}(t)\right]\mathbf{x} \tag{7.4-74}$$

Since, from Eq. (7.4-72), the partial derivative of $f(\mathbf{x}, t)$ with respect to t is

$$\frac{\partial f}{\partial t} = \mathbf{x}'\frac{\partial \mathbf{P}(t)}{\partial t}\mathbf{x} \tag{7.4-75}$$

combining Eqs. (7.4-74) and (7.4-75) leads to the following differential equation for $\mathbf{P}(t)$:

$$\frac{\partial \mathbf{P}(t)}{\partial t} = \frac{1}{\lambda}\mathbf{P}(t)\mathbf{D}(t)\mathbf{D}'(t)\mathbf{P}(t) - 2\mathbf{P}(t)\mathbf{A}(t) - \mathbf{Q}(t) \tag{7.4-76}$$

with the boundary condition given by

$$f(\mathbf{x}, T) = \mathbf{x}'(T)\mathbf{P}(T)\mathbf{x}(T) = 0 \tag{7.4-77}$$

Equation (7.4-76) may be integrated to yield $\mathbf{P}(t)$, using Eqs. (7.4-70) and (7.4-73). Thus one derives the optimum-control signal in matrix notation as

$$m^o = -\frac{1}{\lambda}\mathbf{D}'(t)\mathbf{P}(t)\mathbf{x}(t) \tag{7.4-78}$$

Since $\mathbf{D}'(t)$ is a $1 \times n$ row matrix and $\mathbf{P}(t)$ is an $n \times n$ matrix, the product $\mathbf{D}'(t)\mathbf{P}(t)$ is a $1 \times n$ row matrix. By defining

$$\boldsymbol{\beta}(t) = -\frac{1}{\lambda}\mathbf{D}'(t)\mathbf{P}(t) = [\beta_1(t) \quad \beta_2(t) \quad \cdots \quad \beta_n(t)] \tag{7.4-79}$$

the optimum-control signal may be written as

$$\begin{aligned} m^o(t) &= \boldsymbol{\beta}(t)\mathbf{x}(t) \\ &= \sum_{i=1}^{n} \beta_i(t)x_i(t) \end{aligned} \tag{7.4-80}$$

which is a linear function of the state variable. This control function is often referred to as the *optimum-control law.* Equation (7.4-80) defines

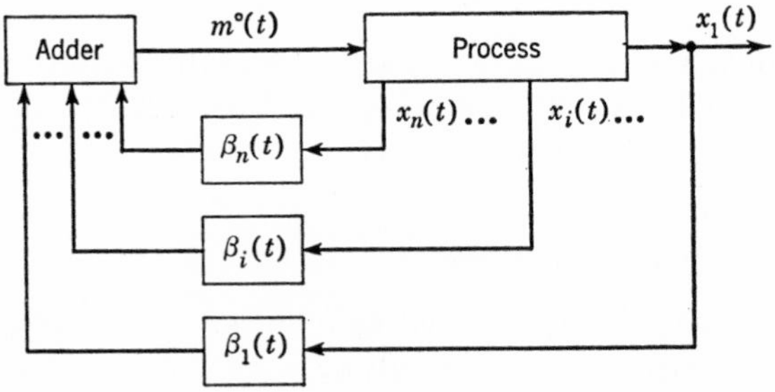

Fig. 7.4-1 Block diagram of an optimum regulator system.

the configuration of the optimum control system, the block diagram of which is depicted in Fig. 7.4-1. From the block diagram of the optimum control system, it is observed that:

1. The number of feedback loops is equal to the order of the control process.
2. The feedback signals are the measurable state variables.
3. The feedback coefficient in each loop is time-varying but independent of the state variables.

The last property results from the assumption that the control process is linear and is optimized with respect to a quadratic criterion.

Quadratic Error Index

As discussed above, an important step in the optimum synthesis of a control system is the formulation of a performance-criterion function. One of the most useful performance-criterion functions in optimum-system design is the error index, which measures the deviations of the state variables from the desired values. The nature of the resulting optimum control is generally determined by the choice of an error index based upon the requirements of the problem at hand. This enables the control engineer to influence the nature of the resulting system by formulating a proper error index. The design of optimum control of a linear nth-order process with respect to an integral error index is considered in the paragraphs to follow.

A commonly used integral error index is of the quadratic form as defined in Eq. (7.4-81):

$$I(m) = \int_0^T \left\{ \sum_{k=1}^{n} \alpha_k(t)[x_k{}^d(t) - x_k(t)]^2 + \lambda m^2(t) \right\} dt \qquad (7.4\text{-}81)$$

where $x_k{}^d(t)$ denotes the desired value corresponding to the state variable $x_k(t)$, and $\alpha_k(t)$ are the time-varying weighting factors which indicate the relative importance of the various terms in the error measure.[54,118,119] In the design of the optimum control, these weighting factors must be selected so as to satisfy the specified performance requirements and physical constraints. The first term of the integrand in Eq. (7.4-81) represents the combined errors at any instant of time t, and the second term describes the cost of control. The multiplier λ may be regarded as a penalty factor. As discussed previously, the second term is introduced as a constraint on the control signals so that saturation of these signals may be avoided. The optimum-design problem requires the determination of an optimum-control signal $m(t)$ which minimizes the performance index given in Eq. (7.4-81).

The condition under which the minimum exists can be derived by applying the principle of optimality. Define the minimum of the integral over the interval (t, T) by

$$f(\mathbf{x}, t) = \min_m \int_t^T \left\{ \sum_{k=1}^{n} \alpha_k(t)[x_k{}^d(t) - x_k(t)]^2 + \lambda m^2(t) \right\} dt \qquad (7.4\text{-}82)$$

Following the formal procedure of functional-equation analysis of dynamic programming yields the condition for a minimum of Eq. (7.4-82),

$$-\frac{\partial f}{\partial t} = \min_m \left\{ \sum_{k=1}^{n} \alpha_k(t)[x_k{}^d(t) - x_k(t)]^2 + \lambda m^2(t) + \sum_{k=1}^{n} \dot{x}_k(t) \frac{\partial f}{\partial x_k} \right\} \qquad (7.4\text{-}83)$$

where $\dot{x}_k(t)$ is defined in Eq. (7.4-69). It is interesting to note that the first two terms on the right-hand side of Eq. (7.4-83) are the same as the terms appearing in the integrand of Eq. (7.4-82). In the above equations, $x_k(t)$ is the kth component of state vector $\mathbf{x}(t)$, which is related to the control signal $m(t)$ by Eq. (7.4-69). The quantity within the braces is a minimum when the partial derivative of this quantity with respect to $m(t)$ is equal to zero. Performing the minimization operation yields the minimizing control signal as given in Eq. (7.4-70).

Substituting Eqs. (7.4-69) and (7.4-70) into Eq. (7.4-83) yields the partial differential equation

$$-\frac{\partial f}{\partial t} = \sum_{k=1}^{n} \alpha_k(t)[x_k{}^d(t) - x_k(t)]^2 + \frac{1}{2\lambda}\left[\sum_{j=1}^{n} d_j(t)\frac{\partial f}{\partial x_j}\right]^2 + \sum_{j=1}^{n}\left[\sum_{k=1}^{n} a_{jk}(t)x_k(t) - \frac{1}{2\lambda} d_j(t)\sum_{k=1}^{n} d_k(t)\frac{\partial f}{\partial x_k}\right]\frac{\partial f}{\partial x_j} \tag{7.4-84}$$

which defines the minimum of the integral, $f(\mathbf{x}, t)$. Thus the optimum-control signal $m^o(t)$ can be determined by using Eq. (7.4-70), provided that Eq. (7.4-84) can be solved for the minimum function $f(\mathbf{x}, t)$. Since the integrand of the criterion function is a quadratic expression, the function $f(\mathbf{x}, t)$ can be written in the form

$$f(\mathbf{x}, t) = b(t) + 2\sum_{j=1}^{n} b_j(t)x_j(t) = \sum_{i=1}^{n}\sum_{j=1}^{n} b_{ij}(t)x_i(t)x_j(t) \tag{7.4-85}$$

where $b(t)$, $b_j(t)$, and $b_{ij}(t)$ are the parameters to be determined from Eqs. (7.4-84) and (7.4-85). It is noted that

$$b_{ij}(t) = b_{ji}(t) \tag{7.4-86}$$

Once these parameters are determined, the optimum-control signal follows immediately by taking the partial derivatives of $f(\mathbf{x}, t)$ with respect to x_j and substituting into Eq. (7.4-70). The partial derivatives of $f(\mathbf{x}, t)$ with respect to x_j are found to be

$$\frac{\partial f}{\partial x_j} = 2b_j(t) + \sum_{i=1}^{n} b_{ij}(t)x_i(t) \tag{7.4-87}$$

Thus, combining Eqs. (7.4-70) and (7.4-87) yields the optimum-control law as

$$m^o(t) = r(t) + \sum_{i=1}^{n} \beta_i(t)x_i(t) \tag{7.4-88}$$

where
$$r(t) = -\frac{1}{\lambda} \sum_{j=1}^{n} d_j(t) b_j(t) \tag{7.4-89}$$

and
$$\beta_i(t) = -\frac{1}{\lambda} \sum_{j=1}^{n} d_j(t) b_{ij}(t) \tag{7.4-90}$$

The optimum-control law is a linear function of the state variables, as expected.

The expansion defined in Eq. (7.4-85) is referred to as a parametric expansion by Merriam, since the coefficients $b_j(t)$ and $b_{ij}(t)$ turn out to be the parameters in the optimum-control law. The block diagram of the optimum control system is readily derived from Eq. (7.4-88) and is shown in Fig. 7.4-2. This optimum control system contains n time-varying feedback loops for the n state variables, with the feedback coefficient equal to $\beta_i(t)$. In addition, this optimum control system is subject to an input $r(t)$,

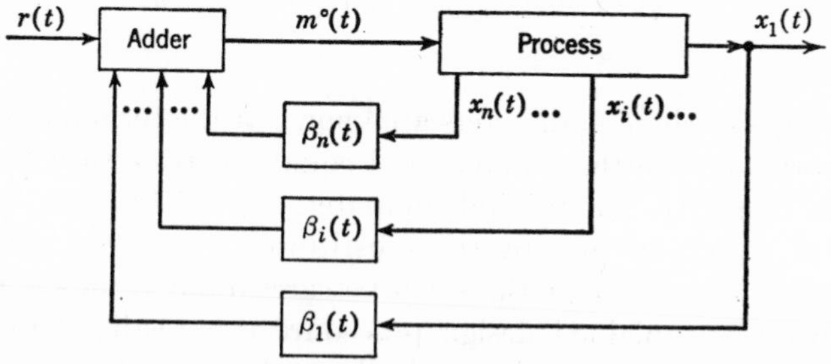

Fig. 7.4-2 Block diagram of an optimum control system.

which is defined in Eq. (7.4-89). This input will be reduced to zero when the desired values of the state variables are set at zero.

Taking the partial derivatives of Eq. (7.4-85) with respect to time t and with respect to state variables x_j and substituting these derivatives into Eq. (7.4-84) results in the following expression after simplification:

$$K_0 + \sum_{i=1}^{n} K_i x_i(t) + \sum_{i=1}^{n} \sum_{j=1}^{n} K_{ij} x_i(t) x_j(t) = 0 \tag{7.4-91}$$

where the K coefficient consists of terms containing the desired state variables $x_k{}^d(t)$, the weighting factors $\alpha_k(t)$, the elements $a_{jk}(t)$ and $d_j(t)$ of the **A** and **D** matrices, and the parameters $b(t)$, $b_j(t)$, and $b_{ij}(t)$. If Eq. (7.4-91) is to be valid for all possible values of the state variables, each K coefficient must be equal to zero. This leads to a set of $1 + n + n(n+1)/2$ independent ordinary first-order differential equations,

$$\begin{aligned} K_0 &= 0 \\ K_i &= 0 \qquad i, j = 1, 2, 3, \ldots, n \\ K_{ij} &= 0 \end{aligned} \tag{7.4-92}$$

which define the parameters $b(t)$, $b_j(t)$, and $b_{ij}(t)$. These first-order differential equations are called the Riccatian differential equations in mathematics literature. Since, at the end of the optimum trajectory, $t = T$, the minimum function $f(\mathbf{x}, t)$ given in Eq. (7.4-82) is equal to zero:

$$f(\mathbf{x}, T) = 0 \tag{7.4-93}$$

Then it follows, from Eq. (7.4-85), that

$$b(T) + 2\sum_{j=1}^{n} b_j(T)x_j(T) + \sum_{i=1}^{n}\sum_{j=1}^{n} b_{ij}(T)x_i(T)x_j(T) = 0 \tag{7.4-94}$$

which yields the $1 + n + n(n + 1)/2$ boundary conditions for the Riccatian differential equations as

$$\begin{aligned} b(T) &= 0 \\ b_j(T) &= 0 \qquad i, j = 1, 2, \ldots, n \\ b_{ij}(T) &= 0 \end{aligned} \tag{7.4-95}$$

Since the values of these parameters are known at the terminal point $t = T$, it is necessary to solve these differential equations backward in time. To facilitate solving them on a digital computer, Eqs. (7.4-95) are transformed into a set of equations in τ by the substitution $\tau = T - t$. The solution of these new differential equations can be carried out from $t = 0$ to $t = T$.

The previously explained design procedure can readily be extended to design of control processes with multiple control-signal inputs. Detailed derivation is left to the interested reader as an exercise. To illustrate the design of optimum control systems by the above techniques, the following two examples are given.

Example 7.4-2 A Simple Control Process

Consider a simple control process described by the differential equation

$$\dot{x} = km$$

At $t = T$, $x(T) = x_f$. Determine the optimum-control signal which minimizes the integral-criterion function

$$I(m) = \int_0^T F(x, m, t)\, dt$$

where

$$F(x, m, t) = ax^2 + \lambda m^2$$

Let the minimum of the integral-criterion function over the interval (t, T) be

$$f(x, t) = \min_m \left\{\int_t^T F(x, m, t)\, dt\right\}$$

Following the formal procedure leads to the functional equation

$$-\frac{\partial f}{\partial t} = \min_m \left\{ax^2 + \lambda m^2 + km\,\frac{\partial f}{\partial x}\right\}$$

By elementary calculus, it is found that the minimum is assumed at

$$m^o = -\frac{k}{2\lambda}\frac{\partial f}{\partial x}$$

Then, by substitution, the condition for the given integral-criterion function to be a minimum is

$$-\frac{\partial f}{\partial t} = ax^2 - \frac{k^2}{4\lambda}\left(\frac{\partial f}{\partial x}\right)^2$$

Assume that the function $f(x, t)$ is quadratic in x and of the form

$$f(x, t) = b_1(t) + 2b_2(t)x + b_3(t)x^2$$

Then the partial derivative of the minimum function $f(x, t)$ with respect to t is

$$\frac{\partial f}{\partial t} = \dot{b}_1(t) + 2\dot{b}_2(t)x + \dot{b}_3(t)x^2$$

and the partial derivative of $f(x, t)$ with respect to x is

$$\frac{\partial f}{\partial x} = 2b_2(t) + 2b_3(t)x$$

Substitution of the partial derivative into the condition for a minimum yields

$$-[\dot{b}_1(t) + 2\dot{b}_2(t)x + \dot{b}_3(t)x^2] = ax^2 - \frac{k^2}{\lambda}[b_2(t) + b_3(t)x]^2$$

Equating terms of like powers leads to the Riccatian differential equations

$$\begin{aligned}\lambda\dot{b}_1(t) &= k^2b_2{}^2(t)\\ \lambda\dot{b}_2(t) &= k^2b_2(t)b_3(t)\\ \lambda\dot{b}_3(t) &= k^2b_3{}^2(t) - a\end{aligned}$$

Since at $t = T$, $f(x, T) = 0$,

$$b_1(T) + 2b_2(T)x(T) + b_3(T)x^2(T) = 0$$

which yields the boundary conditions for the Riccatian differential equations. The boundary conditions are

$$b_1(T) = b_2(T) = b_3(T) = 0$$

By the substitution of $t = \tau + T$, the Riccatian differential equations become

$$\lambda \dot{b}_1(\tau) = k^2 b_2^2(\tau)$$
$$\lambda \dot{b}_2(\tau) = k^2 b_2(\tau) b_3(\tau)$$
$$\lambda \dot{b}_3(\tau) = k^2 b_3^2(\tau) - a$$

with the initial conditions at $\tau = 0$ given by

$$b_1(0) = b_2(0) = b_3(0) = 0$$

The optimum-control signal $m^o(t)$ is determined by solving these equations for the parameters b_1, b_2, and b_3. The solution is readily obtained with the aid of a digital computer.

Example 7.4-3 Aircraft Landing System†

Consider the aircraft-landing problem studied in Secs. 1.3 and 3.2. The aircraft dynamics is characterized by

$$\dot{x}_1 = x_2$$
$$\dot{x}_2 = a_{22}x_2 + a_{23}x_3$$
$$\dot{x}_3 = x_4$$
$$\dot{x}_4 = a_{42}x_2 + a_{43}x_3 + a_{44}x_4 + K_0 m$$

where the state variables x_1, x_2, x_3, and x_4 represent the altitude, the altitude rate, the pitch angle, and the pitch-angle rate, respectively. The coefficients are

$$K_0 = K\omega_0^2 T_0 \qquad a_{22} = -\frac{1}{T_0} \qquad a_{23} = \frac{V}{T_0}$$

$$a_{42} = \frac{1}{VT_0^2} - \frac{2\zeta\omega_0}{VT_0} + \frac{\omega_0^2}{V}$$

$$a_{43} = \frac{1}{T_0^2} + \frac{2\zeta\omega_0}{T_0} - \omega_0^2$$

$$a_{44} = \frac{1}{T_0} - 2\zeta\omega_0$$

where ζ, ω_0, K, and T_0 are the aircraft parameters defined in Sec. 1.3. In this illustrative example it is assumed that

$$\zeta = 0.5$$
$$\omega_0 = 1 \text{ rad/sec}$$
$$K = -0.95 \text{ sec}^{-1}$$
$$T_0 = 2.5 \text{ sec}$$

† From F. J. Ellert and C. W. Merriam, III, Synthesis of Feedback Controls Using Optimization Theory: An Example, *IEEE Trans. Autom. Control*, vol. AC-8, no. 2, pp. 89–103, April, 1963.

The performance index to be considered in this study is

$$I(m) = \int_0^T \left\{ \sum_{k=1}^{4} \alpha_k(t)[x_k{}^d(t) - x_k(t)]^2 + m^2(t) \right\} dt$$

Making use of Eq. (7.4-88), the optimum-control law is found to be

$$m^o(t) = -K_0 b_4(t) - K_0 b_{41}(t) x_1(t) - K_0 b_{42} x_2(t) - K_0 b_{43}(t) x_3(t) - K_0 b_{44}(t) x_4(t)$$

Since $\lambda = 1$, $d_j(t) = K_0$ for $j = 4$ and $d_j(t) = 0$ for $j \neq 4$.

Using Eqs. (7.4-91) and (7.4-92) leads to the following 15 Riccatian differential equations:

$$\dot{b}(t) = K_0{}^2 b_4{}^2(t) - \alpha_4(t)[x_4{}^d(t)]^2 - \alpha_3(t)[x_3{}^d(t)]^2 - \alpha_2(t)[x_2{}^d(t)]^2 - \alpha_1(t)[x_1{}^d(t)]^2$$

$$\dot{b}_1(t) = K_0{}^2 b_4(t) b_{41}(t) - \alpha_1(t) x_1{}^d(t)$$
$$\dot{b}_2(t) = K_0{}^2 b_4(t) b_{42}(t) - b_1(t) - a_{22} b_2(t) - \alpha_2(t) x_2{}^d(t)$$
$$\dot{b}_3(t) = K_0{}^2 b_4(t) b_{43}(t) - a_{23} b_2(t) - a_{43} b_4(t) - \alpha_3(t) x_3(t)$$
$$\dot{b}_4(t) = K_0{}^2 b_4(t) b_{44}(t) - b_3(t) - a_{44} b_4(t) - \alpha_4(t) x_4(t)$$
$$\dot{b}_{11}(t) = K_0{}^2 b_{41}{}^2(t) - \alpha_1(t)$$
$$\dot{b}_{21}(t) = K_0{}^2 b_{41}(t) b_{42}(t) - b_{11}(t) - a_{42} b_{41}(t) - a_{22} b_{21}(t)$$
$$\dot{b}_{22}(t) = K_0{}^2 b_{42}{}^2(t) - 2b_{21}(t) - 2a_{42} b_{42}(t) - 2a_{22} b_{22}(t) - \alpha_2(t)$$
$$\dot{b}_{31}(t) = K_0{}^2 b_{41}(t) b_{43}(t) - a_{23} b_{21}(t) - a_{43} b_{41}(t)$$
$$\dot{b}_{32}(t) = K_0{}^2 b_{42}(t) b_{43}(t) - b_{31}(t) - a_{23} b_{22}(t) - a_{42} b_{43}(t) - a_{43}(t) b_{42}(t) - a_{22}(t) b_{32}(t)$$
$$\dot{b}_{33}(t) = K_0{}^2 b_{43}{}^2(t) - 2a_{23} b_{32}(t) - 2a_{43} b_{43}(t) - \alpha_3(t)$$
$$\dot{b}_{41}(t) = K_0{}^2 b_{41}(t) b_{44}(t) - b_{31}(t) - a_{44} b_{41}(t)$$
$$\dot{b}_{42}(t) = K_0{}^2 b_{42}(t) b_{44}(t) - b_{41}(t) - b_{32}(t) - a_{22} b_{42}(t) - a_{42} b_{44}(t) - a_{44} b_{42}(t)$$
$$\dot{b}_{43}(t) = K_0{}^2 b_{43}(t) b_{44}(t) - b_{33}(t) - a_{23} b_{42}(t) - a_{43} b_{44}(t) - a_{44} b_{43}(t)$$
$$\dot{b}_{44}(t) = K_0{}^2 b_{44}{}^2(t) - 2b_{43}(t) - 2a_{44} b_{44}(t) - \alpha_4(t)$$

Hence the determination of the optimum-control law requires the solution of these first-order differential equations.

Now consider a more specific case for the purpose of illustrating the performance of optimum control for an aircraft landing system. Assume that, for the landing system, the following requirements and constraints are specified:

1. The desired altitude $h_d(t)$ of the airplane during the landing is described by an exponential-linear flare path shown in Fig. 7.4-3. A flare path of this form generally provides a safe and comfortable landing. The duration of the flare-out is 20 sec, including 5 sec over the runway. This value is appropriate for an airplane flying at 175 mph and beginning to flare out

at an altitude of 100 ft. The equations describing the desired flare path are

$$h_d(t) = \begin{cases} 100e^{-t/5} & 0 \le t \le 15 \\ 20 - t & 15 \le t \le 20 \end{cases}$$

The desired rate of ascent $\dot{h}_d(t)$ of the airplane is then given by

$$\dot{h}_d(t) = \begin{cases} -20e^{-t/5} & 0 \le t \le 15 \\ -1 & 15 \le t \le 20 \end{cases}$$

The value -1 ft/sec of $\dot{h}_d(t)$ at touchdown is well below the maximum permissible value of a modern airplane.

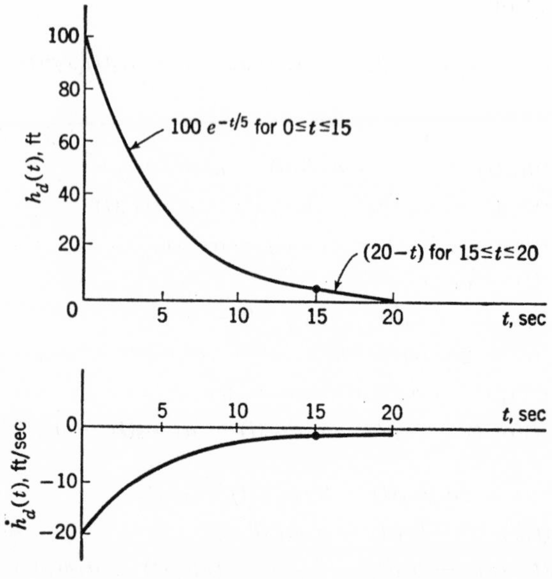

Fig. 7.4-3 The desired altitude and rate of ascent.

2. The pitch angle $\theta(t)$ of the airplane at the desired touchdown $t = T$ must lie between 0 and 10°; thus

$$0° \le \theta(T) \le 10°$$

3. During the landing, the angle of attack $\alpha(t)$ must remain below the stall value of $+18°$. The airplane enters the flare-out phase in equilibrium with an angle of attack of approximately 80 percent of the stall value. Thus the constraints on the angle of attack are

$$\alpha(t) < 18°$$
$$\Delta\alpha(t) < 3.6°$$

4. During the flare-out phase, the elevator deflection $\delta(t)$ is restricted

between the physically limiting values of -35 and $+15°$; thus

$$-35° \leq \delta(t) \leq +15°$$

As an illustration, choose a simple performance-criterion function such that altitude error and elevator deflection are weighted by a constant over

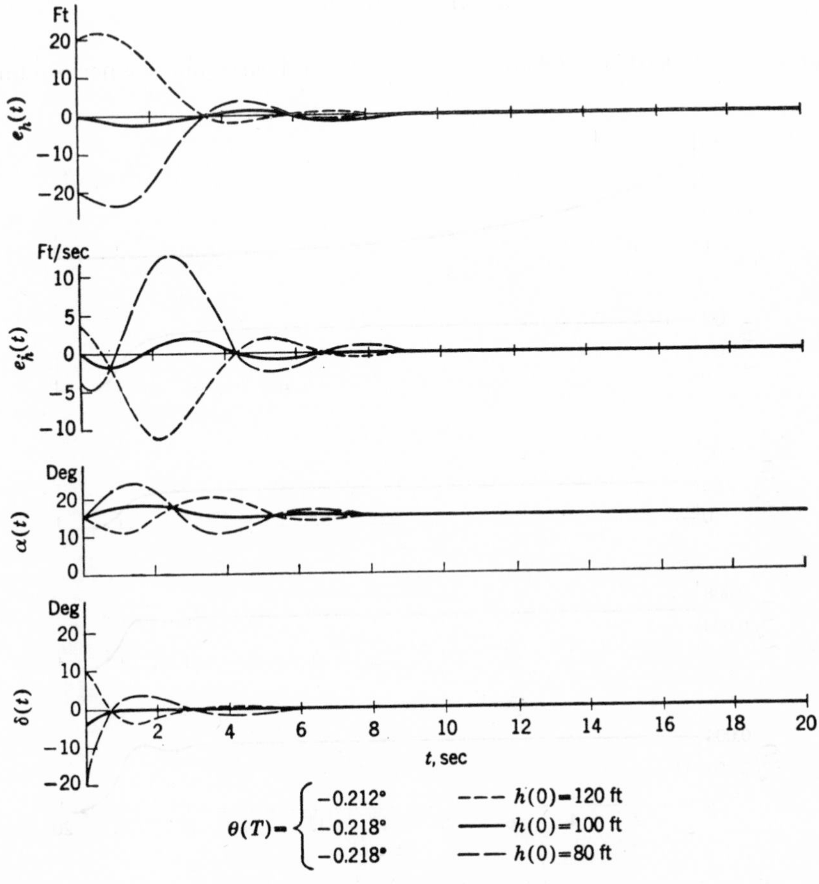

Fig. 7.4-4 Landing-system performance.

the entire 20-sec landing interval and all other weighting factors are zero. The error index then reduces to

$$I(m) = \int_0^{20} \{\alpha_1[x_1{}^d(t) - x_1(t)]^2 + m^2(t)\}\, dt$$

On the basis of this error index, the Riccatian equations can be simplified, since the weighting factors α_2, α_3, and α_4 are equal to zero. It is assumed that the largest altitude error at the beginning of the flare-out is ± 20 ft because of the initial conditions. This altitude error will be corrected by calling for a large positive elevator deflection. The specified largest permissible value is 15°, or 0.262 rad. Assuming that altitude errors and elevator deflection are of equal importance in the performance of the landing system, the weighting factor α_1 may be calculated from the following equation:

$$\alpha_1(20)^2 = (0.262)^2$$

Hence $\alpha_1 = 0.000171$. Choose $\alpha_1 = 0.0001$, and carry out the performance

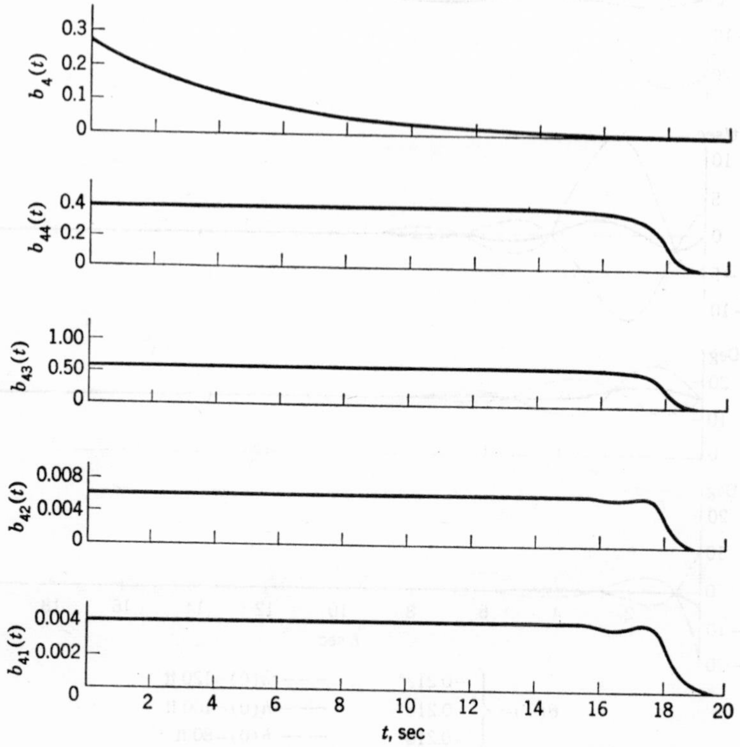

Fig. 7.4-5 Time functions of the input signal and feedback coefficients.

calculations on a digital computer. The performance of the airplane in this case is shown in Fig. 7.4-4. This figure illustrates the performance curves describing the altitude error $e_h(t)$, the rate-of-ascent error $e_{\dot{h}}(t)$, the angle of attack $\alpha(t)$, and the elevator deflection $\delta(t)$. The design based upon this simple performance index results in a control system which meets the performance requirements on altitude, rate of ascent, and elevator deflection. However, the specified constraints on angle of attack and pitch angle at touchdown are not satisfied. By choosing a more sophisticated error index to take into account multiple design factors, an optimum control system may be designed to meet all the specified performance require-

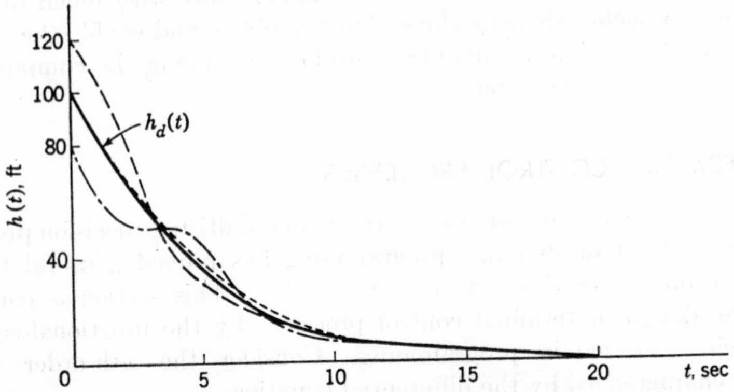

Fig. 7.4-6 Aircraft-landing trajectories for $h(0) = 80, 100, 120$ ft.

ments. This is demonstrated by Ellert and Merriam.† The time functions of the parameters $b(t)$, $b_i(t)$, and $b_{ij}(t)$ are plotted in Fig. 7.4-5. The input signal $b_4(t)$ appears to be similar in waveform to the desired altitude $h_d(t)$ although substantially reduced in amplitude. The feedback coefficients $b_{41}(t)$, $b_{42}(t)$, $b_{43}(t)$, and $b_{44}(t)$ are essentially constant until the last 3 sec of the landing, when they decrease to zero gradually. Thus it can be seen that this landing system is operating essentially open-loop just prior to touchdown. The airplane-landing trajectories for three different initial values of the altitude are sketched in Fig. 7.4-6, which illustrates the deviations of the landing trajectories caused by changes in the initial conditions. This control system follows the desired landing trajectory fairly closely, primarily because of the greater weighting of the altitude errors throughout the landing interval. Solutions to this landing problem cannot readily be obtained without the use of a digital computer. Shown in Fig. 7.4-7 is a simplified flow chart for calculating the feedback coefficients and the landing trajectories under different initial conditions.

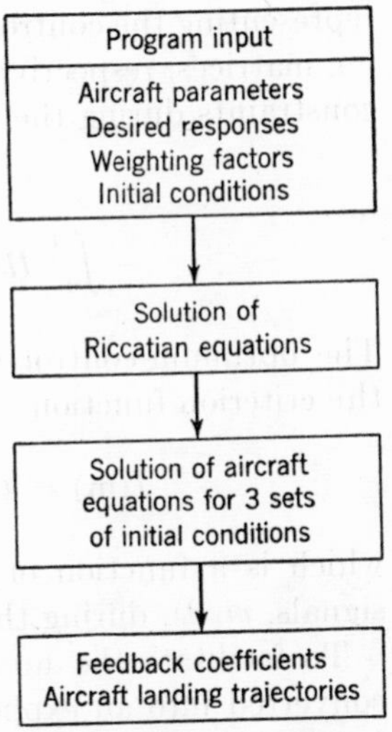

Fig. 7.4-7 A simplified flow chart for optimum-control design.

This example points out several important advantages which can be gained from the application of modern control theory. Modern synthesis techniques can take into account arbitrary initial conditions and multiple

† *Ibid.*

design factors. Modern design procedure leads to an optimum-control configuration and facilitates the solution of more realistic control problems which can be solved by conventional methods only with much difficulty. Modern approaches simplify the stability problem and enable the engineer to devote all his time to analytical studies by leaving the computational drudgery to a digital computer.

7.5 TERMINAL CONTROL PROCESSES

Terminal control processes can be treated as multistage decision processes, and the method of dynamic programming has proved a useful tool for solving problems of this nature.[1,15,16,19,20,22,140] This section is concerned with the design of terminal control processes by the functional-equation approach of dynamic programming. Consider the nth-order control process characterized by the differential equation

$$\dot{\mathbf{x}}(t) = \mathbf{A}\mathbf{x}(t) + \mathbf{D}\mathbf{m}(t) \tag{7.5-1}$$

with the initial conditions given by $\mathbf{x}(0) = \mathbf{x}_0$. In Eq. (7.5-1), $\mathbf{x}$ is an n-vector representing the state of the control process, $\mathbf{m}$ is an r-vector representing the control signal, and $\mathbf{A}$ and $\mathbf{D}$ are the coefficient and the driving matrices, respectively. The control signals are subject to the following constraints during the interval $0 \leq t \leq T$:

$$|m_k| \leq M_k \qquad k = 1, 2, \ldots, r \tag{7.5-2}$$

$$\int_0^T H(\mathbf{m})\, dt \leq c \tag{7.5-3}$$

The optimum-control vector $\mathbf{m}(t)$ is to be determined so as to minimize the criterion function

$$I(\mathbf{m}) = G[x_1(T), x_2(T), \ldots, x_l(T)] \qquad l \leq n \tag{7.5-4}$$

which is a function of the terminal state of the process over all control signals, $m_k(t)$, during the interval of control.

To facilitate the minimization procedure, the criterion function is first converted into an explicit function of the control signals m_k. It has been found that the solution to Eq. (7.5-1) is

$$\mathbf{x}(t) = \mathbf{z}(t) + \int_0^t \mathbf{W}(t-\tau)\mathbf{m}(\tau)\, d\tau \tag{7.5-5}$$

where

$$\mathbf{z}(t) = \boldsymbol{\phi}(t)\mathbf{x}(0) \tag{7.5-6}$$

represents the transient solution, and

$$\mathbf{W}(t-\tau) = \boldsymbol{\phi}(t-\tau)\mathbf{D} \tag{7.5-7}$$

In terms of the components of the vectors, the state variables of the control process are given by

$$x_i(t) = z_i(t) + \int_0^t \Big[\sum_{k=1}^{r} w_{ik}(t-\tau)m_k(\tau) \Big] d\tau \qquad i = 1, 2, \ldots, n \quad (7.5\text{-}8)$$

where $w_{ik}(t-\tau)$ are the elements of $\mathbf{W}(t-\tau)$. The terminal-control problem may now be restated as the determination of the optimum-control vector $\mathbf{m}(t)$ so as to minimize the functional

$$I(\mathbf{m}) = G\Big[z_1(T) + \int_0^T \sum_{k=1}^{r} w_{1k}(t-\tau)m_k(\tau)\,d\tau, \ldots, \\ z_l(T) + \int_0^T \sum_{k=1}^{r} w_{lk}(t-\tau)m_k(\tau)\,d\tau\Big] \quad (7.5\text{-}9)$$

subject to the constraints given in Eqs. (7.5-2) and (7.5-3).

Application of the method of the Lagrange multiplier converts this optimization problem into the minimization of the synthetic function

$$I_1(\mathbf{m}) = G + \lambda \int_0^T H(\mathbf{m})\,d\tau \quad (7.5\text{-}10)$$

with respect to $\mathbf{m}$, which is now constrained only by Eq. (7.5-2). Let the minimum value of I_1 be denoted by $f(z_1, z_2, \ldots, z_l; T)$. Then

$$f(z_1, z_2, \ldots, z_l; T) = \min_{m_k} \Big\{ G\Big[z_1(T) + \int_0^T \sum_k w_{1k}(T-\tau)m_k(\tau)\,d\tau, \ldots, \\ z_l(T) + \int_0^T \sum_k w_{lk}(T-\tau)m_k(\tau)\,d\tau\Big] + \lambda \int_0^T H(m_1, m_2, \ldots, m_r)\,d\tau \Big\} \quad (7.5\text{-}11)$$

which may be written as

$$f(z_1, z_2, \ldots, z_l; T) = \min_{m_k} \Big\{ G\Big[z_1(T) + \int_0^\Delta \sum_k w_{1k}(T-\tau)m_k(\tau)\,d\tau \\ + \int_\Delta^T \sum_k w_{1k}(T-\tau)m_k(\tau)\,d\tau, \ldots, z_l(T) + \int_0^\Delta \sum_k w_{lk}(T-\tau)m_k(\tau)\,d\tau \\ + \int_\Delta^T \sum_k w_{lk}(T-\tau)m_k(\tau)\,d\tau\Big] + \lambda \int_0^\Delta H(m_1, m_2, \ldots, m_r)\,d\tau \\ + \lambda \int_\Delta^T H(m_1, m_2, \ldots, m_r)\,d\tau \Big\} \quad (7.5\text{-}12)$$

where Δ is a very small time interval. By the change of limits,

$$f(z_1, z_2, \ldots, z_l; T) = \min_{m_k} \Big\{ G \Big[z_1(T) + \int_0^\Delta \sum_k w_{1k}(T - \tau) m_k(\tau)\, d\tau + \int_0^{T-\Delta} \sum_k w_{1k}(T - \tau - \Delta) m_k(\tau + \Delta)\, d\tau, \ldots,$$

$$z_l(T) + \int_0^\Delta \sum_k w_{lk}(T - \tau) m_k(\tau)\, d\tau + \int_0^{T-\Delta} \sum_k w_{lk}(T - \tau - \Delta) m_k(\tau + \Delta)\, d\tau \Big] + \lambda \int_0^\Delta H(m_1, m_2, \ldots, m_r)\, d\tau + \lambda \int_0^{T-\Delta} H(m_1, m_2, \ldots, m_r)\, d\tau \Big\} \tag{7.5-13}$$

Invoking the principle of optimality, the functional equation for the terminal-control problem is obtained as

$$f(z_1, z_2, \ldots, z_l; T) = \min_{m_k} \Big\{ f \Big[z_1 + \int_0^\Delta \sum_k w_{1k}(T - \tau) m_k(\tau)\, d\tau, \ldots, z_l + \int_0^\Delta \sum_k w_{lk}(T - \tau) m_k(\tau)\, d\tau; T - \Delta \Big] + \lambda \int_0^\Delta H(m_1, m_2, \ldots, m_r)\, d\tau \Big\} \tag{7.5-14}$$

where the minimum is taken over all m_k defined over the interval $(0, \Delta)$ and satisfying the constraints given in Eq. (7.5-2). An analytical solution to the terminal-control problem is not easy to derive. For computational purposes, the above functional equation may be approximated by the following recurrence relationship:

$$f(z_1, z_2, \ldots, z_l; T) = \min_{m_k} \Big\{ f \Big[z_1 + \Delta \sum_k w_{1k}(T) m_k, \ldots, z_l + \Delta \sum_k w_{lk}(T) m_k; T - \Delta \Big] + \lambda\, \Delta H(m_1, m_2, \ldots, m_r) \Big\} \tag{7.5-15}$$

with

$$f(z_1, z_2, \ldots, z_l; 0) = G[z_1(0), z_2(0), \ldots, z_l(0)] \tag{7.5-16}$$

and the control signals m_k limited to $-M_k$ and $+M_k$.

Linear-criterion Function

The foregoing discussion presents the dynamic-programming approach to the determination of the optimum-control signal to satisfy a general criterion of terminal control for a linear process. The optimum design is reduced to the evaluation of the control sequence by repeated use of a recurrence relationship. Now, by following the above argument, the problem of designing a terminal control system to satisfy a specific criterion function may be studied. Consider the control process discussed in the preceding paragraphs. The control signals are subject to the same constraints. Determine the optimum-control vector **m** which minimizes the linear-criterion function describing the terminal state of the control process:

$$I(\mathbf{m}) = G[\mathbf{x}(T)] = \boldsymbol{\alpha}'\mathbf{x}(T) \tag{7.5-17}$$

where $\boldsymbol{\alpha}$ is a given column vector.

In view of Eq. (7.5-5), the linear criterion given in Eq. (7.5-17) may be expressed as

$$I(\mathbf{m}) = \boldsymbol{\alpha}'\mathbf{z}(T) + \boldsymbol{\alpha}' \int_0^T \mathbf{W}(T - \tau)\mathbf{m}(\tau)\, d\tau \tag{7.5-18}$$

By introducing a Lagrange multiplier, this optimization problem is transformed into the minimization of the synthetic function

$$I_1(\mathbf{m}) = \boldsymbol{\alpha}'\mathbf{z}(T) + \boldsymbol{\alpha}' \int_0^T \mathbf{W}(T - \tau)\mathbf{m}(\tau)\, d\tau + \lambda \int_0^T H(\mathbf{m})\, d\tau \tag{7.5-19}$$

with respect to $\mathbf{m}$, subject to the constraint given in Eq. (7.5-2). Let the minimum of I_1 be

$$f[\mathbf{z}(T), T] = \min_{\mathbf{m}} \left\{ \boldsymbol{\alpha}'\mathbf{z}(T) + \boldsymbol{\alpha}' \int_0^T \mathbf{W}(T - \tau)\mathbf{m}(\tau)\, d\tau + \lambda \int_0^T H(\mathbf{m})\, d\tau \right\} \tag{7.5-20}$$

Carrying out the integration in two parts,

$$\begin{aligned} f(\mathbf{z}, \mathrm{T}) = \min_{\mathbf{m}} \Big\{ & \boldsymbol{\alpha}'\mathbf{z}(T) + \boldsymbol{\alpha}' \int_0^\Delta \mathbf{W}(T - \tau)\mathbf{m}(\tau)\, d\tau \\ & + \boldsymbol{\alpha}' \int_\Delta^T \mathbf{W}(T - \tau)\mathbf{m}(\tau)\, d\tau + \lambda \int_0^\Delta H(\mathbf{m})\, d\tau + \lambda \int_\Delta^T H(\mathbf{m})\, d\tau \Big\} \\ = \min_{\mathbf{m}} \Big\{ & \boldsymbol{\alpha}'\mathbf{z}(T) + \boldsymbol{\alpha}' \int_0^\Delta \mathbf{W}(T - \tau)\mathbf{m}(\tau)\, d\tau \\ & + \boldsymbol{\alpha}' \int_0^{T-\Delta} \mathbf{W}(T - \tau - \Delta)\mathbf{m}(\tau + \Delta)\, d\tau \\ & + \lambda \int_0^\Delta H(\mathbf{m})\, d\tau + \lambda \int_0^{T-\Delta} H(\mathbf{m})\, d\tau \Big\} \end{aligned} \tag{7.5-21}$$

where Δ is a very small time interval. Application of the principle of optimality to Eq. (7.5-21) leads to the functional equation

$$\begin{aligned} f(\mathbf{z}, T) = \min_{\mathbf{m}} \Big\{ & \lambda \int_0^\Delta H(\mathbf{m})\, d\tau \\ & + f\Big[\boldsymbol{\alpha}'\mathbf{z}(T) + \boldsymbol{\alpha}' \int_0^\Delta \mathbf{W}(T - \tau)\mathbf{m}(\tau)\, d\tau;\ T - \Delta \Big] \Big\} \end{aligned} \tag{7.5-22}$$

from which is obtained the recurrence relationship

$$f(\mathbf{z}, T) = \min_{\mathbf{m}} \{\lambda\, \Delta H(\mathbf{m}) + f[\boldsymbol{\alpha}'\mathbf{z}(T) + \boldsymbol{\alpha}'\, \Delta\mathbf{W}(T)\mathbf{m};\ T - \Delta]\} \tag{7.5-23}$$

with

$$f(\mathbf{z}, 0) = \mathbf{z}(0) \tag{7.5-24}$$

and the control signals m_k limited to M_k in magnitude.

As an illustration consider the following terminal-control problem.

Example 7.5-1 A Simple Terminal-control Problem

Consider a second-order control process characterized by

$$\ddot{x}_1(t) + a\dot{x}_1(t) = m(t)$$

with the initial conditions given by

$$x_1(0) = x_{10} \qquad \text{and} \qquad \dot{x}_1(0) = \dot{x}_{10}$$

Determine the optimum-control signal m which minimizes the absolute value of $x_1(t)$ at $t = T$ over all $m(t)$ subject to the constraints

$$|m(t)| \le M \qquad 0 \le t \le T$$

and

$$\int_0^T m^2(t)\, dt \le c$$

In vector-matrix notation, the given differential equation may be expressed as

$$\dot{\mathbf{x}}(t) = \mathbf{A}\mathbf{x}(t) + \mathbf{D}m(t)$$

where

$$\mathbf{A} = \begin{bmatrix} 0 & 1 \\ 0 & -a \end{bmatrix} \qquad \mathbf{D} = \begin{bmatrix} 0 \\ 1 \end{bmatrix} \qquad \mathbf{x} = \begin{bmatrix} x_1 \\ x_2 \end{bmatrix}$$

The solution to the above differential equation is

$$\mathbf{x}(t) = \boldsymbol{\phi}(t)\mathbf{x}_0 + \int_0^t \boldsymbol{\phi}(t - \tau)\mathbf{D}m(\tau)\, d\tau$$

where

$$\boldsymbol{\phi}(t) = \begin{bmatrix} 1 & 1 - e^{-at} \\ 0 & e^{-at} \end{bmatrix} \qquad \text{and} \qquad \mathbf{x}_0 = \begin{bmatrix} x_{10} \\ x_{20} \end{bmatrix}$$

Thus

$$x_1(T) = x_{10} + x_{20}(1 - e^{-aT}) + \int_0^T (1 - e^{-(T-\tau)})m(\tau)\, d\tau$$

Making use of the Lagrange multiplier, this terminal-control problem is converted into the minimization of the functional

$$I(m) = |x_1(T)| + \lambda \int_0^T m^2(\tau)\, d\tau$$

By substitution,

$$I(m) = \left| x_{10} + x_{20}(1 - e^{-aT}) + \int_0^T (1 - e^{-(T-\tau)})m(\tau)\, d\tau \right| + \lambda \int_0^T m^2(\tau)\, d\tau$$

Let

$$f[z_1(T); T] = \min_m I(m)$$

where

$$z_1(T) = x_{10} + x_{20}(1 - e^{-aT})$$

Invoking the principle of optimality yields the functional equation

$$f(z_1, T) = \min_m \left\{ \lambda \int_0^\Delta m^2(\tau)\, d\tau \right.$$
$$\left. + f\left[z_1(T) + \int_0^\Delta (1 - e^{-(T-\tau)})m(\tau)\, d\tau;\ T - \Delta \right] \right\}$$

which, for computational purposes, may be written as

$$f(z_1, T) = \min_m \{\lambda \, \Delta m^2 + f[z_1(T) + \Delta(1 - e^{-(T-\Delta)})m; T - \Delta]\}$$

where Δ is a very small interval of time, $|m| \leq M$, and

$$f(z_1, 0) = |z_1(0)| = |x_{10}|$$

Thus the optimization problem is reduced to one involving a sequence of one-dimensional functions.

By letting $T = N\Delta$, N = a positive integer, the given terminal-control problem may be treated as an N-stage decision process characterized by the recurrence relation

$$f_N(z_1, N\Delta) = \min_m \{\lambda \, \Delta m^2 + f_{N-1}[z_1 + \Delta(1 - e^{-(N-1)\Delta})m, (N-1)\Delta]\}$$

with $f_0(z_1, 0) = |z_1(0)|$. The optimum-control signal can now be determined numerically by following the computational procedure outlined in the preceding sections. The value of λ should be so chosen that the integral constraint is satisfied.

Example 7.5-2 Minimum-integral Control Treated as a Terminal-control Problem

Consider the control system of Example 7.4-1. This minimum-integral-control problem may be treated as a terminal-control problem by introducing an extra state variable. Let

$$x_1 = x$$
$$x_2 = \int_0^t x_1^2 \, dt$$

The criterion function becomes

$$I(m) = \min_m \{x_2(t_1)\}$$

Assume that the minimum of I is $f[x(t_1), t_1]$. Following the formal procedure results in

$$\min_m \left\{(-ax_1 + \gamma m)\frac{\partial f}{\partial x_1} + x_1^2 \frac{\partial f}{\partial x_2} + \frac{\partial f}{\partial t}\right\} = 0$$

Clearly, the minimizing m in this simple example is

$$m = -M \operatorname{sgn} \frac{\partial f}{\partial x_1} = -M \operatorname{sgn} \frac{\partial f}{\partial x}$$

which is in agreement with the result of Example 7.4-1.

7.6 MINIMUM-TIME CONTROL PROCESSES

The problem of minimum-time control has been studied previously, in Secs. 4.7, 5.1, and 6.4, by use of the state-transition method, the variational calculus, and the maximum principle. It has been shown that a linear process or a process with additive control function subject to saturation is of the bang-bang type. In this section, the minimum-time-control problem is investigated from the dynamic-programming point of view.[15,16,18,22,134]

Consider the nonlinear control process characterized by the vector differential equation

$$\dot{\mathbf{x}} = \mathbf{g}(\mathbf{x}, \mathbf{m}, t) \tag{7.6-1}$$

where $\mathbf{x}$ is the $n \times 1$ state vector and $\mathbf{m}$ is the $r \times 1$ control vector. Determine the optimum-control strategy which will transform the process from a given initial state

$$\mathbf{x}(t_0) = \mathbf{x}_0 \tag{7.6-2}$$

to the desired final state

$$x_j(t_f) = x_j^0 \qquad j = 1, 2, \ldots, k \leq n \tag{7.6-3}$$

in minimum time, where the final time t_f is unspecified.

Following Dreyfus,[52] let

$$f(\mathbf{x}, t) = \min_{\mathbf{m}} \{t_f - t\} \tag{7.6-4}$$

be the minimum time to transform the process from the state $\mathbf{x}(t)$ to the desired final state $\mathbf{x}(t_f)$ with the control vector optimally chosen. On the basis of the definition of $f(\mathbf{x}, t)$, it follows that, at the end of the optimum trajectory,

$$\left.\frac{\partial f}{\partial t}\right|_{t=t_f} = 0 \tag{7.6-5}$$

and for x_i not specified at $t = t_f$ by Eq. (7.6-3),

$$\left.\frac{\partial f}{\partial x_i}\right|_{t=t_f} = 0 \tag{7.6-6}$$

Equations (7.6-2), (7.6-3), and (7.6-6) provide the boundary conditions to determine the constants of integration.

Invoking the principle of optimality, the minimum time is given by the functional equation

$$f(\mathbf{x}, t) = \min_{\mathbf{m}} \{\Delta + f(\mathbf{x} + \dot{\mathbf{x}}\Delta, t + \Delta)\} \tag{7.6-7}$$

Expanding $f(\mathbf{x} + \dot{\mathbf{x}}\Delta, t + \Delta)$ into a Taylor's series and simplifying leads to

$$\min_{\mathbf{m}} \left\{\Delta + \frac{\partial f}{\partial \mathbf{x}} \mathbf{g}(\mathbf{x}, \mathbf{m}, t)\Delta + \frac{\partial f}{\partial t}\Delta + \epsilon(\Delta)\right\} = 0 \tag{7.6-8}$$

Passing to the limit as Δ approaches zero reduces Eq. (7.6-8) to

$$\min_{\mathbf{m}} \left\{ \frac{\partial f}{\partial \mathbf{x}} \mathbf{g}(\mathbf{x}, \mathbf{m}, t) + \frac{\partial f}{\partial t} \right\} = -1 \tag{7.6-9}$$

Carrying out the minimization procedure by elementary calculus yields

$$\frac{\partial f}{\partial \mathbf{x}} \frac{\partial \mathbf{g}(\mathbf{x}, \mathbf{m}, t)}{\partial \mathbf{m}} = 0 \tag{7.6-10}$$

and

$$\frac{\partial f}{\partial \mathbf{x}} \mathbf{g}(\mathbf{x}, \mathbf{m}, t) + \frac{\partial f}{\partial t} + 1 = 0 \tag{7.6-11}$$

From Eq. (7.6-11) it can be seen that, in view of Eq. (7.6-5), at the end of the optimum trajectory,

$$\frac{\partial f}{\partial \mathbf{x}} \mathbf{g}(\mathbf{x}, \mathbf{m}, t) \bigg|_{t=t_f} + 1 = 0 \tag{7.6-12}$$

Furthermore, it can be shown by integration that, if the function **g** is time-independent, that is, $\mathbf{g} = \mathbf{g}(\mathbf{x}, \mathbf{m})$, then along the optimum trajectory

$$\frac{\partial f}{\partial \mathbf{x}} \mathbf{g}(\mathbf{x}, \mathbf{m}) + 1 = 0 \tag{7.6-13}$$

When the partial derivative $\partial f/\partial \mathbf{x}$ is known at a point, Eqs. (7.6-10) and (7.6-13) can be solved for the optimum-control vector $\mathbf{m}(x)$.

The differential equation describing the partial derivative $\partial f/\partial \mathbf{x}$ can be derived from Eqs. (7.6-10) and (7.6-13) as follows: Partial differentiation of Eq. (7.6-13) with respect to **x** gives

$$\frac{\partial}{\partial \mathbf{x}}\left(\frac{\partial f}{\partial \mathbf{x}}\right) \mathbf{g}(\mathbf{x}, \mathbf{m}) + \frac{\partial f}{\partial \mathbf{x}} \left[\frac{\partial \mathbf{g}(\mathbf{x}, \mathbf{m})}{\partial \mathbf{x}} + \frac{\partial \mathbf{g}(\mathbf{x}, \mathbf{m})}{\partial \mathbf{m}} \frac{\partial \mathbf{m}}{\partial \mathbf{x}} \right] = 0 \tag{7.6-14}$$

Since

$$\frac{d}{dt}\left(\frac{\partial f}{\partial \mathbf{x}}\right) = \frac{\partial}{\partial \mathbf{x}}\left(\frac{\partial f}{\partial \mathbf{x}}\right) \frac{d\mathbf{x}}{dt} = \frac{\partial}{\partial \mathbf{x}}\left(\frac{\partial f}{\partial \mathbf{x}}\right) \mathbf{g}(\mathbf{x}, \mathbf{m}) \tag{7.6-15}$$

use of Eq. (7.6-10) reduces Eq. (7.6-14) to the Euler-Lagrange equation for the partial derivative $\partial f/\partial \mathbf{x}$,

$$\frac{d}{dt}\left(\frac{\partial f}{\partial \mathbf{x}}\right) + \frac{\partial f}{\partial \mathbf{x}} \frac{\partial \mathbf{g}(\mathbf{x}, \mathbf{m})}{\partial \mathbf{x}} = 0 \tag{7.6-16}$$

In terms of the components of the vectors,

$$\frac{d}{dt}\left(\frac{\partial f}{\partial x_i}\right) + \sum_{j=1}^{n} \frac{\partial f}{\partial x_j} \frac{\partial g_j}{\partial x_i} = 0 \qquad i = 1, 2, \ldots, n \tag{7.6-17}$$

These n differential equations for the partial derivatives $\partial f/\partial x_i$ given in

Eq. (7.6-17), together with the n differential equations for the process specified in Eq. (7.6-1) and the conditions for minimum stated in Eq. (7.6-10), constitute a set of $2n + r$ equations from which the partial derivatives $\partial f/\partial \mathbf{x}$, the optimum-control vector $\mathbf{m}(t)$, and the optimum trajectory $\mathbf{x}(t)$ can be determined.

Since the initial time t_0 is given but the final time t_f is unspecified, it seems desirable to define the minimum-time function $f(\mathbf{x}, t)$ by

$$f(\mathbf{x}, t) = \min_{\mathbf{m}} \int_{t_0}^{t} dt \tag{7.6-18}$$

Based upon this definition, it is noted that, at the beginning of the optimum trajectory, $t = t_0$, $f(x_0, t_0) = 0$, and $\partial f/\partial t = 0$, and at the end of the optimum trajectory, $t = t_f$,

$$f(\mathbf{x}, t_f) = \min_{\mathbf{m}} \int_{t_0}^{t_f} dt = \min_{\mathbf{m}} (t_f - t_0) \tag{7.6-19}$$

and, for x_i not specified by Eq. (7.6-3), $\partial f/\partial x_i = 0$. Carrying out the integration of Eq. (7.6-18) in two steps,

$$\begin{aligned} f(\mathbf{x}, t) &= \min_{\mathbf{m}} \left(\int_{t_0}^{t-\Delta} dt + \int_{t-\Delta}^{t} dt \right) \\ &= \min_{\mathbf{m}} \{\Delta + f(\mathbf{x} - \dot{\mathbf{x}}\Delta, t - \Delta)\} \end{aligned} \tag{7.6-20}$$

This is a functional equation for the minimum-time-control problem. Following the formal procedure results in

$$\frac{\partial f}{\partial \mathbf{x}} \frac{\partial \mathbf{g}(\mathbf{x}, \mathbf{m}, t)}{\partial \mathbf{m}} = 0 \tag{7.6-21}$$

and

$$\frac{\partial f}{\partial \mathbf{x}} \mathbf{g}(\mathbf{x}, \mathbf{m}, t) + \frac{\partial f}{\partial t} - 1 = 0 \tag{7.6-22}$$

from which the Euler-Lagrange equation given in Eq. (7.6-16) or Eq. (7.6-17) can be derived in similar manner.

Process Subject to Additive Control Signals

Now consider the nth-order control process described by the matrix differential equation

$$\dot{\mathbf{x}}(t) = \mathbf{F}[\mathbf{x}(t)] + \mathbf{D}\mathbf{m}(t) \tag{7.6-23}$$

where $\mathbf{x}$ and $\mathbf{m}$ are defined as above, and $\mathbf{D}$ is an $n \times r$ driving matrix with elements d_{ik}. The process is subject to the additive control signals m_k, which are limited by the constraints

$$|m_k| \leq M_k \tag{7.6-24}$$

Determine the optimum-control strategy which will move the process from a given initial state $\mathbf{x}(t_0) = \mathbf{x}_0$ to the equilibrium state $\mathbf{x}(t_f) = \mathbf{0}$ in minimum time, where t_f is unspecified.

By following the previous analysis, the following functional equation is obtained:

$$\min_{\mathbf{m}} \left\{ \frac{\partial f}{\partial \mathbf{x}} [\mathbf{F}(\mathbf{x}) + \mathbf{D}\mathbf{m}(t)] \right\} = 1 \tag{7.6-25}$$

To facilitate the minimization procedure, the vectors and matrices are expressed in terms of their components. Since

$$\dot{x}_i = F_i(\mathbf{x}) + \sum_{k=1}^{r} d_{ik} m_k \tag{7.6-26}$$

where $F_i(\mathbf{x})$ are the components of $\mathbf{F}(\mathbf{x})$, Eq. (7.6-25) can be written as

$$\min_{m_k} \left\{ \sum_{i=1}^{n} \frac{\partial f}{\partial x_i} \left[F_i(\mathbf{x}) + \sum_{k=1}^{r} d_{ik} m_k \right] \right\} = 1 \tag{7.6-27}$$

Examination of Eq. (7.6-27) reveals that the conditions for minimizing the function in the braces with respect to m_k are

$$\sum_{i=1}^{n} \frac{\partial f}{\partial x_i} \sum_{k=1}^{r} d_{ik} m_k < 0 \tag{7.6-28}$$

and

$$|m_k| = M_k \tag{7.6-29}$$

Interchanging the summation operations in Eqs. (7.6-28) yields

$$\sum_{k=1}^{r} m_k \sum_{i=1}^{n} d_{ik} \frac{\partial f}{\partial x_i} < 0 \tag{7.6-30}$$

Thus the optimum-control signals which minimize the time required for transforming the process from a specified initial state to the equilibrium state are given by

$$m_k = -M_k \operatorname{sgn} \sum_{i=1}^{n} d_{ik} \frac{\partial f}{\partial x_i} \tag{7.6-31}$$

This equation points out that the optimum-control signals m_k have magnitudes equal to the maximum permissible values M_k and signs determined by the sign of the function

$$s(t) = \sum_{i=1}^{n} d_{ik} \frac{\partial f}{\partial x_i} \tag{7.6-32}$$

The optimum controller switches between the upper and the lower limits according to the switching function defined in Eq. (7.6-32). The conclusion that this time-optimal control system with the control signals subject to ideal saturation is of the bang-bang type is in agreement with the results derived previously in Secs. 4.7 and 6.4. The partial derivatives $\partial f/\partial x_i$ can be determined from the Euler-Lagrange equations

$$\frac{d}{dt}\left(\frac{\partial f}{\partial x_i}\right) + \sum_{j=1}^{n} \frac{\partial f}{\partial x_j}\frac{\partial F_j}{\partial x_i} = 0 \qquad i = 1, 2, \ldots, n \tag{7.6-33}$$

which follows from Eq. (7.6-17), by using the relationship given in Eq. (7.6-26).

Example 7.6-1 Minimum-time Control of a Second-order Process

Consider the second-order process characterized by differential equations

$$\dot{x}_1 = x_2$$
$$\dot{x}_2 = -ax_2 - bx_1 + m$$

with $|m| \leq M$ and the initial and final conditions

$$x_1(t_0) = x_{10} \qquad x_2(t_0) = x_{20}$$
$$x_1(t_f) = 0 \qquad x_2(t_f) = 0$$

Determine the control signal m so as to move the process from the initial state $\mathbf{x}(t_0) = \mathbf{x}_0$ to the equilibrium state $\mathbf{x}(t_f) = 0$ in minimum time.

In vector-matrix form, the system equation is

$$\dot{\mathbf{x}} = \mathbf{A}\mathbf{x} + \mathbf{D}m$$

where $\mathbf{A} = \begin{bmatrix} 0 & 1 \\ -b & -a \end{bmatrix}$ and $\mathbf{D} = \begin{bmatrix} 0 \\ 1 \end{bmatrix}$

Making use of Eq. (7.6-31), the optimum-control signal is given by

$$m = -M \operatorname{sgn} \frac{\partial f}{\partial x_2}$$

The partial derivative $\partial f/\partial x_2$ can be determined from Eq. (7.6-33). By proper substitution, Eq. (7.6-33) yields

$$\frac{d}{dt}\left(\frac{\partial f}{\partial x_1}\right) - b\frac{\partial f}{\partial x_2} = 0$$
$$\frac{d}{dt}\left(\frac{\partial f}{\partial x_2}\right) - a\frac{\partial f}{\partial x_2} + \frac{\partial f}{\partial x_1} = 0$$

Combining these two equations leads to the differential equation

$$\frac{d^2}{dt^2}\left(\frac{\partial f}{\partial x_2}\right) - a\frac{d}{dt}\left(\frac{\partial f}{\partial x_2}\right) + b\frac{\partial f}{\partial x_2} = 0$$

which can be solved for $\partial f/\partial x_2$. Thus

$$\frac{\partial f}{\partial x_2} = -Ke^{at/2} \sin\left(\tfrac{1}{2}\sqrt{4b - a^2}\, t + \theta\right)$$

provided that $a^2 - 4b < 0$, where K and θ are functions of the boundary conditions. Hence the optimum-control signal is

$$m = M \operatorname{sgn}\left[Ke^{at/2} \sin\left(\tfrac{1}{2}\sqrt{4b - a^2}\, t + \theta\right)\right]$$

This is in agreement with the results obtained in Example 6.4-1 by use of the maximum principle.

7.7 STOCHASTIC AND ADAPTIVE CONTROL PROCESSES

Throughout the treatment in the preceding four sections the concept of dynamic programming is applied to the design of optimum controls for processes which are assumed to be deterministic. The dynamics of the control process is assumed to be completely known and can be described by linear or nonlinear differential equations with known coefficients, together with constraining equations. Application of the functional-equation approach leads to partial differential equations or recurrence equations for the determination of the optimum-control law to minimize or maximize a specified performance-criterion function. However, in many control processes encountered in practice, there are uncertainties and random effects of various kinds. These uncertainties and random effects generally arise because of tolerance in manufacture, parameter variations due to aging, inaccurate knowledge of process dynamics, stochastic inputs, and random external disturbances. When the uncertainties are of a minor nature and the random variations are slight, the feedback principle can be employed to counteract the random effects. On the other hand, should the uncertainty factor become significant and the parameter variations become large, the conventional feedback control may fail to cope with the situations. In order to design optimum control for the processes characterized by uncertainties and large-parameter fluctuations, resort is often had to the new concept of adaptive and learning control. In this section the optimum design of stochastic control process by the method of dynamic programming is discussed, and the design technique is then extended to the study of adaptive and learning control processes. Emphasis is placed upon discrete stochastic and adaptive processes, since they are of fundamental importance and may be used to represent continuous processes. In fact, the design of continuous control processes of moderate complexity by the functional-equation technique of dynamic programming can be carried out only in a discrete, numerical manner.

Stochastic Control[2,16,24,144]

Consider a random-parameter control process characterized by the recurrence relationship

$$\mathbf{x}(k+1) = g[\mathbf{x}(k), \mathbf{r}(k), \mathbf{m}(k)] \tag{7.7-1a}$$

or written as

$$\mathbf{x}_{k+1} = g(\mathbf{x}_k, \mathbf{r}_k, \mathbf{m}_k) \tag{7.7-1b}$$

where $\mathbf{x}$ = the state vector
$\mathbf{r}$ = a vector describing the independent random parameters
$\mathbf{m}$ = the control vector

The initial condition is given by

$$\mathbf{x}(0) = \mathbf{x}_0 \tag{7.7-2}$$

The probability distribution of the random parameter is assumed to be known. An optimum-control problem of particular interest may be formulated as the determination of a control policy which minimizes the expected value of the performance-criterion function

$$J_n = \sum_{k=1}^{N} F(\mathbf{x}_k, \mathbf{r}_k, \mathbf{m}_{k-1}) \tag{7.7-3}$$

which measures the deviation of the system from some desired performance.

Because of the uncertainties involved in the control process it is not reasonable to require that the performance-criterion function J_N defined in Eq. (7.7-3) be minimized as with the deterministic case. Although the expected value of J_N represents a less exact measure of the performance, it is a convenient measure and provides a good compromise.

Let the performance index be

$$I_N = E\left\{\sum_{k=1}^{N} F(\mathbf{x}_k, \mathbf{r}_k, \mathbf{m}_{k-1})\right\} \tag{7.7-4}$$

where E stands for the expected-value operator. For the sake of notational convenience, the random parameters are assumed to possess the common distribution function $dG(\mathbf{r})$. Let $f_N(\mathbf{x}_0)$ be the minimum of I_N with respect to the control vector $\mathbf{m}$, defined by

$$f_N(\mathbf{x}_0) = \min_{\{\mathbf{m}\}} E\left\{\sum_{k=1}^{N} F(\mathbf{x}_k, \mathbf{r}_k, \mathbf{m}_{k-1})\right\} \tag{7.7-5}$$

For $N = 1$,

$$\begin{aligned} f_1(\mathbf{x}_0) &= \min_{\mathbf{m}_0} E\{F(\mathbf{x}_1, \mathbf{r}_1, \mathbf{m}_0)\} \\ &= \min_{\mathbf{m}_0} \int F(\mathbf{x}_1, \mathbf{r}_1, \mathbf{m}_0)\, dG(\mathbf{r}_1) \end{aligned} \tag{7.7-6}$$

For $N \geq 2$, application of the principle of optimality yields the recurrence relationship

$$\begin{aligned} f_N(\mathbf{x}_0) &= \min_{\mathbf{m}_0} E\{F(\mathbf{x}_1, \mathbf{r}_1, \mathbf{m}_0) + f_{N-1}(\mathbf{x}_1)\} \\ &= \min_{\mathbf{m}_0} \int [F(\mathbf{x}_1, \mathbf{r}_1, \mathbf{m}_0) + f_{N-1}(\mathbf{x}_1)]\, dG(\mathbf{r}_1) \end{aligned} \tag{7.7-7}$$

To facilitate numerical computation, the distribution function is taken to be discrete. Then the recurrence relationship given in Eq. (7.7-7) may be expressed as

$$f_N(\mathbf{x}_0) = \min_{\mathbf{m}_0} \left\{ \sum_{i=1}^{L} p_i F(\mathbf{x}_1, \gamma_i, \mathbf{m}_0) + f_{N-1}(\mathbf{x}_1) \right\} \tag{7.7-8}$$

where $\mathbf{r} = \gamma_i$ with probability p_i.

It is interesting to note that the same techniques used in the design of optimum control for deterministic processes have been applied to stochastic control processes, and analogous equations have been derived. The functional-equation technique affords a unified approach for treating both types of control processes.

A stochastic terminal-control problem may be formulated as the determination of the control vector $\mathbf{m}$ which minimizes the expected value of some function of the final state

$$J_N = F(\mathbf{x}_N) \tag{7.7-9}$$

Let the performance index for terminal control be defined by

$$I_N = E\{F(\mathbf{x}_N)\} \tag{7.7-10}$$

and the minimum of I_N with respect to the control vector be

$$f_N(\mathbf{x}_0) = \min_{\{\mathbf{m}\}} E\{F(\mathbf{x}_N)\} \tag{7.7-11}$$

Then, for $N = 1$,

$$f_1(\mathbf{x}_0) = F(\mathbf{x}_0) \tag{7.7-12}$$

and in general for $N \geq 2$,

$$\begin{aligned} f_N(\mathbf{x}_0) &= \min_{\mathbf{m}_0} E\{f_{N-1}[g(\mathbf{x}_0, \mathbf{r}_0, \mathbf{m}_0)]\} \\ &= \min_{\mathbf{m}_0} \int f_{N-1}[g(\mathbf{x}_0, \mathbf{r}_0, \mathbf{m}_0)]\, dG(\mathbf{r}_0) \end{aligned} \tag{7.7-13}$$

Taking the distribution function $dG(\mathbf{r})$ to be discrete, the recurrence relationship becomes

$$f_N(\mathbf{x}_0) = \min_{\mathbf{m}_0} \sum_{i=1}^{L} p_i f_{N-1}[g(\mathbf{x}_0, \gamma_i, \mathbf{m}_0)] \tag{7.7-14}$$

Consider a linear random-parameter process characterized by

$$\mathbf{x}_{k+1} = \boldsymbol{\phi}(k, \mathbf{r}_k)\mathbf{x}_k + \mathbf{G}(k, \mathbf{r}_k)m_k \tag{7.7-15}$$

with $\mathbf{x}(0) = \mathbf{x}_0$ and $|m| \leq 1$. In Eq. (7.7-15), $\mathbf{r}$ is an independent random vector, and $\boldsymbol{\phi}$ and $\mathbf{G}$ are given functions. For simplicity, assume that the random vector $\mathbf{r}_k$ will be either $\mathbf{r}_k^+$ or $\mathbf{r}_k^-$ at the instant k, such that

$$\text{Prob}\,\{\mathbf{r} = \mathbf{r}_k^+\} = p \tag{7.7-16}$$

$$\text{Prob}\,\{\mathbf{r} = \mathbf{r}_k^-\} = 1 - p \tag{7.7-17}$$

where the probability p is assumed to be known. If the value of p is not known, further complications arise, leading to an adaptive control process. As an illustration, consider the problem of minimizing the expected value of the performance-criterion function

$$J_N = \sum_{k=1}^{N} [\mathbf{x}'(k)\mathbf{Q}\mathbf{x}(k) + \lambda m^2(k-1)] \tag{7.7-18}$$

Let the minimum of EJ_N be

$$f_N(\mathbf{x}_0) = \min_{\{m\}} E \sum_{k=1}^{N} [\mathbf{x}'(k)\mathbf{Q}\mathbf{x}(k) + \lambda m^2(k-1)] \tag{7.7-19}$$

For $N = 1$,

$$\begin{aligned} f_1(\mathbf{x}_0) &= \min_{m(0)} E[\mathbf{x}'(1)\mathbf{Q}\mathbf{x}(1) + \lambda m^2(0)] \\ &= \min_{m_0} p[\mathbf{x}^{+\prime}(1)\mathbf{Q}\mathbf{x}^+(1)] + (1-p)[\mathbf{x}^{-\prime}(1)\mathbf{Q}\mathbf{x}^-(1)] + \lambda m_0^2 \end{aligned} \tag{7.7-20}$$

where

$$\mathbf{x}^+(1) = \boldsymbol{\phi}(0, \mathbf{r}_0^+)\mathbf{x}_0 + \mathbf{G}(0, \mathbf{r}_0^+)m_0 \tag{7.7-21a}$$

$$\mathbf{x}^-(1) = \boldsymbol{\phi}(0, \mathbf{r}_0^-)\mathbf{x}_0 + \mathbf{G}(0, \mathbf{r}_0^-)m_0 \tag{7.7-21b}$$

For $N \geq 2$, the minimum of EJ_N is

$$\begin{aligned} f_N(\mathbf{x}_0) &= \min_{m(0)} E[\mathbf{x}'(1)\mathbf{Q}\mathbf{x}(1) + \lambda m^2(0) + f_{N-1}(\mathbf{x}_1)] \\ &= \min_{m(0)} \{p[\mathbf{x}^{+\prime}(1)\mathbf{Q}\mathbf{x}^+(1) + f_{N-1}[\mathbf{x}^+(1)]] \\ &\qquad + (1-p)[\mathbf{x}^{-\prime}(1)\mathbf{Q}\mathbf{x}^-(1) f_{N-1}[\mathbf{x}^-(1)]] + \lambda m(0)\} \end{aligned} \tag{7.7-22}$$

The desired function $f_N(\mathbf{x}_0)$ and the optimum-control policy can be determined computationally from the above recurrence relationships.

Adaptive and Learning Control[2,22,25,26,100,143,144,148]

In the foregoing discussion of stochastic control processes, the probability distribution of the random parameters is assumed to be known in advance. This assumption enables the design to be carried out in the same manner as the design of optimum control for deterministic processes. However, under some circumstances, even less information than was assumed in the stochastic process will be available to the controller concerning the influences of the random parameters upon the behavior of the control process. To achieve optimum control of the process, it is desirable to design the controller with learning capability. Provision is made for the controller to *learn* about the nature of the influences as the process unfolds.

This enables the controller to improve its decision-making ability and the system performance on the basis of the experience and to adapt itself to environment. The concept of adaptation in a complicated system comes from the study of the behavior of living creatures, because there these characteristics are most common and conspicuous. Adaptation means the ability of self-modification and self-adjustment in accordance with varying conditions of environment. It is a fundamental attribute of living organisms. Certainly it is a desirable attribute for a modern control system.

The essential feature of the adaptive control processes is that the situations under which the system will operate are unknown or only partially known. If the equations which characterize the process dynamics or if the signal and disturbance statistics vary with time in a predetermined manner, there is no great increase in the difficulty of designing the control system. This problem does not fall into the category of adaptive control unless there is some uncertainty as to what the equations which describe the process are or as to what the statistics of the signals and disturbances are specified to be. In order to represent this uncertainty mathematically, it is assumed that the characterizing equations depend upon random variables. When the probability distribution of the random variables is known, the problem is referred to as a stochastic control problem. When the probability distribution is unknown or only partially known, the problem is an adaptive control problem. The adaptive and learning control process differs from the ordinary stochastic control process in that it attempts to reevaluate itself in the light of the uncertainties in the control process as they unfold and change.

Referring to the random-parameter process characterized by the recurrence relation defined in Eqs. (7.7-1), if this equation describes the completely augmented system, then the random parameter $\mathbf{r}(k)$ can be considered as representing the uncertainties concerning:

1. The coefficients in the dynamic equations characterizing the original process. This leads to the plant adaptive-control problem.
2. The statistical properties of the reference inputs to the original process if the inputs are random. This describes the signal adaptive-control problem.
3. The statistical properties of the disturbances occurring in the original process. This formulates the disturbance adaptive-control problem.

The random parameter $\mathbf{r}$ can take on values within a finite set $\{\mathbf{r}^{(1)}, \mathbf{r}^{(2)}, \ldots, \mathbf{r}^{(\pi)}\}$. However, in order to simplify the computation, only two values are chosen. Assume that, at the instant k, the random parameter $\mathbf{r}$ takes on two values, $\mathbf{r}_k^+$ and $\mathbf{r}_k^-$, with probabilities p and $1 - p$, respectively, and that the value of the probability of each outcome is not known. The probability p is assumed to be a random variable with an a priori probability-density function $\omega(\xi)$. Although this is an unpleasant situation, the controller is still much more fortunate than one that does not even know the form of the distribution of the random variables or their degree of correlation. At any particular stage of the process when a control decision is made, not only does the process change state physically, but also the adaptive controller determines the estimate of the probability-density function for p and the estimate of the value of p itself.

As the initial estimate of the value of probability p, the expected value of p is chosen:

$$p_0 = \int_0^1 \xi\omega(\xi)\,d\xi \tag{7.7-23}$$

The adaptation and learning process consists in gathering information about the random variable and processing this information according to some decision rule. The decisions resulting from the information processing are used to improve the control, which is chosen initially according to an a priori distribution. As a matter of fact, the initial a priori assumptions about the randomness may be far from correct. By making a number of observations of the random variable, the adaptive controller can determine the correct probability distribution through the process of learning.

Upon observing that $\mathbf{r} = \mathbf{r}_k^+$, the new estimate of the probability-density function for p is given by the a posteriori probability

$$\omega_1(\xi) = P(p = \xi | \mathbf{r} = \mathbf{r}_k^+) \tag{7.7-24}$$

By the Bayes theorem, the probability that $p = \xi$ after $\mathbf{r}_k^+$ has been observed is given by

$$P(p = \xi | \mathbf{r} = \mathbf{r}_k^+) = \frac{P(p = \xi)P(\mathbf{r} = \mathbf{r}_k^+ | p = \xi)}{\int_0^1 P(p = \xi)P(\mathbf{r} = \mathbf{r}_k^+ | p = \xi)\,d\xi} \tag{7.7-25}$$

Since $\quad P(p = \xi) = \omega(\xi) \quad$ and $\quad P(\mathbf{r} = \mathbf{r}_k^+ | p = \xi) = \xi$

the new estimate is

$$\omega_1(\xi) = \frac{\xi\omega(\xi)}{\int_0^1 \xi\omega(\xi)\,d\xi} \tag{7.7-26}$$

Upon observing that $\mathbf{r} = \mathbf{r}_k^-$, the new estimate of the probability-density function is given by the a posteriori probability

$$\omega_2(\xi) = P(p = \xi | \mathbf{r} = \mathbf{r}_k^-) \tag{7.7-27}$$

Applying the Bayes theorem, the conditional probability is

$$P(p = \xi | \mathbf{r} = \mathbf{r}_k^-) = \frac{P(p = \xi)P(\mathbf{r} = \mathbf{r}_k^- | p = \xi)}{\int_0^1 P(p = \xi)P(\mathbf{r} = \mathbf{r}_k^- | p = \xi)\,d\xi} \tag{7.7-28}$$

Since $\quad P(\mathbf{r} = \mathbf{r}_k^- | p = \xi) = 1 - \xi$

the new estimate is given by

$$\omega_2(\xi) = \frac{(1 - \xi)\omega(\xi)}{\int_0^1 (1 - \xi)\omega(\xi)\, d\xi} \tag{7.7-29}$$

Thus, after observing that $\mathbf{r} = \mathbf{r}_k^+$, the new estimate of the value of p itself is

$$P_1 = \int_0^1 \xi\omega_1(\xi)\, d\xi = \frac{\int_0^1 \xi^2\omega(\xi)\, d\xi}{\int_0^1 \xi\omega(\xi)\, d\xi} \tag{7.7-30}$$

and after observing that $\mathbf{r} = \mathbf{r}_k^-$, the new estimate of p is

$$p_2 = \int_0^1 \xi\omega_2(\xi)\, d\xi = \frac{\int_0^1 \xi(1 - \xi)\omega(\xi)\, d\xi}{\int_0^1 (1 - \xi)\omega(\xi)\, d\xi} \tag{7.7-31}$$

The Bayes theorem provides a means of estimating the value of the probability p by modifying the a priori distribution on the basis of the observations that are made in the process of control. If over the past $\mu + \nu$ observations the information pattern has been obtained that the random variables have taken on μ values of $\mathbf{r}^+$ and ν values of $\mathbf{r}^-$, the new estimate of the probability-density function is then given by

$$\omega_{\mu,\nu}(\xi) = \frac{\xi^\mu(1 - \xi)^\nu\omega(\xi)}{\int_0^1 \xi^\mu(1 - \xi)^\nu\omega(\xi)\, d\xi} \tag{7.7-32}$$

and the new estimate of p itself is

$$p_{\mu,\nu} = \frac{\int_0^1 \xi^{\mu+1}(1 - \xi)^\nu\omega(\xi)\, d\xi}{\int_0^1 \xi^\mu(1 - \xi)^\nu\omega(\xi)\, d\xi} \tag{7.7-33}$$

Equations (7.7-32) and (7.7-33) describe the *information pattern* for the adaptive control process. The controller is to act as if this estimate were the exact value of the probability p.

Now consider the problem of minimizing the performance index I_N defined in Eq. (7.7-4). Let $f_N(\mathbf{x}_0, \mu, \nu)$ be the minimum of I_N with respect to the control vector $\mathbf{m}$, starting with the information pattern of initial state $\mathbf{x}_0$, μ values of $\mathbf{r}^+$, and ν values of $\mathbf{r}^-$. Then

$$f_N(\mathbf{x}_0, \mu, \nu) = \min_{\{\mathbf{m}\}} E \sum_{k=1}^{N} F(\mathbf{x}_k, \mathbf{r}_k, \mathbf{m}_k) \tag{7.7-34}$$

For $N = 1$,

$$f_1(\mathbf{x}_0, \mu, \nu) = \min_{\mathbf{m}_0} E\{F(\mathbf{x}_1, \mathbf{r}_1, \mathbf{m}_0)\}$$
$$= \min_{\mathbf{m}_0} \{p_{\mu,\nu}F(\mathbf{x}_1^+, \mathbf{r}_1^+, \mathbf{m}_0) + (1 - p_{\mu,\nu})F(\mathbf{x}_1^-, \mathbf{r}_1^-, \mathbf{m}_0)\} \tag{7.7-35}$$

where
$$\mathbf{x}_1^+ = g(\mathbf{x}_0, \mathbf{r}_0^+, \mathbf{m}_0) \tag{7.7-36a}$$
and
$$\mathbf{x}_1^- = g(\mathbf{x}_0, \mathbf{r}_0^-, \mathbf{m}_0) \tag{7.7-36b}$$

For $N \geq 2$, application of the functional-equation technique yields the recurrence relationship as

$$f_N(\mathbf{x}_0, \mu, \nu) = \min_{\mathbf{m}_0} \{p_{\mu,\nu}[F(\mathbf{x}_1^+, \mathbf{r}_1^+, \mathbf{m}_0) + f_{N-1}(\mathbf{x}_1^+, \mu + 1, \nu)]$$
$$+ (1 - p_{\mu,\nu})[F(\mathbf{x}_1^-, \mathbf{r}_1^-, \mathbf{m}_0) + f_{N-1}(\mathbf{x}_1^-, \mu, \nu + 1)]\} \tag{7.7-37}$$

Equations (7.7-35) and (7.7-37) provide a computational approach for the determination of the optimum-control policy in a systematic, iterative manner.

Example 7.7-1 An Aircraft Landing System[71a]

Consider an aircraft landing system which may be described approximately by a second-order differential equation with random parameters:

$$\frac{d^2h(t)}{dt^2} = r(\rho, V, \delta_1, \delta_2, \delta_3, \delta_4, \delta_5)m(t) \tag{7.7-38}$$

where $h(t)$ = altitude
$m(t)$ = altitude-control signal
r = a coefficient depending on air density ρ, flight velocity V, and aerodynamic coefficients $\delta_1, \delta_2, \delta_3, \delta_4, \delta_5$

At the beginning of the landing process, the initial conditions are given by $h(0)$ and $\dot{h}(0)$. The flight velocity V is assumed to be constant throughout the landing interval T. The random coefficient r is distributed uniformly and independently over any interval $\tau = T/N$, where N denotes the number of sampling periods during the landing interval. For computational convenience, the distribution is assumed to be discrete. The random parameter r is equal to r^+ with probability p, and it is equal to r^- with probability $1 - p$. The probability p is unknown, and it is a random variable with some a priori distribution. It takes on two values p_1 and p_2 with a priori probability ζ and $1 - \zeta$, respectively. Determine the optimum-control signal m which will minimize the mean square of the rate of descent at the moment of landing.

Let

$$\frac{dh(t)}{dt} = x(t)$$

Then Eq. (7.7-38) may be written as

$$\dot{x}(t) = rm(t) \tag{7.7-39}$$

In discrete form, the landing system is characterized by the difference equation

$$x_{k+1} = x_k + r\tau m_k \tag{7.7-40}$$

where $\qquad x_k = x(k\tau) \qquad$ and $\qquad m_k = m(k\tau)$

This terminal-control problem requires the determination of the control signal m so that the performance index

$$I = E\{x^2(T)\} = E\{x^2(N\tau)\} \tag{7.7-41}$$

is minimized.

The design is initiated with the determination of the a posteriori probabilities

$$\alpha(\zeta) = P\{p = p_1 | r = r^+\}$$

and

$$\beta(\zeta) = P\{p = p_1 | r = r^-\}$$

By the Bayes theorem, it is found that

$$\begin{aligned} \alpha(\zeta) &= \frac{P(p = p_1)P(r = r^+|p = p_1)}{P(p = p_1)P(r = r^+|p = p_1) + P(p = p_2)P(r = r^+|p = p_2)} \\ &= \frac{\zeta p_1}{\zeta p_1 + (1 - \zeta)p_2} \end{aligned} \tag{7.7-42}$$

$$\begin{aligned} \beta(\zeta) &= \frac{P(p = p_1)P(r = r^-|p = p_1)}{P(p = p_1)P(r = r^-|p = p_1) + P(p = p_2)P(r = r^-|p = p_2)} \\ &= \frac{\zeta(1 - p_1)}{\zeta(1 - p_1) + (1 - \zeta)(1 - p_2)} \end{aligned} \tag{7.7-43}$$

Let the minimum of I be denoted by $f_N(x_0, \zeta)$, where $x_0 = \dot{h}(0)$ is the initial rate of descent of the aircraft during the landing interval. The minimum of I is a function of the initial speed x_0 and the a priori probability ζ, and is given by

$$f_N(x_0, \zeta) = \min_{\{m_k\}} E\{x^2(T)\} \tag{7.7-44}$$

At any sampling instant $k + 1$, x_{k+1} takes on two values:

$$x_{k+1}^+ = x_k + r^+\tau m_k \tag{7.7-45a}$$

and

$$x_{k+1}^- = x_k + r^-\tau m_k \tag{7.7-45b}$$

For $k = 0$, x_1 takes on the value

$$x_1^+ = x_0 + r^+\tau m_0 \qquad \text{with probability } p_0 \tag{7.7-46a}$$

and the value

$$x_1^- = x_0 + r^-\tau m_0 \qquad \text{with probability } 1 - p_0 \tag{7.7-46b}$$

where p_0 is the expected value of p and is given by

$$p_0 = \zeta p_1 + (1 - \zeta)p_2 \tag{7.7-47}$$

Hence, for $N = 1$,

$$f_1(x_0, \zeta) = \min_{m_0} \{p_0(x_1^+)^2 + (1 - p_0)(x_1^-)^2\} \tag{7.7-48}$$

For $N \geq 2$, invoking the principle of optimality yields

$$f_N(x_0, \zeta) = \min_{m_0} \{p_0 f_{N-1}[x_1^+, \alpha(\zeta)] + (1 - p_0) f_{N-1}[x_1^-, \beta(\zeta)]\} \tag{7.7-49}$$

where $\alpha(\zeta)$, $\beta(\zeta)$, x_1^+, and x_1^- are defined in Eqs. (7.7-42), (7.7-43), (7.7-46*a*), and (7.7-46*b*), respectively. As a result of the first decision, the process will be transformed to one of the two possible states x_1^+ or x_1^- with probabilities p_0 or $1 - p_0$. If the process moves to state x^+, the a posteriori probability $\alpha(\zeta)$ is computed. If the process moves to state x^-, the a posteriori probability $\beta(\zeta)$ is determined.

In a one-stage process, the optimum decision is found by differentiating Eq. (7.7-48) with respect to m_0 and equating the partial derivative to zero. This leads to

$$p_0 r^+ T(x_0 + r^+ T m_0) + (1 - p_0) r^- T(x_0 + r^- T m_0) = 0$$

Hence

$$m_0 = -\frac{D(r)}{D(r^2)} x_0 \tag{7.7-50}$$

where

$$D(r) = p_0 r^+ T + (1 - p_0) r^- T \tag{7.7-51}$$

and

$$D(r^2) = p_0(r^+)^2 T + (1 - p_0)(r^-)^2 T \tag{7.7-52}$$

are functions of ζ. By defining

$$D_i(r) = [p_1 r^+ + (1 - p_1) r^-]T \qquad i = 1, 2 \tag{7.7-53}$$

it can readily be shown that $D(r)$ can be written as

$$D(r) = \zeta D_1(r) + (1 - \zeta) D_2(r) \tag{7.7-54}$$

Similarly, by defining

$$D_i(r^2) = [p_1(r^+)^2 + (1 - p_1)(r^-)^2]T^2 \qquad i = 1, 2 \tag{7.7-55}$$

$D(r^2)$ can be expressed in terms of ζ as

$$D(r^2) = \zeta D_1(r^2) + (1 - \zeta) D_2(r^2) \tag{7.7-56}$$

The minimum for the one-stage process is given by

$$f_1(x_0, \zeta) = W_1(\zeta) x_0^2 \tag{7.7-57}$$

where

$$W_1(\zeta) = 1 - \frac{D^2(r)}{D(r^2)} \tag{7.7-58}$$

By defining

$$g_0(\zeta) = -\frac{D(r)}{D(r^2)} \tag{7.7-59}$$

the optimum decision m_0 may be written as

$$m_0 = g_0(\zeta)x_0 \tag{7.7-60}$$

It can be shown by mathematical induction that

$$f_k(x_0, \zeta) = W_k(\zeta)x_0^2 \tag{7.7-61}$$

In view of Eq. (7.7-61),

$$f_k[x_1^+, \alpha(\zeta)] = W_k[\alpha(\zeta)](x_0 + r^+\tau m_0)^2$$
$$f_k[x_1^-, \beta(\zeta)] = W_k[\beta(\zeta)](x_0 + r^-\tau m_0)^2$$

The minimum for a $(k + 1)$-stage process is

$$f_{k+1}(x_0, \zeta) = \min_{m_0} \{D(\zeta)W_k[\alpha(\zeta)](x_0 + r^+\tau m_0)^2 + [1 - D(\zeta)]W_k[\beta(\zeta)](x_0 + r^-\tau m_0)^2\} \qquad k = 1, 2, \ldots, N - 1 \tag{7.7-62}$$

From this recurrence relationship it is found that the optimum decision is given by

$$m_0 = g_k(\zeta)x_0 \tag{7.7-63}$$

where

$$g_k(\zeta) = -\frac{D[rW_k(\zeta)]}{D[r^2W_k(\zeta)]} \tag{7.7-64}$$

$$D[rW_k(\zeta)] = \zeta D_1[rW_k(\zeta)] + (1 - \zeta)D_2[rW_k(\zeta)] \tag{7.7-65}$$

$$D_i[rW_k(\zeta)] = \{p_i r^+W_k[\alpha(\zeta)] + (1 - p_i)r^-W_k[\beta(\zeta)]\}\tau \qquad i = 1, 2 \tag{7.7-66}$$

$$D[r^2W_k(\zeta)] = \zeta D_1[r^2W_k(\zeta)] + (1 - \zeta)D_2[r^2W_k(\zeta)] \tag{7.7-67}$$

$$D_i[r^2W_k(\zeta)] = \{p_i(r^+)^2W_k[\alpha(\zeta)] + (1 - p_i)(r^-)W_k[\beta(\zeta)]\}\tau^2 \qquad i = 1, 2 \tag{7.7-68}$$

From Eqs. (7.7-62) and (7.7-63) it follows that

$$f_{k+1}(x_0, \zeta) = W_{k+1}(\zeta)x_0^2 \tag{7.7-69}$$

where

$$W_{k+1}(\zeta) = D[W_k(\zeta)] - \frac{D^2[rW_k(\zeta)]}{D[r^2W_k(\zeta)]} \tag{7.7-70}$$

$$D[W_k(\zeta)] = \zeta D_1[W_k(\zeta)] + (1 - \zeta)D_2[W_k(\zeta)] \tag{7.7-71}$$

$$D_i[W_k(\zeta)] = p_iW_k[\alpha(\zeta)] + (1 - p_i)W_k[\beta(\zeta)] \qquad i = 1, 2 \tag{7.7-72}$$

Equations (7.7-57), (7.7-58), (7.7-69), and (7.7-70) are recurrence relationships with which it is possible to evaluate the minimum for an N-stage process $f_N(x_0, \zeta)$.

With the initial state x_0 and initial information ζ, the first optimum decision is

$$m_0 = g_{N-1}(\zeta)x_0 \tag{7.7-73}$$

where $g_{N-1}(\zeta)$ is evaluated from Eqs. (7.7-64) to (7.7-68) and (7.7-70) to (7.7-72), with $k = N - 1$. The second optimum decision should be made after observation of the random variable in the first decision stage. If it is observed that $r = r^+$, the a posteriori probability $\zeta_1 = \alpha(\zeta)$ and the new state

$$x_1^+ = x_0 + r^+ \tau m_0 \tag{7.7-74}$$

are used as the initial information and the initial state for the remaining $N - 1$ stages. The second optimum decision can be determined in similar manner and is given by

$$m_1 = g_{N-2}[\alpha(\zeta)]x_1^+ \tag{7.7-75}$$

If the observed value of r after the first decision is r^-, the a posteriori probability $\beta(\zeta)$ and the new state

$$x_1^- = x_0 + r^- \tau m_0 \tag{7.7-76}$$

are used as the initial information and the initial state for the remaining $N - 1$ stages. The second optimum decision is then given by

$$m_1 = g_{N-2}[\beta(\zeta)]x_1^- \tag{7.7-77}$$

Thus, over the first sampling interval τ, the computer must calculate the a posteriori probability $\alpha(\zeta)$ or $\beta(\zeta)$, the new state x_1, and the second optimum decision m_1.

If the observed value of r after the second decision is r^+, the a posteriori probability $\zeta_2 = \alpha(\zeta_1)$ and the new state

$$x_2^+ = x_1 + r^+ \tau m_1 \tag{7.7-78}$$

are used as the initial information and the initial state for the remaining $N - 2$ stages. In Eq. (7.7-78), if $x_1 = x_1^+$, then $\zeta_1 = \alpha(\zeta)$ and m_1 is given by Eq. (7.7-75); and if $x_1 = x_1^-$, then $\zeta_1 = \beta(\zeta)$ and m_1 is given by Eq. (7.7-77). The third optimum decision can be evaluated in like manner and is given by

$$m_2 = g_{N-3}[\alpha(\zeta_1)]x_2^+ \tag{7.7-79}$$

If the observed value of r after the second decision is r^-, the a posteriori probability $\zeta_2 = \beta(\zeta_1)$ and the new state

$$x_2^- = x_1 + r^- \tau m_1 \tag{7.7-80}$$

are used to determine the third optimum decision, which is

$$m_2 = g_{N-3}[\beta(\zeta_1)]x_2^- \tag{7.7-81}$$

By repeated observation and computation in the above manner, the optimum-control policy $\{m_0, m_1, \ldots, m_{N-1}\}$ for this landing system can be determined. Each new optimum decision is made by using new information resulting from the observation of the random variable.

Now assume that $h(0) = 300$ ft, $\dot{h}(0) = -10$ ft/sec, $T = 100$ sec, $\tau = 5$ sec, $N = 20$, $r^+ = \frac{20}{3}$ ft/sec, $r^- = -\frac{20}{3}$ ft/sec, $p_1 = 0.3$, $p_2 = 0.4$,

$\zeta = 0.8$. The amplitude distribution of random variable r is shown in Fig. 7.7-1. The minimum of the performance index is found to be

$$f_{20}(x_0, \zeta) = 5.5 \text{ ft}^2/\text{sec}^2$$

By following the above procedure the optimum-control signal and the corresponding trajectory are determined and are plotted in Figs. 7.7-2 and 7.7-3, respectively.

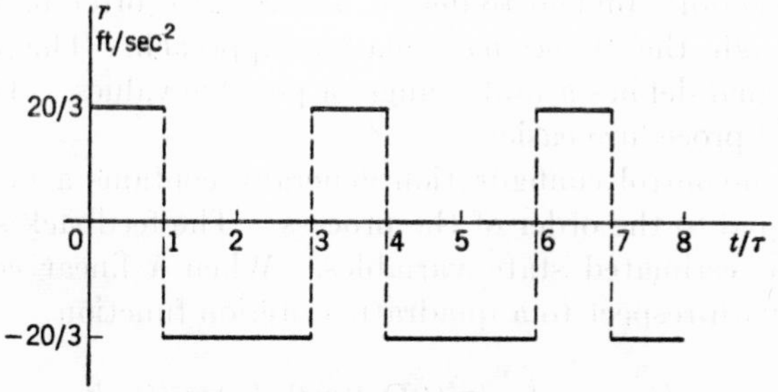

Fig. 7.7-1 Amplitude distribution of the random variable.

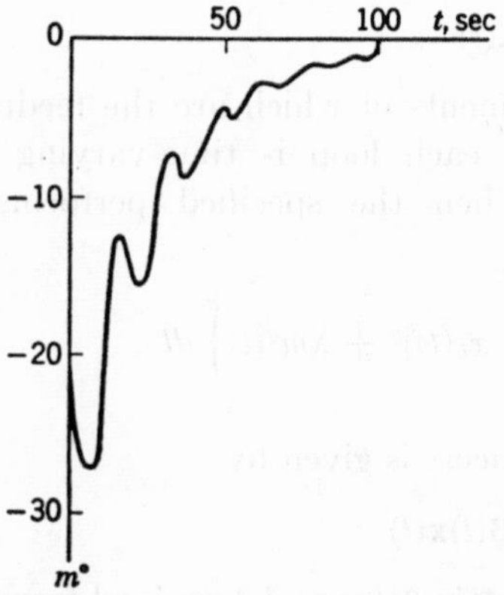

Fig. 7.7-2 Optimum-control signal.

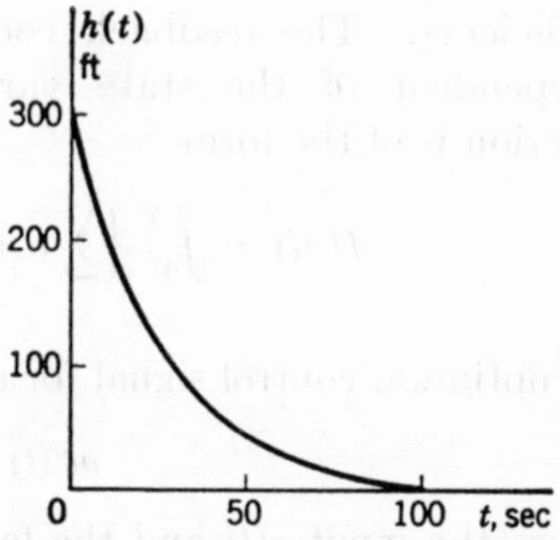

Fig. 7.7-3 The optimum trajectory.

7.8 CONCLUSION

This chapter attempts to present the basic theory of dynamic programming and its application to control-system design. The principle of optimality is discussed, and the functional-equation approach is reviewed. Following the formal analysis, the optimum-control problem can be reduced to the determination of the solution of the Hamilton-Jacobi equation. The functional-equation approach of dynamic programming provides a way of obtaining the computational solution of the optimization problem which does not depend upon the solution of the partial differential equation, thus circumventing the difficulties with the two-point boundary-value problem.

The design of minimum-integral control processes is studied in some detail. The principle of optimality is applied to the derivation of the partial differential equations describing the optimum-control signals. The constraints on control signals are considered in the optimum design. For control processes of moderate complexity, a solution to the partial differential equation is generally difficult to derive, and resort is often had to numerical analysis through the functional-equation approach. The constraint on the control signal defines a finite range of possible values. This makes the computational procedure easier.

An optimum-control configuration generally contains a number of feedback loops equal to the order of the process. The feedback signals are the measurable or estimated state variables. When a linear control process is optimized with respect to a quadratic criterion function

$$I(m) = \int_0^T [\mathbf{x}'(t)\mathbf{Q}(t)\mathbf{x}(t) + \lambda m^2(t)]\, dt$$

the optimum law is found to be

$$m^o(t) = \boldsymbol{\beta}(t)\mathbf{x}(t)$$

where $\boldsymbol{\beta}(t)$ is the feedback matrix the elements of which are the feedback coefficients. The feedback coefficient in each loop is time-varying but independent of the state variables. When the specified performance criterion is of the form

$$I(m) = \int_0^T \left\{\sum_k \alpha_k(t)[x_k{}^d(t) - x_k(t)]^2 + \lambda m^2(t)\right\} dt$$

the optimum-control signal for a linear process is given by

$$m^o(t) = r(t) + \boldsymbol{\beta}(t)\mathbf{x}(t)$$

where the input $r(t)$ and the feedback matrix $\boldsymbol{\beta}(t)$ are determined from the solution to the Riccatian equations. The solution can be obtained with the aid of a digital computer. The design of an aircraft landing system is carried out for illustration.

Both terminal-control and time-optimal-control problems are investigated by use of the dynamic-programming technique. The functional-equation approach is applied to derive the recurrence relationships which are required for the evaluation of the optimum-control signals to minimize the performance-criterion functions

$$I(m) = G[x_1(T), x_2(T), \ldots, x_l(T)]$$

and

$$I(m) = \boldsymbol{\alpha}'\mathbf{x}(T)$$

An analytical solution to the terminal-control problem is generally not easy to derive, and numerical procedures should be followed. Application of the principle of optimality to the minimum-time-control problems leads to the Euler-Lagrange differential equation describing the optimum-control signals. When the process is subject to additive-control signals which are restricted to the upper and lower limits, it is readily shown that the optimum-control signals have their magnitudes equal to the maximum permissible values and the signs determined by the sign of a switching function.

This chapter concludes with a discussion of the design of adaptive and learning control processes. The design of such processes is carried out on the basis of the Bayes theorem and the functional-equation approach of dynamic programming. The adaptation and learning process consists in gathering information about the random variable and processing this information according to some decision rule. The decisions resulting from the information processing are used to improve the control, which is chosen initially according to an a priori distribution. Certain information patterns are derived by making a number of observations of the random variables. On the basis of the information pattern, the adaptive controller can determine the correct probability distribution through the process of learning. An aircraft landing system is used to illustrate the design procedure.

Although the dynamic-programming approach provides a systematic computational procedure, it does not necessarily remove any computational difficulties. Multistage decision processes of high dimension cannot be solved in a routine manner because of the unwieldiness of the storage requirements involved in the computation.

References

Suggested references are Aoki,[1–5] Aris,[6] Bellman,[14–20,22] Bellman and Kalaba,[25,26] Desoer,[48] Dreyfus,[52,53] Ellert and Merriam,[54] Freimer,[57] Grishin,[71a] Guignabodet,[72] Joseph and Tou,[82] Kallay,[83,84] Krug and Letskii,[100] Leitmann,[112] Lewis and Tou,[115] Merriam,[118,119] Miele and Cappelleri,[120] Rozonoer,[134] Tou,[137,140,141a] Tou and Fu,[143] Tou and Joseph,[144,145] Tou and Lewis,[146] and Tou and Wilcox.[148]

8

COMPUTER CONTROL THEORY

The technology of automatic control experienced its earliest rapid growth during World War II and the decade following. Throughout this period control-system design followed closely the feedback-amplifier technology. The classical design of control systems ordinarily involves the selection of appropriate compensating networks for insertion within the feedback system in order to obtain satisfactory performance of the overall system. Confronted with difficult control problems, the engineer turns eagerly to the computer tool, but initially often with little success, since the conventional design theories do not indicate how the added flexibility of the digital computer could be effectively utilized to solve complex problems. Based upon the classical control theory, application of digital techniques often involves little more than the realization of classical lead or lag compensating networks by logical elements or by a digital computer. To utilize fully the digital techniques in solving difficult control problems, the engineer has recourse to modern approaches in order to achieve greater success in optimum design. Current trends in control-system theory reflect the ability to use digital computers to obtain numerical solutions to complex problems. As the reliability of digital computers increases and their size, weight, and cost decrease, the trend toward the use of special-purpose digital computers as an integral part of control systems to process a large amount of data and to implement complex control laws is a natural outcome. With the availability of digital computers and digital controllers, the design of control systems can take into consideration more realistic aspects than was possible in the past. It is conceivable that many control systems designed in the

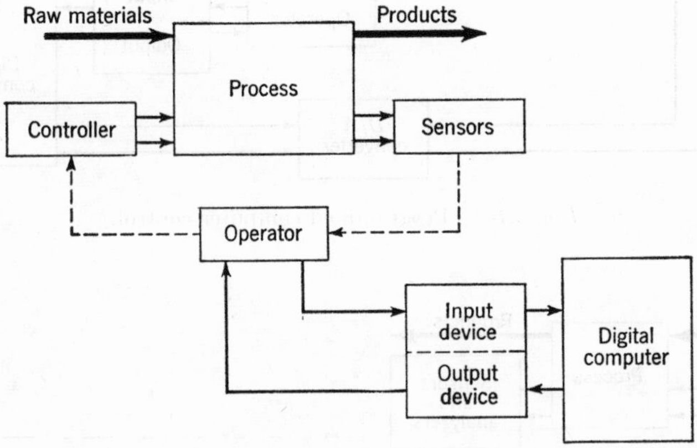

Fig. 8.1-1 Off-line computer control.

future will incorporate special-purpose digital computers as control-system components. The optimum design of computer control systems is the central topic of discussion in this chapter.

8.1 COMPUTER–CONTROL APPROACH

Digital computers can be used to control a process or plant in a number of ways. The possible approaches range from periodic off-line calculations to real-time closed-loop control. An off-line application of a digital computer to process control is illustrated in Fig. 8.1-1. In an off-line computer control of this kind, readings from process instruments and results from laboratory analyses are gathered by an operator for use in control calculations. The calculated results then serve as the basis for adjustments of process conditions. The off-line computer-control scheme may be sufficient if the process will undergo slow changes.

A digital computer may be used as a program controller, as shown in Fig. 8.1-2. The computer receives its information from an operator, but it is connected to the process so that it may exercise direct control. This approach results in a program-controlled system. Figure 8.1-3 depicts a scheme in which a digital computer is used as a data logger and operating-guide calculator. The sensing devices of the process are connected via

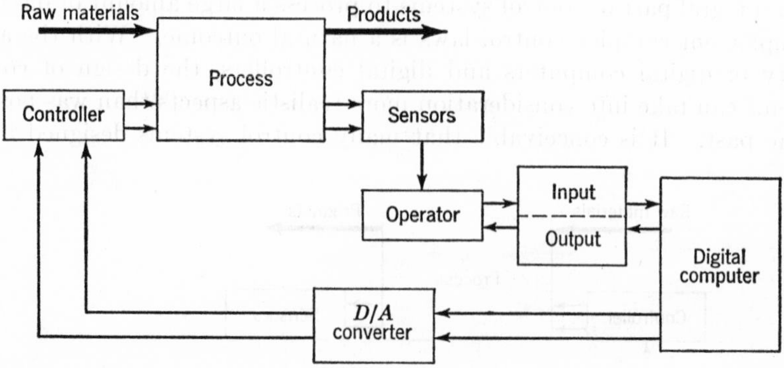

Fig. 8.1-2 Programmed computer control.

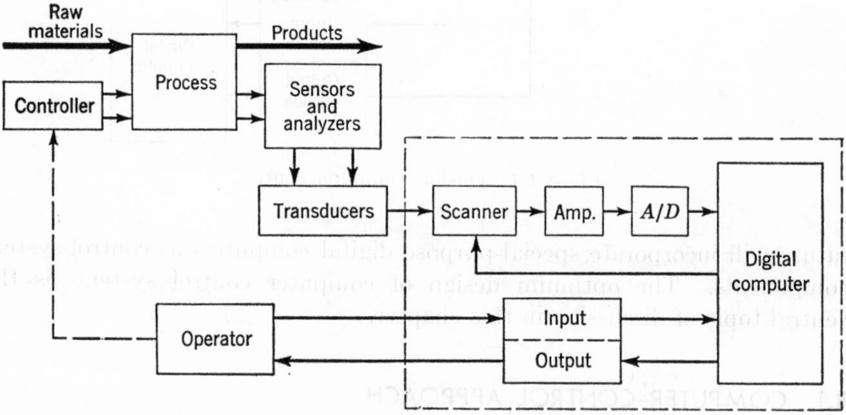

Fig. 8.1-3 Computer used as data logger and operating guide.

converters to the computer in this control system. The converters change the original signals into a form acceptable to the computer. The computer outputs are raw process data or functions of the original readings, such as yields or efficiencies, which may help the operator to adjust the process to a better set of conditions. This scheme is useful when process relationships are being established.

By far the most desirable computer control system is the real-time closed-loop computer control system, as shown in Fig. 8.1-4. The computer reads the process instruments, calculates the best operating conditions, and resets the process controllers automatically. In normal operations, the operator receives data on performance of the process-computer system via a typewriter or special output devices and can modify system operation by inserting new constants or complete programs via a tape reader or other input devices. In emergency operation, the operator can assume control, running

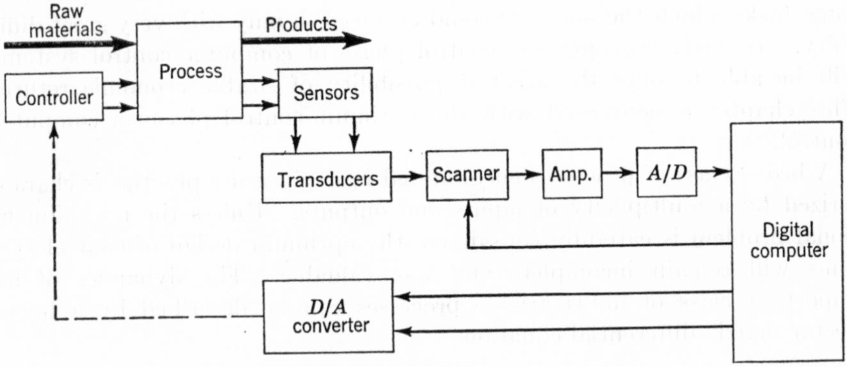

Fig. 8.1-4 A real-time computer control system.

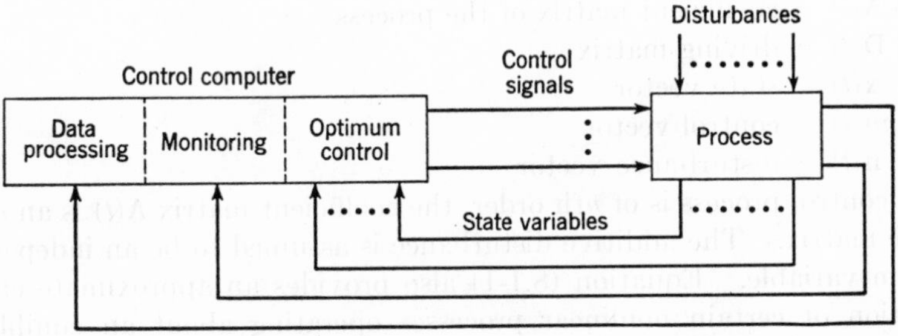

Fig. 8.1-5 Block diagram of a computer control system.

the process in the same way as before installation of the computer. Closed-loop computer control systems become distinctly valuable when process changes occur so frequently and the adjustments and decisions to be made depend on such complex relationships that a human operator cannot respond correctly in the time available. Rapid changes in raw-material characteristics and chemical compositions, random disturbances, ignorance of process dynamics, and conflicting objectives make it difficult or even impossible for any human operator to achieve continuously the kind of performance he might be able to realize occasionally. The digital computer in the control system usually performs the functions of monitoring, data processing, and optimum control, as summarized in Fig. 8.1-5. In the monitoring phase, the computer accomplishes such operations as scanning, alarming, diagnosis, and supervisory control. In the data-processing phase, the computer carries out such operations as data acquisition, data logging, performance calculation, and display. In the optimum-control phase, the computer determines the control laws and makes the optimal decisions so as to achieve system optimization. It is interesting to note that both the monitoring and the data-processing phases represent the direct mechanization of the operator's tasks; however, the optimum-control phase performs some tasks which the operator could accomplish only with very great difficulty. In fact, the optimum-control phase of computer control systems will be able to offer the greatest possibility of sizable economic return. This chapter is concerned with the optimum-control phase in computer control.[139,140,145]

A broad class of processes encountered in engineering practice is characterized by a multiplicity of inputs and outputs. Unless the multidimensional problem is carefully considered, the optimum design of control systems will remain incomplete and less valuable. The dynamics of an important class of multivariable processes can be described by a linear vector-matrix differential equation

$$\dot{\mathbf{x}}(t) = \mathbf{A}(t)\mathbf{x}(t) + \mathbf{D}(t)\mathbf{m}(t) + \mathbf{n}(t) \tag{8.1-1}$$

where $\mathbf{A}(t)$ = coefficient matrix of the process
$\mathbf{D}(t)$ = driving matrix
$\mathbf{x}(t)$ = state vector
$\mathbf{m}(t)$ = control vector
$\mathbf{n}(t)$ = disturbance vector

If the control process is of nth order, the coefficient matrix $\mathbf{A}(t)$ is an $n \times n$ square matrix. The additive disturbance is assumed to be an independent random variable. Equation (8.1-1) also provides an approximate characterization of certain nonlinear processes operating about an equilibrium state. It has been shown in Sec. 2.4 that the solution to Eq. (8.1-1) is

$$\mathbf{x}(t) = \boldsymbol{\phi}(t, t_0)\mathbf{x}(t_0) + \int_{t_0}^{t} \boldsymbol{\phi}(t, \tau)[\mathbf{D}(\tau)\mathbf{m}(\tau) + \mathbf{n}(\tau)]\, d\tau \tag{8.1-2}$$

where $\boldsymbol{\phi}(t, t_0)$ is referred to as the transition matrix and satisfies the homogeneous differential equation

$$\frac{d\boldsymbol{\phi}(t, t_0)}{dt} = \mathbf{A}(t)\boldsymbol{\phi}(t, t_0) \tag{8.1-3}$$

and the relationship

$$\boldsymbol{\phi}(t_0, t_0) = \mathbf{I} \tag{8.1-4}$$

which is the identity matrix. In computer control systems, $m(\tau) = m(kT)$

for $kT < \tau \leq (k+1)T$, and the solution expressed in discrete form is given by the state-transition equation

$$\mathbf{x}(k+1) = \boldsymbol{\phi}(k)\mathbf{x}(k) + \mathbf{G}(k)\mathbf{m}(k) + \mathbf{u}(k) \tag{8.1-5}$$

where

$$\boldsymbol{\phi}(k) = \boldsymbol{\phi}(\overline{k+1}\,T, kT) \tag{8.1-6}$$

$$\mathbf{G}(k) = \int_{kT}^{(k+1)T} \boldsymbol{\phi}(\overline{k+1}\,T, \tau)\mathbf{D}(\tau)\,d\tau \tag{8.1-7}$$

$$\mathbf{u}(k) = \int_{kT}^{(k+1)T} \boldsymbol{\phi}(\overline{k+1}\,T, \tau)\mathbf{n}(\tau)\,d\tau \tag{8.1-8}$$

In Eq. (8.1-5), the sampling period T is dropped for the sake of convenience.

As discussed in the preceding chapters, an important step in the optimum design of control systems is the formulation of a performance index which, to a large extent, determines the nature of the resulting optimum control. The resulting control scheme may be linear, nonlinear, stationary, or time-varying, depending upon the form of the performance index. Consequently, the control engineer can influence the characteristics of the resulting system by the manner in which he formulates the performance index based upon the requirements of the problem at hand. These requirements generally include not only the performance specifications, but also any restrictions on the form of the optimum control to ensure physical realizability. The performance index of interest in the following discussion on computer control systems is of the quadratic form defined below:

$$I_N = \sum_{k=1}^{N} [\mathbf{x}'(k)\mathbf{Q}(k)\mathbf{x}(k) + \lambda\mathbf{m}'(k-1)\mathbf{H}(k-1)\mathbf{m}(k-1)] \tag{8.1-9a}$$

or, more generally,

$$I_N = \sum_{k=1}^{N} \{[\mathbf{x}^d(k) - \mathbf{x}(k)]'\mathbf{Q}(k)[\mathbf{x}^d(k) - \mathbf{x}(k)] + \lambda\mathbf{m}'(k-1)\mathbf{H}(k-1)\mathbf{m}(k-1)\} \tag{8.1-9b}$$

where $\mathbf{x}^d(k)$ = desired state vector
$\mathbf{Q}, \mathbf{H}$ = positive-definite symmetric matrices
λ = a constant multiplier

The choice of a positive-definite matrix guarantees the uniqueness and linearity of the control law and asymptotic stability of the control system for a controllable plant. The quadratic performance criterion has the advantage that it leads generally to a workable analysis.

The expansion of Eq. (8.1-9*b*) leads to a weighted sum of squares of the error $x_j^d - x_j$ and the control signals m_j, with the weighting determined by the elements of matrices **Q** and **H**. For instance, if **Q** and **H** are unity matrices, the weighting factors are unity. The first term on the right-hand side of Eq. (8.1-9*b*) may be used to specify the deviation of the process from the desired condition at any time kT, and the second term provides an energy constraint on the control signals. The first term is a representation of economic penalties arising from response errors, and the second term may be regarded as the cost of control. The multiplier λ may be considered as a penalty factor. The addition of the second term provides a mathematically convenient way to ensure against saturating the control signals. The multiplier λ can be determined directly from engineering considerations. It may be chosen so that the square of the control signal is less than the certain limit where saturation occurs.

The quadratic performance index given above is quite versatile. By suitably changing the elements of matrix $\mathbf{Q}$ any one state variable of the process can be made more important and effective in specifying the control-system performance than any other item describing the operating condition. In like manner, by choosing the appropriate elements for $\mathbf{H}$, the desired energy constraints may be imposed upon the corresponding control signals. Furthermore, Eqs. (8.1-9) describe a time-weighted performance criterion when the matrices $\mathbf{Q}$ and $\mathbf{H}$ are functions of k. The quadratic performance index may be used to synthesize terminal control systems. Such a system attempts to reduce a functional of system error or state variables to zero at the terminal point of the optimum trajectory. Equation (8.1-9*a*) or (8.1-9*b*) can be used as the performance index for a terminal control system, provided that the matrix $\mathbf{Q}$ is a diagonal matrix and the diagonal elements of $\mathbf{Q}$ are either impulse functions or zero.

The optimum-control problem is then formulated as follows:

Determine the control law or control policy, $\{\mathbf{m}(j)\}$, $j = 0, 1, 2, \ldots,$ $N - 1$, which will minimize the expected value of the performance index specified by Eqs. (8.1-9) subject to the relationship of Eq. (8.1-5), for any arbitrary initial state $\mathbf{x}(0)$, and other performance requirements and physical constraints. Because of the uncertainties involved in the random disturbance, it is not appropriate to minimize the performance index I_N. The expected value of I_N is a convenient measure of the performance, although it represents a less exact measure.

Clearly, when the optimum-control problem is formulated as above, it may be viewed as an N-stage decision process. The dynamic-programming technique appears to be a logical approach and a powerful tool for the design of optimum computer control. The optimum design involves, in essence, the determination of the sequence of control vectors

$$\mathbf{m}(0), \mathbf{m}(1), \mathbf{m}(2), \ldots, \mathbf{m}(N-1) \tag{8.1-10}$$

so that the expected value of the performance index I_N is minimized. These control vectors may be considered as the successive decisions which are made during the course of optimum control. This is the same type of N-stage decision process as discussed in Sec. 7.2. Here the state-transition equation is analogous to the transformation function

$$\mathbf{x}^k = g(\mathbf{x}^{k-1}, \mathbf{m}^{k-1}) \tag{8.1-11}$$

and the performance index given by Eq. (8.1-9) may be likened to the return function

$$R = \sum_{j=1}^{N} r(\mathbf{x}^j, \mathbf{m}^j) \tag{8.1-12}$$

It is observed that the minimum of EI_N depends upon the initial state $\mathbf{x}(0)$ and the number of stages N. The symbol E denotes the expected-value operator. This chapter is concerned with the optimum design of computer control systems by the method of dynamic programming.

8.2 TIME-INVARIANT CONTROL PROCESSES

This section is devoted to the study of computer control for time-invariant processes. It is assumed that all the state variables of the process are accessible for measurement and observation. The optimum-control law for a linear time-invariant process is determined to fulfill a quadratic performance criterion. Since the optimal computer control problem may be viewed as a multistage decision process, the determination of the optimum-control law is best carried out by means of the dynamic-programming technique.[137,141a,144]

Consider an nth-order linear process described by the vector-matrix differential equation

$$\dot{\mathbf{x}}(t) = \mathbf{A}\mathbf{x}(t) + \mathbf{D}m(t) \tag{8.2-1}$$

The control process is assumed to be time-invariant, and the external random disturbance is ignored. The design of digital control systems is generally initiated with the characterization of the process dynamics in discrete form. The dynamic equations of the process defined in Eq. (8.2-1) may be converted to the discrete version by using the relationship

$$x_i(\overline{k+1}\,T) = x_i(kT) + Tx_{i+1}(kT) \tag{8.2-2}$$

where x_i denotes the state variables of the process, $\dot{x}_i = x_{i+1}$, $i = 1, 2, 3, \ldots, n$, and T is the chosen sampling period. The linear process may also be characterized in discrete form by the state-transition equation

$$\mathbf{x}(k+1) = \boldsymbol{\phi}(1)\mathbf{x}(k) + \mathbf{h}(1)m(k) \tag{8.2-3}$$

where the sampling period T is dropped for simplicity. It is noted that Eq. (8.2-3) is reducible to the discrete version of Eq. (8.2-1) resulting from the application of Eq. (8.2-2), if the transition matrix $\boldsymbol{\phi}$ is expanded into a power series and approximated by the first two terms. The design problem in this section is concerned with the determination of the optimum-control law which minimizes a quadratic performance index of the form

$$I_N = \sum_{k=1}^{N} [\mathbf{x}'(k)\mathbf{Q}\mathbf{x}(k) + \lambda m^2(k-1)] \tag{8.2-4}$$

for a specified initial state $\mathbf{x}(0)$, and subject to the relationship given in Eq. (8.2-3) or the discrete version of Eq. (8.2-1). The optimum design with respect to the performance index defined in Eq. (8.1-9*b*) can be carried out in like manner, and is thus left to the reader as an exercise.

Let the minimum value of performance index I_N be denoted by

$$f_N[\mathbf{x}(0)] = \min_{\substack{m(0)\\ m(1)\\ \cdots\cdots\\ m(N-1)}} \sum_{k=1}^{N} [\mathbf{x}'(k)\mathbf{Q}\mathbf{x}(k) + \lambda m^2(k-1)] \tag{8.2-5}$$

Putting this into a more general form yields the minimum value for the last $N - j$ stages of the N-stage process given by

$$f_{N-j}[\mathbf{x}(j)] = \min_{\substack{m(j)\\ m(j+1)\\ \cdots\cdots\\ m(N-1)}} \sum_{k=j+1}^{N} [\mathbf{x}'(k)\mathbf{Q}\mathbf{x}(k) + \lambda m^2(k-1)]$$

$$j = 0, 1, 2, \ldots, N-1 \tag{8.2-6}$$

When $j = 0$, Eq. (8.2-6) reduces to Eq. (8.2-5), and it is apparent that

$$f_0[\mathbf{x}(0)] = 0 \tag{8.2-7}$$

Suppose that the return from the first $j - 1$ stages is optimum. Then the output of the remaining $N - j$ stages is equal to the output from the jth stage plus the optimum output from the remaining $N - \overline{j+1}$ stages; that is, the output is

$$[\mathbf{x}'(j+1)\mathbf{Q}\mathbf{x}(j+1) + \lambda m^2(j)] + f_{N-\overline{j+1}}[\mathbf{x}(j+1)] \tag{8.2-8}$$

Invoking the principle of optimality reduces Eq. (8.2-6) to

$$f_{N-j}[\mathbf{x}(j)] = \min_{m(j)} \{\mathbf{x}'(j+1)\mathbf{Q}\mathbf{x}(j+1) + \lambda m^2(j) + f_{N-\overline{j+1}}[\mathbf{x}(j+1)]\} \tag{8.2-9}$$

Starting with $f_0[\mathbf{x}(N)] = 0$, there follows

$$f_1[\mathbf{x}(N-1)] = \min_{m(N-1)} \{\mathbf{x}'(N)\mathbf{Q}\mathbf{x}(N) + \lambda m^2(N-1)\} \tag{8.2-10}$$

$$f_2[\mathbf{x}(N-2)] = \min_{m(N-2)} \{\mathbf{x}'(N-1)\mathbf{Q}\mathbf{x}(N-1) + \lambda m^2(N-2) + f_1[\mathbf{x}(N-1)]\} \tag{8.2-11}$$

$$\cdots\cdots\cdots\cdots\cdots\cdots\cdots\cdots\cdots\cdots\cdots\cdots$$

$$f_N[\mathbf{x}(0)] = \min_{m(0)} \{\mathbf{x}'(1)\mathbf{Q}\mathbf{x}(1) + \lambda m^2(0) + f_{N-1}[\mathbf{x}(1)]\} \tag{8.2-12}$$

Since the functional f is quadratic in $\mathbf{x}$, it can be shown by mathematical induction that both f_{N-j} and $f_{N-\overline{j+1}}$ are expressible in quadratic forms. Assume that

$$f_{N-j}[\mathbf{x}(j)] = \mathbf{x}'(j)\mathbf{P}(N-j)\mathbf{x}(j) \tag{8.2-13}$$

and

$$f_{N-\overline{j+1}}[\mathbf{x}(j+1)] = \mathbf{x}'(j+1)\mathbf{P}(N-\overline{j+1})\mathbf{x}(j+1) \tag{8.2-14}$$

where $\mathbf{P}$'s are $n \times n$ symmetrical matrices which are used to express Eqs. (8.2-13) and (8.2-14) in quadratic form. Then, by substitution, the following relationship is formed:

$$\mathbf{x}'(j)\mathbf{P}(N-j)\mathbf{x}(j) = \min_{m(j)} \{\mathbf{x}'(j+1)\mathbf{S}(N-\overline{j+1})\mathbf{x}(j+1) + \lambda m^2(j)\} \tag{8.2-15}$$

where

$$\mathbf{S}(N-\overline{j+1}) = \mathbf{Q} + \mathbf{P}(N-\overline{j+1}) \tag{8.2-16}$$

In view of Eqs. (8.2-3) and (8.2-13), the functional $f_{N-j}[\mathbf{x}(j)]$ may be written as

$$\begin{aligned} f_{N-j}[\mathbf{x}(j)] &= \mathbf{x}'(j)\mathbf{P}(N-j)\mathbf{x}(j) \\ &= \min_{m(j)} \{[\boldsymbol{\phi}(1)\mathbf{x}(j) + \mathbf{h}(1)m(j)]'\mathbf{S}(N-\overline{j+1}) \\ &\qquad \times [\boldsymbol{\phi}(1)\mathbf{x}(j) + \mathbf{h}(1)m(j)] + \lambda m^2(j)\} \end{aligned} \tag{8.2-17}$$

Since the N-stage decision process has been reduced to a sequence of N single-stage decision processes, the minimization procedure may be readily carried out through ordinary differentiation. Taking the derivative of the functions inside the braces with respect to $m(j)$ and equating it to zero leads to

$$\begin{aligned} 2[\mathbf{h}'(1)\mathbf{S}(N-\overline{j+1})\mathbf{h}(1) + \lambda]m(j) &+ \mathbf{h}'(1)\mathbf{S}(N-\overline{j+1})\boldsymbol{\phi}(1)\mathbf{x}(j) \\ &+ \mathbf{x}'(j)\boldsymbol{\phi}(1)\mathbf{S}(N-\overline{j+1})\mathbf{h}(1) = 0 \end{aligned} \tag{8.2-18}$$

Making use of the symmetry property of the $\mathbf{S}$ matrix and simplifying yields

$$[\mathbf{h}'(1)\mathbf{S}(N-\overline{j+1})\mathbf{h}(1) + \lambda]m(j) = \mathbf{h}'(1)\mathbf{S}(N-\overline{j+1})\boldsymbol{\phi}(1)\mathbf{x}(j) \tag{8.2-19}$$

Hence the optimum-control law or strategy for the given control problem is

$$m^o(j) = \mathbf{B}(N-j)\mathbf{x}(j) \tag{8.2-20}$$

where

$$\mathbf{B}(N-j) = -\frac{\mathbf{h}'(1)[\mathbf{Q} + \mathbf{P}(N-\overline{j+1})]\boldsymbol{\phi}(1)}{\mathbf{h}'(1)[\mathbf{Q} + \mathbf{P}(N-\overline{j+1})]\mathbf{h}(1) + \lambda} \tag{8.2-21}$$

It is to be noted that the optimum-control law is a linear function of the state variables, and the feedback control system is a time-varying system. The feedback matrix $\mathbf{B}$ varies with time. For $j = N - 1$,

$$\mathbf{B}(1) = -\frac{\mathbf{h}'(1)\mathbf{Q}\boldsymbol{\phi}(1)}{\mathbf{h}'(1)\mathbf{Q}\mathbf{h}(1) + \lambda} \tag{8.2-22}$$

since $\mathbf{P}(0) = \mathbf{0}$. Similarly, for $j = N - 2, N - 3, \ldots, 0$, the feedback matrices are

$$\mathbf{B}(2) = -\frac{\mathbf{h}'(1)[\mathbf{Q} + \mathbf{P}(1)]\boldsymbol{\phi}(1)}{\mathbf{h}'(1)[\mathbf{Q} + \mathbf{P}(1)]\mathbf{h}(1) + \lambda} \tag{8.2-23}$$

$$\mathbf{B}(3) = -\frac{\mathbf{h}'(1)[\mathbf{Q} + \mathbf{P}(2)]\boldsymbol{\phi}(1)}{\mathbf{h}'(1)[\mathbf{Q} + \mathbf{P}(2)]\mathbf{h}(1) + \lambda} \tag{8.2-24}$$

$$\cdots\cdots\cdots\cdots\cdots\cdots\cdots\cdots$$

$$\mathbf{B}(j) = -\frac{\mathbf{h}'(1)[\mathbf{Q} + \mathbf{P}(j-1)]\boldsymbol{\phi}(1)}{\mathbf{h}'(1)[\mathbf{Q} + \mathbf{P}(j-1)]\mathbf{h}(1) + \lambda} \tag{8.2-25}$$

$$\cdots\cdots\cdots\cdots\cdots\cdots\cdots\cdots$$

$$\mathbf{B}(N) = -\frac{\mathbf{h}'(1)[\mathbf{Q} + \mathbf{P}(N-1)]\boldsymbol{\phi}(1)}{\mathbf{h}'(1)[\mathbf{Q} + \mathbf{P}(N-1)]\mathbf{h}(1) + \lambda} \tag{8.2-26}$$

The feedback matrices can be readily evaluated if the recurrence relationship for the $\mathbf{P}$ matrices is determined. Substituting Eq. (8.2-20) into the right-hand side of Eq. (8.2-17) yields the minimum value as

$$\begin{aligned}\mathbf{x}'(j)\mathbf{P}(N-j)\mathbf{x}(j) &\\ = \mathbf{x}'(j)[\boldsymbol{\phi}(1) + \mathbf{h}(1)\mathbf{B}(N-j)]'\mathbf{S}(N - \overline{j+1})\,&[\boldsymbol{\phi}(1) + \mathbf{h}(1)\mathbf{B}(N-j)]\mathbf{x}(j)\\ &+ \lambda\mathbf{x}'(j)\mathbf{B}'(N-j)\mathbf{B}(N-j)\mathbf{x}(j)\end{aligned} \tag{8.2-27}$$

Comparing both sides of Eq. (8.2-27) leads to

$$\begin{aligned}\mathbf{P}(N-j) &\\ = [\boldsymbol{\phi}(1) + \mathbf{h}(1)\mathbf{B}(N-j)]'[\mathbf{Q} + \mathbf{P}(N - \overline{j+1})]\,&[\boldsymbol{\phi}(1) + \mathbf{h}(1)\mathbf{B}(N-j)]\\ &+ \lambda\mathbf{B}'(N-j)\mathbf{B}(N-j)\end{aligned} \tag{8.2-28}$$

which is the desired recurrence relationship for the determination of the $\mathbf{P}$ matrices. This recurrence relationship, together with Eq. (8.2-21), provides a computational algorithm for the evaluation of the feedback matrix $\mathbf{B}(N-j)$, which, in turn, determines the optimum-control law. Starting with $\mathbf{P}(0) = \mathbf{0}$, repeated application of the recurrence relationships given in Eqs. (8.2-21) and (8.2-28) yields $\mathbf{B}(1)$, $\mathbf{P}(1)$, $\mathbf{B}(2)$, $\mathbf{P}(2)$, etc. For instance, substituting Eq. (8.2-22) into Eq. (8.2-28) with $j = N - 1$ gives $\mathbf{P}(1)$, which determines $\mathbf{B}(2)$ upon substituting into Eq. (8.2-23). The matrix $\mathbf{P}(2)$ is then obtained by the substitution of Eq. (8.2-23) into Eq. (8.2-28) with $j = N - 2$. The other values of the $\mathbf{B}$ and $\mathbf{P}$ matrices may be determined in like manner. In a computer control system the above computational algorithm is programmed on the digital computer of the system to generate a sequence of optimum-control signals.

With reference to the performance index defined in Eq. (8.2-4), when $N \to \infty$, the control process becomes an infinite-stage process. Equation (8.2-9) reduces to

$$f[\mathbf{x}(j)] = \min_{m(j)} \{\mathbf{x}'(j+1)\mathbf{Q}\mathbf{x}(j+1) + \lambda m^2(j) + f[\mathbf{x}(j+1)]\} \tag{8.2-29}$$

Letting

$$f[\mathbf{x}(j)] = \mathbf{x}'(j)\mathbf{P}\mathbf{x}(j) \tag{8.2-30}$$

$$f[\mathbf{x}(j+1)] = \mathbf{x}'(j+1)\mathbf{P}\mathbf{x}(j+1) \tag{8.2-31}$$

where the matrix $\mathbf{P}$ is invariant in j, it can be shown, by following the same argument as above, that the optimum-control law is given by

$$m^o(j) = \mathbf{B}\mathbf{x}(j) \tag{8.2-32}$$

where the feedback matrix is

$$\mathbf{B} = -\frac{\mathbf{h}'(1)[\mathbf{Q} + \mathbf{P}]\boldsymbol{\phi}(1)}{\mathbf{h}'(1)[\mathbf{Q} + \mathbf{P}]\mathbf{h}(1) + \lambda} \tag{8.2-33}$$

and where the $\mathbf{P}$ matrix may be determined from the following equation:

$$\begin{aligned} \mathbf{P} - [\boldsymbol{\phi}(1) + \mathbf{h}(1)\mathbf{B}]'\mathbf{P}[\boldsymbol{\phi}(1) + \mathbf{h}(1)\mathbf{B}] \\ = [\boldsymbol{\phi}(1) + \mathbf{h}(1)\mathbf{B}]'\mathbf{Q}[\boldsymbol{\phi}(1) + \mathbf{h}(1)\mathbf{B}] + \lambda\mathbf{B}'\mathbf{B} \end{aligned} \tag{8.2-34}$$

Since the feedback matrix $\mathbf{B}$ is a constant row matrix independent of the sequence, the feedback control system remains time-invariant.

The above discussions are concerned with the optimum design of computer control, which is restricted to linear processes subject to only one control signal. In fact, the above design procedure can be readily extended to control processes subject to a multitude of control signals. Consider the linear multidimensional control process characterized by the vector-matrix equation

$$\dot{\mathbf{x}}(t) = \mathbf{A}\mathbf{x}(t) + \mathbf{D}\mathbf{m}(t) \tag{8.2-35}$$

where $\mathbf{x}$ = an n-vector representing the state variables
$\mathbf{m}$ = an r-vector representing the control signals
$\mathbf{A}$ = an $n \times n$ coefficient matrix
$\mathbf{D}$ = an $n \times r$ driving matrix

The state-transition equation describing this process is given by

$$\mathbf{x}(k+1) = \boldsymbol{\phi}(1)\mathbf{x}(k) + \mathbf{h}(1)\mathbf{m}(k) \tag{8.2-36}$$

where the sampling period T is dropped for simplicity. Assume that the performance index is given by

$$I_N = \sum_{k=1}^{N} \mathbf{x}'(k)\mathbf{Q}\mathbf{x}(k) \tag{8.2-37}$$

Following the previous argument, the optimum-control law is obtained as

$$\mathbf{m}^o(j) = \mathbf{B}(N-j)\mathbf{x}(j) \tag{8.2-38}$$

where the feedback matrix $\mathbf{B}(N-j)$ is

$$\begin{aligned} \mathbf{B}(N-j) = -[\mathbf{h}'(1)\{\mathbf{Q} + \mathbf{P}(N - \overline{j+1})\}\mathbf{h}(1)]^{-1} \\ \times [\mathbf{h}'(1)\{\mathbf{Q} + \mathbf{P}(N - \overline{j+1})\}\boldsymbol{\phi}(1)] \end{aligned} \tag{8.2-39}$$

The recurrence relation for $\mathbf{P}(N-j)$ is found to be

$$\mathbf{P}(N-j) = [\boldsymbol{\phi}(1) + \mathbf{h}(1)\mathbf{B}(N-j)]'[\mathbf{Q} + \mathbf{P}(N-\overline{j+1})] [\boldsymbol{\phi}(1) + \mathbf{h}(1)\mathbf{B}(N-j)] \tag{8.2-40}$$

As in the case of single-input systems, starting with $\mathbf{P}(0) = \mathbf{0}$, repeated application of the recurrence relationships defined in Eqs. (8.2-39) and (8.2-40) yields successively the matrices $\mathbf{B}(1)$, $\mathbf{P}(1)$, $\mathbf{B}(2)$, $\mathbf{P}(2)$, etc., which determine the optimum-control law for the given multidimensional control process.

When the control process is subject to command inputs or reference inputs, $\mathbf{r}(t)$, the above design procedure is also applicable. In this situation the inputs are also described by state variables known as input state variables, and the process is represented by an augmented system. When the

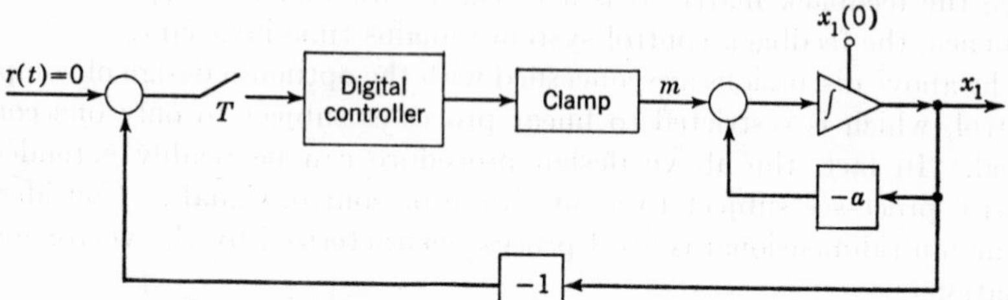

Fig. 8.2-1 State-variable diagram of a simple digital control system.

design of the system is carried out with respect to a quadratic performance index, the optimum-control law is shown to be a linear function of the plant state variables as well as the input state variables. When a performance index other than quadratic is used as a measure of the performance, the optimum-control law is generally a nonlinear function of the plant state variables as well as the input state variables, and possibly kT:

$$\mathbf{m}^o(kT) = \boldsymbol{\beta}[\mathbf{x}(kT), \mathbf{r}(kT), kT] \tag{8.2-41}$$

To illustrate the application of the theories discussed above, the following numerical examples are worked out.

Example 8.2-1 A Regulator Problem

The state-variable diagram of a simple digital control system is shown in Fig. 8.2-1. The control process is characterized by the differential equation

$$\dot{x} + ax = bm$$

Determine the optimum-control sequence $m^o(k)$ which minimizes the quadratic performance index

$$I_N = \sum_{k=1}^{N} [x^2(k) + \lambda m^2(k-1)]$$

The reference input is set at zero.

From the state-variable diagram it is found by inspection that

$$\phi(T) = e^{-aT} \qquad h(T) = \frac{b}{a}(1 - e^{-aT})$$

Then the state-transition equation is given by

$$x(k+1) = e^{-aT}x(k) + \frac{b}{a}(1 - e^{-aT})m(k)$$

Since $Q = 1$ and $P(0) = 0$, it follows from Eq. (8.2-22) that the first feedback coefficient is

$$B(1) = \frac{-ab(1 - e^{-aT})e^{-aT}}{b^2(1 - e^{-aT})^2 + a^2\lambda}$$

Making use of Eq. (8.2-28) yields

$$P(1) = \frac{a^2\lambda e^{-2aT}}{a^2\lambda + b^2(1 - e^{-aT})^2}$$

Substituting into Eq. (8.2-23) gives the second feedback coefficient as

$$B(2) = \frac{-ae^{-aT}[a^2\lambda(1 + e^{-2aT}) + b^2(1 - e^{-aT})^2]}{b(1 - e^{-aT})[a^2\lambda(1 + e^{-2aT}) + b^2(1 - e^{-aT})^2] + \lambda[a^2\lambda + b^2(1 - e^{-aT})^2]}$$

The successive feedback coefficients $B(3), B(4), \ldots, B(N)$ can be determined in like manner. Hence the optimum-control sequence is

$$\begin{aligned}
m^o(0) &= B(N)x(0) \\
m^o(1) &= B(N-1)x(1) \\
&\cdots\cdots\cdots\cdots \\
m^o(N-2) &= B(2)x(N-2) \\
m^o(N-1) &= B(1)x(N-1)
\end{aligned}$$

The feedback coefficients vary with time, and the control system is thus time-varying.

Example 8.2-2 A Second-order Process

Consider a second-order process characterized by the differential equation

$$\ddot{x} + a\dot{x} + bx = m$$

The reference input r is set at zero. Determine the optimum-control law which minimizes the sum of the square of the system error,

$$I_N = \sum_{k=1}^{N} [e(k)]^2$$

where $e(k)$ denotes the system error at $t = kT$.

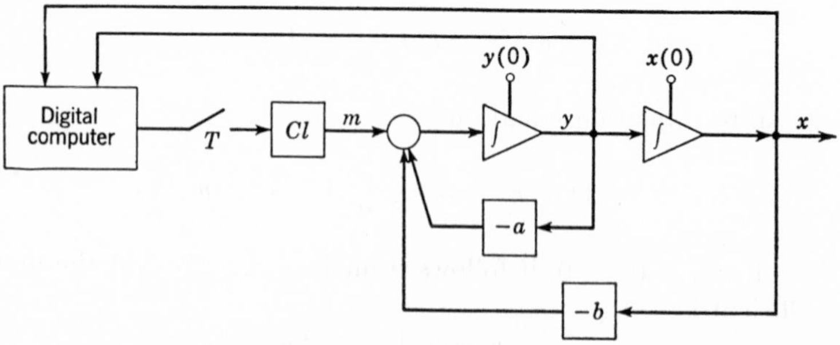

Fig. 8.2-2 State-variable diagram of the system in Example 8.2-2.

The state-variable diagram of the system is shown in Fig. 8.2-2. Let x and y be the state variables of the process; then the system equations become

$$\dot{x} = y$$
$$\dot{y} = -bx - ay + m$$

In terms of the state vector, the system is characterized by

$$\dot{\mathbf{x}} = \mathbf{A}\mathbf{x} + \mathbf{D}m$$

where $$\mathbf{A} = \begin{bmatrix} 0 & 1 \\ -b & -a \end{bmatrix} \quad \text{and} \quad \mathbf{D} = \begin{bmatrix} 0 \\ 1 \end{bmatrix}$$

The system error e is given by $e = r - x = -x$, since $r = 0$. Thus the performance index may be written as

$$I_N = \sum_{k=1}^{N} x_k^2$$

where $$x_k = x(kT)$$

One commonly used discrete version of the system equations is given by

$$x_{k+1} = x_k + Ty_k$$
$$y_{k+1} = y_k + T(-bx_k - ay_k + m_k)$$

This example illustrates the use of the discrete system equations instead of the state-transition equations in the determination of the optimum-control law. Let the minimum of I_N be $f_N(x_1, y_1)$. Then

$$f_N(x_1, y_1) = \min_{m_k} \sum_{k=1}^{N} x_k^2$$

$$f_1(x_1, y_1) = \min_{m_1} x_1^2 = x_1^2$$

Invoking the principle of optimality, for $N > 1$,

$$f_N(x_1, y_1) = \min_{m_1} \{x_1^2 + f_{N-1}[x_1 + Ty_1, y_1 + T(-bx_1 - ay_1 + m_1)]\}$$

Assume that

$$f_{N-1}(x_1, y_1) = \alpha_{N-1}x_1^2 + \beta_{N-1}x_1y_1 + \gamma_{N-1}y_1^2$$

Then

$$\begin{aligned} f_{N-1}(x_2, y_2) &= \alpha_{N-1}x_2^2 + \beta_{N-1}x_2y_2 + \gamma_{N-1}y_2^2 \\ &= \alpha_{N-1}(x_1 + Ty_1)^2 + \beta_{N-1}(x_1 + Ty_1)\,[y_1 + (-bx_1 - ay_1 + m_1)T] \\ &\qquad + \gamma_{N-1}[y_1 + (-bx_1 - ay_1 + m_1)T]^2 \end{aligned}$$

$$\frac{\partial[x_1^2 + f_{N-1}]}{\partial m_1} = \beta_{N-1}(x_1 + Ty_1) + 2\gamma_{N-1}[y_1 + (-bx_1 - ay_1 + m_1)T] = 0$$

Rearranging,

$$y_1 + (-bx_1 - ay_1 + m_1)T = -\frac{\beta_{N-1}}{2\gamma_{N-1}}(x_1 + Ty_1)$$

The minimum of I_N is then given by

$$f_N(x_1, y_1) = x_1^2 + \alpha_{N-1}(x_1 + Ty_1)^2 - \frac{\beta_{N-1}^2}{4\gamma_{N-1}}(x_1 + Ty_1)^2$$

which may be written as

$$f_N(x_1, y_1) = \alpha_N x_1^2 + \beta_N x_1 y_1 + \gamma_N y_1^2$$

where

$$\alpha_N = 1 + \alpha_{N-1} - \frac{\beta_{N-1}^2}{4\gamma_{N-1}}$$

$$\beta_N = 2T\alpha_{N-1} - \frac{T\beta_{N-1}^2}{2\gamma_{N-1}}$$

$$\gamma_N = T^2\alpha_{N-1} - \frac{T^2\beta_{N-1}^2}{4\gamma_{N-1}}$$

Since

$$f_1(x_1, y_1) = x_1^2 \qquad \alpha_1 = 1,\ \beta_1 = 0,\ \gamma_1 = 0$$

making use of the above recurrence relations gives

$$\begin{aligned} \alpha_2 &= 2 & \beta_2 &= 2T & \gamma_2 &= T^2 \\ \alpha_3 &= 2 & \beta_3 &= 2T & \gamma_3 &= T^2 \end{aligned}$$

and, in general,

$$\alpha_k = 2 \qquad \beta_k = 2T \qquad \gamma_k = T^2$$

Since the optimum-control law $m^o(1)$ is found to be

$$m^o(1) = \frac{2a\gamma_{N-1}T - 2\gamma_{N-1} - \beta_{N-1}T}{2\gamma_{N-1}T} y(1) + \frac{2b\gamma_{N-1}T - \beta_{N-1}}{2\gamma_{N-1}T} x(1)$$

substituting the proper values into this expression yields

$$m^o(1) = \left(a - \frac{2}{T}\right) y(1) + \left(b - \frac{1}{T^2}\right) x(1)$$

which is the optimum-control law at the first sampling instant.

The optimum-control law $m^o(j)$ at the jth sampling instant may be determined in like manner. In view of the principle of optimality, the minimum of the remaining $N - j$ stages of the N-stage process is

$$\begin{aligned} f_{N-j}[x(j+1), y(j+1)] &= \min_{\substack{m(j+1)\\ m(j+2)\\ \cdots\cdots \\ m(N-1)}} \sum_{k=j+1}^{N} [x(k)]^2 \\ &= \min_{m_{j+1}} \{x_{j+1}^2 + f_{N-\overline{j+1}}(x_{j+2}, y_{j+2})\} \end{aligned}$$

Using the discrete system equations,

$$\begin{aligned} f_{N-j}(x_{j+1}, y_{j+1}) &= \min_{m_{j+1}} \{x_{j+1}^2 + f_{N-\overline{j+1}}[x_{j+1} + Ty_{j+1}, \\ &\qquad\qquad y_{j+1} + (-bx_{j+1} - ay_{j+1} + m_{j+1})]\} \\ f_{N-\overline{j+1}}(x_j, y_j) &= \min_{m_j} \{x_j^2 + f_{N-j}[x_j + Ty_j, y_j + (-bx_j - ay_j + m_j)]\} \end{aligned}$$

Now let

$$f_{N-j}(x_{j+1}, y_{j+1}) = \alpha_{N-j}x_{j+1}^2 + \beta_{N+j}x_{j+1} + \gamma_{N-j}y_{j+1}^2$$

Using the discrete system equations,

$$\begin{aligned} f_{N-j}(x_{j+1}, y_{j+1}) &= \alpha_{N-j}(x_j + Ty_j)^2 \\ &\quad + \beta_{N-j}(x_j + Ty_j)\,[y_j + (-bx_j - ay_j + m_j)T] \\ &\quad + \gamma_{N-j}[y_j + (-bx_j - ay_j + m_j)T]^2 \\ \frac{\partial[x_j^2 + f_{N-j}]}{\partial m_j} &= \beta_{N-j}(x_j + Ty_j) + 2\gamma_{N-j}[y_j + (-bx_j - ay_j + m_j)T] = 0 \end{aligned}$$

which yields the optimum-control law as

$$m_j^o = \frac{2\gamma_{N-j}(aT - 1) - \beta_{N-j}T}{2\gamma_{N-j}T} y_j + \frac{2b\gamma_{N-j}T - \beta_{N-j}}{2\gamma_{N-j}T} x_j$$

The minimum of $x_j^2 + f_{N-j}$ is

$$f_{N-\overline{j+1}}(x_j, y_j) = x_j^2 + \alpha_{N-j}(x_j + Ty_j)^2 - \frac{\beta_{N-j}^2}{4\gamma_{N-j}} (x_j + Ty_j)^2$$

which reduces to

$$f_{N-\overline{j+1}}(x_j, y_j) = \alpha_{N-j+1}x_j^2 + \beta_{N-j+1}x_jy_j + \gamma_{N-j+1}y_j^2$$

by the substitution

$$\alpha_{N-j+1} = 1 + \alpha_{N-j} - \frac{\beta_{N-j}^2}{4\gamma_{N-j}}$$

$$\beta_{N-j+1} = 2T\alpha_{N-j} - \frac{T\beta_{N-j}^2}{2\gamma_{N-j}}$$

$$\gamma_{N-j+1} = T^2\alpha_{N-j} - \frac{T^2\beta_{N-j}^2}{4\gamma_{N-j}}$$

For $j = N - 1$, $N = 1$, $f_1(x_1, y_1) = x_1^2$, the coefficients are given by $\alpha_1 = 1$,

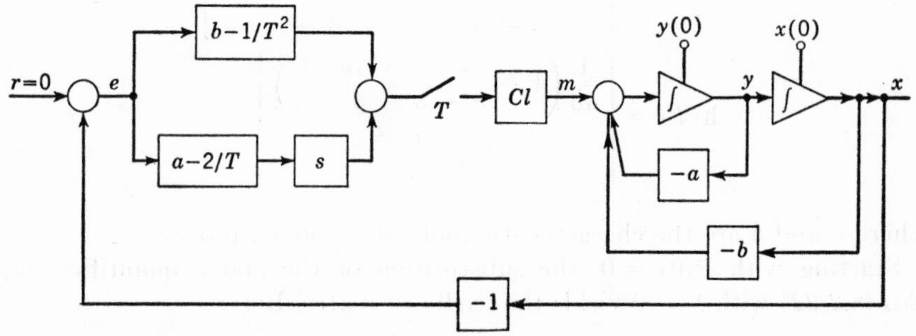

Fig. 8.2-3 A mechanization of the control system in Example 8.2-2.

$\beta_1 = 0$, and $\gamma_1 = 0$. Utilizing the above recurrence relations yields

$$\alpha_k = 2 \qquad \beta_k = 2T \qquad \gamma_k = T^2$$

Hence the optimum-control law is

$$m^o(j) = \left(a - \frac{2}{T}\right)y(j) + \left(b - \frac{1}{T^2}\right)x(j)$$

Since this feedback control system is relatively simple and is time-invariant, the optimum-control law may be mechanized by means of a controller in the forward branch, as shown in Fig. 8.2-3. The realization of the optimum control in this fashion leads to a control configuration which is obtainable by the classical approach.

For the sake of comparison, the optimum-control law is also determined by using the state-transition equations, which provide a more accurate representation of the process dynamics in discrete form. The performance index may be written as

$$I_N = \sum_{k=1}^{N} x_k{}^2 = \sum_{k=1}^{N} \mathbf{x}'(k)\mathbf{Q}\mathbf{x}(k)$$

where $$\mathbf{Q} = \begin{bmatrix} 1 & 0 \\ 0 & 0 \end{bmatrix} \qquad \mathbf{x} = \begin{bmatrix} x \\ y \end{bmatrix}$$

The elements of the **Q** matrix can be determined from the performance index by expanding the matrix notation and equating the corresponding coefficients, as exemplified in Sec. 2.3. The transition matrix and the **h** matrix are found to be

$$\boldsymbol{\phi}(T) = \begin{bmatrix} \dfrac{\beta e^{-\alpha T} - \alpha e^{-\beta T}}{\beta - \alpha} & \dfrac{e^{-\alpha T} - e^{-\beta T}}{\beta - \alpha} \\ \dfrac{\alpha\beta(e^{-\beta T} - e^{\alpha T})}{\beta - \alpha} & \dfrac{\beta e^{-\beta T} - \alpha e^{-\alpha T}}{\beta - \alpha} \end{bmatrix}$$

$$\mathbf{h}(T) = \begin{bmatrix} \dfrac{1}{\alpha\beta}\left(1 - \dfrac{\beta e^{-\alpha T}}{\beta - \alpha} + \dfrac{\alpha e^{-\beta T}}{\beta - \alpha}\right) \\ \dfrac{e^{\alpha T} - e^{-\beta T}}{\beta - \alpha} \end{bmatrix}$$

where α and β are the characteristic roots of the given process.

Starting with $\mathbf{P}(0) = 0$, the substitution of the above quantities into Eq. (8.2-22) with $\lambda = 0$ yields the feedback matrix $\mathbf{B}(1)$:

$$\mathbf{B}(1) = \begin{bmatrix} \dfrac{\alpha\beta(\alpha e^{-\beta T} - \beta e^{-\alpha T})}{\beta(1 - e^{-\alpha T}) - \alpha(1 - e^{-\beta T})} & \dfrac{\alpha\beta(e^{-\beta T} - e^{-\alpha T})}{\beta(1 - e^{-\alpha T}) - \alpha(1 - e^{-\beta T})} \end{bmatrix}$$

The other feedback matrices, which are generally different from $\mathbf{B}(1)$, may be determined by repeated application of Eqs. (8.2-21) and (8.2-28) with $\lambda = 0$. It is interesting to note that the use of the state-transition equation for discrete characterization leads to a time-varying feedback control system, while use of the discrete state equations results in a time-invariant system.

8.3 TIME-VARYING CONTROL PROCESSES

The optimum-design procedure discussed in the preceding section is derived under the assumption that the control process is linear and time-invariant and that the random external disturbance may be ignored. By extending the previous design techniques, this section considers linear control processes which are time-varying and subject to additive external random disturbances.[140, 141a, 144, 145] The basic assumption that all the state variables of the process are accessible for measurement and observation is still valid in the optimum design presented in this section.

The system design is initiated with the process characterization by a vector-matrix differential equation

$$\dot{\mathbf{x}}(t) = \mathbf{A}(t)\mathbf{x}(t) + \mathbf{D}(t)\mathbf{m}(t) + \mathbf{n}(t) \tag{8.3-1}$$

where $\mathbf{x}(t)$ = an n-vector representing the state variables
$\mathbf{m}(t)$ = an r-vector representing the control signals
$\mathbf{n}(t)$ = an s-vector representing the random external disturbance
$\mathbf{A}(t)$ = an $n \times n$ matrix
$\mathbf{D}(t)$ = an $n \times r$ matrix

Both matrices **A** and **D** are functions of time. The additive disturbance is assumed to be an independent random variable with zero mean. The process dynamics characterized by Eq. (8.3-1) may be described with discrete system equations by making use of the basic difference equation

$$x_i(\overline{k+1}\ T) = x_i(kT) + Tx_{i+1}(kT) \tag{8.3-2}$$

where the state variables x_i are related by $\dot{x}_i = x_{i+1}$, as discussed in the preceding section. More often, the state-transition equation

$$\mathbf{x}(k+1) = \boldsymbol{\phi}(k)\mathbf{x}(k) + \mathbf{G}(k)\mathbf{m}(k) + \mathbf{u}(k) \tag{8.3-3}$$

is used to characterize the process dynamics in discrete form. In Eq. (8.3-3), the sampling period T is dropped for convenience, and $\boldsymbol{\phi}(k)$, $\mathbf{G}(k)$, and $\mathbf{u}(k)$ are defined in Eqs. (8.1-6), (8.1-7), and (8.1-8), respectively. In the following discussion, the optimum-control system is designed with respect to a performance index of the form specified in Eq. (8.1-9a) and repeated here:

$$I_N = \sum_{k=1}^{N} [\mathbf{x}'(k)\mathbf{Q}(k)\mathbf{x}(k) + \lambda\mathbf{m}'(k-1)\mathbf{H}(k-1)\mathbf{m}(k-1)] \tag{8.3-4}$$

The optimum design aims at the determination of the optimum-control law which minimizes the expected value of the performance index I_N.

Let the minimum of the expected value of the performance index be denoted by

$$\begin{aligned} f_N[\mathbf{x}(0)] &= \min_{\mathbf{m}(i)} EI_N \qquad i = 0, 1, 2, \ldots, N-1 \\ &= \min_{\substack{\mathbf{m}(0)\\ \mathbf{m}(1)\\ \cdots\cdots\\ \mathbf{m}(N-1)}} E\left\{\sum_{k=1}^{N} [\mathbf{x}'(k)\mathbf{Q}(k)\mathbf{x}(k) + \lambda\mathbf{m}'(k-1)\mathbf{H}(k-1)\mathbf{m}(k-1)]\right\} \end{aligned} \tag{8.3-5}$$

where E stands for the expected-value operator over the sample space of **u**. This expression may be put into a more general form, denoting the minimum value of the last $N - j$ stages of the N-stage process:

$$f_{N-j}[\mathbf{x}(j)] = \min_{\mathbf{m}(i)} EI_{N-j} \qquad i = j, j+1, \ldots, N-1$$

$$f_{N-j}[\mathbf{x}(j)] = \min_{\substack{\mathbf{m}(j)\\ \mathbf{m}(j+1)\\ \cdots\cdots \\ \mathbf{m}(N-1)}} E\left\{ \sum_{k=j+1}^{N} [\mathbf{x}'(k)\mathbf{Q}(k)\mathbf{x}(k) + \lambda \mathbf{m}'(k-1)H(k-1)\mathbf{m}(k-1)]\right\} \qquad j = 0, 1, 2, \ldots, N-1 \quad (8.3\text{-}6)$$

When $j = 0$, Eq. (8.3-6) reduces to Eq. (8.3-5), and it is apparent that $f_0[\mathbf{x}(0)] = 0$.

Now suppose that the return from the first $j - 1$ stages is optimum. Then the output of the remaining $N - j$ stages is equal to the output from the jth stage plus optimum output from the remaining $N - \overline{j+1}$ stages; that is, the output is given by

$$[\mathbf{x}'(j+1)\mathbf{Q}(j+1)\mathbf{x}(j+1) + \lambda\mathbf{m}'(j)\mathbf{H}(j)\mathbf{m}(j)] + f_{N-\overline{j+1}}[\mathbf{x}(j+1)] \quad (8.3\text{-}7)$$

Invoking the principle of optimality,

$$f_{N-j}[\mathbf{x}(j)] = \min_{\mathbf{m}(j)} E\{[\mathbf{x}'(j+1)\mathbf{Q}(j+1)\mathbf{x}(j+1) + \lambda\mathbf{m}'(j)\mathbf{H}(j)\mathbf{m}(j)] + f_{N-\overline{j+1}}[\mathbf{x}(j+1)]\} \quad (8.3\text{-}8)$$

Following the same argument as in Sec. 8.2, it can be assumed that

$$f_{N-j}[\mathbf{x}(j)] = \mathbf{x}'(j)\mathbf{P}(N-j)\mathbf{x}(j) \quad (8.3\text{-}9)$$

and

$$f_{N-\overline{j+1}}[\mathbf{x}(j+1)] = \mathbf{x}'(j+1)\mathbf{P}(N-\overline{j+1})\mathbf{x}(j+1) \quad (8.3\text{-}10)$$

where **P**'s are positive-definite symmetrical matrices.

Substituting Eqs. (8.3-9) and (8.3-10) into Eq. (8.3-8) and defining

$$\mathbf{S}(N-\overline{j+1}) = \mathbf{Q}(j+1) + \mathbf{P}(N-\overline{j+1}) \quad (8.3\text{-}11)$$

yields

$$\begin{aligned}\mathbf{x}'(j)\mathbf{P}(N-j)\mathbf{x}(j) &= \min_{\mathbf{m}(j)} E\{\mathbf{x}'(j+1)[\mathbf{Q}(j+1) + \mathbf{P}(N-\overline{j+1})]\mathbf{x}(j+1) + \lambda\mathbf{m}'(j)\mathbf{H}(j)\mathbf{m}(j)\} \\ &= \min_{\mathbf{m}(j)} E\{\mathbf{x}'(j+1)\mathbf{S}(N-\overline{j+1})\mathbf{x}(j+1) + \lambda\mathbf{m}'(j)\mathbf{H}(j)\mathbf{m}(j)\} \quad (8.3\text{-}12)\end{aligned}$$

The expected value on the right-hand side of Eq. (8.3-12) is defined by

$$J_{N-j} = E\{\mathbf{x}'(j+1)\mathbf{S}(N-\overline{j+1})\mathbf{x}(j+1) + \lambda\mathbf{m}'(j)\mathbf{H}(j)\mathbf{m}(j)\} \quad (8.3\text{-}13)$$

In view of Eq. (8.3-3), the expected value J_{N-j} may be written as

$$\begin{aligned} J_{N-j} = E\{&\mathbf{x}'(j)\mathbf{L}_{\phi\phi}(N - \overline{j+1})\mathbf{x}(j) + \mathbf{m}'(j)\mathbf{L}_{G\phi}(N - \overline{j+1})\mathbf{x}(j) \\ &+ \mathbf{x}'(j)\mathbf{L}_{\phi G}(N - \overline{j+1})\mathbf{m}(j) + \mathbf{m}'(j)[\mathbf{L}_{GG}(N - \overline{j+1}) + \lambda\mathbf{H}(j)]\mathbf{m}(j) \\ &+ [\mathbf{x}'(j)\boldsymbol{\phi}'(j) + \mathbf{m}'(j)\mathbf{G}'(j)]\mathbf{S}(N - \overline{j+1})\mathbf{u}(j) \\ &+ \mathbf{u}'(j)\mathbf{S}(N - \overline{j+1})[\boldsymbol{\phi}(j)\mathbf{x}(j) + \mathbf{G}(j)\mathbf{m}(j)] \\ &+ \mathbf{u}'(j)\mathbf{S}(N - \overline{j+1})\mathbf{u}(j)\} \end{aligned} \tag{8.3-14}$$

where the following identities are used:

$$\mathbf{L}_{\phi\phi}(N - \overline{j+1}) \triangleq \boldsymbol{\phi}'(j)\mathbf{S}(N - \overline{j+1})\boldsymbol{\phi}(j) \tag{8.3-15}$$
$$\mathbf{L}_{GG}(N - \overline{j+1}) \triangleq \mathbf{G}'(j)\mathbf{S}(N - \overline{j+1})\mathbf{G}(j) \tag{8.3-16}$$
$$\mathbf{L}_{G\phi}(N - \overline{j+1}) \triangleq \mathbf{G}'(j)\mathbf{S}(N - \overline{j+1})\boldsymbol{\phi}(j) \tag{8.3-17}$$
$$\mathbf{L}_{\phi G}(N - \overline{j+1}) \triangleq \boldsymbol{\phi}'(j)\mathbf{S}(N - \overline{j+1})\mathbf{G}(j) \tag{8.3-18}$$

Since $\mathbf{u}(j)$ is a vector of independent random variables, Eq. (8.3-14) may be simplified to

$$\begin{aligned} J_{N-j} = \mathbf{x}'(j)&\mathbf{L}_{\phi\phi}(N - \overline{j+1})\mathbf{x}(j) + \mathbf{m}'(j)\mathbf{L}_{G\phi}(N - \overline{j+1})\mathbf{x}(j) \\ + \mathbf{x}'(j)&\mathbf{L}_{\phi G}(N - \overline{j+1})\mathbf{m}(j) + \mathbf{m}'(j)[L_{GG}(N - \overline{j+1}) + \lambda\mathbf{H}(j)]\mathbf{m}(j) \\ &+ E\{\mathbf{u}'(j)\mathbf{S}(N - \overline{j+1})\mathbf{u}(j)\} \end{aligned} \tag{8.3-19}$$

Now the minimization of J_{N-j} may be readily carried out through ordinary differentiation, since the N-stage decision process has been reduced to a sequence of N single-stage decision processes. Differentiating Eq. (8.3-19) with respect to $\mathbf{m}(j)$ and making use of the symmetry property of the matrices yields

$$\frac{dJ_{N-j}}{d\mathbf{m}(j)} = 2\mathbf{L}_{G\phi}(N - \overline{j+1})\mathbf{x}(j) + 2[\mathbf{L}_{GG}(N - \overline{j+1}) + \lambda\mathbf{H}(j)]\mathbf{m}(j) \tag{8.3-20}$$

Equating the derivative to zero and solving for $\mathbf{m}(j)$ gives the optimum-control law as

$$\mathbf{m}^o(j) = \mathbf{B}(N - j)\mathbf{x}(j) \tag{8.3-21}$$

where $\mathbf{B}(N - j) = [\mathbf{L}_{GG}(N - \overline{j+1}) + \lambda\mathbf{H}(j)]^{-1}\mathbf{L}_{G\phi}(N - \overline{j+1})$ (8.3-22)

is the feedback matrix which is dependent upon time. The optimum-control law is a linear function of the state variables of the system. Since the feedback matrix **B** involves the unknown matrix **P**, the optimum-control law is still undefined until the **P** matrix is determined. A recurrence relationship between matrices **P** and **B** can be found from Eqs. (8.3-12) and (8.3-21). This recurrence relationship, together with Eq. (8.3-22), provides a computational algorithm for the evaluation of the feedback matrix $\mathbf{B}(N - j)$.

Substituting Eq. (8.3-21) into Eq. (8.3-12) and making use of Eq. (8.3-19) yields the minimum value as

$$\begin{aligned}
\mathbf{x}'(j)\mathbf{P}(N-j)\mathbf{x}(j) \\
&= \mathbf{x}'(j)\mathbf{L}_{\phi\phi}(N-\overline{j+1})\mathbf{x}(j) + [\mathbf{B}(N-j)\mathbf{x}(j)]'\mathbf{L}_{G\phi}(N-\overline{j+1})\mathbf{x}(j) \\
&\quad + \mathbf{x}'(j)\mathbf{L}_{\phi G}(N-\overline{j+1})[\mathbf{B}(N-j)\mathbf{x}(j)] \\
&\quad + [\mathbf{B}(N-j)\mathbf{x}(j)]'[\mathbf{L}_{GG}(N-\overline{j+1}) + \lambda\mathbf{H}(j)][\mathbf{B}(N-j)\mathbf{x}(j)] \\
&\quad + \min_{\mathbf{m}} E\{\mathbf{u}'(j)\mathbf{S}(N-\overline{j+1})\mathbf{u}(j)\} \\
&= \mathbf{x}'(j)\mathbf{L}_{\phi\phi}(N-\overline{j+1})\mathbf{x}(j) + \mathbf{x}'(j)\mathbf{B}'(N-j)\mathbf{L}_{G\phi}(N-\overline{j+1})\mathbf{x}(j) \\
&\quad + \mathbf{x}'(j)\mathbf{L}_{\phi G}(N-\overline{j+1})\mathbf{B}(N-j)\mathbf{x}(j) \\
&\quad + \mathbf{x}'(j)\mathbf{B}'(N-j)[\mathbf{L}_{GG}(N-\overline{j+1}) + \lambda\mathbf{H}(j)]\mathbf{B}(N-j)\mathbf{x}(j) \\
&\quad + \min_{\mathbf{m}} E\{\mathbf{u}'(j)\mathbf{S}(N-\overline{j+1})\mathbf{u}(j)\} \qquad (8.3\text{-}23)
\end{aligned}$$

In view of Eq. (8.3-22), the preceding equation is reduced to

$$\mathbf{x}'(j)\mathbf{P}(N-j)\mathbf{x}(j) = \mathbf{x}'(j)[\mathbf{L}_{\phi\phi}(N-\overline{j+1}) + \mathbf{L}_{\phi G}(N-\overline{j+1})\mathbf{B}(N-j)]\mathbf{x}(j) + \min_{\mathbf{m}} E\{\mathbf{u}'(j)\mathbf{S}(N-\overline{j+1})\mathbf{u}(j)\} \qquad (8.3\text{-}24)$$

Since **Q** and **P** are positive-definite matrices, then, by Eq. (8.3-11), **S** is also positive-definite. The minimum of the expected value of $\mathbf{u}'(j)\mathbf{S}(N-\overline{j+1})\mathbf{u}(j)$ in Eq. (8.3-24) can be taken as zero. In this case, Eq. (8.3-24) becomes

$$\mathbf{x}'(j)\mathbf{P}(N-j)\mathbf{x}(j) = \mathbf{x}'(j)[\mathbf{L}_{\phi\phi}(N-\overline{j+1}) + \mathbf{L}_{\phi G}(N-\overline{j+1})\mathbf{B}(N-j)]\mathbf{x}(j) \qquad (8.3\text{-}25)$$

Comparing both sides of the preceding equation yields

$$\mathbf{P}(N-j) = \mathbf{L}_{\phi\phi}(N-\overline{j+1}) + \mathbf{L}_{\phi G}(N-\overline{j+1})\mathbf{B}(N-j) \qquad (8.3\text{-}26)$$

Starting with $\mathbf{P}(0) = 0$ for $j = N-1$, Eq. (8.3-22) gives the value of the feedback matrix at the first sampling instant:

$$\mathbf{B}(1) = -[\mathbf{L}_{GG}(0) + \lambda\mathbf{H}(N-1)]^{-1}\mathbf{L}_{G\phi}(0) \qquad (8.3\text{-}27)$$

and Eq. (8.3-26) yields the value of **P**(1) as

$$\mathbf{P}(1) = \mathbf{L}_{\phi\phi}(0) + \mathbf{L}_{\phi G}(0)\mathbf{B}(1) \qquad (8.3\text{-}28)$$

where

$$\mathbf{L}_{\phi\phi}(0) = \boldsymbol{\phi}'(N-1)\mathbf{Q}(N)\boldsymbol{\phi}(N-1) \qquad (8.3\text{-}29)$$

$$\mathbf{L}_{\phi G}(0) = \boldsymbol{\phi}'(N-1)\mathbf{Q}(N)\mathbf{G}(N-1) \qquad (8.3\text{-}30)$$

For $j = N-2$, Eq. (8.3-22) gives **B**(2) and Eq. (8.3-26) determines **P**(2). In like manner, **B**(3), **P**(3), **B**(4), **P**(4), etc., can be successively evaluated.

The recurrence relationships defined in Eqs. (8.3-22) and (8.3-26) provide the necessary computational algorithm for the determination of the optimum-control law. These two recurrence relationships point out that, even though the process to be controlled is time-invariant, the feedback control system is a time-varying system, since the feedback matrix $\mathbf{B}(N - j)$ varies with time. When Eq. (8.1-9*b*) is used to define the performance index instead of Eq. (8.3-4), the optimum-control law can be determined by following an analogous procedure. In a computer control system, the computational algorithm is programmed on the digital computer of the system which will generate a sequence of optimum-control signals to satisfy the performance criterion.

In summary, the optimum-control law possesses two important properties:

1. The optimum-control vector $\mathbf{m}^o(j)$ is linearly related to the state vector $\mathbf{x}(j)$ of the process by

$$\mathbf{m}^o(j) = \mathbf{B}(N - j)\mathbf{x}(j) \tag{8.3-31}$$

The feedback matrix $\mathbf{B}(N - j)$ generally varies with time.

2. If the control process is subjected to additive independent random disturbances and the optimum-control law given in Eq. (8.3-31) is used, the control system is still optimum in the sense that the expected value of a quadratic performance index is minimized.

Example 8.3-1 A Control Process Subject to Random Disturbances[145]

Consider a simple control system which consists of a d-c motor driving a load. This system is characterized by the transfer function

$$G(s) = \frac{1}{s(s + 1)}$$

The dynamic element is subject to a disturbance at the input terminal. The spectral density of this disturbance is

$$S_1(\omega) = \frac{1}{\omega^2 + 4}$$

The input to the system is assumed to be a step function whose measurement is contaminated by a noise which is independent of the disturbance and has a spectral density

$$S_2(\omega) = \frac{1}{\omega^2 + 0.25}$$

The magnitude of the step input is assumed to range anywhere between $-\pi$ and $+\pi$. The sampling period of this system is equal to 0.5 sec. Determine the control law $m^o(kT)$ which minimizes the performance index

$$J_N = E \sum_{k=1}^{N} [x_1(kT) - x_4(kT)]^2$$

where x_1 and x_4 represent the output and the input, respectively.

Based upon well-known statistical theory, it can be shown that the disturbance at the input terminal may be considered as the output of a linear filter with a transfer function

$$G_{n3}(s) = \frac{1}{s+2}$$

subject to a white-noise input having spectral density equal to unity. The state-variable diagram of the augmented system is shown in Fig. 8.3-1,

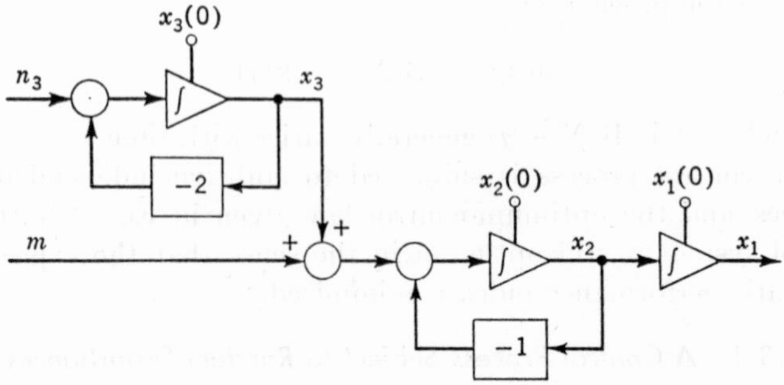

Fig. 8.3-1 State-variable diagram of the process and the external disturbance.

in which x_3 is a new state variable and n_3 is a white noise with spectral density equal to 1.

The state-variable diagram of the input element is shown in Fig. 8.3-2. The step-input signal is the output of an integrator, and is denoted by x_4. The noise which contaminates the input can be considered to be generated by passing white noise through a linear filter with a transfer function

$$G_{n5}(s) = \frac{1}{s+0.5}$$

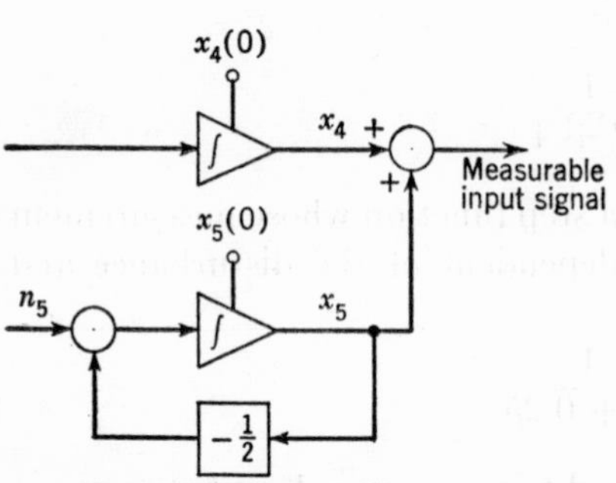

Fig. 8.3-2 State-variable diagram for the input elements.

In Fig. 8.3-2, the white-noise input of spectral density 1 is denoted by n_5.

Let **x** be the state vector with components $x_1, x_2, \ldots, x_5$, and **n** be the disturbance vector with components $n_1, n_2, \ldots, n_5$. Then the system can be described by the vector differential equation

$$\dot{\mathbf{x}}(t) = \mathbf{A}\mathbf{x}(t) + \mathbf{d}m(t) + \mathbf{n}(t)$$

where the coefficient matrix **A** is

$$\mathbf{A} = \begin{bmatrix} 0 & 1 & 0 & 0 & 0 \\ 0 & -1 & 1 & 0 & 0 \\ 0 & 0 & -2 & 0 & 0 \\ 0 & 0 & 0 & 0 & 0 \\ 0 & 0 & 0 & 0 & -\frac{1}{2} \end{bmatrix}$$

Since there is only one control signal and

$$\dot{x}_2 = -x_2 + x_3 + m$$

the driving matrix **d** is a column matrix,

$$\mathbf{d} = \begin{bmatrix} 0 \\ 1 \\ 0 \\ 0 \\ 0 \end{bmatrix}$$

Examination of Figs. 8.3-1 and 8.3-2 gives the disturbance vector as

$$\mathbf{n} = \begin{bmatrix} 0 \\ 0 \\ n_3 \\ 0 \\ n_5 \end{bmatrix}$$

Referring to Fig. 8.3-1, it is found that, for $T = 0.5$ sec, the transition matrix is

$$\boldsymbol{\phi}(T) = \begin{bmatrix} 1 & 0.393 & 0.077 & 0 & 0 \\ 0 & 0.607 & 0.239 & 0 & 0 \\ 0 & 0 & 0.368 & 0 & 0 \\ 0 & 0 & 0 & 1 & 0 \\ 0 & 0 & 0 & 0 & 0.779 \end{bmatrix}$$

From Eq. (8.1-7), the matrix $\mathbf{G}(kT)$ is obtained. Since matrices **A** and **d** are time-invariant, $\mathbf{G}(k)$ is a constant matrix given by

$$\mathbf{G}(kT) = \begin{bmatrix} 0.107 \\ 0.393 \\ 0 \\ 0 \\ 0 \end{bmatrix}$$

The given performance index may be written as

$$J_N = E \sum_{k=1}^{N} \mathbf{x}'(kT)\mathbf{Q}\mathbf{x}(kT)$$

where $\mathbf{x}'(kT)\mathbf{Q}\mathbf{x}(kT) = \{x_1(kT) - x_4(kT)\}^2$ and

$$\mathbf{Q} = \begin{bmatrix} 1 & 0 & 0 & -1 & 0 \\ 0 & 0 & 0 & 0 & 0 \\ 0 & 0 & 0 & 0 & 0 \\ -1 & 0 & 0 & 1 & 0 \\ 0 & 0 & 0 & 0 & 0 \end{bmatrix}$$

To determine the optimum-control law, use is made of Eqs. (8.3-22) and (8.3-26). It is found that, for $0 \leq k \leq N$, the feedback matrix $\mathbf{B}$ is

$$\mathbf{B} = [-9.346 \quad -3.373 \quad -0.720 \quad 9.346 \quad 0]$$

Hence, from Eq. (8.3-21), the control signal which minimizes the specified performance index is given by

$$m^o(kT) = 9.346\{x_4(kT) - x_1(kT)\} - 3.673x_2(kT) - 0.720x_3(kT)$$

Unfortunately, this control law is not physically realizable, since the state variable x_4 is contaminated by noise, and is thus not measurable, and the state variable x_3 is fictitious, introduced only for the sake of convenience, and cannot be directly measured. A complete solution to this problem is discussed in the following sections. It is to be noted that this example illustrates the concept of introducing the input state variables and the augmented system. To unify the design procedure, the inputs and disturbances are characterized by state variables, and the original control process is represented by the augmented system.

8.4 MULTIVARIABLE PROCESSES WITH INACCESSIBLE STATE VARIABLES

In the preceding sections the design of optimum control is carried out under the assumption that all the state variables of the process are accessible for measurement and observation. It is found that the optimum-control law is a linear function of the state variables. However, in many control processes encountered in practice, some of the state variables are not accessible for measurement and observation. Only the output signals can be measured directly. In a chemical process, certain parameters, such as the reaction rate, which characterize the chemical reactor cannot be measured. In the aircraft-control problem discussed in Sec. 1.3, the second and the third derivatives of the altitude h are not readily measurable,

This section is concerned with the design of optimum control for multivariable processes with inaccessible state variables.[82,141,144,145]

Under many realistic situations, not all the state variables of a control process are accessible for direct measurement. These measurable variables are often referred to as the output variables and are denoted by y_1, y_2, . . . , y_p. These variables constitute the components of the output vector $\mathbf{y}$. In the following discussion the output variables are assumed to be linear functions of the state variables, and they are related by the linear transformation

$$\mathbf{y}(k) = \mathbf{M}\mathbf{x}(k) \tag{8.4-1}$$

where $\mathbf{x}$ = an n-vector
$\mathbf{y}$ = a p-vector
$\mathbf{M}$ = a $p \times n$ matrix with $p \leq n$

When there are fewer output variables than state variables, matrix $\mathbf{M}$ is nonsquare and cannot be inverted. The matrix $\mathbf{M}$ is referred to as the *output matrix,* or the *measurement matrix.* In the synthesis procedures discussed previously, the optimum-control signal $m^o(k)$ is determined as a function of the state variables, which ultimately appear as signals in the feedback loops of the control system. Consequently, when some of the state variables are inaccessible, the optimum-control signal $m^o(k)$ will remain undetermined and unrealizable. In this situation, the optimum design aims at the determination of a physically realizable optimum-control signal on the basis of the measured output vectors $\mathbf{y}(k)$, $\mathbf{y}(k-1)$, . . . , $\mathbf{y}(0)$. It is shown in the following discussion that, for a linear system characterized by the state-transition equation given in Eq. (8.3-3), the realizable control vector which minimizes the expected value of the performance index defined in Eq. (8.3-4) is given by

$$\hat{\mathbf{m}}^o(k/k) = \mathbf{B}(N-k)\hat{\mathbf{x}}(k/k) \tag{8.4-2}$$

where $\mathbf{B}(N-k)$ is the feedback matrix determined in the preceding sections, and $\hat{\mathbf{x}}(k/j)$ is the optimum estimate of the state vector $\mathbf{x}(k)$ based upon the measured output vectors $\mathbf{y}(j)$, $\mathbf{y}(j-1)$, . . . , $\mathbf{y}(0)$, in the sense that the expected value

$$E\{[\mathbf{x}(k) - \hat{\mathbf{x}}(k/j)]'[\mathbf{x}(k) - \hat{\mathbf{x}}(k/j)]\} \tag{8.4-3}$$

is a minimum. The determination of the feedback matrix $\mathbf{B}$ and the evaluation of the best estimates $\hat{\mathbf{x}}$ may be carried out independently.

Let the state vector $\mathbf{x}(k)$ be represented by the sum of its orthogonal projection $\hat{\mathbf{x}}(k/k)$ on subspace $\mathbf{Y}(j)$ and its normal component $\tilde{\mathbf{x}}(k/k)$:

$$\mathbf{x}(k) = \hat{\mathbf{x}}(k/k) + \tilde{\mathbf{x}}(k/k) \tag{8.4-4}$$

$\mathbf{Y}(j)$ is a subspace of $\mathbf{X}(k)$ if $j \leq k$. The optimum-control vector $\mathbf{m}^o(k)$

may be similarly represented:

$$\mathbf{m}^o(k) = \hat{\mathbf{m}}^o(k/k) + \tilde{\mathbf{m}}^o(k/k) \tag{8.4-5}$$

where $\hat{\mathbf{m}}^o(k/k)$ and $\tilde{\mathbf{m}}^o(k/k)$ denote the orthogonal projection of $\mathbf{m}^o(k)$ on subspace $\mathbf{Y}(j)$ and the normal component, respectively. Equations (8.4-4) and (8.4-5) follow from the properties of orthogonal projection summarized in Sec. 2.2. It has been shown that, when the state variables are all measurable, the optimum-control law for a linear process designed with reference to a quadratic performance criterion is, as given by Eq. (8.3-21),

$$\mathbf{m}^o(k) = \mathbf{B}(N - k)\mathbf{x}(k) \tag{8.4-6}$$

Combining Eqs. (8.4-4), (8.4-5), and (8.4-6) yields

$$\hat{\mathbf{m}}^o(k/k) + \tilde{\mathbf{m}}^o(k/k) = \mathbf{B}(N - k)\hat{\mathbf{x}}(k/k) + \mathbf{B}(N - k)\tilde{\mathbf{x}}(k/k) \tag{8.4-7}$$

By making use of the basic properties of orthogonal projections, it follows from Eq. (8.4-7) that

$$\hat{\mathbf{m}}^o(k/k) = \mathbf{B}(N - k)\hat{\mathbf{x}}(k/k) \tag{8.4-8}$$

and

$$\tilde{\mathbf{m}}^o(k/k) = \mathbf{B}(N - k)\tilde{\mathbf{x}}(k/k) \tag{8.4-9}$$

The orthogonal projection $\hat{\mathbf{m}}^o(k/k)$ which represents the best estimate of $\mathbf{m}^o(k)$ is linearly related to the best estimate of $\mathbf{x}(k)$. The normal component of $\mathbf{m}^o(k)$ represents the estimation error. It is noted that the estimate $\hat{\mathbf{m}}^o(k/k)$ is physically realizable, since it is a function of the estimate $\hat{\mathbf{x}}(k/k)$, which can be determined from the measured output signals. Now, if it can be shown that, when the best estimate of $\mathbf{m}^o(k)$ is used instead of the optimum-control vector itself, the performance of the control system is still optimum in the specified sense, the control vector given in Eq. (8.4-2) describes the optimum-control law. To be more specific, it is required to show that the optimum estimate $\hat{\mathbf{m}}^o(k/k)$ minimizes the error caused by the substitution of the estimates for the actual control signals.

With reference to the performance index given in Eq. (8.3-4), it is noted that the minimum of the expected value of I_N depends only upon the number of stages N and the initial-state vector $\mathbf{x}(0)$. Let the minimum of the expected value of I_N be denoted by

$$f_N[\mathbf{x}(0)] = \min_{\mathbf{m}(j)} EI_N \qquad j = 1, 2, \ldots, N \tag{8.4-10}$$

Using Eq. (8.3-4),

$$f_N[\mathbf{x}(0)] = \min_{\mathbf{m}(j)} E\left\{\sum_{k=1}^{N} [\mathbf{x}'(k)\mathbf{Q}(k)\mathbf{x}(k) + \lambda\mathbf{m}'(k-1)\mathbf{H}(k-1)\mathbf{m}(k-1)]\right\} \tag{8.4-11}$$

It is clear that, when $\mathbf{m}(j) = \mathbf{m}^o(j)$, $EI_N = f_N$ and $EI_N - f_N = 0$. However, when $\mathbf{m}(k) \neq \mathbf{m}^o(k)$, $EI_N - f_N > 0$, and an error is introduced, since by definition f_N is the minimum of EI_N. Consequently, the problem is to determine an estimate of $\mathbf{m}^o(k)$ which will minimize the error $EI_N - f_N$ caused by the unavailability of $\mathbf{m}^o(k)$. This estimate is referred to as the best estimate. It is interesting to note that the best estimate is given by the orthogonal projection $\hat{\mathbf{m}}(k/k)$, and thus Eq. (8.4-2) provides the optimum-control law for processes with inaccessible state variables.

Invoking the principle of optimality, the minimum value $f_N[\mathbf{x}(0)]$ for the N-stage control process with $N > 1$ may be expressed as

$$f_N[\mathbf{x}(0)] = \min_{\mathbf{m}(0)} E\{\mathbf{x}'(1)\mathbf{Q}(1)\mathbf{x}(1) + \lambda\mathbf{m}'(0)\mathbf{H}(0)\mathbf{m}(0) + f_{N-1}[\mathbf{x}(1)]\} \quad (8.4\text{-}12)$$

where $\mathbf{x}(1)$ is related to $\mathbf{m}(0)$ through Eq. (8.3-3).

For $N = 1$, the minimum is

$$f_1[\mathbf{x}(0)] = \min_{m(0)} E\{\mathbf{x}'(1)\mathbf{Q}(1)\mathbf{x}(1) + \lambda\mathbf{m}'(0)\mathbf{H}(0)\mathbf{m}(0)\} \quad (8.4\text{-}13)$$

The statement that the estimate $\mathbf{m}(k/k)$ is optimum in the sense that it minimizes $EI_N - f_N$ can be verified from Eqs. (8.4-12) and (8.4-13) by letting $N = 1, 2, \ldots$.

For a one-stage process, the performance index reduces to

$$I_1 = \mathbf{x}'(1)\mathbf{Q}(1)\mathbf{x}(1) + \lambda\mathbf{m}'(0)\mathbf{H}(0)\mathbf{m}(0) \quad (8.4\text{-}14)$$

Since, from Eq. (8.3-3),

$$\mathbf{x}(1) = \boldsymbol{\phi}(0)\mathbf{x}(0) + \mathbf{G}(0)\mathbf{m}(0) + \mathbf{u}(0) \quad (8.4\text{-}15)$$

the performance index I_1 is given by

$$I_1 = [\boldsymbol{\phi}(0)\mathbf{x}(0) + \mathbf{G}(0)\mathbf{m}(0) + \mathbf{u}(0)]'\mathbf{Q}(1)[\boldsymbol{\phi}(0)\mathbf{x}(0) + \mathbf{G}(0)\mathbf{m}(0) + \mathbf{u}(0)] + \lambda\mathbf{m}'(0)\mathbf{H}(0)\mathbf{m}(0) \quad (8.4\text{-}16)$$

Expanding the right-hand side of Eq. (8.4-16) and dropping the arguments yields

$$I_1 = \mathbf{x}\boldsymbol{\phi}'\mathbf{Q}(1)\boldsymbol{\phi}\mathbf{x} + \mathbf{m}'[\mathbf{G}'\mathbf{Q}(1)\mathbf{G} + \lambda\mathbf{H}(0)]\mathbf{m} + \mathbf{u}'\mathbf{Q}(1)\mathbf{u} + 2\mathbf{x}'\boldsymbol{\phi}'\mathbf{Q}(1)\mathbf{G}\mathbf{m} + 2\mathbf{u}'\mathbf{Q}(1)\mathbf{G}\mathbf{m} + 2\mathbf{x}'\boldsymbol{\phi}'\mathbf{Q}(1)\mathbf{u} \quad (8.4\text{-}17)$$

In deriving Eq. (8.4-17), use is made of the symmetry property of the matrices $\mathbf{Q}$ and $\mathbf{H}$.

The expected value of I_1 is given by

$$J_1 = EI_1 = \mathbf{x}'\boldsymbol{\phi}'\mathbf{Q}(1)\boldsymbol{\phi}\mathbf{x} + \mathbf{m}'[\mathbf{G}'\mathbf{Q}(1)\mathbf{G} + \lambda\mathbf{H}(0)]\mathbf{m} + 2\mathbf{x}'\boldsymbol{\phi}'\mathbf{Q}(1)\mathbf{G}\mathbf{m} + E\{\mathbf{u}'\mathbf{Q}(1)\mathbf{u}\} \quad (8.4\text{-}18)$$

The quantity J_1 is a minimum when the partial derivative of J_1 with respect to $\mathbf{m}(0)$ is equal to zero. Thus

$$\frac{\partial J_1}{\partial \mathbf{m}} = 2[\lambda \mathbf{H}(0) + \mathbf{G}'\mathbf{Q}(1)\mathbf{G}]\mathbf{m} + 2[\mathbf{G}'\mathbf{Q}(1)\boldsymbol{\phi}\mathbf{x}] \tag{8.4-19}$$

and

$$[\lambda \mathbf{H}(0) + \mathbf{G}'\mathbf{Q}(1)\mathbf{G}]\mathbf{m}^o = -[\mathbf{G}'\mathbf{Q}(1)\boldsymbol{\phi}]\mathbf{x} \tag{8.4-20}$$

where $\mathbf{m}^o$ is the minimizing control vector. The minimum value of J_1 is found to be

$$f_1 = \mathbf{x}'\boldsymbol{\phi}'\mathbf{Q}(1)\boldsymbol{\phi}\mathbf{x} + \mathbf{m}^{o\prime}[\mathbf{G}'\mathbf{Q}(1)\mathbf{G} + \lambda\mathbf{H}(0)]\mathbf{m}^o + 2\mathbf{x}'\boldsymbol{\phi}\mathbf{Q}(1)\mathbf{G}\mathbf{m}^o + E\{\mathbf{u}'\mathbf{Q}(1)\mathbf{u}\} \tag{8.4-21}$$

The difference between EI_1 and f_1 is

$$EI_1 - f_1 = \mathbf{m}'[\mathbf{G}'\mathbf{Q}(1)\mathbf{G} + \lambda\mathbf{H}(0)]\mathbf{m} - \mathbf{m}^{o\prime}[\mathbf{G}'\mathbf{Q}(1)\mathbf{G} + \lambda\mathbf{H}(0)]\mathbf{m}^o + 2\mathbf{x}'\boldsymbol{\phi}'\mathbf{Q}(1)\mathbf{G}(\mathbf{m} - \mathbf{m}^o) \tag{8.4-22}$$

In view of the symmetry property of $\mathbf{Q}$, the third term on the right-hand side of Eq. (8.4-22) may be written as

$$\mathbf{x}'\boldsymbol{\phi}'\mathbf{Q}(1)\mathbf{G}(\mathbf{m} - \mathbf{m}^o) = (\mathbf{m} - \mathbf{m}^o)'\mathbf{G}'\mathbf{Q}(1)\boldsymbol{\phi}\mathbf{x} \tag{8.4-23}$$

Making use of Eq. (8.4-20) and factorizing reduces Eq. (8.4-22) to

$$EI_1 - f_1 = (\mathbf{m} - \mathbf{m}^o)'[\mathbf{G}'\mathbf{Q}(1)\mathbf{G} + \lambda\mathbf{H}(0)](\mathbf{m} - \mathbf{m}^o) \tag{8.4-24}$$

This equation clearly indicates that $f_1 = EI_1$ when $\mathbf{m} = \mathbf{m}^o$. Replacing $\mathbf{m}$ by $\hat{\mathbf{m}} + \tilde{\mathbf{m}}$ and $\mathbf{m}^o$ by $\hat{\mathbf{m}}^o + \tilde{\mathbf{m}}^o$ in Eq. (8.4-24) yields the difference as

$$\begin{aligned} EI_1 - f_1 = (\hat{\mathbf{m}} - \hat{\mathbf{m}}^o)'[\mathbf{G}'\mathbf{Q}(1)\mathbf{G} + \lambda\mathbf{H}(0)](\hat{\mathbf{m}} - \hat{\mathbf{m}}^o) \\ + (\tilde{\mathbf{m}} - \tilde{\mathbf{m}}^o)'[\mathbf{G}'\mathbf{Q}(1)\mathbf{G} + \lambda\mathbf{H}(0)](\tilde{\mathbf{m}} - \tilde{\mathbf{m}}^o) \\ + 2(\hat{\mathbf{m}} - \hat{\mathbf{m}}^o)'[\mathbf{G}'\mathbf{Q}(1)\mathbf{G} + \lambda\mathbf{H}(0)](\tilde{\mathbf{m}} - \tilde{\mathbf{m}}^o) \end{aligned} \tag{8.4-25}$$

Thus the difference $EI_1 - f_1$ is a function of $\hat{\mathbf{m}}$ and $\tilde{\mathbf{m}}$. The minimum of $EI_1 - f_1$ is determined by differentiating $EI_1 - f_1$ with respect to $\hat{\mathbf{m}}$ and $\tilde{\mathbf{m}}$ and equating the partial derivatives to zero. This leads to the condition for minimum error as

$$2[\mathbf{G}'\mathbf{Q}(1)\mathbf{G} + \lambda\mathbf{H}(0)][(\hat{\mathbf{m}} - \hat{\mathbf{m}}^o) + (\tilde{\mathbf{m}} - \tilde{\mathbf{m}}^o)] = 0 \tag{8.4-26}$$

where the matrix $[\mathbf{G}'\mathbf{Q}(1)\mathbf{G} + \lambda\mathbf{H}(0)]$ is nonsingular. From Eq. (8.4-26) it follows that $EI_1 - f_1$ is minimized if

$$\hat{\mathbf{m}} = \hat{\mathbf{m}}^o \qquad \text{and} \qquad \tilde{\mathbf{m}} = \tilde{\mathbf{m}}^o \tag{8.4-27}$$

This completes the proof for a one-stage process.

Now consider a two-stage process. The minimum of the performance index is

$$f_2[\mathbf{x}(0)] = \min_{\mathbf{m}(0)} E\{\mathbf{x}'(1)Q(1)\mathbf{x}(1) + \lambda\mathbf{m}'(0)H(0)\mathbf{m}(0) + f_1[\mathbf{x}(1)]\} \tag{8.4-28}$$

From Eq. (8.4-20) it is found that the minimizing control vector is given by

$$\mathbf{m}^o = -[\mathbf{G}'\mathbf{Q}(1)\mathbf{G} + \lambda\mathbf{H}(0)]^{-1}[\mathbf{G}'\mathbf{Q}(1)\boldsymbol{\phi}]\mathbf{x} \tag{8.4-29}$$

Substituting $\mathbf{m}^o$ into Eq. (8.4-21) and simplifying yields

$$f_1[\mathbf{x}(0)] = \mathbf{x}'(0)\mathbf{R}(0)\mathbf{x}(0) + E\{\mathbf{u}'(0)\mathbf{Q}(1)\mathbf{u}(0)\} \tag{8.4-30}$$

where

$$\mathbf{R}(0) = [\boldsymbol{\phi}'(0)\mathbf{Q}(1)\boldsymbol{\phi}(0)] - [\boldsymbol{\phi}'(0)\mathbf{Q}(1)\mathbf{G}(0)][\mathbf{G}'(0)\mathbf{Q}(1)\mathbf{G}(0) + \lambda\mathbf{H}(0)]^{-1}[\mathbf{G}'(0)\mathbf{Q}(1)\boldsymbol{\phi}(0)] \tag{8.4-31}$$

Making use of Eq. (8.4-30),

$$f_2[\mathbf{x}(0)] = \min_{\mathbf{m}(0)} E\{\mathbf{x}'(1)\mathbf{S}(1)\mathbf{x}(1) + \lambda\mathbf{m}'(0)\mathbf{H}(0)\mathbf{m}(0) + \mathbf{u}(1)\mathbf{Q}(2)\mathbf{u}(1)\} \tag{8.4-32}$$

where

$$\mathbf{S}(1) = \mathbf{Q}(1) + \mathbf{R}(1) \tag{8.4-33}$$

Let

$$I_2 = \mathbf{x}'(1)\mathbf{S}(1)\mathbf{x}(1) + \lambda\mathbf{m}'(0)\mathbf{H}(0)\mathbf{m}(0) + \mathbf{u}'(1)\mathbf{Q}(2)\mathbf{u}(1) \tag{8.4-34}$$

It can readily be shown that the expected value of I_2 is

$$J_2 = EI_2 = \mathbf{x}'\boldsymbol{\phi}'\mathbf{S}(1)\boldsymbol{\phi}\mathbf{x} + \mathbf{m}'[\mathbf{G}'\mathbf{S}(1)\mathbf{G} + \lambda\mathbf{H}(0)]\mathbf{m} + 2\mathbf{x}'\boldsymbol{\phi}'\mathbf{S}(1)\mathbf{G}\mathbf{m} + E\{\mathbf{u}'\mathbf{S}(1)\mathbf{u}\} + E\{\mathbf{u}'(1)\mathbf{Q}(2)\mathbf{u}(1)\} \tag{8.4-35}$$

By elementary calculus the condition for minimizing EI_2 is found to be

$$[\mathbf{G}'\mathbf{S}(1)\mathbf{G} + \lambda\mathbf{H}(0)]\mathbf{m}^o = -[\mathbf{G}'\mathbf{S}(1)\boldsymbol{\phi}]\mathbf{x} \tag{8.4-36}$$

The minimum of J_2 is given by

$$f_2 = \mathbf{x}'\boldsymbol{\phi}'\mathbf{S}(1)\boldsymbol{\phi}\mathbf{x} + \mathbf{m}^{o\prime}[\mathbf{G}'\mathbf{S}(1)\mathbf{G} + \lambda\mathbf{H}(0)]\mathbf{m}^o + 2\mathbf{x}'\boldsymbol{\phi}'\mathbf{S}(1)\mathbf{G}\mathbf{m}^o + E\{\mathbf{u}'\mathbf{S}(1)\mathbf{u}\} + E\{\mathbf{u}'(1)\mathbf{Q}(2)\mathbf{u}(1)\} \tag{8.4-37}$$

Subtracting Eq. (8.4-37) from Eq. (8.4-35) yields the difference $EI_2 - f_2$ as

$$EI_2 - f_2 = \mathbf{m}'[\mathbf{G}'\mathbf{S}(1)\mathbf{G} + \lambda\mathbf{H}(0)]\mathbf{m} - \mathbf{m}^{o\prime}[\mathbf{G}'\mathbf{S}(1)\mathbf{G} + \lambda\mathbf{H}(0)]\mathbf{m}^o + 2\mathbf{x}'\boldsymbol{\phi}'\mathbf{S}(1)\mathbf{G}(\mathbf{m} - \mathbf{m}^o) \tag{8.4-38}$$

which may be simplified to

$$EI_2 - f_2 = (\mathbf{m} - \mathbf{m}^o)'[\mathbf{G}'\mathbf{S}(1)G + \lambda\mathbf{H}(0)](\mathbf{m} - \mathbf{m}^o) \tag{8.4-39}$$

Since this equation is of the same form as Eq. (8.4-24), it can be shown by following similar argument that $EI_2 - f_2$ is minimized when the best estimate $\hat{\mathbf{m}}^o(k/k)$ is used. This completes the proof for a two-stage control process. A more complete proof is presented in Ref. 140.

The foregoing discussions point out that, to design optimum control for multivariable processes with inaccessible state variables, it is necessary to find the best estimate of all the state variables from a knowledge of the measured output signals. An optimum multivariable computer control system thus comprises an estimator and an optimum controller, as illustrated in Fig. 8.4-1. The estimator is employed to determine the best estimate of the state variable from the measured output variables, and the controller is used to generate an optimum-control law on the basis of the estimates of the state variables. The estimation and the control may be carried out independently, and the design of the optimum controller is studied in Secs. 8.2 and 8.3. The digital computer in the control system is programmed to perform the functions of both the estimator and the controller.

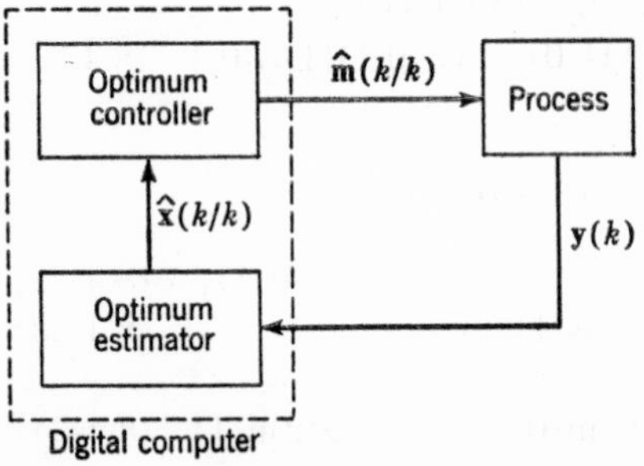

Fig. 8.4-1 Block diagram of a computer control system.

Example 8.4-1 A Control Process with Inaccessible State Variables

Consider the system of Example 8.3-1. It is assumed that the state variable x_1 can be measured directly and that, in the measurement of the state variable x_2, the measuring instrument introduces an additive measurement error of zero mean with standard deviation equal to $\frac{1}{2}$. The measurement error, which is denoted by $w_3(kT)$, is assumed to be essentially independent from one sampling instant to another.

The output signals which can actually be measured are the components of the output vector $\mathbf{y}(k)$ given by

$$\mathbf{y}(k) = \mathbf{M}\mathbf{x}(k) + \mathbf{w}(k)$$

where the sampling period T is dropped for simplicity and the measurement matrix $\mathbf{M}$ is

$$\mathbf{M} = \begin{bmatrix} 0 & 0 & 0 & 1 & 1 \\ 1 & 0 & 0 & 0 & 0 \\ 0 & 1 & 0 & 0 & 0 \end{bmatrix}$$

and the measurement error vector $\mathbf{w}(k)$ is

$$\mathbf{w}(k) = \begin{bmatrix} 0 \\ 0 \\ w_3(k) \end{bmatrix}$$

The measurable output signals are

$$\begin{aligned} y_1(k) &= x_4(k) + x_5(k) \\ y_2(k) &= x_1(k) \\ y_3(k) &= x_2(k) + w_3(k) \end{aligned}$$

From Eq. (8.4-2), the optimum-control law is given by

$$\hat{m}^o(k/k) = 9.346\{\hat{x}_4(k/k) - \hat{x}_1(k/k)\} - 3.673\hat{x}_2(k/k) - 0.72\hat{x}_3(k/k)$$

Thus, once the estimates $\hat{x}_1$, $\hat{x}_2$, $\hat{x}_3$, and $\hat{x}_4$ are determined, the optimization problem will have been solved.

The determination of the state variables from the output variables is discussed in the following section.

8.5 DESIGN OF OPTIMUM ESTIMATOR

The preceding section introduces the concept of optimum estimation and optimum control in the design of control systems with inaccessible state variables. The design procedure is subdivided into two parts:

1. The design of an estimator which determines the best estimates of all the state variables on the basis of the measured output variables
2. The design of an optimum controller which generates the optimum-control law by use of the estimates of the state variables

Before the design of the optimum control is completed, the optimum-estimation problem must be studied. This section is concerned with the determination of the optimum estimate of the state vector $\mathbf{x}(k)$ based upon the measured values of the output vector $\mathbf{y}(j)$ for $j \leq k$ and presents a computational algorithm for the design of the optimum estimator.[82,141,144,145]

The optimum estimate of the state vector $\mathbf{x}(k)$ is determined from the measured values of the output vector $\mathbf{y}(j)$ for $j \leq k$. It is assumed that the measurement begins at $t = 0$ and that the measured values are contaminated with noise. The measured output vector $\mathbf{y}(k)$ and the state vector $\mathbf{x}(k)$ are related by a linear function

$$\mathbf{y}(k) = \mathbf{Mx}(k) + \mathbf{w}(k) \tag{8.5-1}$$

where vector $\mathbf{w}(k)$ denotes the random measurement noise which has zero mean, and matrix $\mathbf{M}$ is the measurement matrix which transforms the state vector into the measured output vector in the absence of measurement noise. The problem of optimum estimation can be formulated as the determination of the best estimate of $\mathbf{x}(k)$ for $k \geq j$, on the basis of the measured values of the components of $\mathbf{y}(i)$ with $0 \leq i \leq j$, such that a certain performance criterion is minimized. In the design of the optimum estimator the minimum-mean-square-error criterion is used. The estimate of $\mathbf{x}(k)$ is said to be optimum if the mean-square error

$$\overline{\varepsilon^2} = E[\mathbf{x}(k) - \mathbf{a}(k/j)]'[\mathbf{x}(k) - \mathbf{a}(k/j)] \tag{8.5-2}$$

is minimized. In this expression, the vector $\mathbf{a}(k/j)$ represents any estimate of the state vector $\mathbf{x}(k)$ based upon the measured values of $\mathbf{y}(i)$ with

$0 \le i \le j$. The estimates are assumed to be linear combinations of the past and present values of $\mathbf{y}(j)$.

Now let $\mathbf{X}(k)$ be the set of all random vectors described by

$$\sum_{i=0}^{k} \mathbf{A}_i \mathbf{x}(i) \tag{8.5-3}$$

and $\mathbf{Y}(j)$ be the set of all random vectors described by

$$\sum_{i=0}^{j} \mathbf{B}_i \mathbf{y}(i) \tag{8.5-4}$$

where $\mathbf{A}_i$ is an $n \times n$ matrix and $\mathbf{B}_i$ is an $n \times p$ matrix. Both matrix $\mathbf{A}_i$ and matrix $\mathbf{B}_i$ are nonrandom; $\mathbf{X}(k)$ defines a finite-dimensional vector space over the real numbers; and $\mathbf{Y}(j)$ describes a subspace of $\mathbf{X}(k)$ if $j \le k$. An estimate of $\mathbf{x}(k)$ made at instant j is a linear combination of the past and present values of $\mathbf{y}(j)$ and is an element of $\mathbf{Y}(j)$. Let $\hat{\mathbf{x}}(k/j)$ be the orthogonal projection of $\mathbf{x}(k)$ to the subspace $\mathbf{Y}(j)$, and $\tilde{\mathbf{x}}(k/j)$ be the normal component of the $\mathbf{x}(k)$. Then, by using the properties of orthogonal projection which are summarized in Sec. 2.2, it can be shown that

$$\mathbf{x}(k) = \hat{\mathbf{x}}(k/j) + \tilde{\mathbf{x}}(k/j) \tag{8.5-5}$$

and that the orthogonal projection is equal to the best estimate of $\mathbf{x}(k)$ that can be obtained from the measured values of $\mathbf{y}(j), \mathbf{y}(j-1), \ldots, \mathbf{y}(0)$, and the normal component accounts for the estimation error.

Consider the nth-order control process characterized by the state-transition equation

$$\mathbf{x}(k+1) = \boldsymbol{\phi}(k)\mathbf{x}(k) + \mathbf{G}(k)\mathbf{m}(k) + \mathbf{u}(k) \tag{8.5-6}$$

The components of $\mathbf{x}(k)$ are the actual state variables. To design the optimum estimator it is desirable that the relationship between optimum estimates and the transition matrix first be established. Let $\boldsymbol{\psi}(k)$ be an $n \times n$ matrix defined by

$$\boldsymbol{\psi}(k) = \boldsymbol{\phi}(k) + \mathbf{G}(k)\mathbf{B}(N-k) \tag{8.5-7}$$

The vector $\boldsymbol{\psi}(k)\hat{x}(k/k)$ is an element of subspace $\mathbf{Y}(k)$. Utilizing the properties of orthogonal projections, it can be shown that the vector

$$\mathbf{x}(k+1) - \boldsymbol{\psi}(k)\hat{\mathbf{x}}(k/k) \tag{8.5-8}$$

is orthogonal to every element of subspace $\mathbf{Y}(k)$, and the orthogonality property leads to the equation

$$\hat{\mathbf{x}}[(k+1)/k] = \boldsymbol{\psi}(k)\hat{\mathbf{x}}(k/k) \tag{8.5-9}$$

Combining Eqs. (8.5-7) and (8.5-9) yields the relationship between optimum estimates and and the transition matrix as

$$\hat{\mathbf{x}}[(k+1)/k)] = \boldsymbol{\phi}(k)\hat{\mathbf{x}}(k/k) + \mathbf{G}(k)\hat{\mathbf{m}}(k/k) \qquad (8.5\text{-}10)$$

In view of Eqs. (8.5-1) and (8.5-5) and the nature of the measurement noise, the estimate of the output vector is related to the estimate of the state vector by

$$\hat{\mathbf{y}}(k/j) = \mathbf{M}\hat{\mathbf{x}}(k/j) \qquad (8.5\text{-}11)$$

and the estimation error is given by

$$\tilde{\mathbf{y}}(k/j) = \mathbf{M}\tilde{\mathbf{x}}(k/j) + \mathbf{w}(k) \qquad (8.5\text{-}12)$$

The vector $\mathbf{M}\hat{\mathbf{x}}(k/j)$ is an element of subspace $\mathbf{Y}(j)$, and the vector $\mathbf{M}\tilde{\mathbf{x}}(k/j)$ is orthogonal to this subspace.

Assume that $\mathbf{Z}(k+1)$ represents the set of all vectors of the form

$$\mathbf{A}^o(k+1)\tilde{\mathbf{y}}[(k+1)/k] \qquad (8.5\text{-}13)$$

where $\mathbf{A}^o$ is an $n \times p$ matrix. Then any vector in subspace $\mathbf{Z}(k+1)$ is orthogonal to every vector in subspace $\mathbf{Y}(k)$. The subspaces $\mathbf{Y}(k)$ and $\mathbf{Z}(k+1)$ are orthonormal to each other, and they are related by

$$\mathbf{Y}(k+1) = \mathbf{Y}(k) + \mathbf{Z}(k+1) \qquad (8.5\text{-}14)$$

Hence the orthogonal projections of vector $\mathbf{x}(k+1)$ on the three vector spaces $\mathbf{Y}(k+1)$, $\mathbf{Y}(k)$, and $\mathbf{Z}(k+1)$ satisfy the relationship

$$\hat{\mathbf{x}}[(k+1)/(k+1)] = \hat{\mathbf{x}}[(k+1)/k] + \mathbf{A}^o(k+1)\tilde{\mathbf{y}}[(k+1)/k] \qquad (8.5\text{-}15)$$

Substituting Eq. (8.5-9) into Eq. (8.5-15) and replacing $k+1$ by k yields

$$\hat{\mathbf{x}}(k/k) = \boldsymbol{\psi}(k-1)\hat{\mathbf{x}}[(k-1)/(k-1)] + \mathbf{A}^o(k)\tilde{\mathbf{y}}[k/(k-1)] \qquad (8.5\text{-}16)$$

Replacing j by $k-1$ in Eq. (8.5-11) leads to

$$\hat{\mathbf{y}}[k/(k-1)] = \mathbf{M}\hat{\mathbf{x}}[k/(k-1)] \qquad (8.5\text{-}17)$$

Equations (8.5-16) and (8.5-17) provide the computational algorithm for the construction of the optimum estimator. From these two equations the block diagram of the optimum estimator is drawn in Fig. 8.5-1, in which the input to the estimator is the measured output vector $\mathbf{y}(k)$ and the output from the estimator is the estimated state variables. The block diagram of a modified optimum estimator is illustrated in Fig. 8.5-2, which points out that optimum estimation requires the estimated control vector at the previous sampling instant as an input. It is noted from Eq. (8.5-16) that the conversion matrix $\mathbf{A}^o$ is still unknown. The next step in the design of the optimum estimator is to derive a computational algorithm for evaluating the conversion matrix.

One approach to the evaluation of the conversion matrix is to derive the recurrence relationship between the covariance matrix $\mathbf{C}(k+1)$ and the conversion matrix $\mathbf{A}^o(k)$. The covariance matrix $\mathbf{C}(k+1)$ is defined as

$$\mathbf{C}(k+1) = E\{\tilde{\mathbf{x}}[(k+1)/k]\tilde{\mathbf{x}}'[(k+1)/k]\} \tag{8.5-18}$$

It follows from Eq. (8.5-5) that the estimation error is given by

$$\tilde{\mathbf{x}}[(k+1)/k] = \mathbf{x}(k+1) - \hat{\mathbf{x}}[(k+1)/k] \tag{8.5-19}$$

Using Eqs. (8.5-6), (8.5-7), and (8.5-9), the estimation error may be expressed as

$$\tilde{\mathbf{x}}[(k+1)/k] = \boldsymbol{\psi}(k)\mathbf{x}(k) - \boldsymbol{\psi}(k)\hat{\mathbf{x}}(k/k) + \mathbf{u}(k) \tag{8.5-20}$$

In view of Eqs. (8.5-5), (8.5-11), and (8.5-15), the estimation error may be

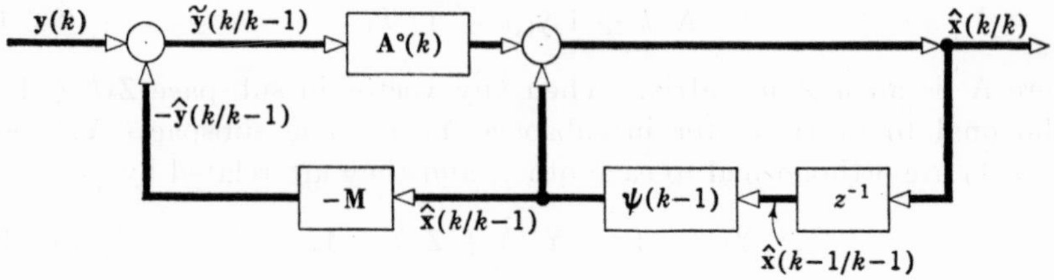

Fig. 8.5-1 Block diagram of an optimum estimator.

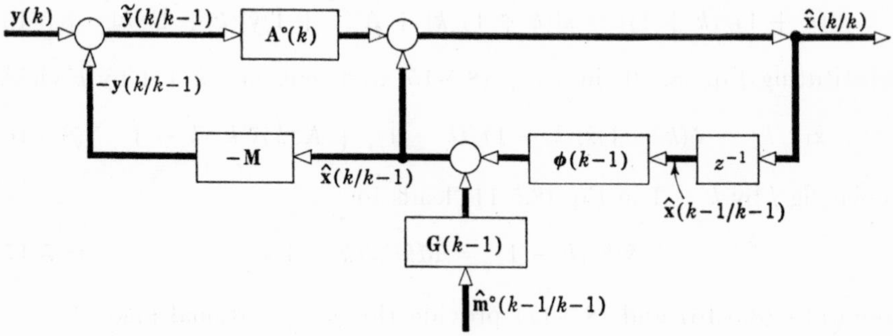

Fig. 8.5-2 Block diagram of a modified optimum estimator.

reduced to the following expression by substitution and rearranging:

$$\tilde{\mathbf{x}}[(k+1)/k] = \boldsymbol{\psi}(k)[\mathbf{I} - \mathbf{A}^o(k)\mathbf{M}]\tilde{\mathbf{x}}[k/(k-1)] - \boldsymbol{\psi}(k)\mathbf{A}^o(k)\mathbf{w}(k) + \mathbf{u}(k) \tag{8.5-21}$$

Thus the covariance defined in Eq. (8.5-18) is given by

$$\mathbf{C}(k+1) = \boldsymbol{\psi}(k)[\mathbf{I} - \mathbf{A}^o(k)\mathbf{M}]\mathbf{C}(k)[\mathbf{I} - \mathbf{A}^o(k)\mathbf{M}]\boldsymbol{\psi}'(k) + \boldsymbol{\psi}(k)\mathbf{A}^o(k)\mathbf{W}(k)\mathbf{A}^{o\prime}(k)\boldsymbol{\psi}'(k) + \mathbf{R}(k) \tag{8.5-22}$$

where $\mathbf{R}(k)$ and $\mathbf{W}(k)$ are defined by

$$\mathbf{R}(k) = E\{\mathbf{u}(k)\mathbf{u}'(k)\} \tag{8.5-23}$$

and

$$\mathbf{W}(k) = E\{\mathbf{w}(k)\mathbf{w}'(k)\} \tag{8.5-24}$$

Since the orthogonal projection of state vector $\mathbf{x}(k+1)$ on subspace $\mathbf{Z}(k+1)$ is

$$\hat{\mathbf{z}}[(k+1)/(k+1)] = \mathbf{A}^o(k+1)\tilde{\mathbf{y}}[(k+1)/k] \tag{8.5-25}$$

the corresponding estimation error is

$$\tilde{\mathbf{z}}[(k+1)/(k+1)] = \mathbf{x}(k+1) - \mathbf{A}^o(k+1)\tilde{\mathbf{y}}[(k+1)/k] \tag{8.5-26}$$

which is a vector of independent random variables with zero mean. It can be shown that

$$E\{[\mathbf{x}(k+1) - \mathbf{A}^o(k+1)\tilde{\mathbf{y}}[(k+1)/k]]\tilde{\mathbf{y}}'[(k+1)/k]\} = 0 \tag{8.5-27}$$

which reduces to

$$\mathbf{C}(k+1)\mathbf{M}' = \mathbf{A}^o(k+1)[\mathbf{M}\mathbf{C}(k+1)\mathbf{M}' + \mathbf{W}(k+1)] \tag{8.5-28}$$

where the covariance matrices $\mathbf{C}(k+1)$ and $\mathbf{W}(k+1)$ are defined in Eqs. (8.5-18) and (8.5-24), respectively. Hence the conversion matrix $\mathbf{A}^o(k+1)$ is given by

$$\mathbf{A}^o(k+1) = [\mathbf{C}(k+1)\mathbf{M}'][\mathbf{M}\mathbf{C}(k+1)\mathbf{M}' + \mathbf{W}(k+1)]^{-1} \tag{8.5-29}$$

The matrix $[\mathbf{M}\mathbf{C}(k+1)\mathbf{M}' + \mathbf{W}(k+1)]$ is assumed to be nonsingular. Equations (8.5-22) and (8.5-29) provide a computational algorithm for the determination of the conversion matrix $\mathbf{A}^o$. Starting with a given value of covariance $\mathbf{C}(0)$, Eq. (8.5-29) yields $\mathbf{A}^o(0)$, and Eq. (8.5-22) gives the covariance $\mathbf{C}(1)$. The conversion matrix $\mathbf{A}^o(1)$ is obtained from Eq. (8.5-29) by the substitution of the calculated value of $\mathbf{C}(1)$. Equation (8.5-22) is then used to compute the covariance $\mathbf{C}(2)$, which determines the conversion matrix $\mathbf{A}^o(2)$ upon substitution into Eq. (8.5-29). Hence repeated application of the recurrence relationship given in Eqs. (8.5-29) and (8.5-22) yields the conversion matrices $\mathbf{A}^o(0)$, $\mathbf{A}^o(1)$, $\mathbf{A}^o(2)$, . . . , $\mathbf{A}^o(k)$, . . . , successively. In a computer control system, the above computational algorithm is programmed on the digital computer of the system.

Example 8.5-1 The Optimum Estimation of State Variables

Consider the control system of Example 8.3-1. Since the measurement-error vector is

$$\mathbf{w}(k) = \begin{bmatrix} 0 \\ 0 \\ w_3(k) \end{bmatrix}$$

and the standard deviation of measurement error $w_3(k)$ is $\frac{1}{2}$ and the mean-square value is $\frac{1}{4}$, the covariance matrix $\mathbf{W}(k)$ is found to be

$$\mathbf{W}(k) = \begin{bmatrix} 0 & 0 & 0 \\ 0 & 0 & 0 \\ 0 & 0 & \frac{1}{4} \end{bmatrix}$$

It follows from Eqs. (8.1-8) and (8.5-23) that the covariance matrix $\mathbf{R}(k)$ is given by

$$\begin{aligned} \mathbf{R}(k) &= \int_{kT}^{(k+1)T} \int_{kT}^{(k+1)T} E\{\boldsymbol{\phi}(\overline{k+1}\,T, \tau)\mathbf{n}(\tau)\mathbf{n}'(\sigma)\boldsymbol{\phi}'(\overline{k+1}\,T, \sigma)\}\,d\tau\,d\sigma \\ &= \int_{kT}^{(k+1)T} \int_{kT}^{(k+1)T} \boldsymbol{\phi}(\overline{k+1}\,T, \tau)E\{\mathbf{n}(\tau)\mathbf{n}'(\tau)\}\boldsymbol{\phi}'(\overline{k+1}\,T, \sigma)\,d\tau\,d\sigma \end{aligned}$$

By noting that the disturbance vector is

$$\mathbf{n}(\tau) = \begin{bmatrix} 0 \\ 0 \\ n_3(\tau) \\ 0 \\ n_5(\tau) \end{bmatrix}$$

and that both n_3 and n_5 are white noise with spectral density equal to 1, it is found that the covariance $E\{\mathbf{n}(\tau)\mathbf{n}'(\tau)\}$ is given by

$$E\{\mathbf{n}(\tau)\mathbf{n}'(\tau)\} = \begin{bmatrix} 0 & 0 & 0 & 0 & 0 \\ 0 & 0 & 0 & 0 & 0 \\ 0 & 0 & \delta(\tau-\sigma) & 0 & 0 \\ 0 & 0 & 0 & 0 & 0 \\ 0 & 0 & 0 & 0 & \delta(\tau-\sigma) \end{bmatrix}$$

where $\delta(\tau - \sigma)$ is an impulse function which is equal to unity at $\tau = \sigma$, and zero otherwise. Hence the covariance matrix $\mathbf{R}(k)$ is

$$\mathbf{R}(k) = \int_{kT}^{(k+1)T} \begin{bmatrix} 0 & 0 & \alpha & 0 & 0 \\ 0 & 0 & \beta & 0 & 0 \\ 0 & 0 & \lambda & 0 & 0 \\ 0 & 0 & 0 & 0 & 0 \\ 0 & 0 & 0 & 0 & 0 \end{bmatrix} \boldsymbol{\phi}'(\overline{k+1}\,T, \sigma)\,d\sigma$$

where

$$\begin{aligned} \alpha &= \tfrac{1}{2}(1 + e^{-2(\overline{k+1}\,T-\sigma)}) - e^{-(\overline{k+1}\,T-\sigma)} \\ \beta &= e^{-(\overline{k+1}\,T-\sigma)} - e^{-2(\overline{k+1}\,T-\sigma)} \\ \lambda &= e^{-2(\overline{k+1}\,T-\sigma)} \\ \mu &= e^{-0.5(\overline{k+1}\,T-\sigma)} \end{aligned}$$

Finally, it is found that

$$\mathbf{R}(k) = \begin{bmatrix} 7 \times 10^{-4} & 3 \times 10^{-3} & 6.8 \times 10^{-3} & 0 & 0 \\ 3 \times 10^{-4} & 0.014 & 0.043 & 0 & 0 \\ 6.8 \times 10^{-3} & 0.043 & 0.216 & 0 & 0 \\ 0 & 0 & 0 & 0 & 0 \\ 0 & 0 & 0 & 0 & 0.394 \end{bmatrix}$$

To determine the covariance $\mathbf{C}(0)$, it is observed that $x_3(0)$ and $x_5(0)$ are independent random variables with zero mean, and their variances are calculated from their spectral densities as $\frac{1}{4}$ and 1, respectively. Both $x_1(0)$ and $x_4(0)$ are assumed to be uniformly distributed between $-\pi$ and $+\pi$, and $x_2(0)$ is identically zero. Thus the covariance matrix $\mathbf{C}(0)$ is given by

$$\mathbf{C}(0) = E\{\mathbf{x}(0)\mathbf{x}'(0)\} = \begin{bmatrix} \frac{\pi^2}{3} & 0 & 0 & 0 & 0 \\ 0 & 0 & 0 & 0 & 0 \\ 0 & 0 & \frac{1}{4} & 0 & 0 \\ 0 & 0 & 0 & \frac{\pi^2}{3} & 0 \\ 0 & 0 & 0 & 0 & 1 \end{bmatrix}$$

The conversion matrices $\mathbf{A}^o(k)$ can then be determined from Eqs. (8.5-22) and (8.5-29). They are found to be

$$\mathbf{A}^o(0) = \begin{bmatrix} 0 & 1 & 0 \\ 0 & 0 & 0 \\ 0 & 0 & 0 \\ 0.767 & 0 & 0 \\ 0.233 & 0 & 0 \end{bmatrix} \qquad \mathbf{A}^o(1) = \begin{bmatrix} 0 & 1 & 0 \\ 0 & 3.38 & 0.010 \\ 0 & 7.14 & 0.041 \\ 0.393 & 0 & 0 \\ 0.607 & 0 & 0 \end{bmatrix}$$

$$\mathbf{A}^o(2) = \begin{bmatrix} 0 & 1 & 0 \\ 0 & 3.01 & 0.011 \\ 0 & 5.75 & 0.055 \\ 0.363 & 0 & 0 \\ 0.637 & 0 & 0 \end{bmatrix} \qquad \mathbf{A}^o(3) = \begin{bmatrix} 0 & 1 & 0 \\ 0 & 2.94 & 0.010 \\ 0 & 5.27 & 0.056 \\ 0.336 & 0 & 0 \\ 0.664 & 0 & 0 \end{bmatrix}$$

$$\mathbf{A}^o(4) = \begin{bmatrix} 0 & 1 & 0 \\ 0 & 2.93 & 0.010 \\ 0 & 5.30 & 0.056 \\ 0.313 & 0 & 0 \\ 0.687 & 0 & 0 \end{bmatrix} \quad \cdots$$

This completes the optimum synthesis of the given control system. The optimum estimator and optimum controller can be realized by programming on a general-purpose digital computer or can be mechanized by building a special-purpose digital computer. The measured output variables $y_1(k)$, $y_2(k)$, and $y_3(k)$ and the control signal $m(k-1)$ are fed into the optimum estimator to generate the desired estimates $\hat{x}_1(k/k)$, $\hat{x}_2(k/k)$, $\hat{x}_3(k/k)$, and $\hat{x}_4(k/k)$, which in turn are fed back into the optimizer to generate the optimum-control law. It should be noted that, even though the given control system is time-invariant, the conversion matrix $\mathbf{A}^o(k)$ varies with k, and therefore the resulting optimum-control system is a time-varying system.

8.6 CONCLUSION

This chapter discusses an approach to the design of computer control systems. The digital computer in the control system usually performs the functions of monitoring, data processing, and optimum control. The third phase of operation is considered, and optimization is performed with respect to the quadratic performance index

$$I_N = \sum_{k=1}^{N} [\mathbf{x}'(k)\mathbf{Q}(k)\mathbf{x}(k) + \lambda\mathbf{m}'(k-1)\mathbf{H}(k-1)\mathbf{m}(k-1)]$$

The control process is assumed to be linear. The optimum-design problem is solved by use of the dynamic-programming theory.

When all the state variables are accessible for measurement and observation, the optimum-control vector $\mathbf{m}^o(k)$ is a linear function of the state vector $\mathbf{x}(k)$:

$$\mathbf{m}^o(k) = \mathbf{B}(N-k)\mathbf{x}(k)$$

The feedback matrix $\mathbf{B}(N-k)$ generally varies with time, and the optimum control system is a time-varying system. If the control process is subjected to additive independent random disturbances and the above optimum-control law is used, the system is still optimum in the sense that the expected value of the quadratic performance index is minimized.

When the control processes contain inaccessible state variables, the optimum-control law is given by

$$\hat{\mathbf{m}}^o(k/k) = \mathbf{B}(N-k)\hat{\mathbf{x}}(k/k)$$

where $\hat{\mathbf{x}}(k/k)$ is the best estimate of the state vector $\mathbf{x}(k)$ based upon the measured output vectors $\mathbf{y}(j)$, $\mathbf{y}(j-1)$, . . . , $\mathbf{y}(0)$, in the sense that the expected value of the estimation error is a minimum. Optimum control requires the feedback of all the estimated state variables. It has been shown that an optimum control system with respect to a quadratic performance index can be designed by optimizing independently the controller and the estimator. Optimum controller and optimum estimator can be designed separately to yield a system which is optimum in the overall sense. A computational algorithm for optimum estimation is derived, and recurrence relationships for the evaluation of the control law are determined. To unify the design procedure, the inputs and disturbances are characterized by state variables, and the original control process can be represented by an augmented system.

References

Suggested references are Aoki,[5] Aris,[6] Bellman,[15,18] Guignabodet,[72] Joseph and Tou,[82] Kalman,[86] Kalman and Koepcke,[93] Lewis and Tou,[115] Tou,[137,140,141a] Tou and Joseph,[144,145] and Tou and Lewis.[146]

PROBLEMS

2.1 Show that the intersection of a finite number of convex sets is also a convex set.

2.2 Show that two hyperplanes are parallel if they have the same unit normal.

2.3 Show that a triangle and its interior form a simplex in the two-dimensional case.

2.4 Show that if a set of n-dimensional vectors is linearly independent, then any subset of these vectors is also linearly independent.

2.5 Given

$$\mathbf{A} = \begin{bmatrix} a_{11} & a_{12} \\ a_{21} & a_{22} \end{bmatrix}$$

$$\mathbf{\Lambda} = \mathbf{T}^{-1}\mathbf{A}\mathbf{T} = \begin{bmatrix} \lambda_1 & 0 \\ 0 & \lambda_2 \end{bmatrix}$$

where λ_1 and λ_2 are eigenvalues of $\mathbf{A}$. Show that

$$e^{\mathbf{A}t} = \mathbf{T}e^{\mathbf{\Lambda}t}\mathbf{T}^{-1}$$

and determine $\mathbf{T}$ in terms of eigenvalues.

2.6 Show that two eigenvectors of a real symmetric matrix corresponding to different eigenvalues are orthogonal.

2.7 Show that, if the eigenvalues of matrix $\mathbf{A}$ are distinct, matrix $\mathbf{A}$ can be transformed into a diagonal matrix

$$\mathbf{T}^{-1}\mathbf{A}\mathbf{T} = \begin{bmatrix} \lambda_1 & 0 & \cdots & 0 \\ 0 & \lambda_2 & \cdots & 0 \\ \cdots & \cdots & \cdots & \cdots \\ 0 & 0 & \cdots & \lambda_n \end{bmatrix}$$

where $\lambda_1, \lambda_2, \ldots, \lambda_n$ are the eigenvalues of matrix $\mathbf{A}$, and matrix $\mathbf{T}$ is formed by using the corresponding eigenvectors as columns.

2.8 Given

$$\dot{\mathbf{x}} = \mathbf{A}\mathbf{x} + \mathbf{d}m$$

where the components x_i of the vector $\mathbf{x}$ are related by

$$\begin{aligned} \dot{x}_1 &= x_2 \\ \dot{x}_2 &= x_3 \\ &\cdots\cdots \\ \dot{x}_{n-1} &= x_n \\ \dot{x}_n &= b_n x_1 + b_{n-1} x_2 + b_{n-2} x_3 + \cdots + b_1 x_n + dm \end{aligned}$$

The matrix $\mathbf{A}$ is transformed into a diagonal matrix such that

$$\mathbf{T}^{-1}\mathbf{AT} = \begin{bmatrix} \lambda_1 & 0 & \cdots & 0 \\ 0 & \lambda_2 & \cdots & 0 \\ \cdots & \cdots & \cdots & \cdots \\ 0 & 0 & \cdots & \lambda_n \end{bmatrix}$$

where $\lambda_1, \lambda_2, \ldots, \lambda_n$ are the eigenvalues of matrix $\mathbf{A}$. Show that matrix $\mathbf{T}$ is given by

$$T = \begin{bmatrix} 1 & 1 & 1 & \cdots & 1 \\ \lambda_1 & \lambda_2 & \lambda_3 & \cdots & \lambda_n \\ \lambda_1^2 & \lambda_2^2 & \lambda_3^2 & \cdots & \lambda_n^2 \\ \cdots & \cdots & \cdots & \cdots & \cdots \\ \lambda_1^{n-1} & \lambda_2^{n-1} & \lambda_3^{n} & \cdots & \lambda_n^{n-1} \end{bmatrix}$$

2.9 Referring to the Sylvester expansion theorem of Sec. 2.3, show that
(*a*) $[\mathbf{F}(\lambda_i)]^r = \mathbf{F}(\lambda_i)$.
(*b*) $\sum_{i=1}^{n} \mathbf{F}(\lambda_i) = \mathbf{I}$.

2.10 Use the Cayley-Hamilton theorem to derive an expression for $\mathbf{A}^{-1}$ as a polynomial in $\mathbf{A}$, provided that the matrix $\mathbf{A}$ is nonsingular.

2.11 Discuss various methods for evaluating $f(\mathbf{A})$, where $\mathbf{A}$ is an $n \times n$ constant matrix.

2.12 By use of Hamilton's variational principles, derive the hamiltonian canonical equations.

3.1 Draw the state-variable diagram for (*a*) a first-order hold; (*b*) a fractional-order hold.

3.2 Derive the state-variable diagram for (*a*) a square-wave input signal; (*b*) a

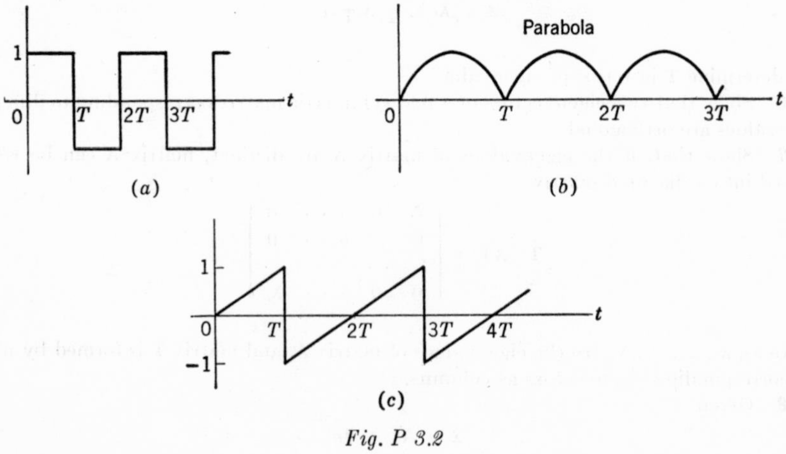

Fig. P 3.2

parabolic-wave input signal; (*c*) a sawtooth input signal; (*d*) $r(t) = e^{-at} \sin \omega t$; (*e*) a stochastic input with power-spectral density

$$\Phi_{rr}(\omega) = \frac{1}{1 + \omega^2}$$

3.3 Determine the state-variable diagrams for the dynamic systems described by
(*a*) $\ddot{x}(t) + a\dot{x}(t) + bx(t) = c\dot{m}(t) + dm(t)$.
(*b*) $\dddot{x}(t) + 4\ddot{x}(t) + 5\dot{x}(t) + 2x(t) = m(t)$.

3.4 Derive the state-variable diagrams for the system shown in Fig. P 3.4 (*a*) by direct programming; (*b*) by parallel programming; (*c*) by iterative programming. Write down the state differential equations and the state-transition equations for each case.

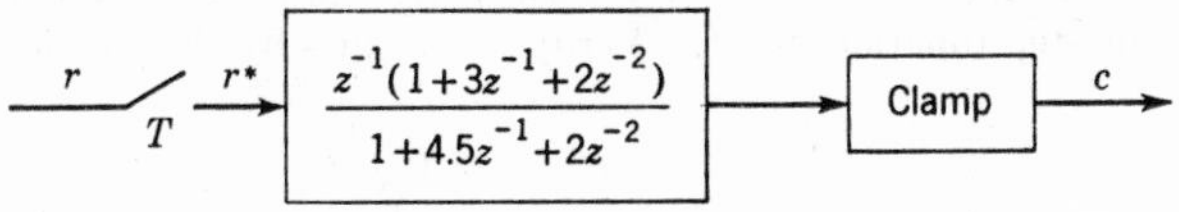

Fig. P 3.4

3.5 Draw the state-variable diagram for a *k*th-order hold.

3.6 Determine the overall transition matrix for the system shown in Fig. P 3.6.

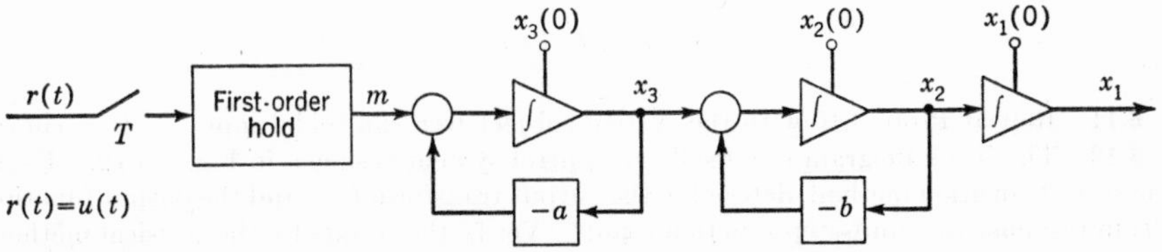

Fig. P 3.6

3.7 Determine the overall transition matrices for the dynamic systems described in Prob. 3.3, where in (*a*) $m(t) = t$, and in (*b*) $m(t) = \sin \omega t$.

3.8 Referring to Fig. P 3.8, the transfer matrix $\mathbf{G}(s)$ of the system is

$$\mathbf{G}(s) = \begin{bmatrix} \dfrac{10}{s(s+1)} & \dfrac{1}{s} \\ \dfrac{1}{s} & \dfrac{10}{s(s+1)} \end{bmatrix}$$

(*a*) Write down the state differential equation in vector-matrix notations.
(*b*) Draw the state-variable diagram for the multivariable system.
(*c*) Determine the output $\mathbf{c}(t)$ in response to step-function input

$$\mathbf{r}(t) = \begin{bmatrix} R_1u(t) \\ R_2u(t) \end{bmatrix}$$

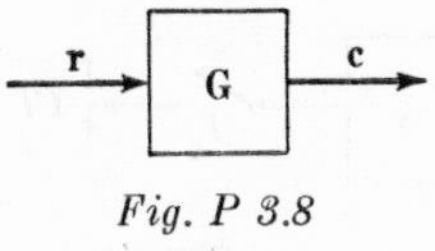

Fig. P 3.8

3.9 Shown in Fig. P 3.9 is a simple system subject to a sawtooth input.
(*a*) Determine the **A** matrix, the **B** matrix, and the overall transition matrix **Φ** for the system.

(*b*) Find the output $c(t)$ by the state-transition method and by the Laplace-transform method.

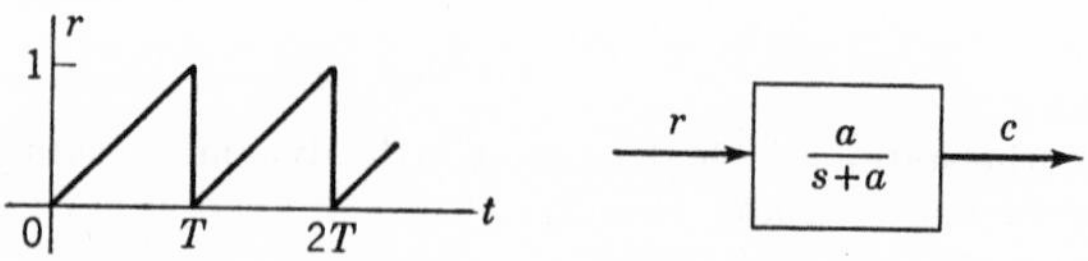

Fig. P 3.9

3.10 The state-variable diagram of a simple discrete-data control system is shown in Fig. P 3.10. Determine the output transform $X_1(z)$ and the output function $x_1(t)$ in response to a unit-step-function input. Verify the results by the classical method.

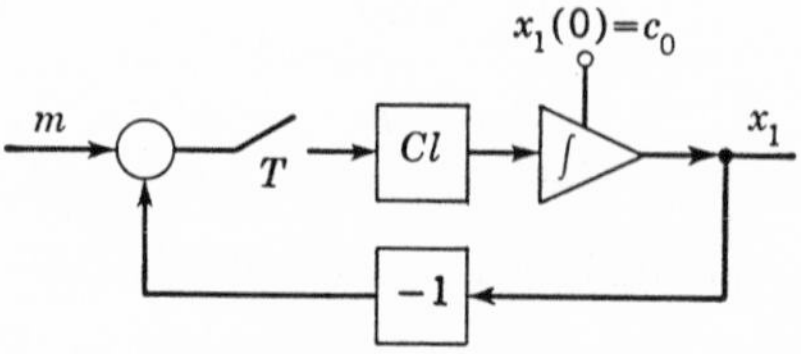

Fig. P 3.10

3.11 Repeat Prob. 3.10 with the system subject to a sinusoidal input, $m(t) = \sin \omega t$.

3.12 The block diagram of a feedback control system is shown in Fig. P 3.12. Using the state-transition method, determine the output transform $C(z)$ and the output function $c(t)$ in response to a unit-step-function input. Verify the results by the classical method.

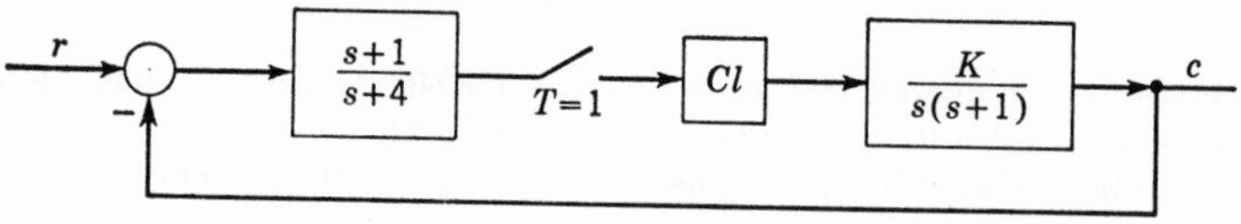

Fig. P 3.12

3.13 Repeat Prob. 3.13 with the system subject to a sinusoidal input $r(t) = \sin \omega t$.

3.14 With reference to the system in Prob. 3.12, determine the maximum allowable gain K for stability by the state-transition method and by the classical method.

3.15 The block diagram of a feedback discrete-data control system is depicted in Fig. P 3.15. It is given that the input signal is a unit-step function, the sampling period is 1 sec, and the initial conditions on the control process are $c(0^+) = 1$ and $\dot{c}(0^+) = 1$. Find the output response $c(t)$ by the state-transition method and by the modified z-transform method.

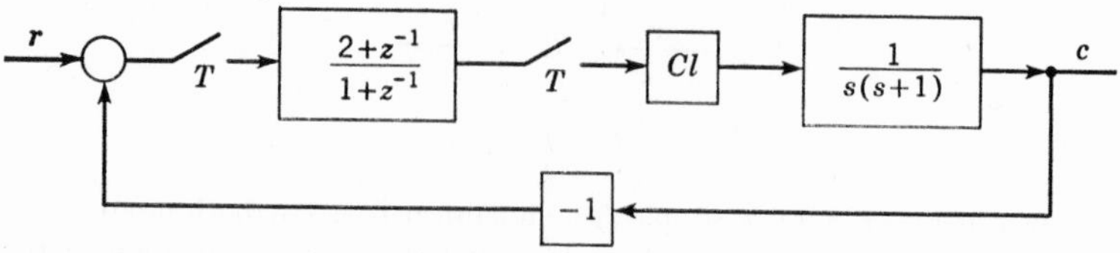

Fig. P 3.15

3.16 Shown in Fig. P 3.16 is the state-variable diagram of a multirate sampled-data control system. The samplers in the forward branch and in the feedback branch operate with sampling periods $\frac{1}{2}$ sec and $\frac{1}{3}$ sec, respectively. Zero initial conditions are assumed.

(*a*) Determine the maximum allowable gain for stability.

(*b*) Evaluate the system response to a unit-step-function input with gain constant $K = 1$.

(*c*) Repeat (*b*) when the system is subject to an input $r(t) = (1 + t)u(t)$.

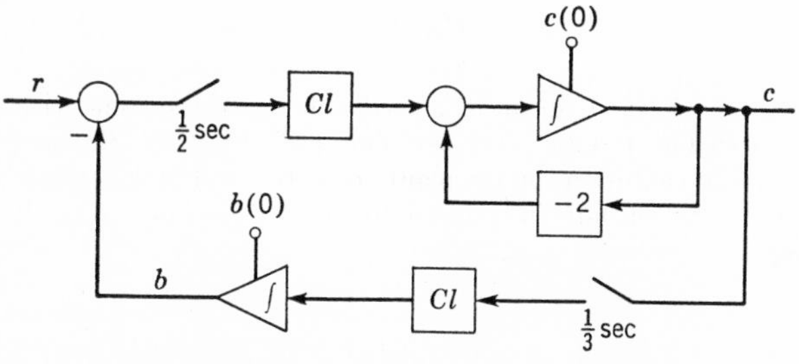

Fig. P 3.16

3.17 Repeat Prob. 3.16 when the initial conditions on the integrators are assumed to be $c(0^+) = 5$ and $b(0^+) = 1$.

3.18 The state-variable diagram of a nonsynchronized sampled-data feedback control system is shown in Fig. P 3.18. The samplers S_1 and S_2 operate with the same sampling period equal to 0.5 sec, but they are not synchronized.

(*a*) Determine the maximum allowable gain for stability when the slip factor of the sampler S_2 is 0.25, 0.5, 0.75.

(*b*) What is the best slip factor for system stability?

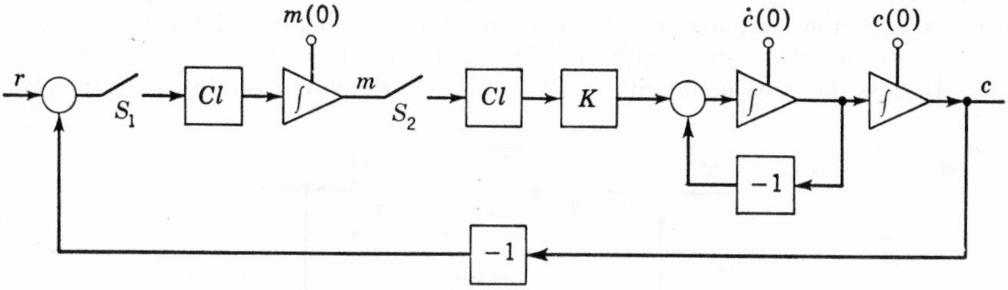

Fig. P 3.18

3.19 Shown in Fig. P 3.19 is the state-variable diagram of a cyclic-variable multirate sampled-data control system. The sampler S operates at a constant rate with sampling period equal to 1 sec. The sample S_v is a cyclic variable-rate sampler which samples at $t = 0,\ T/4;\ T,\ 5T/4;\ \ldots\ ;\ kT,\ (k + \frac{1}{4})T;\ \ldots$. The period of the variable sampler S_v is assumed to be 1 sec.

(*a*) Investigate the stability of this system.

(*b*) With the gain constant K equal to 1, determine the system output in response to a unit-step-function input.

(*c*) Repeat (*b*) with the input $r(t) = (1 - e^{-t})u(t)$.

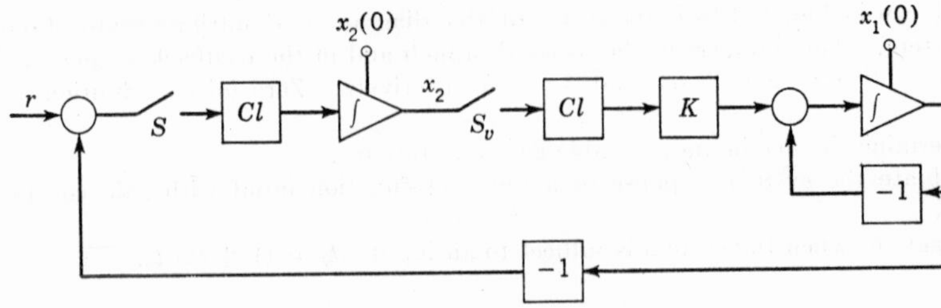

Fig. P 3.19

3.20 The state-variable diagram of a feedback control system with finite sampling duration is shown in Fig. P 3.20. The sampling period is 1 sec, the sampling duration is 0.4 sec, and the initial conditions on the plant are $x_1(0^+) = 1$ and $x_2(0^+) = 1$. Determine the system output function $x_1(t)$ in response to a unit-step-function input, and sketch the output response.

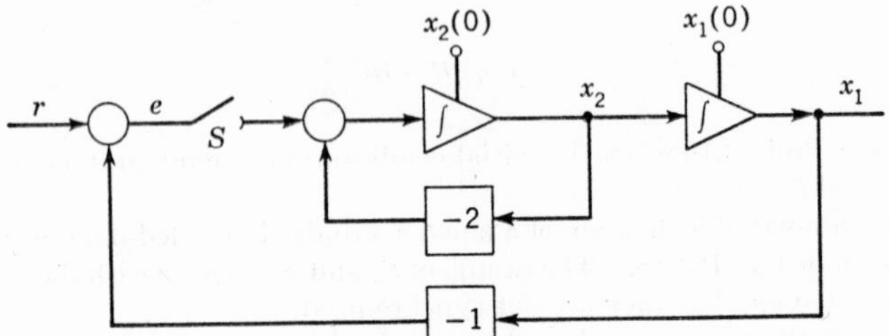

Fig. P 3.20

3.21 Referring to the feedback control system with finite sampling duration shown in Fig. P 3.21, the sampling period is 1 sec and the sampling duration is 0.6 sec.

(*a*) Determine the system output $c(t)$ in response to (1) $r(t) = e^t$ and (2) $r(t) = u(t)$.

(*b*) Discuss the system stability and the effects of the initial conditions of the plant.

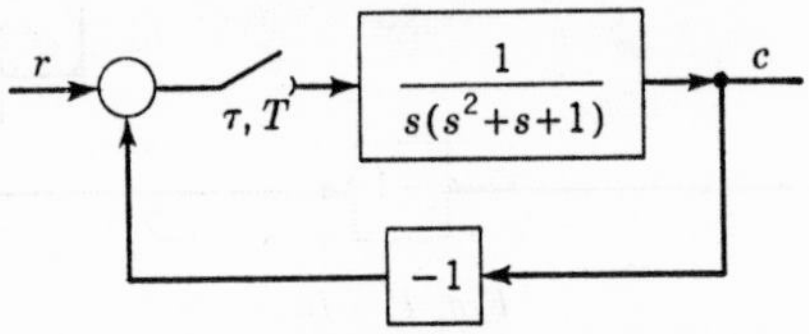

Fig. P 3.21

3.22 Consider the pulse-width-modulated control system shown in Fig. P 3.22. The transfer function of the control process is

$$G(s) = \frac{K}{s(1 + 0.1s)}$$

The initial conditions on the control process are assumed to be $c(0^+) = 0$ and $\dot{c}(0^+) = 0$. The pulse-width modulator possesses the following properties: the sampling period is

1 sec; the magnitude of the pulse is equal to unity; and the width of the pulse is equal to the value of the corresponding sample. With $K = 1$, determine the output of the system in response to a unit-step-function input. Discuss the stability of the system.

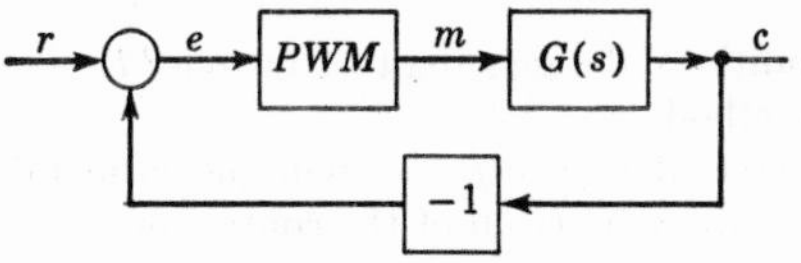

Fig. P 3.22

3.23 Repeat Prob. 3.22, but now the system is incorporated with a pulse-width modulator possessing the properties that the sampling period is 0.1 sec, the magnitude of the pulse is equal to unity, and the width of the pulse is equal to the logarithm of the corresponding sample.

3.24 The state-variable diagram of a variable-gain feedback control system is shown in Fig. P 3.24. The variable-gain element is characterized by $K(t) = 1 + e^{-t}$. The initial conditions for the control process are $c(0^+) = 1$ and $\dot{c}(0^+) = 1$.

(*a*) Determine the system output in response to a unit-step-function input.

(*b*) Evaluate the system output in response to a sawtooth input.

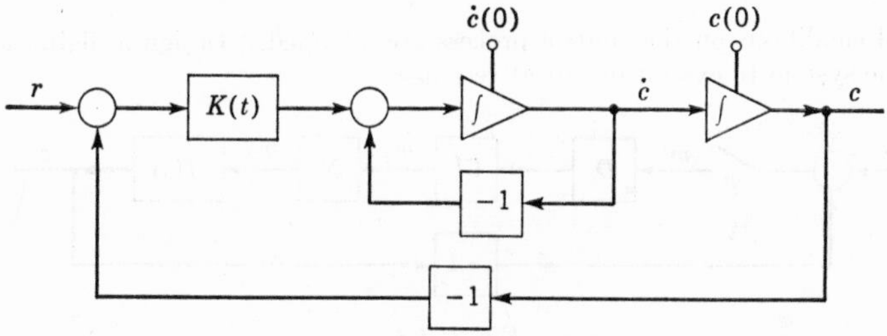

Fig. P 3.24

3.25 Show that the relationship given in Eq. (3.5-19) holds.

4.1 For the discrete-data control system shown in Fig. P 4.1, the sampling period is taken as 0.2 sec and the control process has the transfer function

$$G(s) = \frac{10}{s(1 + 0.1s)(1 + 0.05s)}$$

Zero initial conditions are assumed. By use of the state-transition method, design a digital controller $D(z)$ for deadbeat performance. Verify the result by the classical method. Discuss the effects of the initial conditions of the control process.

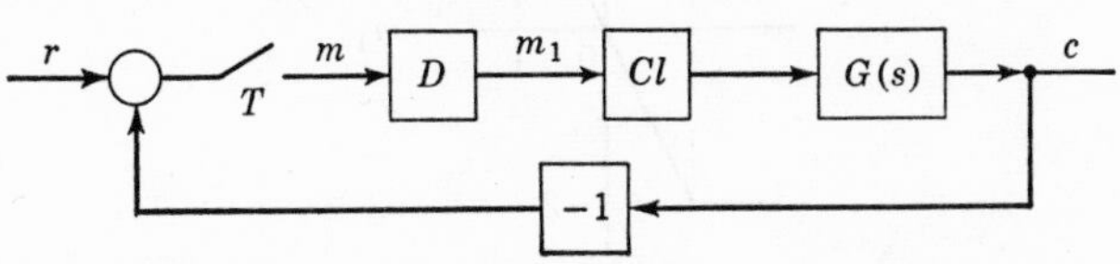

Fig. P 4.1

4.2 Consider the discrete-data control system shown in Fig. P 4.1. The sampling period is equal to 1 sec, and the transfer function of the control process is

$$G(s) = \frac{1}{(s+1)^2}$$

Assuming zero initial conditions, design a digital controller $D(z)$ for deadbeat performance by the state-transition method.

4.3 Consider the discrete-data control system shown in Fig. P 4.1. The sampling period is 1 sec, and the transfer function of the control process is

$$G(s) = \frac{4(s+1)}{s(s+2)}$$

Assuming zero initial conditions:

(*a*) Design a digital controller $D(z)$ for deadbeat performance.

(*b*) Discuss the effect of zeros upon response time.

4.4 Referring to the nonlinear digital control system shown in Fig. P 4.4, the sampling period is 1 sec, the transfer function of the control process is

$$G(s) = \frac{4(s+1)}{s(s+2)}$$

and the nonlinear element is characterized by the input-output relationship

$$m_2 = m_1 - m_1^3$$

Zero initial conditions on the control process are assumed. Design a digital controller $D(z)$ for the system to exhibit deadbeat response.

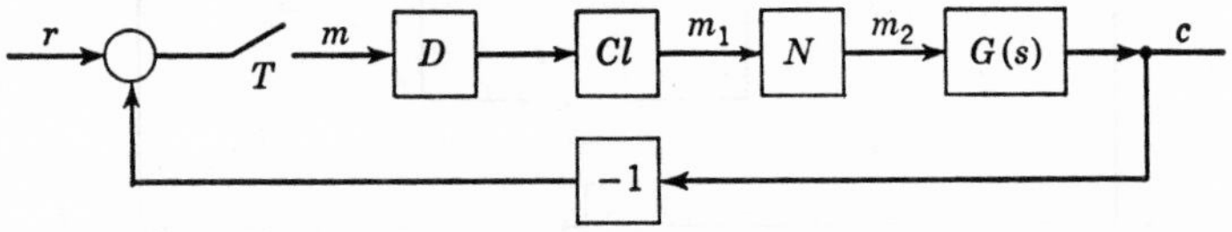

Fig. P 4.4

4.5 Consider the nonlinear digital control system shown in Fig. P 4.4. The control process has the transfer function

$$G(s) = \frac{4}{s(s+1)(s+2)}$$

The nonlinear element is described by the input-output characteristic as shown in Fig. P 4.5. This system is subject to a step-function input $r(t) = 10u(t)$.

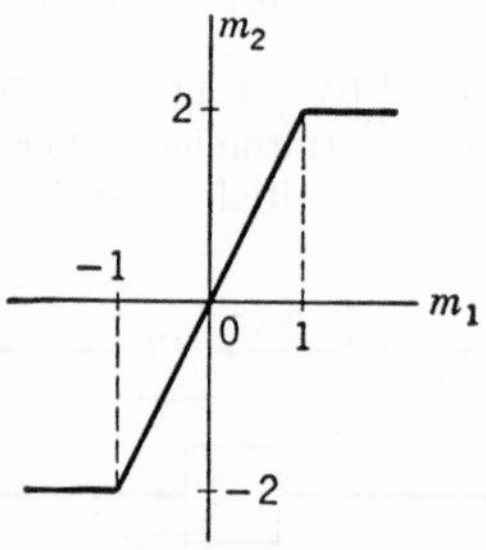

Fig. P 4.5

(*a*) Design a digital controller $D(z)$ for deadbeat performance.

(*b*) Determine the maximum step-function input for the system to settle in three sampling periods; in four sampling periods; in five sampling periods; and design the desired digital controller $D(z)$ in each case.

4.6 With reference to the nonlinear digital control system shown in Fig. P 4.4, the sampling period is 1 sec and the transfer function of the control process is

$$G(s) = \frac{10(s+1)}{s(s^2+s+1)}$$

The characteristic of the nonlinear element is illustrated in Fig. P 4.5. This system is subject to a unit-step-function input.

(*a*) Design a digital controller $D(z)$ for deadbeat performance.

(*b*) Determine the maximum step-function input for the system to deadbeat in three sampling periods; in four sampling periods; in five sampling periods; and design the desired digital controller $D(z)$ in each case.

4.7 Repeat Prob. 4.5, but now the transfer function of the control process is

$$G(s) = \frac{1}{s(s+1)}$$

The system is subject to a unit-step-function input, and the nonlinearities are illustrated in Fig. P 4.7*a* and *b*, respectively.

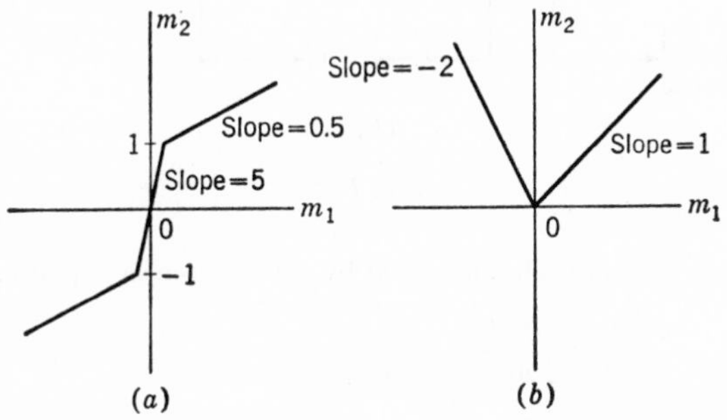

Fig. P 4.7

4.8 Repeat Prob. 4.7, but this time the nonlinear elements have the input-output characteristics shown in Fig. P 4.8*a* and *b*.

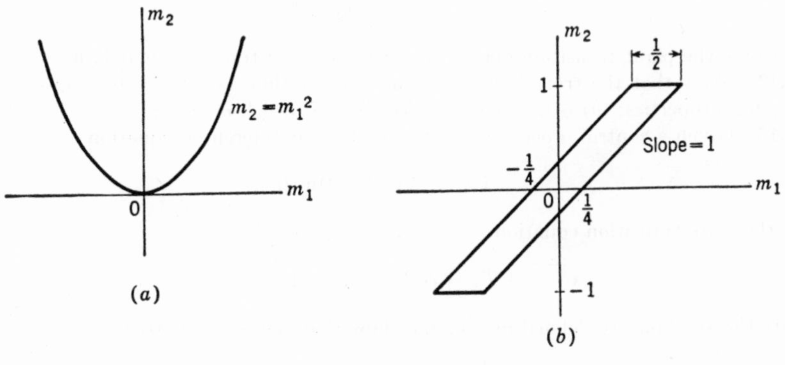

Fig. P 4.8

4.9 Determine the $\boldsymbol{\Phi}$ matrix, the $\boldsymbol{\phi}$ matrix, the $\mathbf{h}$ matrix, and the state-transition equation for the systems shown in Fig. P 4.9.

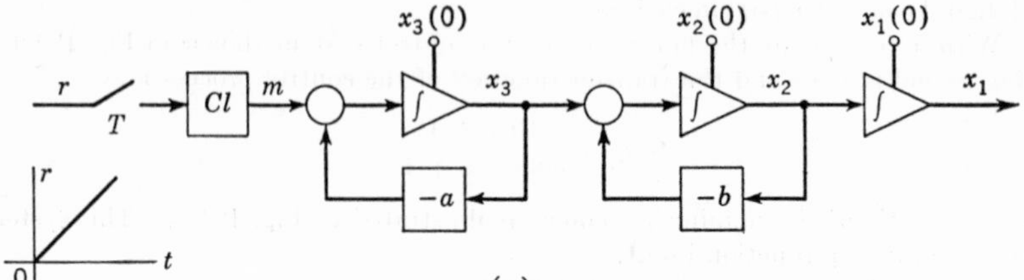

(*a*)

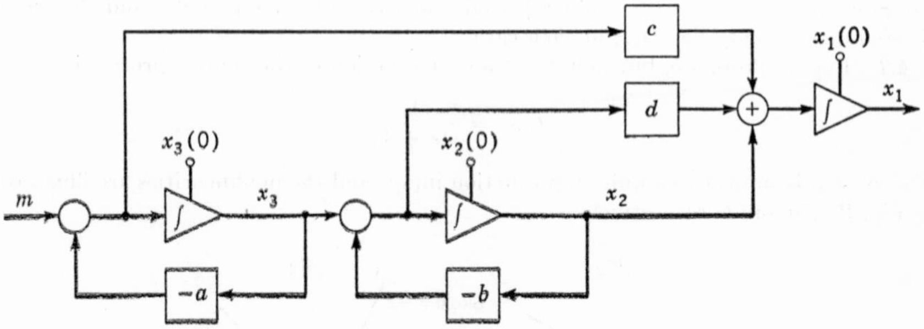

(*b*)

Fig. P 4.9

4.10 A dynamic system is characterized by the differential equation

$$\frac{d^3x(t)}{dt^3} + \frac{d^2x(t)}{dt^2} + \frac{dx(t)}{dt} + x(t) = \frac{dm(t)}{dt} + m(t)$$

Convert this ordinary differential equation into vector-matrix form, and determine the plant transition matrix $\boldsymbol{\phi}$ and the control transition matrix $\mathbf{h}$.

4.11 For the control process characterized by the following set of first-order differential equations,

$$\dot{x}_1 = x_2$$
$$\dot{x}_2 = -ax_2 - bx_1 + m$$

determine the plant transition matrix $\boldsymbol{\phi}$ and the control transition matrix $\mathbf{h}$.

4.12 Show that the transition matrix of a linear time-varying system possesses the following properties: (*a*) $\boldsymbol{\phi}(t;\lambda)\boldsymbol{\phi}(\lambda;\tau) = \boldsymbol{\phi}(t;\tau)$; (*b*) $\boldsymbol{\phi}^{-1}(t;\tau) = \boldsymbol{\phi}(\tau;t)$.

4.13 Given a control process characterized by the differential equation

$$\dot{\mathbf{x}}(t) = \mathbf{A}\mathbf{x}(t) + \mathbf{D}\mathbf{m}(t)$$

and the state-transition equation

$$\mathbf{x}(\overline{k+1}\,T) = \boldsymbol{\phi}(T)\mathbf{x}(kT) + \mathbf{h}(T)\mathbf{m}(kT)$$

where the symbols are defined in Sec. 4.3, show that the set of matrices

$$\mathbf{s}_i = \boldsymbol{\phi}(-iT)\mathbf{h}(T) \qquad i = 1, 2, \ldots, n$$

form a basis in space S if and only if, for every eigenvalue λ of $\mathbf{A}$,

$$[\text{Im}\ \lambda]T \neq k\pi$$

where T is the sampling period, k is a positive integer, and Im λ denotes the imaginary part of λ.

4.14 Show that an nth-order continuous process characterized by

$$\dot{\mathbf{x}}(t) = \mathbf{A}\mathbf{x}(t) + \mathbf{d}m(t)$$

is completely controllable if and only if the vectors

$$\mathbf{d}, \mathbf{A}\mathbf{d}, \mathbf{A}^2\mathbf{d}, \ldots, \mathbf{A}^{n-1}\mathbf{d}$$

are linearly independent.

4.15 Show that the linear independency condition for controllability also holds for control processes with multiple inputs. The necessary and sufficient condition for controllability is that n columns in the basis matrices $\mathbf{s}_i$, $i = 1, 2, \ldots, n$, be linearly independent.

4.16 The dynamics of a control process is characterized by the differential equation

$$\frac{d^2x(t)}{dt^2} + (a - 2b \cos 2t)x(t) = m(t)$$

(*a*) Find $x(t)$.

(*b*) Determine the state-transition equation for the discrete case.

4.17 An electronic system is characterized by the differential equation

$$\frac{d^2x(t)}{dt^2} + a(t)\frac{dx(t)}{dt} + bx(t) = m(t)$$

where $a(t) = R_0(1 + \alpha \cos \omega_1 t)$, $0 < \alpha \ll 1$, $m(t) = E \cos \omega_2 t$, and b is a constant.

(*a*) Find $x(t)$.

(*b*) Determine the state-transition equation for the discrete case.

4.18 Consider a control process with transfer function

$$G(s) = \frac{10}{s(s+1)(s+2)}$$

and initial states $x_1(0) = 1$, $x_2(0) = 1$, and $x_3(0) = 1$. Determine the optimum-control strategy $m^o(kT)$ which will move the process from the given initial state to the equilibrium state in minimum time.

4.19 Repeat Prob. 4.18 with

$$G(s) = \frac{10(s+2)}{s^2(s+1)}$$

4.20 Repeat Prob. 4.18 with

$$G(s) = \frac{1}{s(s^2+s+1)}$$

4.21 Consider a multivariable control process with transfer matrix given by

$$\mathbf{G}(s) = \begin{bmatrix} \dfrac{10}{s(s+1)} & \dfrac{1}{s} \\ \dfrac{1}{s} & \dfrac{10}{s(s+1)} \end{bmatrix}$$

This process is subject to a control vector $\mathbf{m} = [m_2 \quad m_2]'$, and the initial conditions on the integrators of the state-variable diagram are assumed to be all equal to 1. Determine the optimum-control strategy $\mathbf{m}^o(kT)$ which is required to move the process from the given initial state to the equilibrium state in minimum time.

4.22 The dynamics of a control process is described by the following set of differential equations:

$$\dot{x}_1 = x_2$$
$$\dot{x}_2 = -2\zeta x_2 - x_1 + m$$

where x_1 and x_2 are the state variables, m is the control signal, and ζ is the damping constant. The control signal m is constrained by $|m| \leq 1$.

(*a*) Determine the switching boundary for various values of ζ: $\zeta = 1.5$, $\zeta = 0.5$, $\zeta = 0$, $\zeta = -0.5$, $\zeta = -1.5$.

(*b*) Plot the switching boundaries.

(*c*) Assuming that the initial state is $x_1(0) = 4$, $x_2(0) = 3$, find the optimum trajectory for each case.

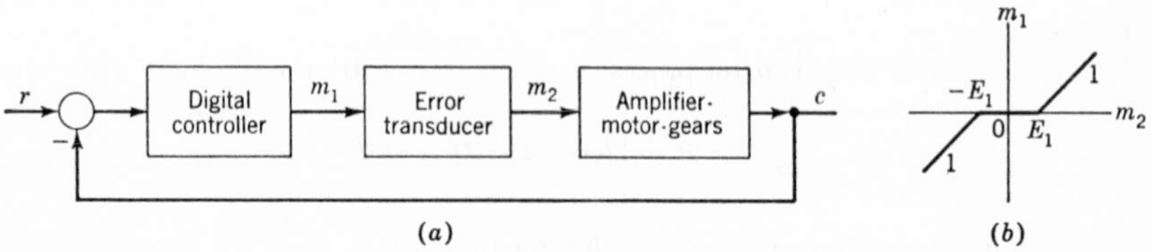

Fig. P 4.23

4.23 Shown in Fig. P 4.23*a* is an electromechanical control system. The transfer function of the amplifier, motor, and gears is

$$G(s) = \frac{10}{s^2(s+1)}$$

and the input-output characteristic of the error transducer is illustrated in Fig. P 4.23*b*.

Design a digital controller $D(z)$ so that the system will respond with deadbeat performance to step-function inputs of magnitudes ranging between 1 and 10.

4.24 Shown in Fig. P 4.24 is a simple discrete-data control system. The control signal m is subject to saturation such that $|m| \leq 4$. Determine the optimum-control sequences $\{m^o\}$ which are required to move the process from the initial states (*a*) $x_1(0) = 1$, $x_2(0) = 1$ and (*b*) $x_1(0) = 10$, $x_2(0) = -10$ to the equilibrium state in minimum time.

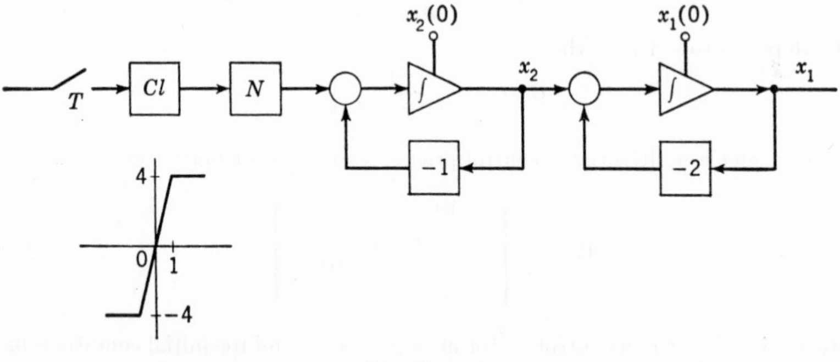

Fig. P 4.24

4.25 Referring to the discrete-data control system shown in Fig. P 4.25, the control process possesses a pair of complex poles and the control signal is restricted to +1 and −1. The transfer function $G(s)$ is

$$G(s) = \frac{10}{s^2 + s + 1}$$

Determine the optimum-control sequence $\{m^o\}$ for moving the process from the initial state $x_1(0) = 1$, $x_2(0) = 1$, to the equilibrium state in minimum time.

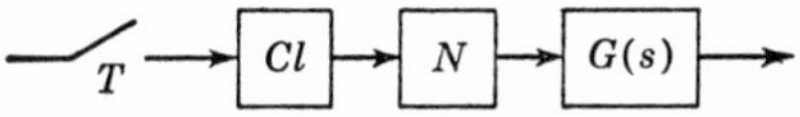

Fig. P 4.25

4.26 Repeat Prob. 4.25 with the transfer function of the process given by

$$G(s) = \frac{1}{s(s^2 + s + 1)}$$

and the initial state $x_1(0) = 1$, $x_2(0) = 1$, $x_3(0) = 1$.

4.27 The state-variable diagram of a cyclic variable-rate sampled-data control process is shown in Fig. P 4.27. The sampler S_v samples at $t = 0, T/4; T, 5T/4; \ldots; kT, (k + \frac{1}{4})T; \ldots$. The sampling period T is assumed to be 1 sec, and the initial-state vector of the control process is $\mathbf{x}(0) = [1 \quad 2 \quad 1]'$. The control signal is subject to the constraint $|m| \leq 1$. Find the least number of sampling periods for the process to reach the equilibrium state from the given initial state, and determine the desired optimum-control sequence $\{m^o\}$ and the optimum-control law.

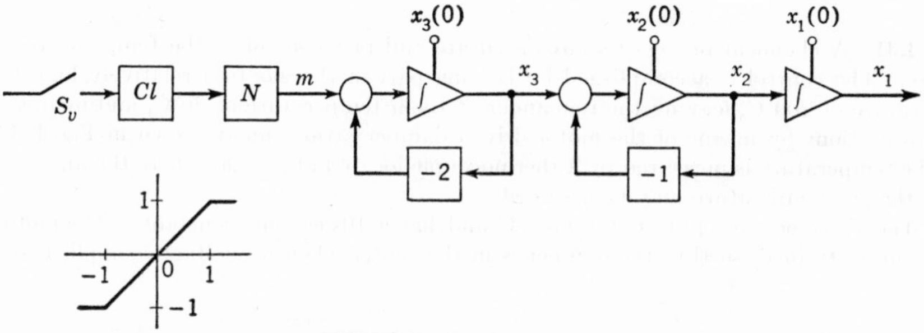

Fig. P 4.27

4.28 Consider the multivariable control process of Prob. 4.21. It is now assumed that the control signals are subject to the constraints $|m_1| \leq 1$ and $|m_2| \leq 1$. Determine the control sequence $\{\mathbf{m}^o\}$ for time-optimal control of the process.

4.29 Shown in Fig. P 4.29 is the state-variable diagram of a finite-width discrete-data system with control signals subject to saturation. The sampling period is 1 sec, the pulse width is 0.2 sec, and $|m| \leq 1$.

Design a digital control for moving the system from the initial state $\mathbf{x}(0) = [1 \quad 2]'$ to the equilibrium state in minimum time.

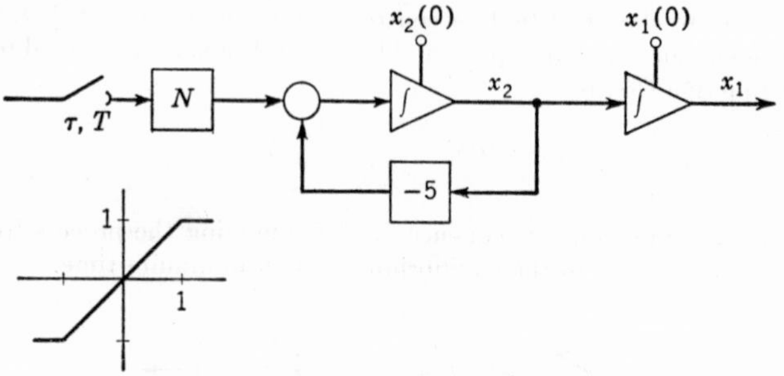

Fig. P 4.29

4.30 A simple pulse-width-modulated system is illustrated in Fig. P 4.30. The control process is characterized by transfer function

$$G(s) = \frac{1}{s(1 + 0.1s)}$$

and the initial conditions are given by $x(0) = 1$ and $\dot{x}(0) = 1$. The sampling period is 1 sec, and the pulse-width modulator generates a train of pulses of unity magnitude, the width of which is equal to the value of the corresponding sample.

Design a digital control to move the system from the given initial state to the equilibrium state in minimum time.

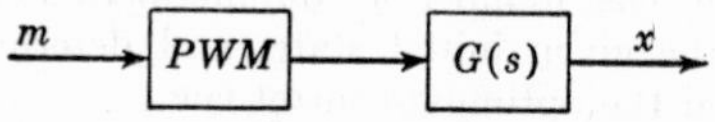

Fig. P 4.30

4.31 A chemical process requires accurate and fast control of the temperature of a gas. The control is accomplished by heating part of the gas to a relatively high temperature of 200°C, leaving the remainder at room temperature of 20°C, and mixing the two portions by means of the motor-driven damper arrangement shown in Fig. P 4.31. The temperature is measured by a thermocouple located at a point where the uniformity of the gas temperature may be assumed.

The thermocouple puts out 1 mv/°C and has a 10-sec time constant. The motor is spring-restrained, so that the damper is in the center when no voltage is applied to the

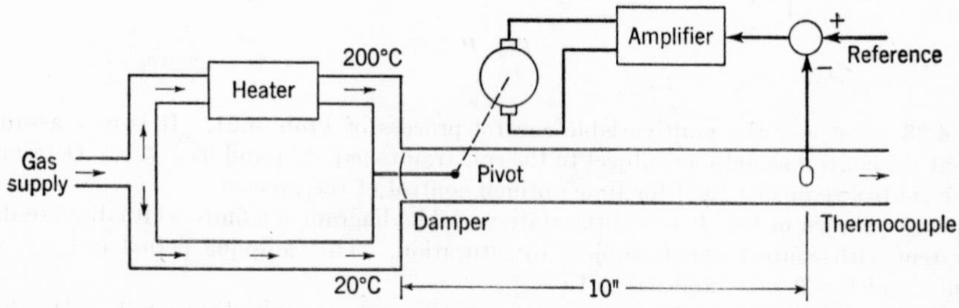

Fig. P 4.31

amplifier. At ± 1 mv at the amplifier grid, the damper moves from the neutral position to a point where air flow through one channel is cut off completely. The variation of air flow through each channel with damper position is assumed to be linear. The motor time constant is 1 sec, the total rate of gas flow is constant at 200 in.^{3}/sec, the pipe has a cross-sectional area of 2 in.^{2}, and the thermocouple is located at a distance of 10 in. from the damper.

Design an optimum controller for the system to exhibit deadbeat response.

4.32 For horizontal flight, the control characteristics of a missile frequently can be described by the differential equation relating the control-surface deflection $\theta(t)$ and the angular heading of the missile, $c(t)$:

$$T_m \frac{d^2c(t)}{dt^2} + \frac{dc(t)}{dt} = K_1\theta(t)$$

where K_1 = radians per second of c per radian of θ, and T_m = missile time constant in seconds.

An amplifier and power boost with gain K_2 is used to provide the control power, where K_2 = radians deflection of control surface per volt input to amplifier.

Assume that

$$T_m = 2 \text{ sec} \qquad K_1 = 2.5 \qquad K_2 = 100$$

and the control-surface deflection is limited to ± 1 rad. Design an optimum controller so that the system will respond with minimum-time performance.

4.33 Consider the roll control for an airplane by a digital controller as shown in Fig. P 4.33. The combined autopilot and airplane characteristic is given by the transfer function

$$G(s) = \frac{1.5}{s(1 + s/3)(1 + s/25)}$$

The gain constant of the preamplifier is equal to 10.

Design a digital controller so that the roll control for the airplane will exhibit deadbeat performance.

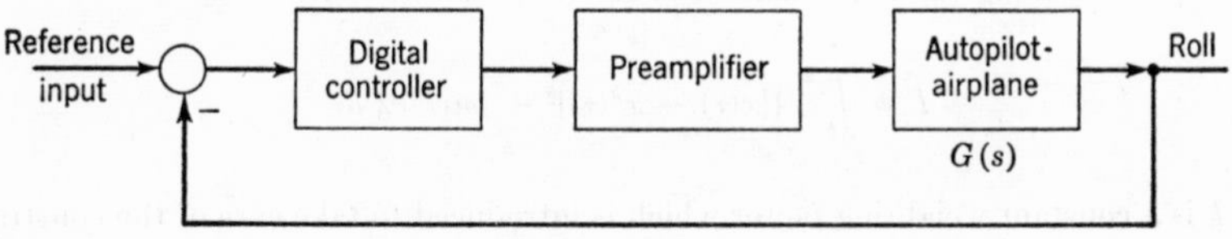

Fig. P 4.33

4.34 The pitch control of an airplane is complicated by the oscillatory response of the airplane itself and by the additional delay due to the path time constant. Shown in Fig. P 4.34 is the block diagram of a proposed pitch-control system for the airplane. The transfer function of the combined autopilot and airplane is

$$G_1(s) = \frac{10(1 + s)}{s(1 + s/10)(1 + 1.4s/5 + s^2/5^2)}$$

and the transfer function of the path is

$$G_2(s) = \frac{1}{1 + s}$$

Design a digital controller for the steering system so that the airplane path will respond to the stepwise inputs with deadbeat performance.

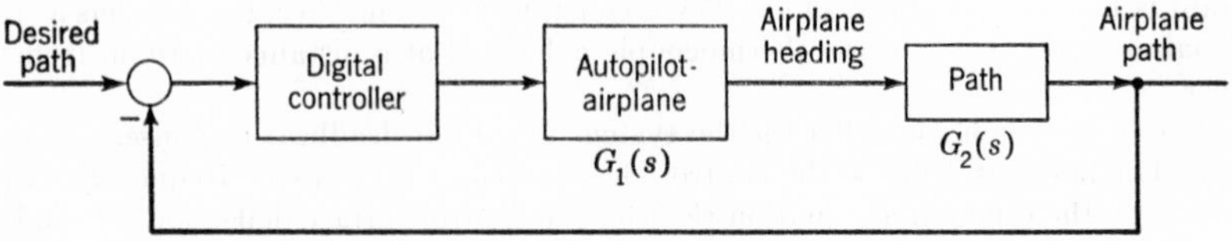

Fig. P 4.34

4.35 Work out the design procedure for the minimum-time control of a multi-input system. The control signals are subject to saturation constraint.

4.36 Extend the method of coordinate transformation developed in Sec. 4.5 to the design of minimum-time control for discrete systems subject to control-signal saturation.

5.1 Consider an nth-order process characterized by the differential equation

$$\frac{d^n x(t)}{dt^n} + \alpha_{n-1}\frac{d^{n-1}x(t)}{dt^{n-1}} + \cdots + \alpha_k \frac{d^k x(t)}{dt^k} + \cdots + \alpha_1 \frac{dx(t)}{dt} + \alpha_0 x(t) = m(t)$$

where the coefficients α_k are known constants and the control signal is subject to the constraint

$$|m| \leq 1$$

Determine the Euler-Lagrange equations for the optimum-control signal to minimize the performance index

$$I = \int_t^\infty [x(\tau) - x^d(\tau)]^2 \, d\tau$$

If the effect of the constraint on control signal m is taken into account in the optimization process by considering the minimization of the performance index

$$I = \int_t^\infty \{[x(\tau) - x^d(\tau)]^2 + [m(\tau)]^k\} \, d\tau$$

where k is a constant weighting factor which is introduced to take care of the constraint, show that the Euler-Lagrange equations are

$$\dot{x}_1 + \sum_{k=1}^{n} \alpha_{n-k} x_k = m$$

$$\dot{x}_k = x_{k-1} \qquad k = 2, 3, \ldots, n$$

$$\dot{\lambda}_k = \alpha_{n-k}\lambda_k - \lambda_{k+1} \qquad k = 1, 2, \ldots, n-1$$

$$\dot{\lambda}_n = \alpha_0 \lambda_1 + x_n - x^d$$

where

$$m = \operatorname{sgn}(\lambda_1) \left| \frac{2}{r} \lambda_1 \right|^{1/(r-1)}$$

and λ_k denote the Lagrange multipliers. By imposing the constraint in this way, the derivatives of the variables generated by the Euler-Lagrange equations remain continuous. This results in a significant computational advantage.

5.2 Given a control process characterized by

$$\frac{d^n x(t)}{dt^n} + a_{n-1}\frac{d^{n-1}x(t)}{dt^{n-1}} + \cdots + a_1\frac{dx(t)}{dt} + a_0 x(t) = b_0 m(t) + b_1\frac{dm(t)}{dt} + \cdots + b_r\frac{d^r m(t)}{dt^r}$$

with $x(t)$ representing the output signal, $m(t)$ denoting the control signal, and the initial conditions given by

$$\left.\frac{d^k x(t)}{dt^k}\right|_{t=0} = x_k(0) \qquad k = 0, 1, \ldots, n-1$$

and

$$\left.\frac{d^j m(t)}{dt^j}\right|_{t=0} = m_j(0) \qquad j = 0, 1, \ldots, r-1$$

determine the optimum-control signal $m(t)$ which minimizes the performance index

$$I = \int_0^\infty m^2(t)\, dt$$

subject to the constraint

$$\int_0^{t_f} m^2(t)\, dt = K$$

and at $t = t_f^+$,

$$\left.\frac{d^j m(t)}{dt^j}\right|_{t=t_f^+} = m_j(t_f)$$

5.3 A linear control process is characterized by

$$\frac{d^n x(t)}{dt^n} + a_{n-1}\frac{d^{n-1}x(t)}{dt^{n-1}} + \cdots + a_1\frac{dx(t)}{dt} + a_0 x(t) = b_0 m(t) + \sum_{i=1}^{r} b_i\frac{d^i m(t)}{dt^i}$$

The control signal $m(t)$ is subject to the constraint

$$\int_0^{t_f} m^2(t)\, dt = K$$

and $m(t) = 0$ for $t > t_f$, where t_f represents the time of regulation. Design an optimum controller which minimizes the control-energy function

$$I = \int_0^{t_f} |m(t)|\, dt$$

5.4 Consider a linear nth-order control process described by

$$\dot{\mathbf{x}}(t) = \mathbf{A}\mathbf{x}(t) + \mathbf{D}m(t)$$

with the initial conditions given by $\mathbf{x}(0)$. The control signal $m(t)$ satisfies the control-energy constraint

$$\int_0^{t_f} m^2(t)\, dt = K$$

Design an optimum controller to move the process from the given initial state $\mathbf{x}(0)$ to the zero state in the shortest time.

5.5 By use of the variational calculus, study the bang-bang servo problem.

5.6 Derive a solution for the Mayer problem as formulated in Sec. 5.1.

5.7 Consider a simple second-order system described by

$$\ddot{x}(t) + \dot{x}(t) = m(t)$$

The system output is subject to the constraint

$$x(t) \geq 0$$

Design an optimum controller to minimize the performance index

$$I = \int_t^T \{[x(t) - x^d(t)]^2 + [m(t)]^2\}\, dt$$

where $x^d(t)$ represents the desired output of the system.

5.8 Given a second-order system characterized by

$$\ddot{x}(t) = m(t)$$

determine the condition for minimizing the performance index

$$I = \int_t^{t_f} \{[x(t) - x^d(t)]^2 + [m(t)]^2\}\, dt$$

The state variable $x(t)$ is subject to the constraint

$$x(t) \geq 0$$

5.9 A second-order control process is characterized by

$$\ddot{x}(t) + \dot{x}(t) + x(t) = m(t)$$

with boundary conditions $\mathbf{x}(0) = \mathbf{x}_0$, $\mathbf{x}(t_f) = \mathbf{0}$. Determine the control signal $m(t)$ which will take the process from a given initial state to the equilibrium state in minimum time. The control signal is subject to the constraint

$$\int_0^{t_f} m^2(t)\, dt = 1$$

5.10 Given a second-order control system described by the differential equation

$$\ddot{x}(t) + \dot{x}(t) + x(t) = m(t)$$

where the control signal is subject to the constraint

$$\int_0^{t_f} m^2(t)\, dt = 10$$

determine the optimum-control signal $m^o(t)$ which will move the system from the initial state $x(0) = 1$, $\dot{x}(0) = 2$, to the equilibrium state $x(t_f) = \dot{x}(t_f) = 0$ in minimum time.

5.11 Show that the fundamental necessary condition for the integral

$$I = \int_{t_0}^{t_f} F[x_1(t), \dot{x}_1(t), \ldots, x_1^{(n)}(t); x_2(t), \dot{x}_2(t), \ldots, x_2^{(n)}(t); \ldots; x_r(t), \dot{x}_r(t), \ldots, x_r^{(n)}(t); t]\, dt$$

to be an extremum is

$$\frac{\partial F}{\partial x_i} - \frac{d}{dt}\frac{\partial F}{\partial \dot{x}_i} + \cdots + (-1)^n \frac{d^n}{dt^n}\frac{\partial F}{\partial x_i^{(n)}} = 0$$

where the integrand F is differentiable, the end points are fixed, and

$$x_i^{(n)}(t) \triangleq \frac{d^n x_i(t)}{dt^n}$$

5.12 Determine the transversality conditions for the problem of finding the extrema of the integral

$$I = \int_{t_0}^{t_f} F[x(t), \dot{x}(t), y(t), \dot{y}(t), t]\, dt$$

with the boundary points $P_0(x_0, y_0, t_0)$ fixed and $P_1(x_1, y_1, t_f)$ movable.

(*a*) $P_1(x_1, y_1, t_f)$ can move along a certain curve $x_1 = c_1(t_f)$ and $y_1 = c_1(t_f)$.

(*b*) $P_1(x_1, y_1, t_f)$ can move on a surface $x_1 = \varphi(y_1, t_f)$.

6.1 The dynamics of a linear control process is described by the differential equations

$$\dot{x}_i(t) = \sum_{j=1}^{n} a_{ij}x_j(t) + d_i m(t)$$

where the x_i denote the state variables of the system and the a_{ij} and d_i are constant coefficients. The control signal is subject to the constraint

$$|m(t)| \leq 1$$

Show that the optimum-control signal to minimize the functional

$$I = \int_0^\infty \left[\sum_{i=1}^{n} \alpha_i x_i^2(t) + \lambda m^2(t) \right] dt$$

is given by

$$m(t) = \begin{cases} \dfrac{1}{2\lambda} \displaystyle\sum_{i=1}^{n} d_i p_i & \text{for } \left| \dfrac{1}{2\lambda} \displaystyle\sum_{i=1}^{n} d_i p_i \right| \leq 1 \\ 1 & \text{for } \dfrac{1}{2\lambda} \displaystyle\sum_{i=1}^{n} d_i p_i \geq 1 \\ -1 & \text{for } \dfrac{1}{2\lambda} \displaystyle\sum_{i=1}^{n} d_i p_i \leq -1 \end{cases}$$

and the optimum-control law is

$$m(\mathbf{x}) = \begin{cases} \dfrac{1}{2\lambda} \displaystyle\sum_{i=1}^{n} \beta_i x_i & \text{for } \left| \dfrac{1}{2\lambda} \displaystyle\sum_{i=1}^{n} \beta_i x_1 \right| \leq 1 \\ 1 & \text{for } \dfrac{1}{2\lambda} \displaystyle\sum_{i=1}^{n} \beta_i x_i \geq 1 \\ -1 & \text{for } \dfrac{1}{2\lambda} \displaystyle\sum_{i=1}^{n} \beta_i x_i \leq -1 \end{cases}$$

where the p_i are as defined in Sec. 6.2, the β_i are given by

$$\beta_i = \sum_{j=1}^{n} d_j \mu_{ji}$$

and

$$p_i(0) = \sum_{j=1}^{n} \mu_{ij} x_j(0)$$

6.2 Consider the linear process characterized by

$$\dot{\mathbf{x}}(t) = \mathbf{A}(t)\mathbf{x}(t) + \mathbf{D}(t)\mathbf{m}(t) \qquad \mathbf{x}(0) = \mathbf{x}_0$$

Show that, if there exists an optimum-control policy $\mathbf{m}$ such that the integral

$$\int_{t_0}^{t_f} F[\mathbf{x}(t) - \mathbf{x}^d(t)]\, dt$$

is minimized, where $\mathbf{x}^d(t)$ is the desired state vector, there exists an optimum relay control; that is,

$$|m_i| = M_i$$

for all t within the interval (t_0, t_f).

6.3 A second-order control system is characterized by the differential equation

$$\ddot{x}(t) = m(t)$$

where the control signal $m(t)$ is subject to the physical constraint

$$|m(t)| \leq M$$

for all t.

Determine the optimum-control signal $m^o(t)$ which will move the system from a given initial state $\mathbf{x}(0)$ to the equilibrium state in minimum time.

6.4 Consider the control system of Prob. 6.3. Determine the optimum-control signal $m^o(t)$ which will move the system from a given initial state $\mathbf{x}(0)$ to the equilibrium state and will minimize the total fuel consumption during the course of optimum control. The fuel consumption is given by

$$I = \int_0^{t_f} |m(t)|\, dt$$

The control trajectory terminates at t_f, which is not specified.

6.5 Consider the second-order control system of Prob. 6.3. Determine the optimum-control signal $m^o(t)$ that will minimize the fuel consumption in the process of moving the system from a given initial state $\mathbf{x}(0)$ to the equilibrium state in time t_f. The fuel consumption is measured by

$$I = \int_0^{t_f} |m(t)|\, dt$$

The time of control t_f is subject to the constraint that

$$t_f \leq \alpha t^0$$

where α is a given constant greater than 1, and t^0 is the minimum time required to move the system from a specified initial state $\mathbf{x}(0)$ to the equilibrium state as determined in Prob. 6.3.

6.6 A second-order system subject to a delayed control signal is described by differential equations

$$\begin{aligned} \dot{x}_1(t) &= x_2(t) \\ \dot{x}_2(t) &= -ax_1(t) - bx_2(t) + m(t - \tau) \end{aligned}$$

where a and b are prespecified constants, and τ represents the time delay for the application of the control signal which is constrained by $|m(t)| \leq 1$ for all t. Determine the optimum-control signal $m^o(t)$ which will move the system from a given initial state $\mathbf{x}(0)$ to the equilibrium state in the shortest possible time.

6.7 Consider the control system of Prob. 6.6. Determine the optimum-control signal $m^o(t)$ which will minimize the total energy required to move the system from a given initial state $\mathbf{x}(0)$ to the equilibrium state. The total energy of control is measured by the performance index

$$I = \int_0^{t_f} m^2(t)\, dt$$

where t_f denotes the time at which the system reaches the equilibrium state.

6.8 Given a second-order control system containing a transportation lag described by

$$\begin{aligned}\dot{x}_1(t) &= -a_1x_1(t) - b_1x_2(t - \tau)\\ \dot{x}_2(t) &= -a_2x_1(t) - b_2x_2(t) + m(t)\end{aligned}$$

with the boundary conditions

$$\begin{aligned}x_1(0) &= x_{10}\\ x_2(t) &= c(t) \qquad \text{for } -\tau \le t \le 0\\ x_1(t_f) &= 0\\ x_2(t_f) &= 0\end{aligned}$$

Determine the optimum-control signal $m^o(t)$ which will move the system from a specified initial state $\mathbf{x}(0)$ to the equilibrium state in minimum time. The control signal is bounded by $|m(t)| \le 1$ for all t.

6.9 Consider the control system of Prob. 6.8. Determine the optimum-control signal $m^o(t)$ which minimizes the total energy required to move the system from a given initial state $\mathbf{x}(0)$ to the equilibrium state. The total energy of control is measured by the performance index

$$I = \int_0^{t_f} m^2(t)\, dt$$

The system will reach the equilibrium state at t_f.

6.10 Given an nth-order system described by

$$\dot{\mathbf{x}}(t) = \mathbf{f}[\mathbf{x}(t); t] + \mathbf{m}(t)$$

where $\mathbf{x}$, $\mathbf{f}$, and $\mathbf{m}$ are n-vectors, show that, if $\|\mathbf{m}(t)\| \le 1$ for all $t \ge 0$ and

$$\|\mathbf{x}(t)\| = \sqrt{\sum_{i=1}^{n} x_i^2(t)}$$

is constant along trajectories of the homogeneous system $\dot{\mathbf{x}}(t) = \mathbf{f}[\mathbf{x}(t); t]$, then the optimum-control law which minimizes the time required to move the system from a given initial state $\mathbf{x}(0)$ to the equilibrium state and the integral

$$I = \int_0^{t_f} \|\mathbf{m}(t)\|\, dt$$

is given by

$$\mathbf{m}^o(t) = -\frac{\mathbf{x}(t)}{\|\mathbf{x}(t)\|}$$

6.11 Given a second-order control system characterized by

$$\begin{aligned}\dot{x}_1(t) &= x_2(t)\\ \dot{x}_2(t) &= -x_1(t) - x_2(t) + m(t)\end{aligned}$$

with initial conditions $\mathbf{x}(0)$ and constraint on the control signal $|m(t)| \le 1$, determine the optimum-control signal $m^o(t)$ which minimizes the system error at the end of the trajectory:

$$e(T) = x^d(T) - x_1(T)$$

where $x^d(T)$ is the desired system response, and $x_1(T)$ is the actual response at the terminal time T.

6.12 Consider the aircraft landing system studied in Example 7.4-3. It is desired that the altitude error at the touchdown point be reduced to the smallest possible value without exceeding the elevator-deflection limits. This specified performance may be attained by minimizing the error index

$$I(m) = \int_0^{t_f} \{[x_1{}^d(t_f) - x_1(t_f)]^2 + m^2(t)\}\, dt$$

where $t_f = 20$ sec, at which the trajectory terminates. Determine an optimum-control law for this terminal control system.

6.13 A control process is characterized by the vector differential equation

$$\dot{\mathbf{x}}(t) = \mathbf{X}(\mathbf{x}, t) + \mathbf{D}(t)\mathbf{m}(t)$$

with the control signals subject to the constraint

$$\int_0^T g(\mathbf{m})\, dt = c$$

where c is a given constant. Determine the optimum-control vector $\mathbf{m}^o$ which minimizes the performance index

$$I = x_1(T) + x_2(T)$$

6.14 Given a second-order control system described by

$$\ddot{x}(t) + \dot{x}(t) + x(t) = m(t)$$

with the control signal m constrained by $|m| \leq 1$, and the initial conditions given by $x(0)$ and $\dot{x}(0)$, determine the optimum-control signal $m^o(t)$ and the optimum-control law $m^o(x, \dot{x})$ which will move the system from a given initial state $\mathbf{x}(0)$ to the equilibrium state in the shortest time. Plot the switching boundary and the trajectory of motion with initial conditions $x(0) = 1$ and $\dot{x}(0) = 2$.

6.15 Write a term paper on the comparison between Pontryagin's maximum principle and the Mayer problem.

6.16 Given the system equation

$$\dot{\mathbf{x}}(t) = \mathbf{A}(t)\mathbf{x}(t)$$

the solution of which is $\mathbf{x}(t) = \boldsymbol{\phi}(t, t_0)\mathbf{x}(t_0)$, where $\boldsymbol{\phi}(t)$ satisfies $\dot{\boldsymbol{\phi}}(t) = \mathbf{A}(t)\boldsymbol{\phi}(t)$ with $\boldsymbol{\phi}(t_0) = \mathbf{1}$, and the adjoint equation

$$\dot{\mathbf{y}}(t) = -\mathbf{A}'(t)\mathbf{y}(t)$$

the solution of which is $\mathbf{y}(t) = \boldsymbol{\psi}(t, t_0)\mathbf{y}(t_0)$, where $\boldsymbol{\psi}(t)$ satisfies $\boldsymbol{\psi}(t) = -\mathbf{A}'(t)\boldsymbol{\psi}(t)$ with $\boldsymbol{\psi}(t_0) = \mathbf{1}$, show that

$$\dot{\boldsymbol{\psi}}(t) = [\boldsymbol{\phi}^{-1}(t)]'$$

6.17 With reference to the temperature control system described in Prob. 4.31, using the maximum principle, design an optimum controller which will move the system from a given initial state $\mathbf{x}(0)$ to the equilibrium state in minimum time.

6.18 Consider the temperature control system described in Prob. 4.31. Applying the maximum principle, design an optimum controller which minimizes the integral of the square of the error during the interval to move the system from a specified initial state $\mathbf{x}(0)$ to the equilibrium state.

6.19 Work out Prob. 4.32 by using the maximum principle.

6.20 Consider the roll control system for an airplane described in Prob. 4.33. Using the maximum principle, design an optimum controller so that the system may be taken from a given initial state to the equilibrium state in the shortest possible time.

7.1 The dynamics of an nth-order control process is characterized by

$$\dot{\mathbf{x}}(t) = \mathbf{A}\mathbf{x}(t) + \mathbf{D}m(t)$$

which is subject to the boundary conditions

$$x_1(0) = x_{10} \qquad x_2(0) = x_{20} \qquad \cdots \qquad x_n(0) = x_{n0} \qquad m(0) = m_0$$
$$x_1(\infty) = x_2(\infty) = \cdots = x_n(\infty) = m(\infty) = 0$$

Determine the optimum-control law which minimizes the performance criterion

$$I(m) = \int_0^\infty \left[\sum_{k=1}^{n} \alpha_k x_k^2(t) + \lambda m^2(t) \right] dt$$

by use of (*a*) the variational calculus, (*b*) the maximum principle, and (*c*) the method of dynamic programming.

7.2 Referring to the control process of Prob. 7.1, the control signal is subject to the constraints

$$|m| \le M_1 \qquad \text{and} \qquad |\dot{m}| \le M_2$$

where M_1 and M_2 are positive numbers. Determine the optimum-control law for minimizing the specified performance criterion by use of (*a*) the variational calculus, (*b*) the maximum principle, and (*c*) the dynamic programming.

7.3 With reference to the control process of Prob. 7.1, the control signal is subject to the saturation constraint

$$|m(t)| \le 1$$

for all t during the control interval. Determine the optimum-control law for minimizing the given performance criterion.

7.4 A second-order control process is characterized by the differential equation

$$\ddot{x}(t) + \dot{x}(t) = m(t)$$

where the control signal is subject to the physical constraint

$$|m(t)| \le M$$

for all t. Determine the optimum-control law $m^o(\mathbf{x})$ which will move the process from a given initial state to the equilibrium state in minimum time.

7.5 Consider the control process of Prob. 7.4. The control trajectory is assumed to terminate at time t_f, which is not specified. Determine the optimum-control law $m^o(\mathbf{x})$ which will move the process from a given initial state $\mathbf{x}(0)$ to the equilibrium state and will minimize the total fuel consumption during the course of optimum control. The fuel consumption is given by

$$I = \int_0^{t_f} |m(t)|\, dt$$

7.6 A second-order control process is characterized by the differential equation

$$\ddot{x}(t) + x(t) = m(t)$$

with initial conditions $x(0) = c_1$ and $\dot{x}(0) = c_2$. Determine the optimum-control policy

$m^o(k)$ which minimizes the performance criterion

$$I(x) = \int_0^T [x^2(t) + \dot{x}^2(t)]\, dt$$

7.7 Consider the control process of Prob. 5.4. By use of the dynamic-programming technique, determine the optimum-control law m^o which will move the process from the given initial state $\mathbf{x}(0)$ to the equilibrium state in minimum time.

7.8 Consider the control process of Prob. 5.9. Determine the optimum-control signal by use of the dynamic-programming technique.

7.9 Determine the optimum-control signal for the process described in Prob. 6.6 via dynamic programming.

7.10 Using the dynamic-programming technique, work out Prob. 6.7.

7.11 Consider the second-order control system of Prob. 6.8. Determine the optimum-control signal $m^o(t)$ by use of the dynamic-programming approach.

7.12 Work out Prob. 6.9 by applying the dynamic-programming method.

7.13 Design the terminal control system described in Prob. 6.11 by using the dynamic-programming technique.

7.14 Using the method of dynamic programming, design the aircraft landing system described in Prob. 6.12.

7.15 Write a term paper to compare the maximum principle and the dynamic programming for the design of optimum control systems.

7.16 Consider the temperature control system described in Prob. 4.31. Using the method of dynamic programming, design an optimum controller which will move the system from a given initial state $\mathbf{x}(0)$ to the equilibrium state in minimum time.

7.17 With reference to the temperature control system described in Prob. 4.31, applying the dynamic-programming technique, design an optimum controller which minimizes the integral of the square of the error during the interval to move the system from an initial state $\mathbf{x}(0)$ to the equilibrium state.

7.18 Work out Prob. 4.32 by use of dynamic programming.

7.19 Consider the roll control system for an airplane described in Prob. 4.33. Applying the dynamic-programming technique, design an optimum controller which will take the system from a specified initial state to the equilibrium state in minimum time.

7.20 A linear nth-order process subject to multiple control inputs is characterized by

$$\dot{\mathbf{x}}(t) = \mathbf{A}(t)\mathbf{x}(t) + \mathbf{D}(t)\mathbf{m}(t)$$

Determine the optimum-control law $\mathbf{m}^o(\mathbf{x})$ which minimizes the quadratic performance criterion

$$I(m) = \int_0^T [\mathbf{x}'\mathbf{Q}(t)\mathbf{x} + \mathbf{m}'\mathbf{H}(t)\mathbf{m}]\, dt$$

where $\mathbf{Q}(t)$ is an $n \times n$ symmetrical matrix and $\mathbf{H}(t)$ is an $r \times r$ symmetrical matrix.

7.21 The dynamics of a servomechanism may be approximately described by the differential equation

$$\ddot{x}(t) + r\dot{x}(t) = m(t)$$

where the coefficient r is a random parameter, and the control signal m is subject to the constraint

$$|m(t)| \le 1$$

for all t. The random parameter is equal to 10 with probability p, and it is equal to -10 with probability $1 - p$. The probability p is unknown, but it is known that p can take on two values, $p_1 = 0.2$ and $p_2 = 0.7$, with a priori probability $\zeta = 0.6$ and $1 - \zeta = 0.4$, respectively. The amplitude distribution of r is illustrated in Fig. 7.7-1. The sampling period τ is 1 sec, and the initial conditions are $x(0) = 1$, $\dot{x}(0) = 1$. Determine an optimum-control policy which minimizes the performance index

$$J = E\{x^2(10\tau)\}$$

7.22 Consider the aircraft landing system discussed in Example 7.4-3. Now assume that the short-period gain constant K is a random parameter, which is equal to $-0.5\ \text{sec}^{-1}$ with probability p and equal to $-1.0\ \text{sec}^{-1}$ with probability $1 - p$. It is known that p can take on two values $p_1 = 0.6$ and $p_2 = 0.2$ with a priori probability 0.8 and 0.2, respectively. Determine an optimum control policy which minimizes the error index

$$I(m) = \sum_{k=1}^{20} \{0.01[x_1{}^d(k) - x_1(k)]^2 - m^2(k-1)\}$$

and the optimum landing trajectory. The sampling period is assumed to be 1 sec. Discuss the effect of the initial altitude of the aircraft during the flare-out upon the landing trajectory.

8.1 An nth-order linear process subject to a single-control input is characterized by

$$\dot{\mathbf{x}}(t) = \mathbf{A}\mathbf{x}(t) + \mathbf{D}m(t)$$

Show that the optimum-control law which minimizes the quadratic performance index

$$I_n = \sum_{k=1}^{N} \{[\mathbf{x}^d(k) - \mathbf{x}(k)]'\mathbf{Q}[\mathbf{x}^d(k) - \mathbf{x}(k)]\}$$

is

$$m^o(\mathbf{x}) = \mathbf{B}(N-k)\mathbf{x}(k) + \mathbf{C}(N-k)\mathbf{x}^d(k)$$

Determine the recurrence relationships for the computation of the matrices $\mathbf{B}(N-k)$ and $\mathbf{C}(N-k)$.

8.2 Repeat Prob. 8.1 for an nth-order process subject to multiple control inputs characterized by the differential equation

$$\dot{\mathbf{x}}(t) = \mathbf{A}\mathbf{x}(t) + \mathbf{D}\mathbf{m}(t)$$

Determine the optimum-control law $\mathbf{m}^o(\mathbf{x})$.

8.3 A linear control process is characterized in discrete form by the state-transition equation

$$\mathbf{x}(\overline{k+1}\,T) = \boldsymbol{\phi}(T)\mathbf{x}(kT) + \mathbf{h}(T)m(kT)$$

(*a*) Show that the optimum-control law which minimizes the quadratic performance index

$$I_N = \sum_{k=1}^{\infty} [\mathbf{x}'(kT)\mathbf{Q}\mathbf{x}(kT)]$$

is

$$m^o(kT) = \mathbf{B}\mathbf{x}(kT)$$

where

$$\mathbf{B} = -\frac{\mathbf{h}'(T)[\mathbf{Q} + \mathbf{P}]\boldsymbol{\phi}(T)}{\mathbf{h}'(T)[\mathbf{Q} + \mathbf{P}]\mathbf{h}(T)}$$

(*b*) Determine the recurrence relationship for the computation of matrix **P**.

8.4 Determine the conditions such that the quadratic performance criterion

$$I_N = \sum_{k=1}^{N} \{[\mathbf{x}^d(k) - \mathbf{x}(k)]'\mathbf{Q}[\mathbf{x}^d(k) - \mathbf{x}(k)]\}$$

will characterize (*a*) a minimum-time control process and (*b*) a terminal control process.

8.5 Give a more complete proof that, in the case of inaccessible state variables, the optimum-control law which minimizes the expected value of the performance index defined in Eq. (8.3-4) is

$$\hat{\mathbf{m}}^o(k/k) = \mathbf{B}(N - k)\hat{\mathbf{x}}(k/k)$$

The estimated state vector $\hat{\mathbf{x}}(k/k)$ is based upon the measured output vectors $\mathbf{y}(j)$, $\mathbf{y}(j-1), \ldots, \mathbf{y}(0)$, with $j \leq k$, in the sense that the expected value

$$E\{[\mathbf{x}(k) - \hat{\mathbf{x}}(k/j)]'[\mathbf{x}(k) - \hat{\mathbf{x}}(k/j)]\}$$

is a minimum.

8.6 Consider a linear control process characterized by

$$\dddot{x} + 6\ddot{x} + 11\dot{x} + 6x = m$$

Design a digital controller which minimizes the performance index

$$I_N = \sum_{k=1}^{N} [r(k) - x_1(k)]^2$$

where x_1 denotes the output of the process, and r is the input signal which is assumed to be a unit-step function. The sampling period is equal to 1 sec.

8.7 Prove by mathematical induction that Eq. (8.2-13) is valid.

8.8 Given a linear process characterized by the transfer function

$$G(s) = \frac{1}{s(s^2 + 3s + 2)}$$

The class of inputs for which the digital control system is to be optimized is defined by $d^2r(t)/dt^2 = 0$. The sampling period is equal to 1 sec. Design an optimum digital controller which minimizes the performance index

$$I_N = \sum_{k=1}^{N} [r(k) - c(k)]^2$$

where r is the input, and c the output, of the system.

8.9 Consider the linear process of Prob. 8.8. Design an optimum digital controller which minimizes the performance index

$$I_N = \sum_{k=1}^{N} \{[r(k) - c(k)]^2 + [\dot{r}(k) - \dot{c}(k)]^2\}$$

8.10 A linear digital control process is characterized by the state-transition equation

$$\mathbf{x}(k+1) = \boldsymbol{\phi}(1)\mathbf{x}(k) + \mathbf{h}(1)m(k)$$

The sampling period is assumed to be 1 sec. The control signal is subject to the constraint

$$|m| \leq 1$$

Design an optimum digital controller so that the performance index

$$I_N = \sum_{k=1}^{N} \mathbf{x}'(k)\mathbf{Q}\mathbf{x}(k)$$

is minimized.

8.11 Consider the nth-order digital control process of Prob. 8.10. The state variables are subject to the constraint

$$|x_i| \leq X_i \qquad i = 1, 2, \ldots, n$$

Design an optimum digital controller which minimizes the performance index given above.

8.12 Work out Prob. 8.11 when both the control signal and the state variables are subject to the specified constraints.

8.13 The dynamics of a second-order process is characterized by

$$\ddot{x}(t) + [x(t) - 1]\dot{x}(t) + x(t) = m(t)$$

with the initial conditions $x(0) = 0$, $\dot{x}(0) = 1$, and the control signal subject to the constraint

$$|m(t)| \leq 1 \qquad \text{for all } t$$

Design optimum digital controllers which minimize, respectively,

(a) $I_{20} = \sum_{k=1}^{20} \{x^2(k) + [\dot{x}(k) - 10]^2\}$

(b) $I_{20} = \sum_{k=1}^{20} \{x^2(k) + 10m^2(k - 1)\}$

(c) $I_{20} = x^2(20) + \sum_{k=1}^{20} m^2(k - 1)$

The sampling period is assumed to be 1 sec.

8.14 Consider the temperature control system described in Prob. 4.31. Design an optimum digital controller so as to minimize the sum of the square of the sampled error

$$I_N = \sum_{k=1}^{N} [e(k)]^2$$

during the control interval to move the system from a specified initial state $\mathbf{x}(0) = \mathbf{1}$ to the equilibrium state. The sampling period is assumed to be 1 sec.

8.15 Consider the roll control system for an airplane described in Prob. 4.33. Design an optimum digital controller so that the sum of the square of the sampled error

$$I = \sum_{k=1}^{\infty} [e(k)]^2$$

is minimized.

8.16 A third-order, time-invariant process may be described by the state-variable diagram, shown in Fig. P 8.16. At the control input, there occurs an independent random disturbance n with mean value equal to ϵ. The disturbance n may be expressed as $n = v + \epsilon$, where v denotes an independent random variable with zero mean. The reference input r to the control system is assumed to be a step function of magnitude ranging from -10 to $+10$. The output c can be directly measured. The measurement of state variable x_1 introduces some noise which can be considered as an independent random variable with zero mean and standard deviation equal to 0.25. The state variable x_2 is inaccessible for measurement. Design an optimum digital controller which minimizes the error criterion

$$I_N = \sum_{k=1}^{N} [c(k) - r(k)]^2$$

The sampling period is assumed to be 1 sec.

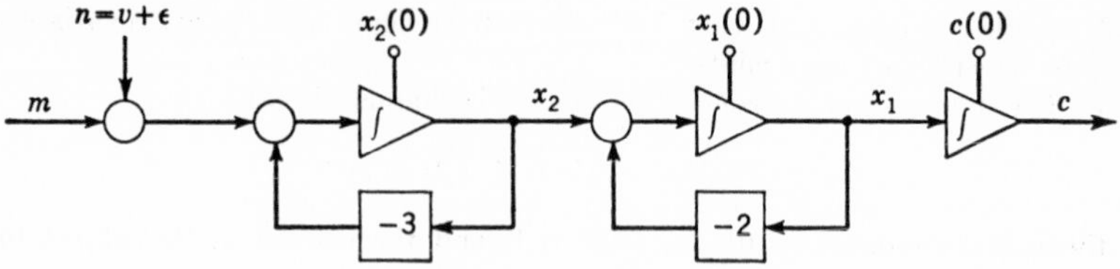

Fig. P 8.16

8.17 Consider a linear control system characterized by the transfer function

$$G(s) = \frac{1}{s(s+1)(s+2)}$$

The dynamic element is subject to a disturbance at the input terminal. The spectral density of the disturbance is

$$S_1(\omega) = \frac{1}{\omega^2 + 0.36}$$

The input to the system is assumed to be a step function the magnitude of which is assumed to range anywhere between −1 and +1. The input signal is contaminated by a noise which is independent of the external disturbance and has a spectral density given by

$$S_2(\omega) = \frac{1}{\omega^2 + 2.25}$$

The state-variable diagram of the control system is shown in Fig. P 8.17. It is assumed that the output state variable x_1 can be measured directly; in measuring the state variable x_2, the instrument introduces an additive measurement error of zero mean with standard deviation equal to 0.8, and the state variable x_3 is inaccessible for measurement. The measurement error is assumed to be independent from one sampling instant to another.

Design an optimum digital controller so that the expected value of the sum of the square of sampled error

$$J_N = E\left\{\sum_{k=1}^{N} [r(k) - x_1(k)]^2\right\}$$

is minimized. The sampling period is assumed to be 1 sec. The initial conditions are $x_1(0) = x_2(0) = x_3(0) = 1$.

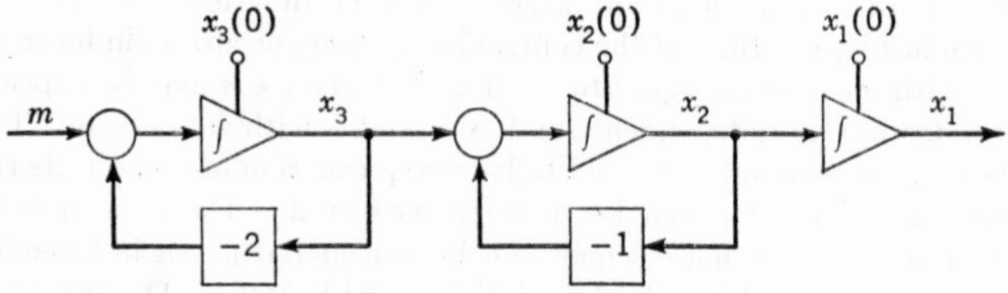

Fig. P 8.17

8.18 Consider an nth-order control process

$$\dot{\mathbf{x}}(t) = \mathbf{A}\mathbf{x}(t) + \mathbf{D}\mathbf{m}(t) + \mathbf{n}(t)$$

which is subject to r control signals and s disturbance signals. The control signals are constrained by the saturation effect such that

$$|m_i| \leq M_i \qquad i = 1, 2, \ldots, r$$

Some of the state variables are not accessible for measurement. The measurable output variables are related to the state variables and control signals by

$$\mathbf{y} = \mathbf{M}\mathbf{x} + \mathbf{K}\mathbf{m}$$

where $\mathbf{y}$ is the $p \times 1$ output vector, $p < n$. Determine the optimum-control law which minimizes the expected value of the quadratic performance index

$$I_N = \sum_{k=1}^{N} [\mathbf{x}'(k)\mathbf{Q}\mathbf{x}(k) + \lambda\mathbf{m}'(k-1)\mathbf{H}m(k-1)]$$

The sampling period is assumed to be 1 sec. $\mathbf{Q}$ and $\mathbf{H}$ are positive-definite symmetrical matrices.

REFERENCES

Aoki, M.

1. On Optimal and Sub-optimal Policies in the Choice of Control Forces for Final-value Systems, *IRE Trans. Autom. Control*, vol. AC-5, no. 3, pp. 171–178, August, 1960.
2. Dynamic Programming Approach to a Final-value Control System with a Random Variable Having an Unknown Distribution Function, *IRE Trans. Autom. Control*, vol. AC-5, no. 4, pp. 270–283, September, 1960.
3. On Minimum of Maximum Expected Deviation from an Unstable Equilibrium Position of Randomly Perturbed Control Systems, *IRE Trans. Autom. Control*, vol. AC-7, no. 2, pp. 1–12, March, 1962.
4. Integrals of Absolute Deviations in Linear Control Systems, *AIEE Trans. Appl. Ind.*, vol. 81, pp. 125–128, July, 1962.
5. On Some Approximation Techniques in Solving Optimization Problems in Control Systems, *J. Basic Eng.*, 1963.

Aris, R.

6. "The Optimal Design of Chemical Reactors: A Study in Dynamic Programming," Academic Press Inc., New York, 1961.

Astrom, K. J., J. E. Bertram, et al.

7. Current States of Linear Optimum Control Theory, *SIAM J. Control*, 1963.

Athans, M.

8. Bang-Bang Control for Tracking Systems, *IRE Trans. Autom. Control*, vol. AC-7, no. 3, pp. 77–78, April, 1962.
9. Minimum-fuel Feedback Control Systems: Second-order Case, *IEEE Trans. Appl. Ind.*, vol. 82, 1963.
10. Optimal Control for Linear Time-invariant Plants, *AIEE Trans. Appl. Ind.*, vol. 82, pp. 321–325, January, 1963.
11. Time-, Fuel-, and Energy-optimal Control of Nonlinear Norm-invariant Systems, *IEEE Trans. Autom. Control*, vol. AC-8, no. 3, pp. 196–202, July, 1963.

Athans, M., P. L. Falb, and R. T. Lacoss

12. Time-optimal Velocity Control of a Spinning Space Body, *AIEE Trans. Appl. Ind.*, vol. 82, 1963.

Athans, M., and O. J. M. Smith

13. Theory and Design of High-order Bang-Bang Control Systems, *IRE Trans. Autom. Control*, vol. AC-6, no. 2, pp. 125–134, May, 1961.

Bellman, R.

14. Dynamic Programming and Lagrange Multipliers, *Proc. Natl. Acad. Sci. U.S.*, vol. 42, pp. 767–769, 1956.
15. On the Application of the Theory of Dynamic Programming to the Study of Control Processes, *Proc. Symp. Nonlinear Circuit Analysis*, April, 1956, pp. 199–213.
16. "Dynamic Programming," Princeton University Press, Princeton, N.J., 1957.
17. Notes on Control Processes: On the Minimum of Maximum Deviation, *Quart. Appl. Math.*, vol. 14, pp. 419–423, January, 1957.
18. Dynamic Programming and the Computational Solution of the Feedback Design Control Problems, *AIEE Spec. Publ.*, T-101, pp. 22–25, 1958.
19. Dynamic Programming and Stochastic Control Processes, *Inform. Control*, vol. 1, pp. 228–239, 1958.
20. Some New Techniques in the Dynamic Programming Solution of Variational Problems, *Quart. Appl. Math.*, vol. 15, pp. 295–305, 1958.
21. "Introduction to Matrix Algebra," McGraw-Hill Book Company, New York, 1960.
22. "Adaptive Control Processes," Princeton University Press, Princeton, N.J., 1961.

Bellman, R., and K. L. Cooke

23. "Differential-difference Equations," Academic Press Inc., New York, 1963.

Bellman, R., I. Glicksberg, and O. Gross

24. On the Bang-Bang Control Problem, *Quart. J. Appl. Math.*, vol. 14, 1956.

Bellman, R., and R. Kabala

25. On Adaptive Control Processes, *IRE Trans. Autom. Control*, vol. AC-4, pp. 1–9, November, 1959.
26. Dynamic Programming and Adaptive Processes: Mathematical Foundation, *IRE Trans. Autom. Control*, vol. AC-5, pp. 5–10, January, 1960.

Berkovitz, L.

27. Variational Methods in Problems of Control and Programming, *J. Math. Analysis Appl.*, vol. 3, pp. 145–169, 1961.

Bertram, J. E.

28. Control by Stochastic Adjustment, *AIEE Trans. Appl. Ind.*, vol. 79, pp. 1–6, January, 1960.

Bliss, G. A.

29. "Lectures on the Calculus of Variations," Chicago University Press, Chicago, 1946.

Boltyanskii, V. G.

30. The Maximum Principle in the Theory of Optimum Processes, *Dokl. Akad. Nauk SSSR*, vol. 119, no. 6, pp. 1070–1073, June, 1958.

Boltyanskii, V. G., R. V. Gamkrelidze, E. F. Mischenko, and L. S. Pontryagin

31. The Maximum Principle in the Theory of Optimal Process of Control, *Proc. First Intern. Congr. Autom. Control*, Eyre and Spottiswoode (Publishers), Ltd., London, 1961.

Boltyanskii, V. G., R. V. Gamkrelidze, and L. S. Pontryagin

32. On the Theory of Optimum Processes, *Dokl. Akad. Nauk SSSR*, vol. 110, no. 1, pp. 7–10; Translation 61-23140, S.L.A. Translation Center, Chicago, 1956.
33. The Theory of Optimal Processes, I, *Izv. Akad. Nauk SSSR, Ser. Mat.*, vol. 24, pp. 3–42, 1959. (See also *Am. Math. Soc. Transl.*, ser. 2, vol. 18, pp. 341–382, January, 1960–1961.)
34. The Theory of Optimal Processes, I, The Maximum Principle, *Usp. Mat. Nauk SSSR*, transl. L. W. Neustadt, STL-TR 61-5110-36, Space Technology Laboratories, Los Angeles, 1960.

Bolza, O.

35. "Lectures on the Calculus of Variations," Dover Publications, Inc., New York, 1960.

Bryson, A. E., and W. F. Denham

36. Multivariable Terminal Control for Minimum Square Deviation from a Nominal Path, *J. Aerospace Sci.*, 1962.

Bushaw, D.

37. Optimal Discontinuous Forcing Terms, in "Contributions to the Theory of Nonlinear Oscillations," vol. 4, pp. 29–58, 1958, Princeton University Press, Princeton, N.J.

Butkovskii, A. G.

38. The Maximum Principle for Optimum Systems with Distributed Parameters, *Automation Remote Control*, vol. 22, no. 10, pp. 1156–1169, March, 1962.

Chandaket, P., and C. T. Leondes

39. Synthesis of Quasi-stationary Optimum Nonlinear Control Systems, I and II, *AIEE Trans. Appl. Ind.*, vol. 81, pp. 313–324, January, 1962.

Chang, J. W.

40. A Program in the Synthesis of Optimal Systems Using Maximum Principle, *Automation Remote Control*, vol. 22, no. 10, pp. 1170–1176, March, 1962.

Chang, S. S. L.

41. Digitized Maximum Principle, *Proc. IRE*, vol. 48, pp. 2030–2031, December, 1960.
42. "Synthesis of Optimum Control Systems," McGraw-Hill Book Company, New York, 1961.

Chestnut, H., R. R. Duersch, and W. M. Gaines

43. Automatic Optimizing of Poorly Defined Processes, I, *AIEE Trans. Appl. Ind.*, 1963.

Clement, P. R.

44. On the Bang-Bang Regulator Problem for Linear Sampled-data Systems, *IEEE Trans. Autom. Control*, vol. AC-8, pp. 180–182, April, 1963.

Coddington, E. A., and N. Levinson

45. "Theory of Ordinary Differential Equations," McGraw-Hill Book Company, New York, 1955.

Cunningham, W. J.

46. An Introduction to Lyapunov's Second Method, *AIEE Trans. Appl. Ind.*, vol. 81, pp. 325–332, January, 1962.

Desoer, C. A.

47. The Bang-Bang Servo Problem Treated by Variational Techniques, *Inform. Control*, vol. 2, pp. 333–348, December, 1959.
48. Pontryagin's Maximum Principle and the Principle of Optimality, *J. Franklin Inst.*, vol. 271, pp. 361–367, 1961.

Desoer, C. A., and J. Wing

49. An Optimal Strategy for a Saturating Sampled-data System, *IRE Trans. Autom. Control*, vol. AC-6, pp. 5–15, February, 1959.
50. A Minimal Time Discrete System, *IRE Trans. Autom. Control*, vol. AC-6, no. 2, 1961.
51. Minimal Time Regulator Problem for Linear Sampled-data Systems (General Theory), *J. Franklin Inst.*, vol. 271, pp. 208–228, September, 1961.

Dreyfus, S. E.

52. Dynamic Programming and the Calculus of Variations, *J. Math. Analysis Appl.*, vol. 1, no. 2, pp. 228–239, September, 1960.
53. Computation Aspects of Variational Problems, *J. Math. Analysis Appl.*, vol. 3, 1961.

Ellert, F. J., and C. W. Merriam III

54. Synthesis of Feedback Control Using Optimization Theory: An Example, *IEEE Trans. Autom. Control*, vol. AC-8, pp. 89–103, April, 1963.

Feldbaum, A. A.

55. Theory of Dual Control, I and II, *Automation Remote Control*, vol. 21, nos. 9 and 10, pp. 874–880, 1033–1039, April and May, 1961.

Florentin, J. J.

56. Optimal Control of Continuous Time, Markov, Stochastic Systems, *J. Electron. Control*, vol. 10, pp. 473–488, June, 1961.

Freimer, M.

57. A Dynamic Programming Approach to Adaptive Control Processes, *IRE Trans. Autom. Control*, vol. AC-4, no. 2, pp. 10–15, 1959.

Friedland, B.

58. A Mathematical Theory of Adaptive Control Processes, *Proc. Natl. Acad. Sci.*, vol. 45, no. 8, pp. 1288–1290, August, 1960.
59. A Minimum Response-time Controller for Amplitude and Energy Constraints, *IRE Trans. Autom. Control*, vol. AC-7, pp. 73–74, January, 1962.
60. The Structure of Optimum Control Systems, *J. Basic Eng.*, 1962.

Fuller, A. T.

61. Optimization of Nonlinear Control Systems with Transient Inputs, *J. Electron. Control*, vol. 8, pp. 465–479, 1960.

62. Phase Space in the Theory of Optimum Control, *J. Electron. Control*, vol. 8, pp. 381–400, 1960.

Gamkrelidze, R. V.

63. On the Theory of Optimum Processes in Linear Systems, *Dokl. Akad. Nauk SSSR*, vol. 116, no. 1, pp. 9–11, January, 1957.
64. On the General Theory of Optimum Processes, *Dokl. Akad. Nauk SSSR*, vol. 123, no. 2, pp. 223–226, 1958; transl. *Automation Express*, March, 1959, pp. 37–39.
65. The Theory of Processes Which Are Optimum for Rapid-action in Linear Systems, *Izv. Akad. Nauk SSSR, Ser. Mat.*, vol. 22, no. 4, pp. 449–474; transl. E. Stear, Report 61-7, Department of English, University of California at Los Angeles, 1958.

Gantmaker, F. R.

66. "The Theory of Matrices," Chelsea Publishing Company, New York, 1959.

Gavrilovic, M., R. Petronic, and D. Siljak

67. Adjoint Method in the Sensitivity Analysis of Optimal Systems, *J. Franklin Inst.*, vol. 276, no. 1, pp. 26–38, July, 1963.

Gilbert, E. G.

68. A Method for the Symbolic Representation and Analysis of Linear Periodic Feedback Systems, *AIEE Trans.*, pt. II, vol. 79, pp. 512–523, January, 1961.
69. Controllability and Observability in Multivariable Control Systems, *SIAM J. Control*, 1963.

Goldstein, H.

70. "Classical Mechanics," Addison-Wesley Publishing Company, Inc., Reading, Mass., 1951.

Gould, L. A., and W. Kipiniak

71. Dynamic Optimization and Control of a Stirred-tank Chemical Reactor, *AIEE Trans. Commun. Electron.*, vol. 80, pp. 734–746, January, 1961.

Grishin, V. P.

71a. On a Calculation Method Related to a Process of Automatic Adaptation, *Automation Remote Control*, vol. 23, no. 12, pp. 1502–1509, June, 1963.

Guignabodet, J.

72. Dynamic Programming: Cumulative Errors in the Evaluation of an Optimal Control Sequence, *J. Basic Eng.*, 1963.

Hadley, G.

73. "Linear Algebra," Addison-Wesley Publishing Company, Inc., Reading, Mass., 1961.

Halmos, P. R.

74. "Finite-dimensional Vector Spaces," D. Van Nostrand Company, Inc., Princeton, N.J., 1958.

Harvey, C. A., and E. B. Lee

75. On the Uniqueness of Time Optimal Control for Linear Processes, *J. Math. Analysis Appl.*, 1962.

Ho, Y. C.

76. A Computational Technique for Optimal Control Problems with State Variable Constraint, *J. Math. Analysis Appl.*, 1961.
77. Solution Space Approach to Optimal Control Problem, *J. Basic Eng.*, ser. D. vol. 83, pp. 53–58, March, 1961.
78. A Successive Approximation Technique for Optimal Control Systems Subject to Input Saturation, *J. Basic Eng.*, vol. 84, 1962.

Hoffman, K., and R. Kunze

79. "Linear Algebra," Prentice-Hall, Inc., Englewood Cliffs, N.J., 1961.

Hsieh, H. C.

80. On the Final Value and Minimum Effort Systems, *J. Franklin Inst.*, vol. 276, no. 2, pp. 154–167, August, 1963.

Hsu, J. C., and W. E. Meserve

81. Decision-making in Adaptive Control Systems, *IRE Trans. Autom. Control*, vol. AC-7, pp. 24–32, January, 1962.

Joseph, P. D., and J. T. Tou

82. On Linear Control Theory, *AIEE Trans.*, vol. 80, pp. 193–196, 1961.

Kallay, N.

83. Dynamic Programming and Nuclear Reactor Design, *Nucl. Sci. Eng.*, October, 1960.
84. An Example of the Application of Dynamic Programming to the Design of Optimal Control Programs, *IRE Trans. Autom. Control*, vol. AC-7, no. 3, pp. 10–21, April, 1962.

Kalman, R. E.

85. Optimal Nonlinear Control of Saturation Systems by Intermittent Action, *IRE WESCON, Conv. Record*, 1957, pt. IV, pp. 130–135.
86. A New Approach to Linear Filtering and Prediction Problems, *J. Basic Eng.*, vol. 82, pp. 35–45, March, 1960.
87. Contributions to the Theory of Optimal Control, *Bol. Soc. Mat. Mex.*, 1960, pp. 102–119.
88. On the General Theory of Control Systems, *Proc. First Intern. Congr. Autom. Control*, Eyre & Spottiswoode (Publishers), Ltd., London, 1961.
89. Mathematical Description of Linear Dynamic Systems, *SIAM J. Control*, 1963.

Kalman, R. E., and J. E. Bertram

90. General Synthesis Procedure for Computer Control of Single-loop and Multi-loop Linear Systems, *AIEE Trans.*, pt. II, vol. 77, pp. 602–609, 1958.
91. A Unified Approach to the Theory of Sampling Systems, *J. Franklin Inst.*, vol. 267, p. 408, 1959.
92. Control System Analysis and Design via the Second Method of Lyapunov, *J. Basic Eng.*, ser. D, vol. 82, pp. 371–393, 1960.

Kalman, R. E., and R. W. Koepcke

93. Optimal Synthesis of Linear Sampling Control Systems Using Generalized Performance Indices, *ASME Trans.*, vol. 80, pp. 1800–1826, November, 1958.

Kipiniak, W.

94. "Dynamic Optimization and Control: A Variational Approach," The M.I.T. Press, Cambridge, Mass., and John Wiley & Sons, Inc., New York, 1961.

Kishi, F. H.

95. The Existence of Optimal Control for a Class of Optimization Problems, *IEEE Trans. Autom. Control*, vol. AC-8, pp. 173–175, April, 1963.

Kranc, G. M., and P. E. Sarachik

96. An Application of Functional Analysis to the Optimal Control Problem, *J. Basic Eng.*, 1963.

Krasovskii, N. N.

97. Concerning the Theory of Optimal Control, *Automation Remote Control*, vol. 18, pp. 1005–1016, 1957.
98. On the Theory of Optimum Regulation, *Automation Remote Control*, vol. 18, pp. 255–294, April, 1959.
99. On the Theory of Optimum Control, *Prikl. Mat. Mekhan.*, vol. 23, pp. 625–639, June, 1959.

Krug, G. K., and E. K. Letskii

100. A Learning Automaton of the Tabular Type, *Automation Remote Control*, vol. 22, no. 10, March, 1962.

Kurzweil, F.

101. Dynamic Synthesis of Higher-order Optimum Saturating Systems, *J. Basic Eng.*, ser. D, vol. 83, pp. 45–52, March, 1961.

Kushner, H. J.

102. Hill Climbing Methods for the Optimization of Multi-parameter Noise-disturbed Systems, *J. Basic Eng.*, 1963.

LaSalle, J. P.

103. Time-optimal Control Systems, *Proc. Natl. Acad. Sci.*, vol. 45, pp. 573–577, 1959.
104. The Time Optimum Control Problem, in "Contributions to the Theory of Nonlinear Oscillations," vol. 5, pp. 1–24, Princeton University Press, Princeton, N.J., 1960.

LaSalle, J. P., and S. Lefschetz

105. "Stability by Lyapunov's Direct Method with Applications," Academic Press Inc., New York, 1961.
106. (Eds.), "International Symposium on Nonlinear Differential Equations and Nonlinear Mechanics," Academic Press Inc., New York, 1963.

Lee, E. B.

107. Mathematical Aspects of the Synthesis of Linear Minimum Response-time Controllers, *IRE Trans. Autom. Control*, vol. AC-5, no. 4, pp. 283–289, September, 1960.
108. Design of Optimum Multi-variable Control Systems, *J. Basic Eng.*, vol. 83, 1961.
109. On the Time Optimal Control of Plants with Numerator Dynamics, *IRE Trans. Autom. Control*, June, 1961.
110. Time Optimal Control of Nonlinear Processes, *J. Basic Eng.*, ser. D, 1961.
111. On the Domain of Controllability for Linear Systems Subject to Control Amplitude Constraints, *IEEE Trans. Autom. Control*, vol. AC-8, pp. 172–173, April, 1963.

Leitmann, G.

112. "Optimization Techniques," Academic Press Inc., New York, 1962.

Lendaris, G. G.

113. The Identification of Linear Systems, *AIEE Trans. Appl. Ind.*, vol. 81, pp. 231–242, September, 1962.

Letov, A. M.

114. Analytic Controller Design, I, II, and III, *Automation Remote Control*, vol. 21, nos. 4–6, pp. 303–436, 389–393, 458–466, November and December, 1960.

Lewis, J. B., and J. T. Tou

115. Optimum Sampled-data Systems with Quantized Control Signals, *IEEE Trans. Appl. Ind.*, 1963.

Li, C. C.

116. A Short Bibliography of Pontryagin's Maximum Principle of the Theory of Optimum Control, *IRE Trans. Autom. Control*, vol. AC-7, pp. 74–75, January, 1962.

McDonald, D. C.

117. Nonlinear Techniques for Improving Servo Performance, *Proc. Natl. Electron. Conf.*, vol. 6, pp. 400–421, 1950.

Merriam, C. W., III

118. Use of a Mathematical Error Criterion in the Design of Adaptive Control Systems, *AIEE Trans.*, vol. 78, pp. 506–512, January, 1959.
119. An Optimization Theory for Feedback Control System Design, *Inform. Control*, vol. 3, pp. 32–59, March, 1960.

Miele, A., and J. O. Cappelleri

120. Topics in Dynamic Programming for Rockets, *Sonderdruck Z. Flugwiss.*, no. 1, pp. 14–21, 1959.

Neustadt, L. W.

121. Synthesizing Time-optimal Controls, *J. Math. Analysis Appl.*, December, 1960.
122. Discrete Time Optimal Control Systems, in J. P. LaSalle and S. Lefschetz (eds.), "International Symposium on Nonlinear Differential Equations and Nonlinear Mechanics," Academic Press Inc., New York, 1963.

Newton, G. C., L. A. Gould, and J. F. Kaiser

123. "Analytical Design of Linear Feedback Controls," John Wiley & Sons, Inc., New York, 1957.

O'Hearn, E. A., and R. K. Smyth

124. Terminal Control System Applications, *IRE Trans. Autom. Control*, vol. AC-6, pp. 142–153, May, 1961.

Pipes, L. A.

125. Solution of Variable Circuits by Matrices, *J. Franklin Inst.*, vol. 224, pp. 767–777, December, 1937.
126. "Matrix Methods for Engineering," Prentice-Hall, Inc., Englewood Cliffs, N.J., 1963.

Pontryagin, L. S.

127. Some Mathematical Problems Arising in Connection with the Theory of Optimal Systems of Automatic Control, *Proc. Acad. Sci. USSR*, October, 1956.
128. Optimum Control Processes, *Usp. Mat. Nauk. SSSR*; transl. *Automation Express*, vol. 1, pp. 15–18; vol. 2, pp. 26–30, January and February, 1959.
129. Optimal Control Processes, *Usp. Mat. Nauk SSSR*, vol. 14, no. 1, p. 85, 1959.

Pontryagin, L. S., V. G. Boltyanskii, R. V. Gamkrelidze, and E. F. Mishchenko

130. "The Mathematical Theory of Optimal Processes," John Wiley & Sons, Inc., New York, 1962.

131. *Proc. Symp. Discrete Adaptive Processes*, AIEE Special Publication, 1962.

132. *Proc. Workshop State Space Techniques for Control Systems*, AIEE Special Publication, 1962.

Roxin, E.

133. A Geometric Interpretation of Pontryagin's Maximum Principle, in J. P. LaSalle and S. Lefschetz (eds.), "International Symposium on Nonlinear Differential Equations and Nonlinear Mechanics," pp. 303–324, Academic Press Inc., New York, 1963.

Rozonoer, L. I.

134. L. S. Pontryagin's Maximum Principles in the Theory of Optimum Systems, I, II, and III, *Automation Remote Control*, vol. 20, pp. 1288–1302, October, 1959; pp. 1405–1421, November, 1959; pp. 1515–1532, December, 1959.

Smith, F. B., Jr.

135. Time-optimal Control of Higher-order Systems, *IRE Trans. Autom. Control*, vol. AC-6, no. 1, pp. 16–21, February, 1961.

Tou, J. T.

136. "Digital and Sampled-data Control Systems," McGraw-Hill Book Company, New York, 1959.
137. Design of Optimum Digital Control Systems via Dynamic Programming, *Proc. Dynamic Programming Workshop, AIEE*, Purdue University Press, Lafayette, Ind., 1961.
138. A Simplified Approach to the Design of Minimum-time Control of Discrete-data Systems Subject to Saturation, *Automatica*, Kiev, U.S.S.R., 1963. (In Russian.)
139. Digitale Regelung von Mehrfachprozessen, *Regelungstechnik*, January, 1963.
140. "Optimum Design of Digital Control Systems," Academic Press Inc., New York, 1963.
141. Optimum Control of Discrete Systems Subject to Saturation, *IEEE Proc.*, 1964.
141a. Dynamic Programming and Modern Control Theory, in R. H. MacMillan, T. J. Higgins, and P. Naslin (eds.), "Progress in Control Engineering," Academic Press Inc., New York, 1964.
142. Synthesis of Discrete Systems Subject to Control Signal Saturation, *J. Franklin Inst.*, May, 1964.

Tou, J. T., and K. S. Fu

143. Digital Control Concepts for Nervous System Synthesis and Simulation, *Proc. Third Intern. Congr. Cybernetics*, 1961.

Tou, J. T., and P. D. Joseph

144. Digital Adaptive Control Systems, II, Purdue University, Control and Information Systems Laboratory, TR 102, Lafayette, Ind., 1961.
145. Modern Synthesis of Computer Control Systems, *IEEE Trans. Appl. Ind.*, vol. 82, 1963.

Tou, J. T., and J. B. Lewis

146. Nonlinear Digital Control Systems, Purdue University, Control and Information Systems Laboratory, TR 201, Lafayette, Ind., 1961.

Tou, J. T., T. T. Lin, and T. Meksawan

146a. A Study of Digital Control Systems, Northwestern University, Computer Sciences Laboratory, TR 103, Evanston, Ill., 1963.

Tou, J. T., and B. Vadhanaphuti

147. Optimum Control of Nonlinear Discrete-data Systems, *AIEE Trans.*, vol. 80, pp. 166–171, 1961.

Tou, J. T., and R. H. Wilcox (eds.)

148. "Computer and Information Sciences," Spartan Book Company, Baltimore, Md., 1964.

Wing, J., and C. A. Desoer

149. The Multiple-input Minimal-time Regulator Problem (General Theory), *IEEE Trans. Autom. Control*, vol. AC-8, pp. 125–136, April, 1963.

Zadeh, L. A.

150. On the Identification Problem, *IRE Trans. Circuit Theory*, vol. CT-3, no. 4, December, 1956.
151. Optimal Control Problems in Discrete-time Systems, in C. T. Leondes (ed.), "Computer Control Systems Technology," McGraw-Hill Book Company, New York, 1961.

Zadeh, L. A., and C. A. Desoer

152. "Linear System Theory," McGraw-Hill Book Company, New York, 1963.

INDEX